Dinosaurs and Other Extinct Saurians: A Historical Perspective

Geological Society books refereeing procedures

The Society makes every effort to ensure that the scientific and production quality of its books matches that of its journals. Since 1997, all book proposals have been refereed by specialist reviewers as well as by the Society's Books Editorial Committee. If the referees identify weaknesses in the proposal, these must be addressed before the proposal is accepted.

Once the book is accepted, the Society Book Editors ensure that the volume editors follow strict guidelines on refereeing and quality control. We insist that individual papers can only be accepted after satisfactory review by two independent referees. The questions on the review forms are similar to those for *Journal of the Geological Society*. The referees' forms and comments must be available to the Society's Book Editors on request.

Although many of the books result from meetings, the editors are expected to commission papers that were not presented at the meeting to ensure that the book provides a balanced coverage of the subject. Being accepted for presentation at the meeting does not guarantee inclusion in the book.

More information about submitting a proposal and producing a book for the Society can be found on its web site: www.geolsoc.org.uk.

It is recommended that reference to all or part of this book should be made in one of the following ways:

Moody, R. T. J., Buffetaut, E., Naish, D. & Martill, D. M. (eds) 2010. *Dinosaurs and Other Extinct Saurians: A Historical Perspective*. Geological Society, London, Special Publications, **343**.

Buffetaut, E. 2010. Spinosaurs before Stromer: early finds of spinosaurid dinosaurs and their interpretations. *In*: Moody, R. T. J., Buffetaut, E., Naish, D. & Martill, D. M. (eds) *Dinosaurs and Other Extinct Saurians: A Historical Perspective*. Geological Society, London, Special Publications, **343**, 175–188.

GEOLOGICAL SOCIETY SPECIAL PUBLICATION NO. 343

Dinosaurs and Other Extinct Saurians: A Historical Perspective

EDITED BY

R. T. J. MOODY
Kingston University, UK

E. BUFFETAUT
CNRS, Ecole Normale Supérieure, Paris, France

D. NAISH and D. M. MARTILL
University of Portsmouth, UK

2010
Published by
The Geological Society
London

THE GEOLOGICAL SOCIETY

The Geological Society of London (GSL) was founded in 1807. It is the oldest national geological society in the world and the largest in Europe. It was incorporated under Royal Charter in 1825 and is Registered Charity 210161.

The Society is the UK national learned and professional society for geology with a worldwide Fellowship (FGS) of over 9000. The Society has the power to confer Chartered status on suitably qualified Fellows, and about 2000 of the Fellowship carry the title (CGeol). Chartered Geologists may also obtain the equivalent European title, European Geologist (EurGeol). One fifth of the Society's fellowship resides outside the UK. To find out more about the Society, log on to www.geolsoc.org.uk.

The Geological Society Publishing House (Bath, UK) produces the Society's international journals and books, and acts as European distributor for selected publications of the American Association of Petroleum Geologists (AAPG), the Indonesian Petroleum Association (IPA), the Geological Society of America (GSA), the Society for Sedimentary Geology (SEPM) and the Geologists' Association (GA). Joint marketing agreements ensure that GSL Fellows may purchase these societies' publications at a discount. The Society's online bookshop (accessible from www.geolsoc.org.uk) offers secure book purchasing with your credit or debit card.

To find out about joining the Society and benefiting from substantial discounts on publications of GSL and other societies worldwide, consult www.geolsoc.org.uk, or contact the Fellowship Department at: The Geological Society, Burlington House, Piccadilly, London W1J 0BG: Tel. +44 (0)20 7434 9944; Fax +44 (0)20 7439 8975; E-mail: enquiries@geolsoc.org.uk.

For information about the Society's meetings, consult *Events* on www.geolsoc.org.uk. To find out more about the Society's Corporate Affiliates Scheme, write to enquiries@geolsoc.org.uk.

Published by The Geological Society from:
The Geological Society Publishing House, Unit 7, Brassmill Enterprise Centre, Brassmill Lane, Bath BA1 3JN, UK

(*Orders*: Tel. +44 (0)1225 445046, Fax +44 (0)1225 442836)
Online bookshop: www.geolsoc.org.uk/bookshop

British Library Cataloguing in Publication Data

A catalogue record for this book is available from the British Library.
ISBN 978-1-86239-311-0

Typeset by Techset Composition Ltd, Salisbury, UK
Printed by CPI Antony Rowe, Chippenham, UK

Distributors

North America
For trade and institutional orders:
The Geological Society, c/o AIDC, 82 Winter Sport Lane, Williston, VT 05495, USA
Orders: Tel. +1 800-972-9892
Fax +1 802-864-7626
E-mail: gsl.orders@aidcvt.com

For individual and corporate orders:
AAPG Bookstore, PO Box 979, Tulsa, OK 74101-0979, USA
Orders: Tel. +1 918-584-2555
Fax +1 918-560-2652
E-mail: bookstore@aapg.org
Website: http://bookstore.aapg.org

India
Affiliated East-West Press Private Ltd, Marketing Division, G-1/16 Ansari Road, Darya Ganj, New Delhi 110 002, India
Orders: Tel. +91 11 2327-9113/2326-4180
Fax +91 11 2326-0538
E-mail: affiliat@vsnl.com

Contents

Dinosaurs and other extinct saurians: a historical perspective – introduction

RICHARD T. J. MOODY[1]*, ERIC BUFFETAUT[2], DARREN NAISH[3] & DAVID M. MARTILL[3]

[1]*Faculty of Science, Kingston University, Penrhyn Road, Kingston KT1 2EE, UK*

[2]*Centre National de la Recherche Scientifique, UMR 8538, Laboratoire de Géologie de l'Ecole Normale Supérieure, 24 rue Lhomond, 75231 Paris Cedex 05, France*

[3]*School of Earth & Environmental Sciences, Burnaby Building, Burnaby Road, University of Portsmouth, Portsmouth PO1 3QL, UK*

**Corresponding author (e-mail: rtjmoody@yahoo.com)*

The discovery of dinosaurs and other large extinct 'saurians', a term under which the Victorians commonly lumped ichthyosaurs, plesiosaurs, pterosaurs and their kin, makes exciting reading. The story of how early 'fossilists' first found the remains of these 'primeval monsters' has been told again and again in popular and semi-popular books about the history of palaeontology. Mary Anning making a living by collecting extinct reptiles along the Dorset coast, William Buckland and Gideon Mantell finding the 'terrible lizards' for which Richard Owen was to coin the word 'Dinosauria', O. C. Marsh and E. D. Cope fighting over new fossil vertebrates in the American West – all of these well-known stories have almost achieved the status of legends, and have often been retold with little regard for historical or scientific accuracy.

The purpose of the present volume is not to retell these tales. The papers in this collection focus on relatively little-known episodes in the discovery and interpretation (from both a scientific and an artistic point of view) of dinosaurs and other Mesozoic animals. They cover a long time span, from the beginnings of scientific palaeontology to the present, and deal with many parts of the world, from the Yorkshire coast to central India, from Bavaria to the Sahara. The characters in these stories include professional palaeontologists and geologists (some of them well known, others more obscure), explorers, amateur fossil collectors and artists, linked together by their interest in Mesozoic creatures. The papers are diverse in their scope and approach, some dealing with a particular researcher or artist, others with a well defined group of fossil organisms or the development of a scientific concept, others with a fossil locality or a region.

A first group of papers concerns collections, those who brought them together and those who studied and curated them. **Evans** focuses on the important role of collections – and therefore collectors – in the early development of vertebrate palaeontology. Although the emphasis is on Britain, examples from The Netherlands and France are also mentioned, all showing how the growth of large collections, which sooner or later found their way into museums, was vital for comparative studies and, therefore, for our understanding of various groups of fossil reptiles. **Torrens** tells the sad story of William Perceval Hunter, a much forgotten naturalist who, among many other pursuits, studied the geology of the Isle of Wight and the large reptiles of the local Wealden, before he ended his life in a lunatic asylum. **Noè & Liston** provide new information about the life and work of Alfred Leeds, one of the most famous collectors of fossil reptiles in Britain, whose superb specimens from the Oxford Clay of the Peterborough area can be seen in many museums in England, Scotland and elsewhere. **Fanti** recalls the role of the sponsored or affluent intelligensia in the development of geology and vertebrate palaeontology as significant sciences in the late nineteenth century with an outline of the curatorial, scientific and inspirational teaching skills of Italian Giovanni Capellini. **Moody & Naish** provide a brief biography of Alan Charig, who in many ways personified British research on dinosaurs during the second half of the twentieth century by both publishing significant scientific contributions and reaching out to the general public through popular books and television programmes. Although many of the scientists who discovered and studied extinct reptiles were men, the contribution of women should not be ignored, as revealed by **Turner *et al.*** Mary Anning has attained an almost iconic status, but she was also the first of a long series of women working on fossil reptiles, some of whom, like Tilly Edinger, achieved prominence in their field,

From: Moody, R. T. J., Buffetaut, E., Naish, D. & Martill, D. M. (eds) *Dinosaurs and Other Extinct Saurians: A Historical Perspective*. Geological Society, London, Special Publications, **343**, 1–3.
DOI: 10.1144/SP343.1 0305-8719/10/$15.00

while others remained obscure despite their contributions.

Quite a few of these collectors were pioneers in their field, who broke new ground by discovering the remains of dinosaurs and other Mesozoic reptiles in regions that had been hitherto virtually untouched by palaeontologists. One of them is Wilhelm (also known as Guillermo) Schulz. **Pereda Suberbiola *et al.*** provide a biographical essay on this German mining geologist who spent most of his working life in Spain in the mid-nineteenth century, and is mostly remembered for his successful search for mineral resources, but was also the first to report Mesozoic reptiles from that country. In a more exotic setting, **Carrano *et al.*** tell the often adventurous story of the discovery of dinosaurs in what was then British India, from the first finds by Sleeman in 1828 (only a few years after the epoch-making discoveries by Buckland and Mantell in England) to Matley's extensive collecting efforts between 1917 and 1933, as a result of which much is now known about the Late Cretaceous dinosaur fauna of India. In some instances, it turns out that discoveries of spectacular dinosaur specimens had been preceded by more obscure finds that attracted little attention. In this vein, **Buffetaut** shows how remains of spinosaurid theropods were discovered well before Ernst Stromer first described *Spinosaurus aegyptiacus*, from the Cretaceous of Egypt, in 1915. Teeth of these unusual dinosaurs were described as early as the 1820s by Mantell and Cuvier, but because of their peculiar morphology they were mistaken for crocodile teeth, a misinterpretation shared by later researchers such as Owen and Sauvage.

While the history of research on extinct 'saurians' contains many instances of outstanding discoveries made by individual scientists, in many cases significant advances have been the result of the efforts of a succession of dedicated researchers over longer periods of time. This is ably illustrated by **Whyte *et al.*** on the discovery of dinosaur remains in the Jurassic of the Yorkshire coast. The story, which began in the early nineteenth century and is still going on today, has taken a new turn with the discovery of abundant footprints that had largely escaped the attention of earlier researchers. Fossil footprints are also the topic of the paper by **Bowden *et al.*** about *Chirotherium*, an ichnite that long remained a mystery, but attracted the attention of a group of dedicated 'footprint hunters' based in Liverpool, who not only tried to identify the track maker but also attempted to reconstruct the environment in which these tracks were made. **Naish** shows how dinosaur discoveries in the Wealden of England during the nineteenth century gradually led such well-known experts as Owen and Seeley to recognize the existence of pneumaticity in dinosaur bones and to speculate about its meaning.

Among the many controversies surrounding dinosaurs, one of the longest-enduring debates has been that about the origin of birds. **Wellnhofer** summarizes the many questions and interpretations raised by the 'primeval bird' *Archaeopteryx*, with its mixture of avian and reptilian characters, from the initial discoveries in the mid-nineteenth century to the present day. **Switek** discusses a directly related and important episode in the history of evolutionary palaeontology, viz. the recognition of the close relationship between birds and dinosaurs, with a detailed examination of Huxley's contribution to the question and how it developed through time. The paper by **Hansen** deals with the controversy about the identification of the digits in theropod dinosaurs and birds. He shows how conflicting interpretations were of considerable importance for the whole question of avian origins and for the now widely accepted idea that dinosaurs were ancestral to birds.

Ever since the first discoveries of skeletons of these flying reptiles, pterosaurs have been the focus of much attention on the part of palaeontologists. **Ösi *et al.*** both revise pterosaur specimens in Hungarian institutions and reconstruct their eventful histories, which in some cases goes back a long time, one of them having been part of the collection of Archduchess Maria Anna in the second half of the eighteenth century. **Martill** deals with discoveries of pterosaurs in England, which began in the early nineteenth century, and shows how their recognition was hampered by various misconceptions, although such renowned palaeontologists as Buckland, Mantell, Owen and Seeley were involved. **Witton** concentrates on the discovery of giant pterosaurs, which was initiated in England but really began with Marsh's find of *Pteranodon* in Kansas in 1870. Huge as it was, *Pteranodon* eventually lost its title of largest flying creature when even larger pterosaurs were found in the second half of the twentieth century.

Beyond scientific descriptions and interpretations, dinosaurs and other extinct saurians have also inspired artists, as illustrated by the last two papers in the volume. **Le Loeuff** depicts the life and work of Mathurin Méheut, a twentieth century painter whose art found wide recognition in his native Brittany. His reconstructions of prehistoric animals, including dinosaurs, ichthyosaurs and pterosaurs produced for the Institute of Geology of the University of Rennes in the 1940s during the German occupation of France, are an aspect of his work that deserves to be better known as an unusual example of palaeontological art. **Liston**, after briefly reviewing more conventional efforts, draws attention to a little-recognized medium for palaeontological reconstruction, viz. the comic strip, and shows how fast it accepted the new image of dinosaurs as active and agile animals conveyed by the 'Dinosaur renaissance' of the 1970s. Finally, **Taylor** provides an entertaining review of how our understanding of the archetypal sauropod dinosaurs developed, showing how some rather outlandish reconstructions required the dislocation of joints to achieve the poses in which they were depicted.

We hope that this volume may reflect the diversity of possible approaches to the history of vertebrate palaeontology in general. Beyond the well-known episodes that have been retold many times, much remains to be investigated. Further studies surely will reveal that the history of vertebrate palaeontology is more complex, richer and more fascinating than presently accepted.

During the preparation of this volume the Natural History Museum, London (NHM) changed the prefix code for its specimen numbers from BMNH to NHMUK. Both codes are to be found in this volume, reflecting the historical bias of specific manuscripts.

The Editors and the History of Geology Group would like to thank the BG Group, Premier Oil, The Curry Fund of the Geologists' Association and The Dinosaur Society for the support given during the lifetime of this project.

The roles played by museums, collections and collectors in the early history of reptile palaeontology

MARK EVANS

New Walk Museum and Art Gallery, 53 New Walk, Leicester LE1 7EA, UK; Department of Geology, University of Leicester, University Road, Leicester LE1 7RH, UK
(e-mail: mark.evans@leicester.gov.uk)

Abstract: The early history of reptile palaeontology is reviewed in order to assess the different roles played by museums, collections and collectors. The formal characterization and description of several fossil reptile groups (mosasaurs, pterosaurs, ichthyosaurs, plesiosaurs and dinosaurs) is then examined in a series of case histories. Fossil reptile bones were collected from the end of the sixteenth century, originally as objects of curiosity. The comprehensive collection of John Woodward (1665–1728) was an exception to this, and fossil reptiles only comprise a small fraction of the total number of specimens. Early discoveries of reptile fossils were interpreted within an anthropocentric context, with later interpretations being based on contemporary exotic faunas. The emergence of the systematic study of comparative anatomy at the end of the eighteenth century allowed more precise identifications of specimen's affinities, and demonstrated that extinction was a reality. Interpretations were no longer constrained by the contemporary biota. Georges Cuvier was instrumental in both of these advances. Collections and museums of comparative biological material were vital to his methods, and to the whole field of comparative anatomy. By the 1840s, fossil reptiles had been classified into separate and distinguishable groups. Private collectors were important for securing new discoveries, but specimens have only survived when they were acquired by institutional museums. Museums and their collections influenced the careers of such early pioneers as Richard Owen, who later became one of the most politically powerful scientists of the nineteenth century. It is hard to conceive how a field such as palaeontology could survive without collections, as fossil reptiles ably demonstrate.

Museums, collections and collectors have always had a very close association with palaeontology. Fossil reptiles are, perhaps, the most familiar palaeontological specimens that we associate with museums. Their very size makes them hard to ignore, and their fearsome-looking teeth and claws are tempered by the knowledge that they are safely extinct. Fossil reptiles, and in particular dinosaurs, are a mainstay of the modern museum visit. Yet, their relationship with museums and collections precedes the relatively recent 1990s craze of 'dinomania' and the film *Jurassic Park* (see Gould 1996, pp. 221–237) by hundreds of years.

With this in mind, this study examines the role of museums, collections and collectors in defining what we now know as fossil reptiles. It reviews the early discovery and interpretation of specimens, and presents case histories where the characterization and description of several fossil reptile groups will be examined. The groups under consideration are usually lumped together as 'dinosaurs' in the popular imagination. However, in reality they belonged to distinct and often distantly related lineages that dominated, respectively, the terrestrial, aerial and aquatic habitats of the Mesozoic Era. The history of ichthyosaur discoveries has been reviewed by Howe *et al.* (1981), Delair & Sarjeant (1975) reviewed the earliest dinosaur discoveries and the history of pterosaur discoveries has been documented by Wellnhofer (1991, 2008). Cadbury (2000) and McGowan (2001) provided more recent treatments of the subject, while Dean (1999) focused on the role of Gideon Mantell. Torrens (1997) explored the politics underlying the scientific discovery of the Dinosauria, and Taylor (1997) focused on the historical significance of Mesozoic marine reptile discoveries. Rudwick has recently provided an in-depth review and analysis of the development of geohistory (Rudwick 2005, 2008), while Knell (2000) has examined the social context of English geology in the first half of the nineteenth century, focusing on the culture of collecting.

Institutional abbreviations: BMNH, Natural History Museum, Cromwell Road, London, UK; MNHN, Muséum National d'Histoire Naturelle, Jardin des Plantes, rue Buffon, Paris, France; MONZ, Museum of New Zealand Te Papa Tongarewa, Wellington, New Zealand; OUMNH, Oxford University Museum of Natural History, Parks Road, Oxford, UK.

From: Moody, R. T. J., Buffetaut, E., Naish, D. & Martill, D. M. (eds) *Dinosaurs and Other Extinct Saurians: A Historical Perspective*. Geological Society, London, Special Publications, **343**, 5–29.
DOI: 10.1144/SP343.2 0305-8719/10/$15.00

The early relationship between museums and fossil reptiles

The interpretation of fossil reptiles developed in tandem with the emergence of the European museum from the sixteenth and seventeenth century 'cabinet of curiosities'. The establishment of museum collections was vital to the emergence of palaeontology (Rudwick 1976, p. 12), and collections obviously continue to be a necessarily central feature of the science to the present day. A cabinet was part of the essential apparatus of a learned gentleman, as listed by Francis Bacon in 1594 (see Impey & Macgregor 1985, p. 1), along with a library, garden, menagerie and laboratory. The *Kunstkammer* of Archduke Ferdinand II (1529–1595) contained 'giant's bones' now thought to have been those of dinosaurs (Scheicher 1985, p. 32). 'Giant's bones' could also be found in the gallery of the physic garden at the University of Pisa in the 1590s (Schupbach 1985, p. 170). These may have been fossil reptile bones, although they could also have been mammalian.

Fossils of all kinds were included in the *naturalia* of cabinets (Edwards 1967; Torrens 1985), but their organic nature was not generally appreciated. Originally a 'fossil' was any object that had been dug from the ground, and so a wide range of objects, with a similarly wide range of organic resemblance, were classified under this term (Rudwick 1976, pp. 1–2). The two dominant intellectual frameworks of the time, Neoplatonism and Aristotelianism, provided persuasive explanations for the organic resemblance of some fossil objects, and made theories of their organic origin unnecessary and counterintuitive (Rudwick 1976, pp. 34–35). Also, the localities in which even the most organic-looking fossils were found demanded a degree of geographical change that was unimaginable at the time. The only explanation was a catastrophic inundation, either the unique universal deluge of *The Bible* or one of a number of local events that was a natural part of the eternally changing Earth of Aristotle (Rudwick 1976, pp. 36–37).

Robert Hooke (1635–1703), Curator of Experiments of the Royal Society, investigated the morphology, composition and location of fossils, and proposed an organic origin for fossils such as ammonites (Hooke 1665, pp. 109–112, 1705, p. 291). However, the most persuasive reason for organic origins was on philosophical grounds, in that 'Nature does nothing in vain' (Hooke 1665, p. 112). This represents a shift from teleological Aristotelianism to the teleological designful universe of natural theology (Rudwick 1976, p. 56). Hooke also made a call for a well-documented collection of 'figur'd stones' to be made 'that from such a History of Observations well rang'd, examin'd and digested, the true original or production of all those kinds of stones might be perfectly and surely known' (Hooke 1665, p. 122). Hooke was so convinced by the teleological argument that fossils such as ammonites were organic, that he accepted their extinction. He hypothesized that new species had subsequently arisen to maintain the fullness of Creation (Rudwick 1976, pp. 61–65).

John Woodward (1665–1728) is probably the most important British geological collector of this period. He was also a diluvialist, and in *An Essay toward a Natural History of the Earth*, published in 1695, he described how the settling out of the flotsam and jetsam from the flood waters produced horizontally stratified rocks and fossils (Edwards 1967, pp. 11–12). Woodward's geological collection contained around 9400 specimens (Price 1989), and it is remarkable not only for its size, but for the nature of its contents. In contrast to the vast majority of collectors Woodward did not concentrate on 'curiosities', but on typical samples of rocks, minerals, fossils and the like. The collection was to be comprehensive and representative, and Woodward scorned collectors who concentrated on the 'abstruse and difficult' before they had 'duly inform'd themselves of Things the most obvious and common' (see Price 1989, p. 80). Much of the collection was from his own field studies, although he also had collecting agents and foreign correspondents. The agents were issued with collecting guidelines that contained detailed descriptions of field data that should be recorded (Torrens 1985, p. 212). On Woodward's death, part of the collection was bequeathed to the University of Cambridge, which purchased the remainder for £1000, while Woodward's estate was to fund a lecturer who would also curate the collection (Price 1989, pp. 83–84). The Woodwardian Collection formed the nucleus of what is now the Sedgwick Museum, and is currently housed in the 'Woodwardian Pew' of the museum.

The Woodwardian cabinets were searched for specimens that could be identified as reptilian during a visit to the Sedgwick Museum. The results of this search are shown in Table 1. Only 23 specimens constituting reptile material could be found. Another six specimens consisted of worn bone pieces that *could* have been reptile, while some of the tentative identifications of conical teeth may prove to be erroneous. The specimens had originally been interpreted as the remains of fish and quadrupeds. The fragmentary nature of these specimens would have made any other interpretation uncalled for. The small contribution of fossil reptiles to Woodward's collection demonstrates not only the rarity of such specimens, but also the all-embracing nature of the collection itself.

Table 1. *Reptilian specimens in Woodward's collection as preserved in the Sedgwick Museum, Cambridge*

Position no.	Old no.	Description and identification
B.20.26	B.9	Costal scute. Turtle
D.10.2	n.2	Rolled bone, black preservation. Dinosaurian?
D.10.8	n.8	Amphicoelous centrum. Ichthyosaurian
D.10.9	n.9	Worn centrum. Plesiosaurian
D.10.10	n.9.x	Two cervical vertebrae. Plesiosaurian (noted by Delair 1969)
D.10.11	n.9.a	Two cervical vertebrae. Plesiosaurian (noted by Delair 1969)
D.10.12	n.9.b	Cervical vertebra with double headed rib facet. Plesiosaurian
D.10.13	n.9.c	Damaged centrum. Possibly ichthyosaurian
D.10.42	n.34	Ichthyosaurian centrum
D.10.43	n.36	Ichthyosaurian centrum
D.10.44	n.36.x	Ichthyosaurian centrum
D.10.95	n.77	Assorted teeth, some crocodilian, others shark
D.25.55	E.d.2	Large amphicoelous centrum. Ichthyosaurian
D.25.56	E.d.3	Large amphicoelous centrum. Ichthyosaurian
D.25.69	E.d.16	Thin recurved tooth. Plesiosaurian?
D.25.70	E.d.17	Conical tooth. Crocodilian?
D.25.71	E.d.18	Conical tooth with two carinae. Crocodilian
D.25.72	E.d.19	Proximal part of laterally compressed tooth, any carinae lost to abrasion. Theropod
D.30.1	a.1	Section of limb bone. Theropod (noted by Delair & Sarjeant 1975)
D.30.5	a.5	Two slightly curved conical teeth. Crocodilian
D.30.13	a.14	Upper jaw with alveoli but no teeth. Crocodilian
D.30.14	a.15	Lower jaw with alveoli but no teeth. Crocodilian
E.27.44	m.80	Two conical teeth, one more compressed than the other. Crocodilian, or possibly small pliosaur

Note: 'Position no.' refers to a numbering system connected with a specimen's position within a specific drawer within a specific cabinet (A, B, etc.). 'Old no.' refers to Woodward's numbering system.

The first published illustration and description of material now known to be dinosaurian was by Robert Plot (1640–1696) in his 1677 *Natural History of Oxfordshire*. Incidentally, it was this publication that caught the eye of Elias Ashmole and persuaded him that Oxford would be a suitable home for the future Ashmolean Museum (Gunther 1939, p. 333). It also assisted Plot in becoming the Ashmolean's first 'Keeper'. The specimen (Fig. 1), a distal femoral condyle identified as belonging to *Megalosaurus* by Delair & Sarjeant (1975, pp. 6–7), was found in a quarry at Cornwell in Oxfordshire (Plot 1677, p. 131), but has not survived. Plot donated his collection to the Ashmolean after he resigned the keepership in 1690, but the whole collection has since been lost, along with the vast majority of the museum's seventeenth-century geological specimens (Gunther 1925, pp. 216, 341 and 375). Plot wondered if the bone was from an elephant brought to Britain by the Romans, but he could find no evidence of this from classical sources (Plot 1677, pp. 133–136). When, in 1676, he compared the bone with that of an elephant he found that they differed in both size and morphology. Plot concluded that his specimen must have come from a human giant, and speculated that the Romans might have brought this giant to Cornwell (Plot 1677, pp. 136–137). In 1763 Richard Brookes (1720–1772) described the same specimen, closely following Plot's description, and figured it under the illustrative caption 'Scrotum humanum' (Brookes 1763, facing 318). Plot himself is often accredited with this identification in popular palaeontological literature (e.g. Norell *et al.* 1995, p. 6). Plot thought that fossil shellfish were produced by a 'plastic force', and suggested

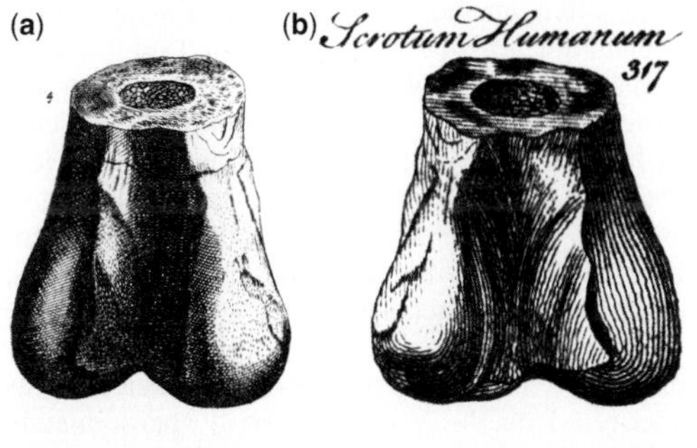

Fig. 1. (**a**) The Cornwell bone, as figured by Plot (1677). (**b**) The same as figured, and named, by Brookes (1763).

that ammonites were formed by the action of two competing salts (Edwards 1967, p. 5), but the internal structure of the bone convinced him it was organic in origin. He considered other fossil 'bones' with no internal structure, which may have been natural casts or nodules, to be the result of the 'plastic power' (Plot 1677, p. 132).

Isolated vertebrae that can now be identified as plesiosaurian were first illustrated in 1605 by Richard Verstegan (*c.* 1550–1640), an Anglo-Dutch Catholic living in Antwerp. He identified them as 'great bones of fishes' and considered them evidence that the island of 'Albion' (i.e. Great Britain) had once been connected to the European mainland (Howe *et al.* 1981, pp. 5–6; Davidson 2000). Similarly, ichthyosaur and plesiosaur vertebrae were identified as *Ichthyospondyli*, or fish vertebrae, by Edward Lhwyd (1660–1709) in his *Lithophylacii Britannici Ichnographia*, published in 1699. Lhwyd, who was Plot's successor as Keeper of the Ashmolean Museum, assembled collections of duplicate specimens for purchase by interested persons. One of these collections, discovered earlier this century by R. T. Gunther, was found to contain a tooth of the thalattosuchian crocodilian *Teleosaurus sp.* (Gunther 1945, p. 559 and plate 13). Lhwyd believed his fossils were due to the growth of an organism's 'seed' that had lodged in the Earth (Rudwick 1976, p. 84).

In 1719 the first articulated specimen of a fossil reptile was described by William Stukely (1687–1765). Robert Darwin (*c.* 1682–1754), great-grandfather of Charles, had drawn his attention to a slab of rock containing a partial skeleton (Fig. 2), which Stukely subsequently purchased for the Repository of the Royal Society (Stukely 1719). The skeleton had been displayed at the parsonage in Elston near Newark, the Darwins' country seat and birthplace of Erasmus Darwin (1731–1802) (King-Hele 1963, p. 13). Robert Darwin

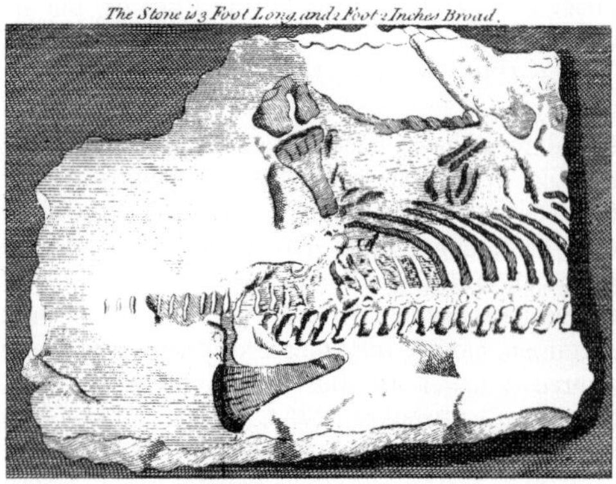

The Stone is 3 Foot Long, and 2 Foot 2 Inches Broad.

Fig. 2. The Elston plesiosaur BMNH R.1330 (from Stukely 1719).

was received by the Royal Society as a guest of Stukely's in recognition of his being 'a person of curiosity' (King-Hele 1999, p. 2). The specimen was thought to have come from the nearby quarries of Fulbeck, and the slab had been used as a 'Landing-place' at a well in Elston before the skeleton was discovered on its underside. The specimen, along with the rest of the Royal Society Repository, was presented to the British Museum in 1781 (Lydekker 1889, p. 259; British Museum (Natural History) 1904, p. 321). It is now on display in Gallery 30 of the Natural History Museum, where it bears the registration number BMNH R.1330 and is identified as *Plesiosaurus dolichodeirus*.

The skeleton was originally said to be human, but Stukely identified it as that of a crocodile or porpoise. This identification seems to derive in part from Stukely's theory that the Fulbeck fossils were deposited against the cliff of the 'Lincolnshire Alpes' by the floodwaters of the Deluge as they receded towards the North Sea. An 'amphibious or marine' animal would survive longer in this 'World of Waters' than a terrestrial animal and so the skeleton would still be articulated when the waters receded (Stukely 1719, p. 967). Stukely also outlined a 'Notion of Petrifaction', deduced from 'Sir Isaac Newton's Doctrine of the Attraction of the Particles of Matter' This accounted not only for the hard rock that surrounded the skeleton, but also for the longevity of ancient buildings and the barrenness of the Middle East (Stukely 1917, pp. 965–967).

Stukely's description places his fossil reptile in the same context as the fossil shells found at Fulbeck. The fossils all have an organic origin, with the Flood being the agent of deposition. Debates on the nature of fossils had tended to concentrate on invertebrate fossils. Fossil bones had generally been recognized as organic in origin, but were given peculiarly anthropocentric interpretations. The existence in antiquity of a race of giants was a common belief (Plot 1677, pp. 136–138; Hooke 1705, p. 327; Rudwick 1976, p. 75), and, as noted above, the remains of fossil reptiles were often attributed to them. Plot's alternative explanation for his bone again relied on a human agency, this time the Roman Empire. Even the Elston skeleton had itself been initially interpreted as human. 'Scientific' interpretations became less anthropocentric during the eighteenth century as concepts of Earth history developed, most fossil reptiles discoveries being identified as cetaceans, pachyderms or crocodiles.

In some cases these discoveries were true crocodilians. In 1758 a fossil crocodilian skeleton was uncovered on the Yorkshire coast, approximately half a mile from Whitby (Fig. 3). This was reported to the Royal Society by Captain William Chapman

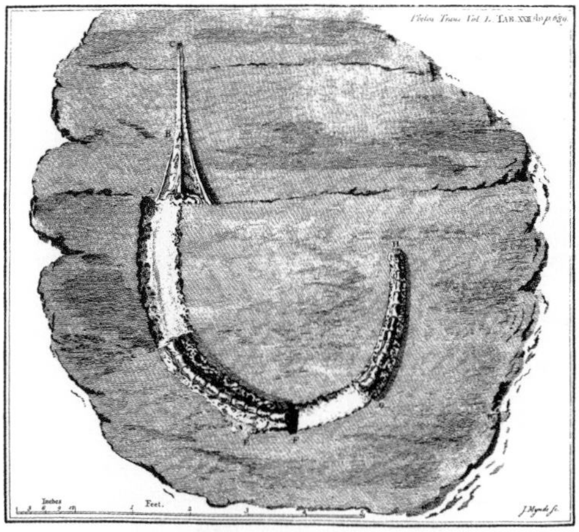

Fig. 3. The crocodile discovered near Whitby (BMNH R.1087a from Chapman 1758).

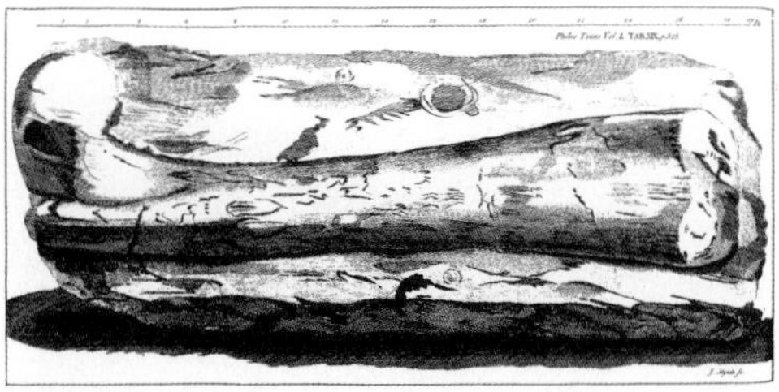

Fig. 4. The fossil femur from Stonesfield (from Platt 1758).

(1713–1793), and a further description was given by civil engineer John Wooler (d. 1783) (Chapman 1758; Wooler 1758). The skeleton was presented to the Society by Chapman's correspondent, John Fothergill, and, like the Elston skeleton, it is currently in the Natural History Museum. It was on display in 1922 in the old fossil reptile gallery, where it was identified as the thalattosuchian *Mystriosaurus chapmani* (British Museum (Natural History) 1922), while Lydekker had earlier listed it as *Steneosaurus chapmani*, BMNH R.1087a (Lydekker 1888, p. 111). This species has since been synonymized with *S. bollensis* (Westphal 1962; Steel 1973). Chapman tentatively identified it as an alligator, while Wooler considered it to be identical to the recently discovered gavial or gharial (Edwards 1756). Wooler's description shows that the concepts of actualism (*sensu* Rudwick 1976, p. 110) and the relative ages of strata were already developing. However, he felt that the universal Deluge was the only force capable of depositing this exotic creature. It is also clear from his statement that 'at the beginning [the cliff] must have extended near a mile further down to the sea' that his time frame of Earth history was of the order of a few thousand years.

At the same time a fossil femur of a large animal was found in a slate pit at Stonesfield in Oxfordshire (Platt 1758). Platt had compared it with the femur of an elephant, but could see no resemblance. He concluded that it belonged to a hippopotamus, rhinoceros 'or some such large animal, of whose anatomy we have not yet a competent knowledge'. From the figure in Platt's paper, the bone (Fig. 4) was that of a dinosaur, probably a theropod. As Benson (2009) has determined that the assemblage of large theropod material from Stonesfield is monospecific, the femur can be referred to *Megalosaurus* Buckland 1824. Platt thought the bone to be antediluvian, and he appears to suggest that its good condition was evidence against deposition by the Flood (Platt 1758, p. 525). Delair & Sarjeant (1975, p. 10) reported that the whereabouts of this specimen was unknown.

Further discoveries of fossil 'crocodiles' and 'cetaceans' were made in the late eighteenth and early nineteenth centuries that can now be attributed to ichthyosaurs and plesiosaurs. The skeleton of a 40 foot 'Young Whale' had been discovered at Weston near Bath by 1766, while the jaw of a supposed crocodile was exhibited in London in 1783 (Torrens 1979*b*, pp. 225–226; Howe *et al.* 1981, p. 6). Both of these fossils are now thought to be ichthyosaurian (Howe *et al.* 1981, p. 7), although the specimens no longer exist. Two fossil reptile specimens were added to the Woodwardian cabinets in Cambridge over this period. A specimen from the quarries of Barrow-upon-Soar, Leicestershire was accessioned in 1779 by Thomas Green, the fifth Woodwardian Professor (Green 1779–1785). The specimen, number D.11.35b, was apparently an ichthyosaur skull (MS note, dated 1967, in Green 1779–1785), and a plaster cast of it is still in Cambridge, although not in the Sedgwick Museum (R. Long pers. comm. 1996). In 1784 a theropod scapula from Stonesfield, noted by Delair & Sarjeant (1975, p. 10), was accessioned as D.11.34a. It had originally been presented by Dr Richard Watson (1737–1816), the Bishop of Llandaff, to Trinity College, before being passed on to the Woodwardian Museum (Green 1779–1785). The theropod scapula was thought to have come from a very large quadruped, while the nature of the ichthyosaur skull had not been 'ascertained' (Green 1779–1785).

Nichols (1795, p. ccv) described the fossil bones in the collections of the Reverends Mounsey and Turner of the Vale of Belvoir, Leicestershire. The majority of these bones, including several partial skeletons, appear to have been plesiosaurian, although some ichthyosaurian vertebrae are also figured (see Fig. 5). Other 'petrified bodies' from

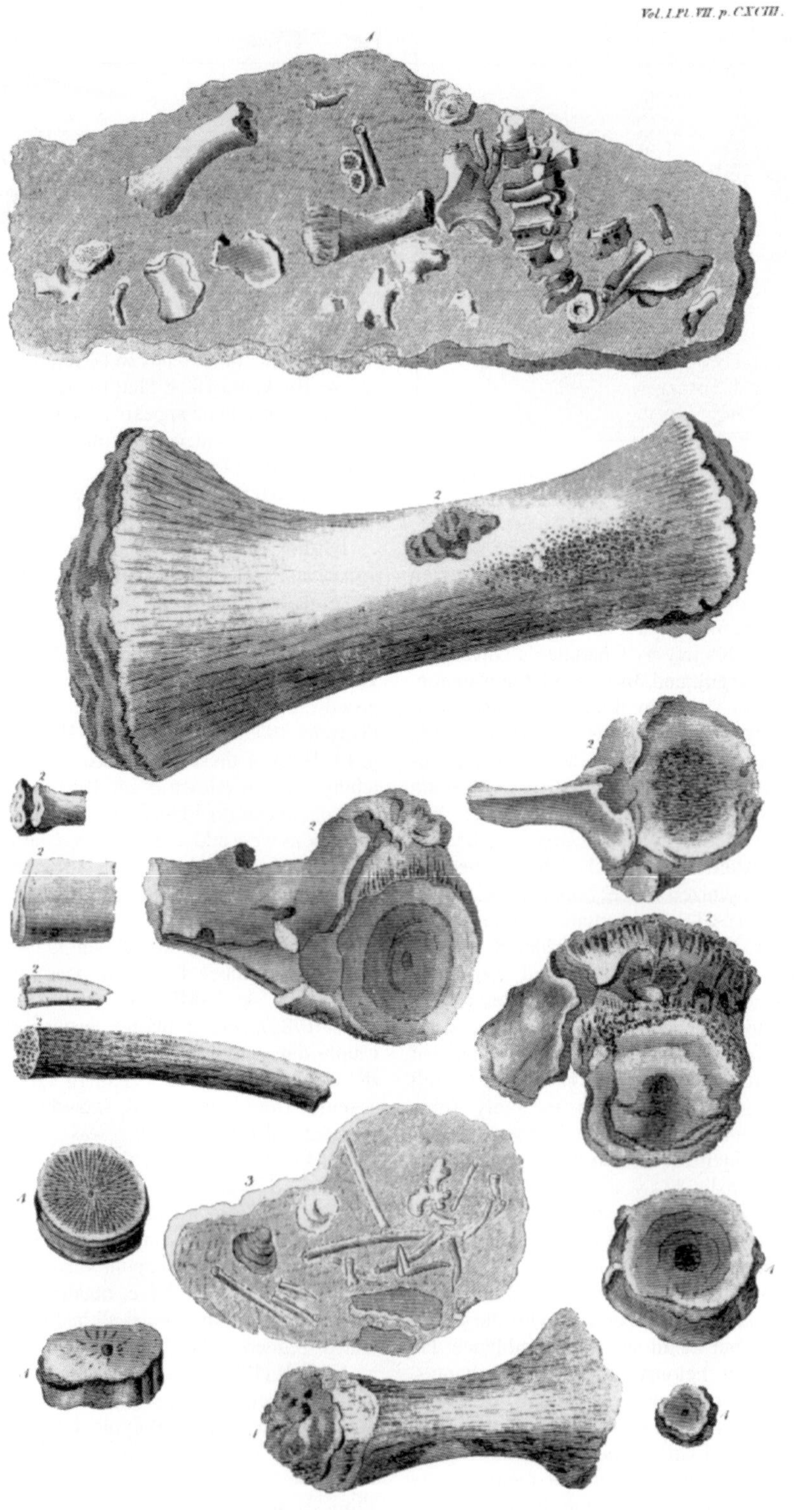

Fig. 5. Fossil reptile specimens from Mounsey's collection figured by Nichols (1795).

the same deposits were thought to be marine, and so the bones were attributed to 'some cetaceous fish' (Nichols 1795, p. ccv). However, Nichols considered the robust plesiosaurian propodials to be the limb bones of 'some short thick quadrupede'. Unfortunately, it would seem that Mounsey's collections have been lost, but Turner's specimen was presented to the British Museum in 1880 by Major Harlowe Turner (Lydekker 1889, p. 264; British Museum (Natural History) 1904, pp. 231–232). It is currently on display in Gallery 30 of the Natural History Museum as BMNH R.45, identified as *Plesiosaurus hawkinsi* (now referred to the genus *Thalassiodracon* Storrs & Taylor 1996).

Another ichthyosaur was found at Weston in 1804 or 1805 by the Rev. Peter Hawker (*c.* 1773–1833), and was identified as a crocodile (Cumberland (1829) gives the date as 1812). This specimen was widely publicized in the scientific circles of the day (Hawker 1807; Howe *et al.* 1981, pp. 9–10) so that it became known as 'Hawker's Crocodile'. Howe *et al.* (1981) suggested that this historic specimen was acquired by Bristol Museum in 1823 only to be destroyed by bombing in November 1940 (Anon. 1941*b*). A 'crocodile' discovered at Wilmcote near Stratford-upon-Avon in 1810 can now be seen to be the jaw of an ichthyosaur and the partial skeleton of a plesiosaur combined (Howe *et al.* 1981, p. 10). The jaw is now in the Sedgwick Museum, but the other half of this chimaeric specimen appears to have been lost.

Even by this time, the relationship between fossil reptiles and collections was essentially unchanged from that of the cabinets of the sixteenth century and their curios. Even isolated vertebrate fossils are much rarer than invertebrate fossils, and an articulated skeleton was something to be wondered at. Private collectors were the main source of specimens, and the majority of their collections have now been dispersed and lost. Even acquisition of specimens by the fledgling museums did not guarantee their survival, as the tragic loss of the collections of Plot and Lhwyd shows. The interpretations of these fossils, whilst being more biological than those of an earlier age, were still firmly rooted in the contemporary fauna of crocodilians, cetaceans and large terrestrial mammals. From this we can see that, although the concept of extinction had been in existence since the time of Hooke, the consensus was still that the ancient world had been very much like the present. With the exception of authentic crocodilians, fossil reptiles were morphologically unlike any group of animals known at that time. Furthermore, meaningful comparisons with extant vertebrates were not easy due to a lack of osteological knowledge, as Platt (1758, p. 526) recognized. The characterization of the various groups of fossil reptiles would only be possible once the field of comparative anatomy had matured to a sufficient level.

Museums and their role in the formal characterization and differentiation of fossil reptile groups

Specimens of fossil reptiles had been in museum collections, both private and public, for several hundred years by the beginning of the nineteenth century. These specimens generated much interest amongst both the scientific community of the day and the general public. However, as the preceding section shows, they had not been characterized and identified as any new type of animal. 'Hawkers Crocodile', for example, had been widely exhibited, publicized and scrutinized (Hawker 1807; Howe *et al.* 1981, pp. 9–10). However, even after all this attention, it still remained a 'crocodile', despite being what would today be recognized as an ichthyosaur.

However, by the time that Richard Owen (1804–1892) published his reports on British fossil reptiles for the British Association for the Advancement of Science (Owen 1840, 1842), all of the groups under consideration below had been distinguished and, to some extent, characterized. Many details are now regarded as inaccurate, but this is due to the relative lack of good specimens in most cases. What is important is that the different fossil reptile groups were an accepted part of the history of life, in whatever way this was interpreted. The case histories of the formal description and characterization of the groups will now be considered in approximately chronological order.

Mosasaurs

In 1766 a Major Drouin started collecting the fossils from the chalk hills surrounding Maastricht in the present-day Netherlands. In his collection, which was subsequently passed on to Teyler's Museum in Haarlem, were some large jaw bones that he thought to be crocodilian (Camper 1786, p. 444; Cuvier 1812*a*, pp. 3–4). The specimen survives as TM 7424 (Mulder 2004). Recently, doubt has been cast on the accepted history of the next step in the chain of events (Bardet & Jagt 1996; Mulder 2004). The prize specimen, a large set of jaws, had been found in the nearby chalk quarries of St Peter's Mountain some time between 1770 and 1774, and ultimately came into the possession of Dr Goddin, Dean of the chapter of Maastricht. The specimen remained in Goddin's possession until 1795, when Maastricht was taken by the French army in 1795. The French commander had been

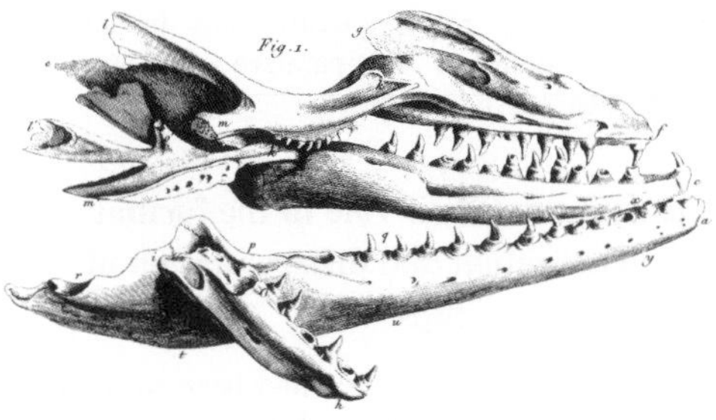

Fig. 6. The jaws of the Great Fossil Animal of Maastricht, MNHN-AC9648 (from Cuvier 1812*a*).

given orders to secure the by-now famous fossil, and Barthélemy Faujas de Saint-Fond (1741–1819), acting as Commissary for the Sciences of the 'Armée du Nord', conveyed it to the Muséum d'Histoire Naturelle in Paris (Faujas de St.-Fond 1799), where it remains (MNHN-AC9648) (Fig. 6). Faujas de Saint-Fond's account of the discovery and collection of the specimen would now seem to be misleading (Mulder 2004), and could be considered an act of propaganda. M. J. Everhart (pers. com.) suggests it was an attempt to justify the confiscation of the specimen by the French authorities. Faujas de Saint-Fond (1799) recounted how Maastricht surgeon and collector J. L. Hoffmann (1710–1782) painstakingly collected the specimen, only to have it unjustly seized by Goddin, who was in turn relieved of it by the scientifically aware French troops. Nevertheless, it seems that Hoffmann had been instrumental in making the various fossil specimens known to the wider world (Mulder 2004).

The large bones and jaws from the Maastricht chalk were originally thought to be crocodilian by most observers. Both Hoffmann and Drouin interpreted the specimens in their collections as such, and Faujas de Saint Fond was of the same opinion in his 1799 description of the natural history of the area. The Dutch anatomist Petrus Camper (1722–1789) was convinced that the bones belonged to 'physeteres or respiring fishes [i.e. cetaceans]', and he dissuaded Hoffmann from publishing a crocodilian interpretation (Camper 1786, pp. 443–444). He even went as far as declaring that the 'pretended crocodile' from Whitby (Chapman 1758; Wooler 1758, see above) was also a cetacean. He considered the palatal teeth, in reality unknown in both crocodilians and cetaceans, as a cetacean character because palatal tooth plates are found in some fish (Camper 1786). Camper purchased the principal specimens from Hoffmann's collection after the latter's death, and in 1784 he presented to the British Museum a mosasaurian lower jaw, now specimen BMNH R.1224 (Lydekker 1888, p. 263; British Museum (Natural History) 1904, pp. 201 and 275).

Adriaan Gilles Camper (1759–1820), son of Petrus, re-examined his father's specimens, and interpreted them as saurian reptiles with resemblances to monitors and iguanas (see Cuvier 1812*a*, p. 6; Owen 1851–1864, p. 29). This view was endorsed and developed by Georges Cuvier (1769–1832). Cuvier was Professor of Comparative Anatomy at the new Muséum d'Histoire Naturelle in Paris, and is often hailed as the father of comparative anatomy and vertebrate palaeontology (see Rudwick 2005 for a full account of Cuvier's career). However, Cuvier had initially been unconvinced by the combination of skull and vertebral material proposed by A. G. Camper, and needed to be persuaded by the latter that this was the case (Theunissen 1986). Cuvier admitted that it might seem strange to some that the Maastricht animal was so much larger than these present-day species, and was marine when there were no known marine lizards in the modern world (Cuvier 1812*a*). However, these apparently common-sense objections did not perturb Cuvier. As he said, he had already seen an elephant-sized tapir and a rhinoceros-sized sloth, so a crocodile-sized monitor lizard wasn't so surprising (Cuvier 1812*a*). His faith in his methodology overcame any reservations over his conclusion. He declared that a single tooth could tell him everything, and that the rest of the skeleton would then arrange itself. Later Hermann Schlegel (1804–1884) asserted that Hoffmann had falsified some of his specimens, and that this had impeded the work of A. G. Camper and Cuvier (Schlegel 1854; Mulder & Theunissen 1986). Mulder & Theunissen (1986) concluded that the available evidence indicates that Hoffmann did not intentionally falsify his specimens, and noted that Schlegel had been the first to correctly reconstruct mosasaurian limbs as paddles.

Despite this characterization of the animal from Maastricht, it still did not have a name. William Daniel Conybeare (1787–1857) referred to it as 'the fossil animal of Maestricht' (Conybeare 1822, pp. 106–107), while William Buckland (1784–1856) called it the 'gigantic monitor of Maestricht' (Buckland 1824, p. 393). The name *Mosasaurus*, from the Latin for the River Meuse, was proposed by Conybeare in the absence of a proper alternative (Parkinson 1822, p. 298). Cuvier accepted this name, whilst noting that the name was one which 'one can adopt while waiting for a generic name better determined from its characters' (Cuvier 1824, p. 338, my translation). Gideon Mantell (1790–1852) completed the animal's Linnaean binomial by erecting 'Mososaurus Hoffmannii' in honour of its alleged discoverer (Mantell 1829, p. 207).

Pterosaurs

The first known pterosaur specimen was initially described by Cosimo Alessandro Collini (1727–1806) in 1784 (Wellnhofer 1991, 2008). In 1764 Collini had been appointed by Karl Theodor (1733–1799), the Elector Palatine, to supervise his Naturalienkabinett at Mannheim. The specimen arrived here between 1767 and 1784, and was probably presented by the Graf of Pappenheim, a town near the lithographical limestone quarries of Solnhofen and Eichstätt in Bavaria (Wellnhofer 1991, 2008). Collini determined that the skeleton was that of neither a bird nor a bat, and he ultimately suggested that it was some form of marine creature (Cuvier 1812*c*, p. 32; Wellnhofer 1991).

Cuvier's attention was drawn to the strange skeleton by a letter he received in 1800 from his friend Jean Hermann (1738–1800), Professor of Medicine in Strasbourg (Taquet & Padian 2004). Hermann accompanied his letter with the first restoration of a pterosaur, and regarded it as forming a better intermediate between birds and mammals than bats. Although he had correctly recognized the form of the wings, Hermann's interpretation did not influence that of Cuvier, who quickly completed his analysis by the end of the year and widely published it in 1801 (Taquet & Padian 2004). All he had to work on was Collini's description and engraving as he believed that the specimen had been lost when the Mannheim cabinet had been transferred to Munich (Cuvier 1812*c*, p. 25). He reviewed Collini's conclusions, and those of other workers. Some thought that the fossil animal was an intermediate form between mammals and birds, while others had interpreted it as a web-footed bird (Cuvier 1812*c*, pp. 33–34). Cuvier analysed all of the alleged resemblances to these groups and concluded that, '[a]u contraire', the animal had reptilian characters. Once again he claimed that a single feature, this time the cylindrical quadrate bone, had demonstrated its reptilian nature to him 'at first sight' (Cuvier 1812*c*, pp. 35–36). The other details of the skeleton confirmed this classification, and Cuvier declared that his anatomical laws had received their full and entire practical application. He recognized that the long fourth finger supported a membrane which formed a wing, and he christened his flying reptile 'Ptero-Dactyle', from the Greek for 'wing finger' (Fig. 7). Lorenz Oken (1779–1851), at that time Professor of Medicine and Natural History at Jena (Kurtesz 1986), Latinized Cuvier's name to *Pterodactylus* in 1818 (Taquet & Padian 2004).

Fortunately, the specimen had not been lost. It was actually in Munich, but was being worked on by Samuel Thomas von Soemmerring (1755–1830) at the Bavarian Academy of Science. He interpreted the fossil as a mammal forming a transitional link between bats and birds (Wellnhofer 1991, p. 24). He named it *Ornithocephalus antiquus*, and in 1817 described a second pterosaur specimen as

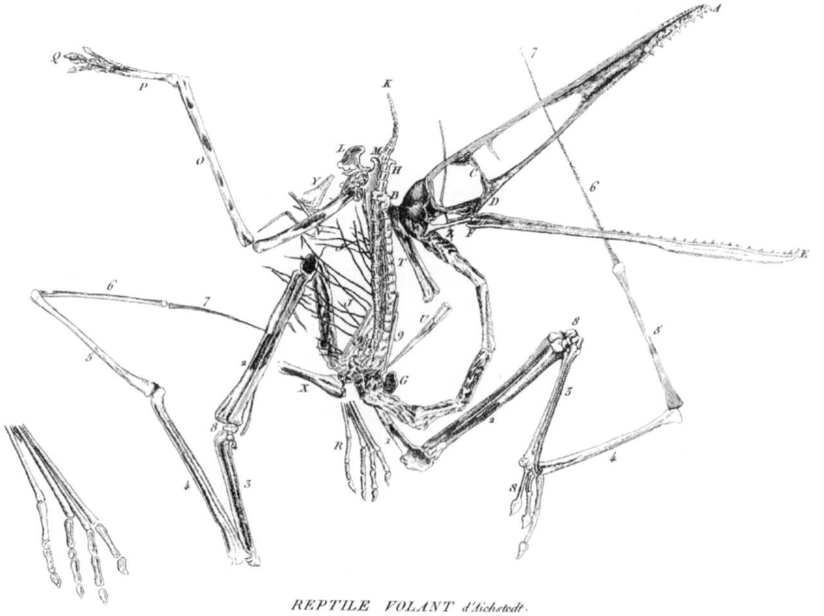

Fig. 7. The Eichstätt Ptero-Dactyle (from Cuvier 1812*c*).

O. brevirostris. Soemmerring presented a restoration in which this specimen was given a wide bat-like wing attached at the ankle. Padian (1987) argued that this restoration was responsible for initiating the tradition of depicting pterosaurs as clumsy gliders rather than as agile bipeds capable of powered flight as he proposed (Padian 1983). Both this specimen and the original Ptero-Dactyle are in the Bayerische Staatssammlung für Paläontologie und historische Geologie in Munich (Wellnhofer 1991, p. 192). The first British pterosaur was described in 1829 by Buckland, and was named *Pterodactylus macronyx* on account of its larger claws (Buckland 1829*a*). It is today known as *Dimorphodon macronyx*. The specimen had been found in 1828 by Mary Anning (1799–1847) at Lyme Regis in Dorset, and is now in the Natural History Museum, registered number BMNH R.1034 (Lydekker 1888, p. 38). Buckland noted that what he now suspected were pterosaur bones had previously been found at Lyme and Stonesfield, but had been attributed to birds (e.g. Buckland 1824, p. 392).

Ichthyosaurs

The history of recognition of ichthyosaurs as a specific group is somewhat convoluted and tortuous, and has been described by Howe *et al.* (1981, pp. 12–20). Although several well-preserved specimens, such as 'Hawker's Crocodile', were well known by the early nineteenth century, the scientific description of ichthyosaurs was initiated by a discovery at Lyme Regis. Joseph Anning (1796–1849) is reputed to have found the skull of this 'crocodile' in 1811, while the remainder of the vertebral column was found by his more famous sister, Mary, the following year (Howe *et al.* 1981, p. 12). Their father, Richard (*c.* 1766–1810), had been selling fossils for some time to supplement his income from cabinet making, and their mother, Mary or Molly (*c.* 1764–1842), also took part in what became the family business (Howe *et al.* 1981, p. 11; Torrens 1995). The fossil was sold to the Lord of the Manor, Henry Henley, for £23, and provided much needed funds for the Anning family following Richard's death. The significant role of the Anning family in the history of palaeontology has been examined by a number of authors (Lang 1936, 1939, 1945, 1960; Delair 1969; Taylor & Torrens 1987; Riley 1991; Torrens 1995). Torrens (1995) has concluded that there has been much confusion between Mary Anning senior and junior in the history of palaeontology; it was very much a family business, at least up until the 1820s. Henley deposited the specimen in William Bullock's (fl. 1795–1840) London Museum of Natural History in Piccadilly. When Bullock auctioned his collection in 1819 (Mullens 1917) the specimen was bought for the British Museum for £47.5s by the then Keeper of Natural History, Charles König (1774–1851) (Howe *et al.* 1981, p. 12). The skull is presently on display in Gallery 30 of the Natural History Museum as *Temnodontosaurus platyodon*, registered number BMNH R.1158 (Fig. 8).

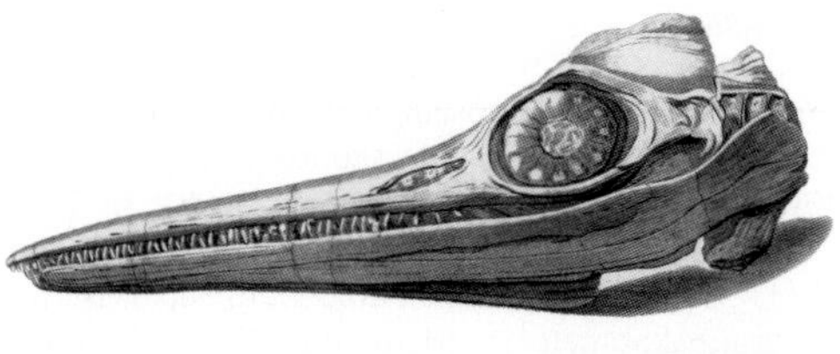

Fig. 8. The Annings's ichthyosaur skull BMNH R.1158, as figured by Home (1814).

This specimen formed the basis of the first of a series of papers on ichthyosaurs by Sir Everard Home (1756–1832), Hunterian Professor at the Royal College of Surgeons (Flower 1898, p. 99). Home was assisted by a network of collectors and correspondents following his first paper on the Anning ichthyosaur (Home 1814). Specimens from the collections of Buckland and James Johnson (*c.* 1764–1844) of Bristol were described and figured in Home's second paper (Home 1816). The third paper (Home 1818) was based on specimens and communications from Peter Hawker and Dr Thomas Coulson Carpenter of Lyme, as well as Buckland and 'Johnston' (i.e. Johnson). Home also received correspondence from Henry Thomas De la Beche (1796–1855), at that time a young collector based in Lyme. Home's two papers of 1819 drew on ichthyosaur specimens from De la Beche and Lt Col. Thomas James Birch (*c.* 1768–1829) of Lincolnshire (Torrens 1979*a*, 1980), and axolotl material from Dr William Elford Leach (1790–1836) (Home 1819*a*, *b*). The final paper in this series (Home 1820) described new specimens collected by Birch at Lyme. Home also had at his disposal the Museum of the Royal College of Surgeons, containing the most extensive anatomical collection in the country.

Home initially interpreted his new animal as a fish, but forming a connecting link with animals higher up in the Great Chain of 'animated beings' (Home 1814, 1816). Rupke (1983) has described the importance of the doctrine of the Chain of Being to the English school of historical geology in the early nineteenth century. Home later drew analogies between the sternum (actually the coracoids) and that of the 'ornithorhynchus', or duck-billed platypus (Home 1818). This convinced Home that it could not be a fish: however, he did not offer an alternative interpretation, and left it

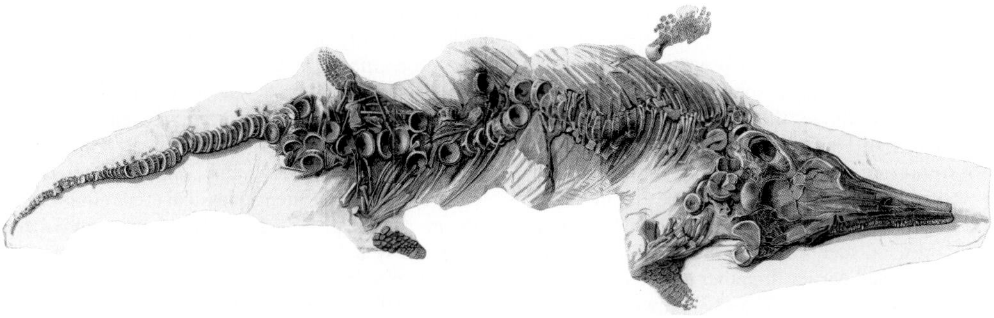

Fig. 9. Birch's complete ichthyosaur, as figured by Home (1819*a*).

somewhat in 'limbo'. The following year Home figured a relatively complete skeleton from Birch's collection that showed the hind limbs (Fig. 9). The animal was definitely not a fish, but had strikingly fish-like vertebrae. It was this character that Home used in trying to find 'the place in the chain of created beings, to which the animal belonged' (Home 1819*b*, p. 212). He saw similarities between these amphicoelous vertebrae and those of a salamander, *Proteus*, and thus concluded that the animal's place in the Chain was between *Proteus* and lizards, and so called it *Proteosaurus*. Home's last paper on '*Proteosaurus*' stuck to this interpretation, and contained observations on the vertebrae and paddle (Home 1820).

However, as De la Beche noted in his diaries for 1818 and 1819, Home's interpretation and christening of the new animal was not popular (see Howe *et al.* 1981, p. 16). König had already named the animal *Ichthyosaurus* in 1817 (Torrens 1995, p. 260), and, although he provided no description, this drew attention to its place in the Great Chain. This is what probably forced Home to propose his own name in 1819 (Home 1819*b*), and he rejected *Ichthyosaurus* as he thought that the animal was closer to lizards than to fish. Home was closer to the modern interpretation than König, but both were still constrained within the framework of a linear Chain of Being.

In the first comprehensive description of ichthyosaur anatomy, De la Beche and Conybeare used König's *Ichthyosaurus*, stating that the animal's analogies with *Proteus* were insufficient to sanction the changing of the earlier name (De la Beche & Conybeare 1821, pp. 563–564). In contrast to Home, who published anatomical snippets on isolated fossils, De la Beche & Conybeare presented a synthesis from many specimens, and attempted a reconstruction of the head. Taylor (1994, p. 181) considered their work on marine reptiles to be some of the first competent British work in vertebrate palaeontology. Both men had made collections of Lower Lias fossils, although De la Beche's seems to have been the more significant (De la Beche & Conybeare 1821, pp. 559–560). In addition to their own collections, they relied on a large network of collectors from the South West: Richard Bright (1754–1840); a Dr Dyer; J. S. Miller (1779–1830); Johnson; George Weare Brackenridge (1775–1856); George Cumberland (1754–1848); a Mr Page; and Birch (De la Beche & Conybeare 1821, p. 560; Taylor 1994). Birch and Johnson possessed the most significant specimens, which are referred to in the paper by De la Beche & Conybeare (1821, pp. 574, 575 and 579). This detailed anatomical description was, in fact, the prologue to the briefer description of a new animal, which they christened *Plesiosaurus* (see later). Cumberland (1829) provided an account of the early discoveries of ichthyosaurs and other marine reptiles, and praised the 'patient labours' of Mary Anning.

In a paper read to the Geological Society in 1819, but not published until 1822, De la Beche named three species of *Ichthyosaurus*, *I. communis*, *I. platyodon* and *I. tenuirostris*, which he distinguished on skull and tooth characters (De la Beche 1822, p. 43). Conybeare (1822, p. 108) formally described these three species along with another, *I. intermedius*. Again, he was working with the assistance of De la Beche, who, along with Birch and the Oxford Museum, provided specimens for research. Conybeare's last paper on marine reptiles (Conybeare 1824) included the first reconstruction of an ichthyosaur, based on a specimen of *I. communis* in the Bristol Institution. This specimen was the first palaeontological donation to the Institution's museum, and had been purchased from the Annings for £50 by a group of donors including Conybeare and De la Beche (Taylor & Torrens 1987, p. 139; Taylor 1994, p. 186). As Taylor (1994) pointed out, the Institution and its museum enabled members to pool their resources and acquire specimens and assorted academic accoutrements that might otherwise be outside their individual budgets.

Plesiosaurs

The recognition of the plesiosaur was a much less protracted affair than that of the ichthyosaur. As was noted above, the primary objective of the 1821 paper of De la Beche & Conybeare was the description of this new creature. This required a thorough understanding of the ichthyosaur's anatomy so that the two could be differentiated. They drew on specimens from the group of collectors mentioned earlier, together with the collection of Alexander Catcott (1725–1779), which was preserved in the Bristol Library Society (Taylor 1994, p. 179). Knell (2000, pp. 194–195) records how Conybeare delegated De la Beche with the search for specimens of their new animal in the local Lyme collections, especially Anning's. Once again, Birch's collection held the most significant specimen, a disarticulated partial skeleton including elements of the forelimb and 63 vertebrae. At least some of this important specimen has, in fact, survived and has been rediscovered in the Oxford University Museum of Natural History. The partial paddle OUMNH J.50146 (Fig. 10) is without doubt the one figured by De la Beche & Conybeare (1821, plate 42, fig. 1) and it is possible that more of the original specimen may be identified in the Oxford collections; research is ongoing. The specimen formed the basis of a reconstruction of the forelimb, which Conybeare admitted was conjectural to some degree. In a short review of fossil 'crocodiles', they recognized that the Elston skeleton (Fig. 2) was a small plesiosaur. Conybeare was suitably charitable towards Cuvier, who had identified it as a crocodile based on the illustration of 1719 (Cuvier 1812*b*, p. 32; De la Beche & Conybeare 1821, p. 591).

The name chosen for the new animal once again reflects the philosophical system underlying palaeontology at the time. It was seen as forming a link in the Chain between the *Ichthyosaurus* and true crocodiles (De la Beche & Conybeare 1821, p. 562), and was christened *Plesiosaurus* from the Greek for 'nearer to reptiles'. Conybeare seems to have come in for some philological criticism of his formulation of this name, and he later endeavoured to demonstrate its classical credentials (Conybeare 1824, p. 381 fn.). This must have been particularly galling as he had been awarded a first class degree in classics at the University of Oxford (Rupke 1983). The importance of the 'connected chain of organized beings' to Conybeare and De la Beche is shown in the long renunciation of Lamarckian transmutation, and has been discussed by Taylor (De la Beche & Conybeare 1821, pp. 560–561 fn.; Taylor 1994, 1997). Interestingly, Cumberland (1829, p. 346) spells the name as 'plethiosaurus', which may indicate the authors' preferred pronunciation.

Conybeare's 1822 paper provided an update on the latest plesiosaur specimens. De la Beche had obtained the anterior portion of a lower jaw, and Conybeare ascribed this to *Plesiosaurus*. It was probably a cast of this specimen that sculptor Francis Legatt Chantrey (1782–1841) donated to the Geological Society's cabinet in 1822 (Anon. 1824, p. 438). The most complete head to date had been found at Street in Somerset by Thomas Clark, Jr (1792–1864) who presented it to the Society in 1823 through Mr Robert Anstice (d. 1849) of Bridgwater (Buckland 1829*b*; Taylor 1997). Conybeare noted the skull's blend of crocodilian, lacertilian and ichthyosaurian characters (Conybeare 1822, p. 120). It is now in the collections of the British Geological Survey (BGS GSM 26035) (Fig. 11), having been transferred along with the British collections of the Geological Society in 1911, and has been identified as

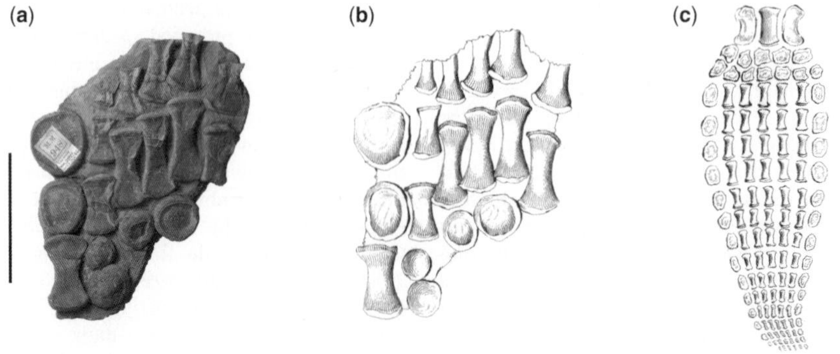

Fig. 10. (**a**) OUMNH J.50146; scale bar, 50 mm; (**b**) as figured in De la Beche & Conybeare (1821); and (**c**) the reconstructed paddle from De la Beche & Conybeare (1821).

Fig. 11. *Thalassiodracon hawkinsi* (BGS GSM 26035), the plesiosaur skull found by Thomas Clarke and presented to the Geological Society in 1823. Scale bar, 50 mm.

Thalassiodracon hawkinsi (Storrs & Taylor 1996). Birch had found the posterior end of a lower jaw and a humerus at Weston near Bath, and had also acquired two specimens showing the pectoral girdle in a crushed state. Conybeare also referred to vertebrae found near Weymouth and in Oxfordshire, the proportions of which differed from the other specimens of *Plesiosaurus*. The genus *Pliosaurus* (best translated as 'more saurian') would later be erected for these, and other, specimens by Owen as a link in the Chain between crocodiles and *Plesiosaurus* (Owen 1842, p. 60). However, in 1822 plesiosaurs were still poorly defined; what was needed was a complete skeleton.

The Annings found this vital specimen (Fig. 12) in the Lias of Lyme Regis in 1823 (Taylor & Torrens 1987; Taylor 1997). It was bought by the Duke of Buckingham (1776–1839) in 1824 for somewhere between £100 and £200 (Taylor 1997, p. 144), who later made it available to Buckland for research. Conybeare had heard about the new specimen from his friend Buckland, and received 'a very fair drawing by Miss Annin [*sic*] of the most magnificent specimen' (letter from Conybeare to De la Beche, dated 4 March 1824, quoted by Lang 1939, pp. 152–153 and Taylor 1997, pp xxiii–xxiv; original in National Museum of Wales). Conybeare then told De la Beche, who was inspecting his estate in Jamaica (McCartney 1977, p. 22), how he had delightedly presented the 'strange monster' to the Bristol Philosophical and Literary Society at the Bristol Institution. The close connections between the work of Conybeare and De la Beche, and the Bristol Institution prompted Taylor (1994) to christen it 'the plesiosaur's birthplace'. Buckland arranged to have the specimen shipped to the Geological Society in London, and entrusted Conybeare with the task of meeting it 'on pain of its falling into the hands of Sir Evd. H. [Sir Everard Home]' (Lang 1939; Taylor 1997). It seems that Buckland did not have confidence in Home's ability to do the skeleton justice after his treatment of the ichthyosaur. M. A. Taylor (pers. comm.) has also suggested that this may reflect the rivalry between the Royal Society and Geological Society identified by Torrens (1997). Conybeare used Anning's drawing to demonstrate to Davy, Home and William Hyde Wollaston (1766–1828) that the disarticulated elements he had earlier integrated into the *Plesiosaurus* really did belong together. He told De la Beche 'I made my Beast roar almost as loud as Buckland's Hyaenas' (Lang 1939; Taylor 1997). The specimen eventually arrived in London, and, after struggling in vain for a day to move it upstairs to the Society's meeting room (Lang 1939; Taylor 1997), Conybeare presented his description of it on 20 February 1824, the same meeting at which Buckland described *Megalosaurus* (see below).

The new skeleton justified Conybeare's previous combination of separate specimens, but the greatest surprise was the long neck and the relative smallness of the head. Indeed, it seems that the strange and unexpected proportions of the new animal caused Cuvier to suspect that it might be a composite of more than one animal, and in a letter he advised Conybeare to make sure that this was not the case (Taquet 2003). In 1821 the paddle had been reconstructed with a fringe of circular bones resembling the phalanges of the ichthyosaurs (Fig. 10c). This made it a perfect intermediate structure in a series from fish, to ichthyosaur, to plesiosaur, to sea turtle and then to 'the usual quadrupedal type' (De la Beche & Conybeare 1821, p. 590), and undoubtedly contributed towards the plesiosaur's placement in the Chain and hence its name. The reconstruction had been based on Birch's specimen (Fig. 10a), in which the originally loose circular bones, either carpals or tarsals, had been glued on 'in consequence of a conjecture of the proprietor' (Conybeare 1824, pp. 387–388 fn.). While it is possible that, although loose, they had been glued into their true taphonomic positions as observed 'in the field', the series of articulated phalanges would suggest otherwise. The new skeleton clearly showed the true structure of the paddles, and Conybeare compared it to that of cetaceans and sea turtles, while still stressing its intermediate structure.

The relative completeness of the specimen allowed Conybeare to draw up a reconstruction of the whole skeleton, and this was presented with the *Ichthyosaurus* reconstruction previously mentioned (Fig. 13). He attempted to reconstruct the plesiosaur's lifestyle, as Buckland had earlier done with hyenas (Buckland 1822), and the nature of the neck led him to give it the species epithet *dolichodeirus*. He also noted a large short-necked plesiosaur from the Kimmeridge Clay of Market Raisin in Buckland's collection at Oxford, for which he proposed the name *Plesiosaurus giganteus*. The type skeleton of *Plesiosaurus dolichodeirus* was bought by the British Museum in 1848 at the sale of the Duke of

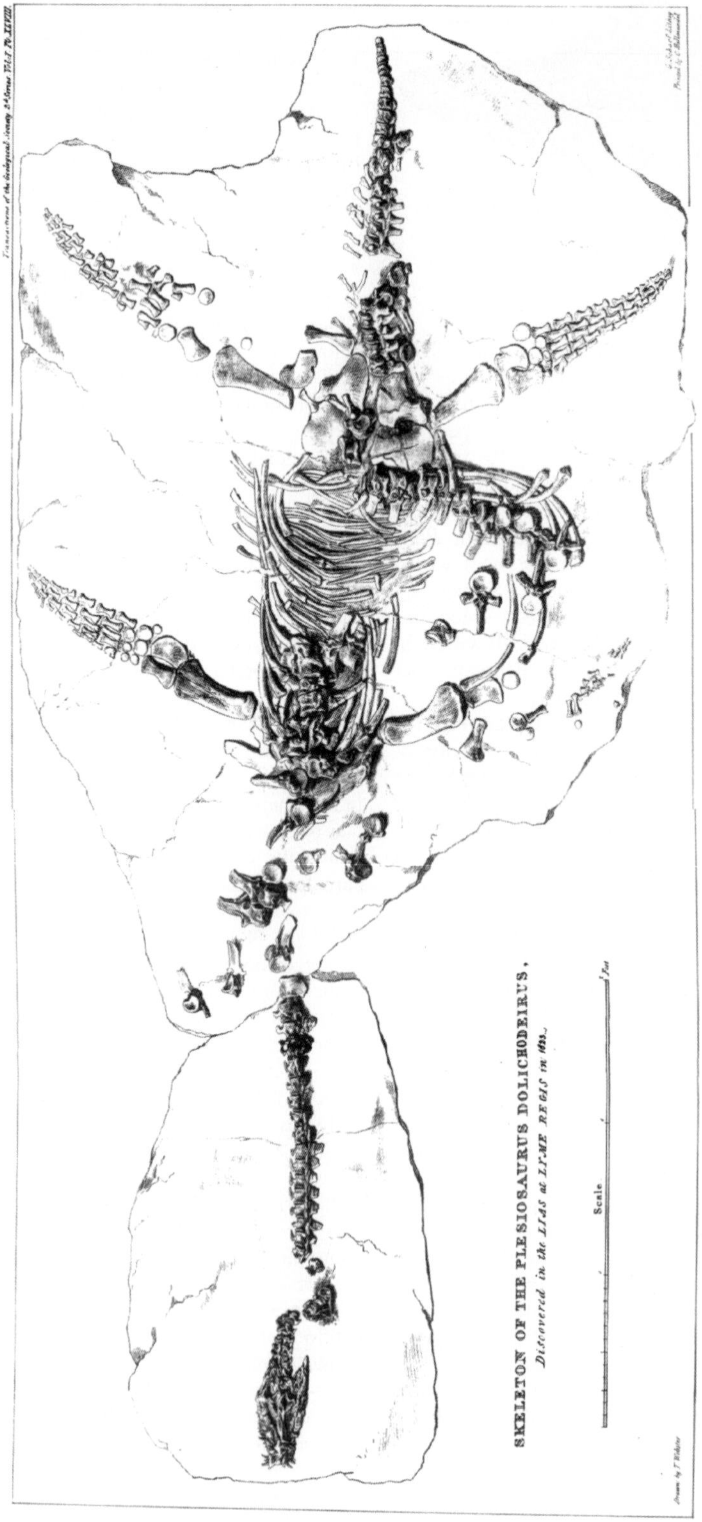

Fig. 12. The first complete plesiosaur (BMNH 22656), found by Mary Anning and described by Conybeare (from Conybeare 1824).

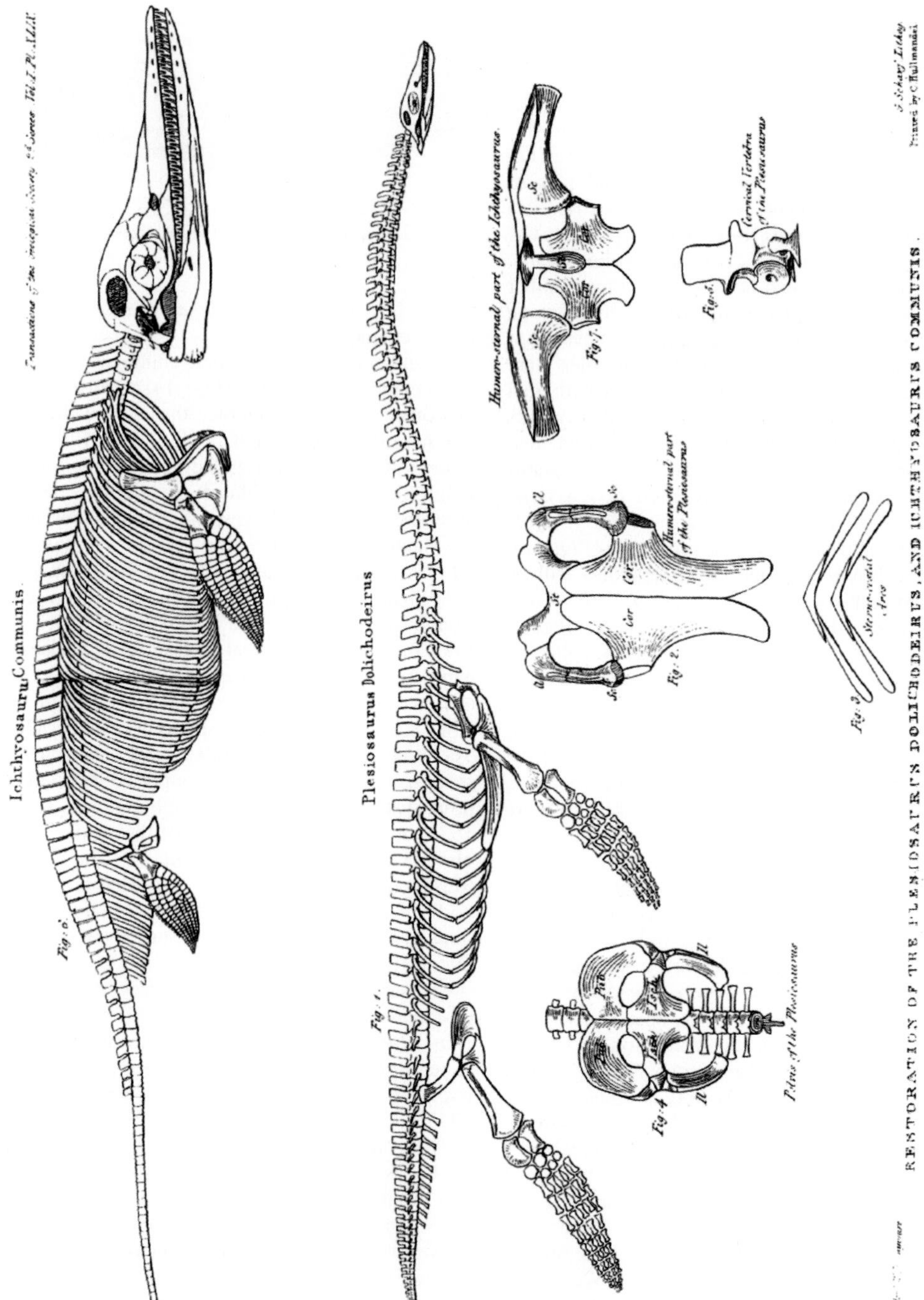

Fig. 13. The first reconstructions of an ichthyosaur and a plesiosaur (from Conybeare 1824).

Buckingham's estate (Lydekker 1889, p. 256; British Museum (Natural History) 1904, pp. 209 and 274). It is presently on display in Gallery 30 of the Natural History Museum, with the registered number 22656.

Dinosaurs

The concept of the Dinosauria as a group was not introduced until 1842, when the second part of Richard Owen's Report on British Fossil Reptiles was published (Owen 1842; Torrens 1992). The three genera concerned, *Megalosaurus*, *Iguanodon*, and *Hylaeosaurus*, had been known for a number of years before Owen grouped them together on the basis of a number of characters. Several of these characters indicated that these reptiles were terrestrial and resembled the 'heavy pachydermal Mammals', while Owen indicated that others showed a blend of crocodilian and 'lacertian' features (Owen 1842, p. 103). The taxonomic status of *Megalosaurus* has recently been reviewed by Benson *et al.* (2008) and Benson (2009), while Paul (2007*a*, *b*) has revised the taxonomy of *Iguanodon*. The historical usage of these names will be followed in this work.

The first of these three dinosaur genera, *Megalosaurus*, was formally described in 1824, followed by *Iguanodon* in 1825 and *Hylaeosaurus* in 1832 (Buckland 1824; Mantell 1825, 1832). Buckland officially unveiled *Megalosaurus*, the 'great Fossil Lizard of Stonesfield', at the same meeting of the Geological Society at which Conybeare spoke on the plesiosaur skeleton (Buckland 1824; Conybeare 1824). Benson *et al.* (2008) recognized that the 'Large jaw bone with two serrated teeth' acquired by the Anatomy School at Christ Church College, Oxford in 1797 (Gunther 1925) was part of Buckland's type series. This partial right dentary has been now designated the lectotype specimen for the taxon (Benson *et al.* 2008). Buckland's published description was based on specimens in the Ashmolean Museum, in the collection of Gideon Algernon Mantell of Lewes in Sussex and a sacrum donated to the Society's collection by Henry Warburton (1784–1858). Mantell informally announced his own specimens after Buckland's talk, and Buckland visited Mantell's collection 2 weeks later, accompanied by Charles Lyell (1797–1875) (Cadbury 2000). Buckland was anxious to include Mantell's specimens in his published paper, to the extent that Warburton wrote him a strongly worded letter to ensure 'fair play' in his capacity as a member of the Society's Publications Committee (Cadbury 2000). However, none of the specimens consisted of articulated or associated elements. This, along with the specimen's relatively low diagnostic value, has resulted in *Megalosaurus* being a poorly characterized taxon.

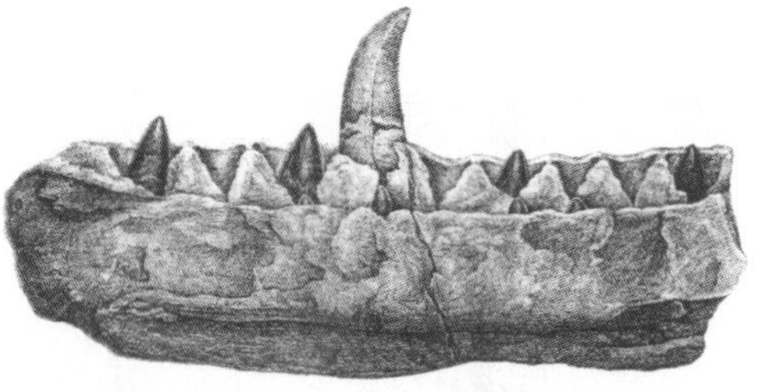

Fig. 14. The lectotype dentary of Buckland's *Megalosaurus* (OUMNH J.13505 from Buckland 1824).

Buckland classified the new animal as a saurian on account of the teeth (Fig. 14), whilst noting that other elements resembled those of quadrupeds (i.e. mammals) (Buckland 1824, p. 390). Buckland reports that Cuvier, extrapolating from the largest femur in Oxford, calculated the animal's length at 40 feet, while the largest individual represented in Mantell's collection was given a length of 60–70 feet by Buckland. This 'enormous magnitude', had prompted Buckland, in association with Conybeare, to name the animal *Megalosaurus*, from the Greek for 'great lizard'. This choice of name must have been something of an open secret, as James Parkinson (1755–1824) used it in his 1822 guide to British fossils (Parkinson 1822). Teeth and bones of crocodiles, turtles and plesiosaurs from the same locality supported Buckland's proposition that it was amphibious (Buckland 1824, p. 392). For a summary of those specimens of Buckland's that can be identified in the Oxford Museum of Natural History see Benson *et al.* (2008). Warburton's specimen is now in the collections of the British Geological Survey (BGS Geol. Soc. Coll. 3887).

The account of the initial discovery of the teeth of *Iguanodon* (Fig. 15) by Mantell's wife, Mary Ann (1795–1869), in 1822 has become firmly established in the folklore of palaeontology (for a relatively recent reiteration see Gardom & Milner 1993). Cleevely & Chapman (1992, p. 355, n. 100) noted that, although there have been doubts as to the authenticity of the story, the fact that Mantell published the story in the first place lends credence to it (see Mantell 1833, p. 268). However, Dean (1999) noted inconsistencies in Mantell's several accounts of the history of the discovery of *Iguanodon*. He considered that the first *Iguanodon* material was probably supplied to Mantell by a Mr Leney, who has been assumed to be a quarryman working the quarries at Cuckfield, Sussex (e.g. Dean 1999; Cadbury 2000; McGowan 2001). However, Tandy & Brook (2007) have

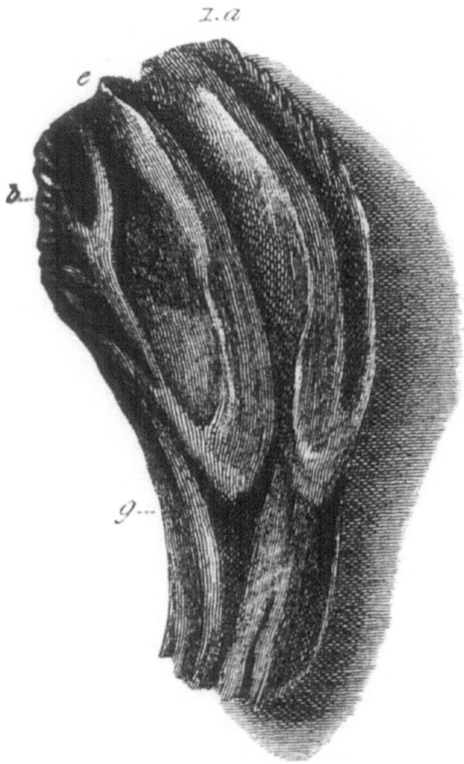

Fig. 15. One of Mantell's original *Iguanodon* teeth (from Mantell 1825).

identified him as James Leney, the village cordwainer, or shoemaker, of Cuckfield. They suggested that he was an acquaintance of Mantell's as the latter's father had also been a cordwainer, and that he acted as a middleman for finds made in the Cuckfield quarries. In June 1820 Leney sent Mantell a consignment of fossils that included teeth, some of which may have been from *Iguanodon*. This intriguing package may have provided the impetus for an unusual visit to the quarries that Mantell made with his family in August. This is probably when Mary Ann Mantell found the teeth attributed to her (Dean 1999). The worn surface of the teeth implied that the animal was a herbivore and, if they were of Wealden age, then they could conceivably belong to a large herbivorous reptile. However, their stratigraphic position could not be unequivocally demonstrated, and Mantell's reptilian interpretation was discouraged (Mantell 1851, pp. 228–229). Lyell conveyed one of the teeth to Cuvier for his opinion and, although at first dismissing it as a rhinoceros tooth, he later agreed that it represented a large herbivorous reptile (Dean 1999). Still searching for a satisfying interpretation of the teeth, Mantell consulted the collections of the Museum of the Royal College of Surgeons. It was here that Mantell, accompanied by William Clift (1778–1849), the curator, and his then assistant, Samuel Stutchbury (1798–1859), discovered that the fossil teeth were reminiscent of those of an iguana (Mantell 1825, pp. 181–182, 1851, p. 230). This supported the giant herbivorous reptile theory, and Mantell named the new animal *Iguanodon*. This was at the suggestion of Conybeare (Mantell 1825, p. 148), who regarded Mantell's originally intended name of 'Iguanosaurus' as unsatisfactory (Dean 1999, p. 85). Mantell continued collecting *Iguanodon* material, with the result that there are now approximately 250 Mantellian *Iguanodon* specimens in the Natural History Museum (Cleevely & Chapman 1992, pp. 347–349). Mantell's collections were purchased by the British Museum in 1838 and 1853 (British Museum (Natural History) 1904, p. 205; Cleevely & Chapman 1992), and some of the original suite of teeth can be seen in the Ronson Gallery of the Natural History Museum. What appears to be the very first discovered tooth that was shown to Cuvier is now in New Zealand (MONZ GH 004839), with annotations identifying it as such by Mantell and Lyell (Yaldwyn *et al.* 1997; Dean 1999, p. 75). The most spectacular of Mantell's specimens is undoubtedly the 'Maidstone Iguanodon' or 'Mantel-piece', an associated skeleton discovered in 1834 (Mantell 1851; Norman 1993). However, the full picture of *Iguanodon* only emerged in 1878, when a fossil assemblage was discovered at Bernissart, Belgium, and 39 relatively complete skeletons were collected (Norman 1985, 1987).

The first example of the third of Owen's dinosaurs was collected by Mantell in 1832 from Tilgate Forest. The specimen (BMNH 3775, Fig. 16) consisted of a partial skeleton representing the anterior end of the animal, minus the limbs, but including a small part of the skull (Carpenter 2001), and was the first articulated dinosaur specimen. Mantell was particularly struck by the apparent mix of crocodile and lizard anatomy in the pectoral girdle, and a row of large bony spines along the vertebral column (Mantell 1832, 1833). He erected a new genus and species, *Hylaeosaurus armatus* ('armoured forest-lizard'), defined by these peculiar characters (Mantell 1832, 1833). Mantell had collected another two partial skeletons by 1837, and these three specimens remain the only definite representatives of this taxon (Mantell 1851, pp. 142–143; Pereda-Suberbiola 1993).

When Owen created the Dinosauria in 1842 he reviewed the anatomy of these three genera, consulting various collections in the process. He examined Buckland's *Megalosaurus* material in Oxford,

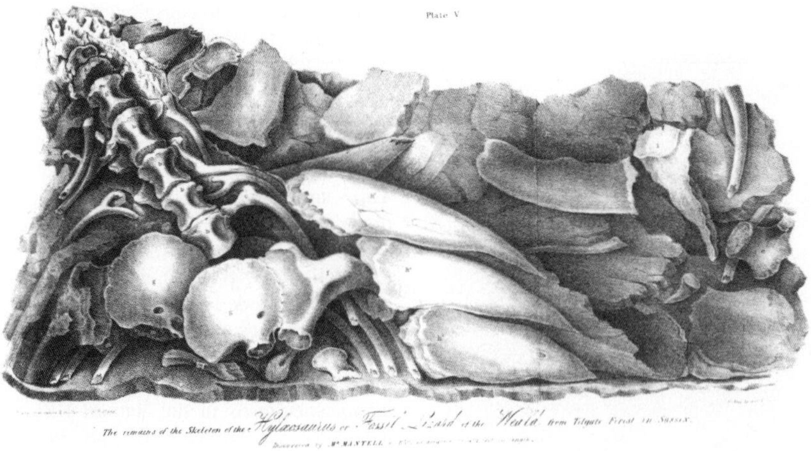

Fig. 16. The type specimen of *Hylaeosaurus armatus*, BMNH 3775 (from Mantell 1833).

and other specimens in the British Museum, the Geological Society's cabinet, and the private collections of George Bax Holmes (1803–1887) in Horsham and William Devonshire Saull (1784–1855) in London. Owen also consulted Wealden specimens collected by Mantell in the British Museum, and he noted that private collections in the Yorkshire town of Malton contained megalosaur teeth from the local oolite rock (Owen 1842, pp. 103–110). All of the specimens of *Hylaeosaurus* that Owen inspected were from the collections of Mantell in the British Museum (Owen 1842, pp. 111–120). In his review of *Iguanodon*, Owen again referred to material in the Mantellian Collection at the British Museum, and the collections of Holmes and Saull (Owen 1842, pp. 120–144). Holmes had been collecting Wealden reptiles since at least 1832–1834. At his death the collection was bought by the Corporation of Brighton for £55, and is currently preserved in the Booth Museum, Brighton (Cooper 1992). An *Iguanodon* sacrum in Saull's collection was a major factor in enabling Owen to erect the Dinosauria (Owen 1842, p. 130). Torrens (1997) considered this historical specimen to be the first true dinosaur specimen as, without it, Owen would not have been able to justify his new group. Saull left his collection to his trustees, who founded an educational institute in London, but neglected the collection. Approximately 200 palaeontological specimens, including the dinosaur specimens, were purchased by the British Museum in 1863 (British Museum (Natural History) 1904, pp. 217 and 322). Only six of Saull's dinosaur specimens, all *Iguanodon*, are included by Lydekker in his 1888 catalogue, and it would seem that the theropod material noted by Owen (1842, p. 109) has been lost.

Discussion

The preceding sections show that museums and collections have played several vital roles in the recognition of the major groups of fossil reptiles. Palaeontology will always be closely associated with museums, being very much object based. Obviously, one needs to have collections so that specimens can be preserved for study, and researchers need access to the specimens to describe them sufficiently. All museum specimens need to be classified, if only for reasons of collection management. Palaeontological specimens come with an inbuilt classification system; that used for the taxa themselves. Once identified and classified, a paleontological collection can be arranged according to biological systematics, stratigraphy or geographical locality. The collection of William 'Strata' Smith (1769–1839) was arranged stratigraphically, initially on the floor of his house, as a practical aid to geological mapping (Knell 2000, p. 95). A secondary biological arrangement was imposed on the collection in 1816 when Smith and his nephew John Phillips (1800–1874) curated the collection prior to its sale to the British Museum (Knell 2000, pp. 95–96). Biological systematics relies on collections as the repositories for the type specimens that validate and define a taxon. Biological taxonomy is based on the classification system of the botanist Carolus Linnaeus (1707–1778), which was founded on his herbarium specimens. The majority of Linnaeus's collection was sold in 1783 to James Edward Smith (1759–1828). On Smith's death, the collection was purchased by the Linnean Society, where it remains to this day (Stafleu 1971, p. 112). The classification of extinct species is necessarily a morphological exercise, for which specimens held in collections are the raw materials. Collections document the diversity present in the natural world, and so can be used in a comparative manner when new specimens come to be classified. This role of collectors, museums and their collections is fundamental to any area of biological or palaeontological study.

Collections form the foundation for what has become the field of comparative anatomy, which was of utmost importance in the description and characterization of the fossil reptiles under consideration. The first English comparative anatomist is identified by Flower (1898, p. 157) as Edward Tyson (1651–1708), 'Reader of Anatomy at Chirurgeon's Hall', who studied the anatomy of a variety of animals, including the chimpanzee and Virginian opossum (Gunther 1925, p. 170). The importance of museum collections in the development of comparative anatomy was recognized by Flower (1898, p. 74), who remarked:

> Our science would make little progress if the objects of our enquiries, once used for examination or description, were then thrown aside, and those coming after were denied the opportunity of which we have availed ourselves. A museum is a register, in a permanent form, of facts, suitable for examination, verification, and comparison one with another.

The museum of the anatomist and surgeon John Hunter (1728–1793) was such a register of anatomical and biological 'facts'. In 1799 his collection was purchased by the Government for £15 000 and entrusted to the care of the Corporation (later the Royal College) of Surgeons (Flower 1898, p. 77). The collection encompassed a very wide range of material, including palaeontological and osteological specimens (see Flower 1898, p. 80 for the complete spectrum of Hunter's collection). Flower considered Hunter's osteological collection to be more extensive than any other of his time, containing as it did two small whale skeletons (Flower 1898, p. 88). The full extent of Hunter's contribution to comparative anatomy can never be fully assessed as the majority of his observations were never published and remained in manuscript form at the time of his death. Unfortunately, the original manuscripts had been burnt in 1823 by Home, who was Hunter's brother-in-law and one of his executors. Clift had transcribed some extracts from these papers before Home took possession of them, and these remnants were subsequently edited and published by Owen in 1861. Home has since been accused of plagiarizing Hunter's observations as his own (Flower 1898, pp. 98–101; Desmond 1989, pp. 246–248). Flower believed that if Hunter's researches, based on specimens in his museum, had been published they would have elevated him to the pioneering status now held by figures such as Cuvier.

Hunter's original collection contained over 80 specimens of fossil reptiles, including 29 of ichthyosaurian origin (Delair 1969, p. 118; Howe *et al.* 1981, p. 16). Unfortunately, the majority of the Museum of the Royal College of Surgeons was destroyed during an air raid in 1941 (Anon. 1941*a*), and this historically important collection has been lost. The museum was consulted by Home in his ichthyosaur researches (Home 1814, 1816, 1818, 1819*a*, *b*, 1820). In his first paper he drew analogies between aspects of the new animal's anatomy and that of fish (both bony and cartilaginous), crocodiles and turtles. The similarities between the ichthyosaur's pectoral girdle and that of the platypus were noticed by Clift when he and Home were examining the collections (Home 1818, p. 26), while Home's search for analogous vertebrae led him to the neotenous amphibians in the collections (Home 1819*b*, p. 213). In 1820 he found some ichthyosaurian vertebrae in the Hunterian collection that had originally been identified as shark vertebrae, but he was finally able to recognize them for what they were (Home 1820, p. 161).

Mantell (1851, p. 230) described how he and Clift had 'ransacked all the draws in the Hunterian Museum that contained jaws and teeth of reptiles' in his search for teeth analogous to those he (or his wife) had discovered. The iguana skeleton that Stutchbury drew to their attention was one which he intended to present to the museum after he had prepared it (Mantell 1851). Although Owen did not refer to any specimens from the museum in his 1842 report, it is worth remembering that the museum was his workplace and home. The political machinations surrounding both Owen's appointment to the museum and his creation of the Dinosauria have been discussed at length by Desmond (1975, pp. 15–18, 1979, 1989, pp. 240–248) and Torrens (1997). Owen was appointed as Clift's assistant in 1827 to catalogue the collection, and was subsequently groomed by the gentlemen surgeons of the 'College' to counter the attacks of reformers. The poor state of the collection's documentation was a direct result of Home's actions, and the loss of Hunter's manuscripts made Owen's task more challenging (Desmond 1989, p. 246). However, the task of having to redescribe Hunter's specimens created the Richard Owen who went on to erect the Dinosauria and become the Superintendent of the Natural History departments of the British Museum.

The Museum of the Royal College of Surgeons also served as a repository for the specimens of the new fossil reptiles, either temporarily or permanently. Birch's complete ichthyosaur, the main object of Home's second paper of 1819, was bought by the College when Birch sold his collection to benefit the Anning family (Torrens 1979*a*,

1995, p. 261). An ichthyosaur discovered in 1818 by William Morgan (*c.* 1773–1852) at Watchet in Somerset was purchased by the College for £25 in 1820 after Birch had offered Morgan £20 for the specimen (Torrens 1980). Home referred to the specimen, but did not publish an illustration, deeming it 'unnecessary' (Home 1820, p. 163). Collectors such as Birch and Johnson sent their latest specimens to Home at the museum to be studied and (hopefully) described in the prestigious *Philosophical Transactions*. The collector's objects were being validated by Home, who, in turn, was being validated by Hunter's collection. This transfer of prestige can also work in the other direction. Knell (2000) has described how the philosophical societies in Yorkshire towns and cities vied with one another, attempting to secure the most impressive fossil reptile skeletons for their fledgling museums and so rise above their local rivals.

The most influential individual of these early years of vertebrate palaeontology and comparative anatomy was undoubtedly Cuvier. His was a teleological approach to the anatomy of both fossil and living animals, in which the functional purpose of a character took precedence over any structural affinity with other organisms (Appel 1987, p. 41). This Aristotelian method was part of Cuvier's objective of establishing rational laws for anatomical science akin to those of the physical sciences (Rudwick 1976, p. 103). However, the development of Cuvier's science would have been impossible without the collections, and other facilities of the Muséum d'Histoire Naturelle. The museum developed from the pre-Revolution Jardin du Roi and Cabinet du Roi, as described by Appel (1987, pp. 16–19), and the collections grew as the revolutionary armies swept across Europe, acquiring specimens such has the fossil animal of Maastricht. By 1822 Cuvier's Cabinet of Comparative Anatomy contained thousands of specimens (see Appel 1987, p. 36 for details), and the Muséum d'Histoire Naturelle had the largest natural history collections in the world. The scientific importance of museum collections was acknowledged by Cuvier, who stated 'the only real virtue of a cabinet, the only rational purpose for governments making collections, is to advance the sciences' (Cuvier 1812*c*, p. 24, my translation). Rudwick (2005, 2008) has described Cuvier's grand research project in vertebrate palaeontology. His methodology inspired English workers such as Conybeare and Buckland (see, for example, Conybeare 1824, p. 389), who then combined it with the tenets of natural theology and the Chain of Being (as in De la Beche & Conybeare 1821, pp. 560–561 fn.). Cuvier's earlier work with fossil mammals had demonstrated the reality of extinction (Rudwick 1976, 2005), and this widened the choice of possible interpretations of new fossils beyond what was known from extant faunas.

Cuvier drew up what he considered to be a non-arbitrary natural system of classification, based around functional characters. Similar characters in different animals represented similarities in function, rather than some underlying abstract ideal (Appel 1987, p. 44). This rationalization of the natural world and the microcosm of his collection was the ultimate objective of all his research (Appel 1987, p. 45). The value of a natural classification system in interpreting new fossil reptiles can be seen in the case of Petrus Camper's interpretation of the Maastricht animal. Camper had a wide concept of what a 'physeter' was that enabled him to ignore the nature of the true teeth and accept the presence of palatal teeth. Hoffmann, apparently a supporter of the Linnaean System, criticized Camper for this approach (Camper 1786, pp. 444–445).

It is not surprising that private collectors and collections were so important at this early period in the history of vertebrate palaeontology before the young science became professionalized. Torrens (1995, p. 281) split the concept of 'collectors' into 'hunters' and 'gatherers', and he classified Mary Anning as a hunter. He also noted that it tends to be the gatherers who become immortalized with their collections rather than the hunters. While we can class collectors such as Saull and Holmes as gatherers, a figure such as Mantell can be seen as a 'hunter–gatherer'. Mantell's involvement in early palaeontology demonstrates another role of collections, in that his interest in geology was greatly encouraged by visiting Parkinson's cabinet during his medical training (Cleevely & Chapman 1992, p. 311). Mantell provided the scientific validation for his own collection, whereas gatherers such as Holmes had to rely on others. Cooper (1992, p. 395) described how Holmes was relying on Owen to publish his specimens, only to be disappointed when Owen later followed his own agenda. The survival of these collections is greatly enhanced by their institutionalization. Turner's plesiosaur survived for at least 85 years before it was presented to the British Museum in 1880, but the majority of the early specimens were not so lucky. The Maastricht mosasaur was forcibly institutionalized by the revolutionary army (see earlier), while Buckland bequeathed his private collection to Oxford University (Gunther 1925, p. 242). Saull's idealistic posthumous plans for his collection failed, but it was rescued by the British Museum (British Museum (Natural History) 1904, p. 322).

The influence of collectors on the description and characterization of fossil reptiles can be seen in the case of the 'improved' plesiosaur paddle (De la Beche & Conybeare 1821, pp. 588–589) (see also Fig. 10). As has already been noted, this undoubtedly contributed to the placement of the new animal in the Chain of Being, and the creation of the name *Plesiosaurus*. Conybeare lays the onus for this on the 'proprietor' (Conybeare 1824, p. 388 fn.). In 1820 Birch admitted in a letter to Mantell (see Torrens 1979*a*, p. 409, 1995, p. 261) that the Annings had found almost all of the specimens in his collection, which he sold later that year for their benefit. Could the 'proprietor' in question have been a Mary Anning, either the mother or the daughter? McGowan (2001) concluded that Conybeare was referring to Mary Anning junior, although Birch's letter to Mantell stresses it was the mother and her children who had originally discovered his specimens. At the time of the 1821 paper the specimen was in Birch's private collection, so Conybeare may have been referring to him as the owner of the 'property'. The role of the Anning family as the source of the specimens they sold to the gentleman collectors and museums was certainly very rarely acknowledged (Price 1986; Taylor & Torrens 1987). The problem of 'improved' fossil reptiles, whatever the motive, has plagued palaeontology ever since. Marine reptiles preserved in shale are particularly susceptible, with limb elements (A. R. I. Cruickshank pers. comm. 1995) or the tail flexures and body outlines of ichthyosaurs being susceptible to 'improvement' (Martill 1987, p. 60, 1993, pp. 84–85; McGowan 1989, p. 413). Composite specimens, such as a recently uncovered 'Iffyosaur', are also not uncommon (Buttler & Howe 2002). More recently, the exceptional preservation of fossils from the Santana Formation of Brazil has been enhanced by local dealers. This was the case in the first Santana dinosaur to be described, and its generic name, *Irritator*, reflects the feelings of the authors when they discovered this (Martill *et al.* 1996). The now infamous 'Archeoraptor' episode, in which components of avian and non-avian dinosaur specimens were combined into a composite 'missing link' (Rowe *et al.* 2001), shows that the fossil market can produce what the science desires. Museum collections can be regarded as a sort of 'quality control' against which new specimens can be judged. However, this does not always apply in the case of unique specimens from new taxa, as Cuvier's unfounded suspicions of the first complete plesiosaur specimen would demonstrate.

Conclusions

This analysis has revealed several ways in which museums, collections and collectors have influenced the early field of reptile palaeontology. With the notable exception of John Woodward's, early collections were assembled for their curiosity value. Anthropocentric interpretations of fossil reptile specimens in these collections gave way to ones based on contemporary exotic faunas. The transition from the cabinets of curiosities to more scientific collecting can be seen in the case histories of mosasaur and pterosaur characterization. The type specimens of both groups were originally cabinet specimens.

Comparative anatomy collections and the science founded on them were vital in understanding and classifying the new animals, and this required individuals such as John Hunter and Cuvier to establish and develop these collections. Recognizing that these collections do not speak for themselves, Flower (1898, pp. 97–98) talked of putting their silent eloquence in some sort of articulate language.

As the examples of Owen and Mantell demonstrate, even at this early stage museums and collections also influenced individuals who went on to have a major effect. Collectors of both the 'hunter' and 'gatherer' variety acted as the link between the specimens and the museums, although entry into a museum did not always guarantee specimen survival. Finally, it is likely that 'improvement' of a specimen, together with the doctrine of the Great Chain of Being, was responsible for the christening of the plesiosaur.

This paper has been updated from a dissertation originally submitted in 1996 towards a Master's Degree in Museum Studies at the University of Leicester. I would like to thank S. Knell (University of Leicester) for his supervision of that dissertation, his comments on early drafts and access to references. I would like to thank D. Naish and M. Taylor for their insightful comments on an earlier version of this paper, and J. Liston for our discussions on the history of fossil reptile discoveries. D. Norman, M. Dorling and, especially, R. Long made me welcome at the Sedgwick Museum, University of Cambridge. P. Jeffery (Oxford University Museum of Natural History) has been very helpful, and R. Forrest assisted in the search for pieces of Colonel Birch's plesiosaur in the Oxford collections.

References

ANON. 1824. A list of donations to the Library, to the Collection of Maps, Plans, Sections, and Models, and to the Cabinet of Minerals belonging to the Geological Society. *Transactions of the Geological Society of London*, Series 2, **1**, 427–439.

ANON. 1941*a*. Air-raid damage to museums. *Museums Journal*, **41**, 78–79.

ANON. 1941*b*. Destruction at Bristol Museum: heavy damage in November air raid. *Museums Journal*, **40**, 272–273.

APPEL, T. A. 1987. *The Cuvier–Geoffroy Debate: French Biology in the Decades Before Darwin*. Oxford University Press, Oxford.

BARDET, N. & JAGT, J. W. M. 1996. *Mosasaurus hoffmanni*, le 'Grand Animal fossile des Carrières de

Maestricht': deux siécles d'histoire. *Bulletin du Muséum national d'Histoire naturelle de Paris*, **(4)18**(C4), 569–593.

BENSON, R. B. J. 2009. An assessment of variability in theropod dinosaur remains from the Bathonian (Middle Jurassic) of Stonesfield and New Park Quarry, UK and taxonomic implications for *Megalosaurus bucklandii* and *Iliosuchus incognitus*. *Paleontology*, **52**, 857–877.

BENSON, R. B. J., BARRETT, P. M., POWELL, H. P. & NORMAN, D. B. 2008. The taxonomic status of *Megalosaurus bucklandii* (Dinosauria, Theropoda) from the Middle Jurassic of Oxfordshire, UK. *Paleontology*, **51**, 419–424.

BENTON, M. J. 1990. *Vertebrate Palaeontology*. HarperCollinsAcademic, London.

BRITISH MUSEUM (NATURAL HISTORY) 1904. *The History of the Collections Contained in the Natural History Departments of the British Museum*. Trustees of the British Museum (Natural History), London.

BRITISH MUSEUM (NATURAL HISTORY) 1922. *A Guide to the Fossil Reptiles, Amphibians, and Fishes in the Department of Geology and Palaeontology in the British Museum (Natural History), Cromwell Road, London, SW 7*. Trustees of the British Museum (Natural History), London.

BROOKES, R. 1763. *The Natural History of Waters, Earths, Stones, Fossils, and Minerals, with their Virtues, Properties and Medicinal Uses: To which is added, The method in which LINNAEUS has treated these subjects*. Volume 5, London.

BUCKLAND, W. 1822. Account of an assemblage of fossil teeth and bones of elephant, rhinoceros, hippopotamus, bear, tiger, and hyaena, and sixteen other animals; discovered in a cave at Kirkdale, Yorkshire, in the year 1821: with a comparative view of five similar caverns in various parts of England, and others on the continent. *Philosophical Transactions of the Royal Society*, **112**, 171–236.

BUCKLAND, W. 1824. Notice on the Megalosaurus or Great Fossil Lizard of Stonesfield. *Transactions of the Geological Society, London*, Series 2, **1**, 390–396.

BUCKLAND, W. 1829*a*. On the discovery of a new species of Pterodactyle in the Lias at Lyme Regis. *Transactions of the Geological Society, London*, Series 2, **3**, 217–222.

BUCKLAND, W. 1829*b*. On the discovery of coprolites or fossil faeces in the Lias at Lyme Regis, and in other formations. *Transactions of the Geological Society, London*, Series 2, **3**, 223–238.

BUTTLER, C. J. & HOWE, S. R. 2002. Ichthyosaur to Iffyosaur: from fact to fiction. *The Geological Curator*, **7**, 305–308.

CADBURY, D. 2000. *The Dinosaur Hunters: A True Story of Scientific Rivalry and the Discovery of the Prehistoric World*. Fourth Estate, London.

CAMPER, P. 1786. Conjectures relative to the petrifactions found in St. Peter's Mountain, near Maestricht. *Philosophical Transactions of the Royal Society*, **76**, 443–456.

CARPENTER, K. 2001. Skull of the polacanthid ankylosaur *Hylaeosaurus armatus* Mantell, 1833, from the Lower Cretaceous of England. *In*: CARPENTER, K. (ed.) *The Armored Dinosaurs*. Indiana University Press, Bloomington, IN, 169–172.

CHAPMAN, W. 1758. An account of the fossile bones of an allegator, found on the sea-shore, near Whitby in Yorkshire. *Philosophical Transactions of the Royal Society*, **50**, 688–691.

CLEEVELY, R. J. & CHAPMAN, S. D. 1992. The accumulation and disposal of Gideon Mantell's fossil collections and their role in the history of British palaeontology. *Archives of Natural History*, **19**, 307–364.

CONYBEARE, W. D. 1822. Additional notices on the fossil Genera Ichthyosaurus and Plesiosaurus. *Transactions of the Geological Society of London*, Series 2, **1**, 103–123.

CONYBEARE, W. D. 1824. On the discovery of an almost perfect skeleton of the Plesiosaurus. *Transactions of the Geological Society of London*, Series 2, **1**, 381–389.

COOPER, J. A. 1992. The life and work of George Bax Holmes (1803–1887) of Horsham, Sussex: a Quaker vertebrate fossil collector. *Archives of Natural History*, **19**, 379–400.

CUMBERLAND, G. 1829. Some account of the order in which the fossil saurians were discovered. *Quarterly Journal of Literature, Science and the Arts*, **27**, 345–349.

CUVIER, G. 1812*a*. Sur le grand animal fossile des carrières de Maestricht. *In*: CUVIER, G. (ed.) *Recherches sur les Ossemens Fossiles de Quadrupèdes*, Tome IV. Paris. (Facsimile reprint, 1969, Bruxelles: Culture et Civilisation).

CUVIER, G. 1812*b*. Sur les ossemens fossiles de Crocodiles, et particulièrement sur ceux des environs du Harve et de Honfleur, avec des remarques sur les squelettes de Sauriens de la Thuringe. *In*: CUVIER, G. (ed.) *Recherches sur les Ossemens Fossiles de Quadrupèdes*, Tome IV. Paris. (Facsimile reprint, 1969, Bruxelles: Culture et Civilisation).

CUVIER, G. 1812*c*. Sur quelques quadrupèdes ovipares fossiles, conservés dans des schistes calcaires. *In*: CUVIER, G. (ed.) *Recherches sur les Ossemens Fossiles de Quadrupèdes*, Tome IV. Paris (Facsimile reprint, 1969, Bruxelles: Culture et Civilisation).

CUVIER, G. 1824. *Recherches sur les Ossemens Fossiles de Quadrupèdes*, Nouvelle Édition Tome V, Partie II, Paris.

DAVIDSON, J. P. 2000. Fish tales: Attributing the first illustration of a fossil shark's tooth to Richard Verstegan (1605) and Nicolas Steno (1667). *Proceedings of the Academy of Natural Sciences of Philadelphia*, **150**, 329–344.

DEAN, D. R. 1999. *Gideon Mantell and the Discovery of Dinosaurs*. Cambridge University Press, Cambridge.

DE LA BECHE, H. T. 1822. Remarks on the geology of the south coast of England, from Bridport Harbour, Dorset, to Babbacombe Bay, Devon. *Transactions of the Geological Society, London*, Series 2, **1**, 40–47.

DE LA BECHE, H. T. & CONYBEARE, W. D. 1821. Notice of the discovery of a new fossil animal, forming a link between the Ichthyosaurus and Crocodile, together with general remarks on the osteology of the

Ichthyosaurus. *Transactions of the Geological Society, London*, **5**, 559–594.

Delair, J. B. 1969. A history of the early discoveries of Liassic ichthyosaurs in Dorset and Somerset (1779–1835). *Proceedings of the Dorset Natural History and Archaeological Society*, **90**, 115–127.

Delair, J. B. & Sarjeant, W. A. S. 1975. The earliest discoveries of dinosaurs. *Isis*, **66**, 5–25.

Desmond, A. J. 1975. *The Hot-blooded Dinosaurs*. Blond & Briggs, London.

Desmond, A. J. 1979. Designing the dinosaur: Richard Owen's response to Robert Edmond Grant. *Isis*, **70**, 224–234.

Desmond, A. J. 1989. *The Politics of Evolution: Morphology, Medicine, and Reform in Radical London*. University of Chicago Press, Chicago, IL.

Edwards, G. 1756. An account of Lacerta (Crocodilus) ventre marsupio donato, faucibus Merganseris rostrum aemulantibus. *Philosophical Transactions of the Royal Society*, **49**, 639–642.

Edwards, W. N. 1967. *The Early History of Palaeontology*. Trustees of the British Museum (Natural History), London.

Faujas de Saint-Fond, B. 1799. *Histoire Naturelle de la Montagne de Saint-Pierre de Maestricht*, Volume 1, H. J. Jansen, Paris.

Flower, W. H. 1898. *Essays on Museums*. Macmillan, London.

Gardom, T. & Milner, A. C. 1993. *The Natural History Museum Book of Dinosaurs*. Virgin Books, London.

Gould, S. J. 1996. *Dinosaur in a Haystack*. Jonathan Cape, London.

Green, T. 1779–1785. *Additional Fossils 1779 &c.* MS notebook, Sedgwick Museum, Cambridge.

Gunther, R. T. 1925. *Early Science in Oxford, Vol. III: Part I. The Biological Sciences; Part II. The Biological Collections*. Printed for subscribers, Oxford.

Gunther, R. T. 1939. *Early Science in Oxford, Vol. XII: Dr. Plot and the Correspondence of the Philosophical Society of Oxford*. Printed for subscribers, Oxford.

Gunther, R. T. 1945. *Early Science in Oxford, Vol. XIV: Life and Letters of Edward Lhwyd*. Printed for subscribers, Oxford.

Hawker, J. 1807. *Gentleman's Magazine*, **77**, 7–8.

Home, E. 1814. Some account of the fossil remains of an animal more nearly allied to fishes than any other of the Classes of animals. *Philosophical Transactions of the Royal Society*, **104**, 571–577.

Home, E. 1816. Some farther account of the fossil remains of an animal, of which a description was given to the Society in 1814. *Philosophical Transactions of the Royal Society*, **106**, 318–321.

Home, E. 1818. Additional facts respecting the fossil remains of an animal, on the subject of which two papers have been printed in the Philosophical Transactions, showing that the bones of the sternum resemble those of the ornithorhynchus paradoxus. *Philosophical Transactions of the Royal Society*, **108**, 24–32.

Home, E. 1819*a*. An account of the fossil skeleton of the Proteo-saurus. *Philosophical Transactions of the Royal Society*, **109**, 209–211.

Home, E. 1819*b*. Reasons for giving the name Proteo-Saurus to the fossil skeleton which has been described. *Philosophical Transactions of the Royal Society*, **109**, 212–216.

Home, E. 1820. On the mode of formation of the canal for containing the spinal marrow, and on the form of the fins (if they deserve that name) of the Proteosaurus. *Philosophical Transactions of the Royal Society*, **110**, 159–164.

Hooke, R. 1665. *Micrographia: or some Physiological Descriptions of Minute Bodies Made by Magnifying Glasses with Observations and Inquiries Thereupon.* (Facsimile reprint, 1961, Dover Publications, New York).

Hooke, R. 1705. Lectures and Discourses of Earthquakes and Subterraneous Eruptions. *In*: Waller, R. (ed.) *The Posthumous Works of Robert Hooke*. London (Facsimile reprint, 1971, Frank Cass & Co., London).

Howe, S. R., Sharpe, T. & Torrens, H. S. 1981. *Ichthyosaurs: A History of Fossil 'Sea-dragons'*. National Museum of Wales, Cardiff.

Impey, O. & MacGregor, A. 1985. Introduction. *In*: Impey, O. & MacGregor, A. (eds) *The Origins of Museums: The Cabinet of Curiosities in Sixteenth- and Seventeenth-century Europe*. Oxford University Press, Oxford, 1–4.

King-Hele, D. G. 1963. *Erasmus Darwin*. Macmillan, London.

King-Hele, D. G. 1999. *Erasmus Darwin: A Life of Unequalled Achievement*. Giles de la Mare, London.

Knell, S. J. 2000. *The Culture of English Geology, 1815–1851: A Science Revealed Through its Collecting*. Ashgate, Aldershot.

Kurtesz, G. A. 1986. Notes on Isis von Oken, 1817–1848. *Isis*, **77**, 497–503.

Lang, W. D. 1936. Mary Anning, 'Fossilist'. *Proceedings of the Geologists' Association*, **47**, 65–67.

Lang, W. D. 1939. Mary Anning (1799–1847), and the pioneer geologists of Lyme. *Proceedings of the Dorset Natural History and Archaeological Society*, **60**, 142–164.

Lang, W. D. 1945. Three letters by Mary Anning, 'fossilist,' of Lyme. *Proceedings of the Dorset Natural History and Archaeological Society*, **66**, 169–173.

Lang, W. D. 1960. Portraits of Mary Anning and other items. *Proceedings of the Dorset Natural History and Archaeological Society*, **81**, 89–91.

Lhwyd, E. 1699. *Lithophylacii Britannici ichnographia. Sive Lapidum aliorumque Fossilium Britannicorum singulari figura insignium, quotquot hactenus vel ipse invenit vel ab amicis accepit, Distributio Classica: Scrinii sui lapidarii Repertorium cum locis singulorum natalibus exhibens. Additis rariorum aliquot figuris aere incisis; cum Epistolis ad Clarissimos Viros de quibusdam circa marina Fossilia & Stirpes minerals praesertim notandis.* 1st edn. Printed for the subscribers, London.

Lydekker, R. 1888. *Catalogue of the Fossil Reptilia and Amphibia in the British Museum (Natural History). Part 1.* British Museum (Natural History), London.

Lydekker, R. 1889. *Catalogue of the Fossil Reptilia and Amphibia in the British Museum (Natural History). Part 2.* British Museum (Natural History), London.

MANTELL, G. A. 1825. Notice on the Iguanodon, a newly discovered fossil reptile, from the sandstone of Tilgate forest, in Sussex. *Philosophical Transactions of the Royal Society*, **115**, 179–186.

MANTELL, G. A. 1829. A tabular arrangement of the organic remains of the county of Sussex. *Transactions of the Geological Society, London*, Series 2, **3**, 201–216.

MANTELL, G. A. 1832. Observations on the remains of the Iguanodon, and other fossil reptiles, of the strata of Tilgate Forest in Sussex. *Proceedings of the Geological Society of London*, **1**, 410–411.

MANTELL, G. A. 1833. *The Geology of the South-East of England.* Longman, Rees, Orme, Browne, Greene and Longman, London.

MANTELL, G. A. 1851. *Petrifactions and Their Teachings; Or a Hand-book to the Gallery of Organic Remains of The British Museum.* Henry G. Bohn, London.

MARTILL, D. M. 1987. Ichthyosaurs with soft tissues: additional comments. *Transactions of the Leicester Literary & Philosophical Society*, **81**, 35–45.

MARTILL, D. M. 1993. Soupy substrates: a medium for the exceptional preservation of ichthyosaurs of the Posidonia Shale (Lower Jurassic) of Germany. *Kaupia*, **2**, 77–97.

MARTILL, D. M., CRUICKSHANK, A. R. I., FREY, E., SMALL, P. G. & CLARKE, M. 1996. A new crested maniraptoran dinosaur from the Santana Formation (Lower Cretaceous) of Brazil. *Journal of the Geological Society, London*, **153**, 5–8.

MCCARTNEY, P. J. 1977. *Henry De la Beche: Observations on an Observer.* Friends of the National Museum of Wales, Cardiff.

MCGOWAN, C. 1989. *Leptopterygius tenuirostris*, and other long-snouted ichthyosaurs from the English Lower Lias. *Palaeontology*, **32**, 409–427.

MCGOWAN, C. 2001. *The Dragon Seekers: How An Extraordinary Circle of Fossilists Discovered The Dinosaurs and Paved the Way for Darwin.* Perseus Publishing, New York.

MULDER, E. W. A. 2004. Maastricht Cretaceous finds and Dutch pioneers in vertebrate palaeontology *In*: TOURET, J. L. R. & VISSER, R. P. W. (eds) *Dutch Pioneers of the Earth Sciences.* Royal Netherlands Academy of Arts and Sciences (KNAW), Amsterdam, 165–176.

MULDER, E. W. A. & THEUNISSEN, B. 1986. Hermann Schlegel's investigation of the Maastricht mosasaurs. *Archives of Natural History*, **13**, 1–6.

MULLENS, W. H. 1917. Some museums of old London II: William Bullock's London Museum. *Museums Journal*, **17**, 51–56, 132–137, 180–187.

NICHOLS, J. 1795. *The History and Antiquities of the County of Leicester*, Volume 1, John Nichols, London. (Republished facsimile, 1971, S.R. Publishers, Wakefield).

NORELL, M. A., GAFFNEY, E. S. & DINGUS, L. 1995. *Discovering Dinosaurs.* Little, Brown & Co., London.

NORMAN, D. B. 1985. *The Illustrated Encyclopedia of Dinosaurs.* Salamander Books, London.

NORMAN, D. B. 1987. On the history of the discovery of fossils at Bernissart in Belgium. *Archives of Natural History*, **14**, 59–75.

NORMAN, D. B. 1993. Gideon Mantell's 'Mantel-piece': the earliest well-preserved ornithischian dinosaur. *Modern Geology*, **18**, 225–245.

OWEN, R. 1840. Report on British Fossil Reptiles: Part I. *Report of the British Association for the Advancement of Science*, **1839**, 43–126.

OWEN, R. 1842. Report on British Fossil Reptiles: Part II. *Report of the British Association for the Advancement of Science*, **1841**, 60–204.

OWEN, R. 1851–1864. A monograph on the fossil Reptilia of the Cretaceous formations. *Palaeontographical Society*, **5**.

PADIAN, K. 1983. A functional analysis of flying and walking in pterosaurs. *Paleobiology*, **9**, 218–239.

PADIAN, K. 1987. The case of the bat-winged pterosaur: typological taxonomy and the influence of pictorial representation on scientific perception. *In*: CZERKAS, S. J. & OLSON, E. C. (eds) *Dinosaurs Past and Present: Volume 11.* Natural History Museum of Los Angeles County and University of Washington Press, London, 65–81.

PARKINSON, J. 1822. *Outlines of Oryctology*, London.

PAUL, G. S. 1994. Big sauropods – really, really big sauropods. *The Dinosaur Report*, Fall, 12–13.

PAUL, G. S. 2007*a*. Turning the old into the new: a separate genus for the gracile iguanodont from the Wealden of England. *In*: CARPENTER, K. (ed.) *Horns and Beaks: Ceratopsian and Ornithopod Dinosaurs.* Indiana University Press, Bloomington, IN, 69–77.

PAUL, G. S. 2007*b*. A revised taxonomy of the iguanodont dinosaur genera and species. *Cretaceous Research*, **29**, 192–216.

PEREDA-SUBERBIOLA, J. 1993. *Hylaeosaurus*, Polacanthus, and the systematics and statigraphy of Wealden armoured dinosaurs. *The Geological Magazine*, **130**, 767–781.

PLATT, J. 1758. An account of the fossile thigh-bone of a large animal, dug up at Stonesfield, near Woodstock, in Oxfordshire. *Philosophical Transactions of the Royal Society*, **50**, 524–527.

PLOT, R. 1677. *The Natural History of Oxfordshire, Being an Essay Toward the Natural History of England.* Printed at the Theater, Oxford.

PRICE, D. 1986. Mary Anning specimens in the Sedgwick Museum, Cambridge. *Geological Curator*, **4**, 319–324.

PRICE, D. 1989. John Woodward and a surviving British geological collection from the early eighteenth century. *Journal of the History of Collections*, **1**, 79–95.

RILEY, S. 1991. *Marine Reptiles: Collectors, Science, and Museums.* MSc dissertation, University of Leicester.

ROWE, T., KETCHAM, R. A., DENISON, C., COLBERT, M., XU, X. & CURRIE, P. J. 2001 The Archaeoraptor forgery. *Nature*, **410**, 539–540.

RUDWICK, M. J. S. 1976. *The Meaning of Fossils: Episodes in the History of Palaeontology*, 2nd edn. University of Chicago Press, Chicago, IL.

RUDWICK, M. J. S. 2005. *Bursting the Limits of Time.* University of Chicago Press, Chicago, IL.

RUDWICK, M. J. S. 2008. Worlds before Adam. University of Chicago Press, Chicago, IL.

RUPKE, N. A. 1983. *The Great Chain of History: William Buckland and the English School of Geology (1814–1849).* Clarendon Press, Oxford.

SCHEICHER, E. 1985. The Collection of Archduke Ferdinand II at Scloss Ambras: Its Purpose, Composition and Evolution. *In*: IMPEY, O. & MACGREGOR, A.

(eds) *The Origins of Museums: The Cabinet of Curiosities in Sixteenth- and Seventeenth-century Europe.* Oxford University Press, Oxford, 29–38.

SCHLEGEL, H. 1854. Note sur le Mosasaure. *Comptes rendus hebdomadaires des séances de l'Académie des Sciences de Paris*, **39**, 799–802.

SCHUPBACH, W. 1985. Some Cabinets of Curiosities in European Academic Institutions. *In*: IMPEY, O. & MACGREGOR, A. (eds) *The Origins of Museums: The Cabinet of Curiosities in Sixteenth- and Seventeenth-century Europe.* Oxford University Press, Oxford, 169–178.

STAFLEU, F. A. 1971. *Linnaeus and the Linneans: The Spread of their Ideas in Systematic Botany, 1735–1789.* I.A.P.T., Utrecht.

STEEL, R. 1973. *Crocodylia. Handbuch der Paläoherpetologie*, Band 16. [*Encyclopedia of Paleoherpetology*, Volume 16.] Gustav Fischer, Stuttgart.

STORRS, G. W. & TAYLOR, M. A. 1996. Cranial anatomy of a new plesiosaur genus from the lowermost Lias (Rhaetian/Hettangian) of Street, Somerset, England. *Journal of Vertebrate Paleontology*, **16**, 403–420.

STUKELY, W. 1719. An Account of the impression of the almost entire sceleton of a large animal in a very hard stone, lately presented to the Royal Society, from Nottinghamshire. *Philosophical Transactions of the Royal Society*, **30**, 963–968.

TANDY, P. & BROOK, A. 2007. Leney the quarryman? *Newsletter of the History of Geology Group of the Geological Society of London*, **29**, 10–11.

TAQUET, P. 2003. Quand les Reptiles marins anglais traversaient la Manche: Mary Anning et Georges Cuvier, deux acteurs de la découverte et de l'étude des Ichthyosaures et des Plésiosaures. *Annales de Paléontologie*, **89**, 37–64.

TAQUET, P. & PADIAN, K. 2004. The earliest known restoration of a pterosaur and the philosophical origins of Cuvier's Ossemens Fossiles. *Comptes Rendus Palevol*, **3**, 157–175.

TAYLOR, M. A. 1994. The plesiosaur's birthplace: the Bristol Institution and its contribution to vertebrate palaeontology. *Zoological Journal of the Linnean Society*, **112**, 179–196.

TAYLOR, M. A. 1997. Before the dinosaur: the historical significance of the fossil marine reptiles. *In*: CALLAWAY, J. M. & NICHOLLS, E. L. (eds) *Ancient Marine Reptiles.* Academic Press, San Diego, CA, xix–xlvi.

TAYLOR, M. A. & TORRENS, H. S. 1987. Saleswoman to a new science: Mary Anning and the fossil fish *Squaloraja* from the Lias of Lyme Regis. *Proceedings of the Dorset Natural History and Archaeological Society*, **108**, 135–148.

THEUNISSEN, B. 1986. The relevance of Cuvier's lois zoologiques for his palaeontological work. *Annals of Science*, **43**, 543–556.

TORRENS, H. S. 1979*a*. Collections and collectors of Note 28: Colonel Birch (*c.* 1768–1829). *Newsletter of the Geological Curators Group*, **2**, 405–412.

TORRENS, H. S. 1979*b*. Geological communication in the Bath area in the last half of the eighteenth century. *In*: JORDANOVA, L. J. & PORTER, R. S. (eds) *Images of the Earth: Essays in the History of the Environmental Sciences. BSHS Monographs*, **1**. British Society for the History of Science, Chalfont St Giles, 215–247.

TORRENS, H. S. 1980. Collections and collectors of Note 28: Colonel Birch (*c.* 1768–1829). *The Geological Curator*, **2**, 561–562.

TORRENS, H. S. 1985. Early collecting in the field of geology. *In*: IMPEY, O. & MACGREGOR, A. (eds) *The Origins of Museums: The Cabinet of Curiosities in Sixteenth- and Seventeenth-century Europe.* Oxford University Press, Oxford, 204–213.

TORRENS, H. S. 1992. When did the dinosaur get its name? *New Scientist*, **134**, 40–44.

TORRENS, H. S. 1995. Mary Anning (1799–1847) of Lyme; 'the greatest fossilist the world ever knew'. *British Journal for the History of Science*, **28**, 257–284.

TORRENS, H. S. 1997. Politics and paleontology: Richard Owen and the invention of dinosaurs. *In*: FARLOW, J. O. & BRETT-SURMAN, M. K. (eds) *The Complete Dinosaur.* Indiana University Press, Bloomington, IN, 175–190.

WELLNHOFER, P. 1991. *The Illustrated Encyclopedia of* Pterosaurs. Crescent Books, New York.

WELLNHOFER, P. 2008. A short history of pterosaur research. *Zitteliana*, **B28**, 7–19.

WESTPHAL, F. 1962. Die Krokodilen des deutschen und englischen oberen Lias. *Palaeontographica, Abteilung A*, **118**, 1–96.

WOOLER, J. 1758. A description of the fossil skeleton of an animal found in the Alum Rock near Whitby. *Philosophical Transactions of the Royal Society*, **50**, 786–790.

YALDWYN, J. C., TEE, G. J. & MASON, A. P. 1997. The status of Gideon Mantell's 'first' *Iguanodon* tooth in the Museum of New Zealand Te Papa Tongarewa. *Archives of Natural History*, **24**, 397–421.

William Perceval Hunter (1812–1878), forgotten English student of dinosaurs-to-be and of Wealden rocks

H. S. TORRENS

Lowermill Cottage, Madeley, Crewe, CW3 9EU, UK (e-mail: gga10@keele.ac.uk)

Abstract: This paper examines the tragic life of William Perceval (wrongly Percival) Hunter (1812–1878), who was active right across natural history in the period 1828–1841. He was a nephew of the 'father of American Geology', William Maclure, but, despite this, has been completely forgotten. He produced a number of books and papers, some of which discussed what were to become dinosaurs in 1842, and the Wealden, and adjoining rocks, which had produced so many of them. Hunter was, notably, one of the first to draw attention to the Isle of Wight as a favoured fossil locality for these, among the many other natural history topics he covered. His problems were initially his itinerancy, then his failure to complete projects, coupled with their publication privately, obscurely and abroad. But the major problem comes from his forgotten end; first, in a Scottish medical 'confinement' from 1841 and, finally, within a major asylum there, until 1878. This left him unable to complete his projects and with an indelible mark on any reputation he might have acquired.

Hunter was only active in the period before dinosaurs were 'invented', or conceptualized, by Richard Owen in April 1842 (Torrens 2011). This was when many major discoveries of large saurians were made, only some of dinosaurs-to-be. Hunter was never a mainstream dino-to-be-student, but he provides a fascinating study of how the historical record treats people. First, he was active across the whole of natural history, and bears no relation to today's specialists. Second, he left no archive, and his life has to be pieced together from fragments and publications. In addition, with financial independence gained from his father, he was, for a decade, itinerant throughout the British Isles and Europe. Few people can subsequently have become so forgotten, despite producing four books. This was the result of Hunter's forgotten end in a Scottish lunatic asylum.

The Hunter and Maclure families

Hunter's Scottish grandfather was Walter Hunter, who married Margaret Glen in Dumfries, SW Scotland on 4 April 1751 (see *International Genealogical Index* www.familysearch.org – hereafter *IGI*). They had at least four children, all baptized there, of whom the eldest was David (1752), then Agnes (1754), Walter (1757) and Grizzel (1759). David Hunter (1752–1822), was William Perceval's father. He migrated south and was, by 1794, a merchant 'of Broad Street, in the City of London' (*Gentleman's Magazine* – hereafter *GM* – **64**, (2), p. 861, 1794), when, on 1 September 1794, he married in Liverpool, where he must have previously spent time on his travels south. His wife was Helen Maclure (1771–?) (IGI), younger sister of the Anglo-American merchant, then geologist, and philanthropist, William Maclure (1763–1840), who was born and received his early education in Ayr (Doskey 1988, p. xvii), 50 miles NW of Dumfries.

They were among the children of David Maclure (*c.* 1733–1799 – baptized in 1734 in Dailly, Ayrshire – *IGI*) and Ann Kennedy, who married in Ayr, 18 July 1759 (*IGI*). This Maclure family was based in Shawwood, Ayr, on that SW Scottish coast. David Maclure was another Anglo-American merchant and was initially based here (Doskey 1988, p. xviii) where he was also landlord to the family of poet Robbie Burns (1759–1796), born in a tiny cottage built by his father in Alloway, Ayrshire. Robbie was the eldest of four sons of William Burnes (1721–1784), gardener and tenant farmer, and his wife, Agnes Brown (1732–1820), of Maybole, Ayrshire (see *Oxford Dictionary of National Biography* – hereafter *ODNB*). The Burns family had moved into a larger farm in Lochlie in May 1777, where they became involved in an infamous lawsuit that concluded in 1784. By then, William Burnes, in failing health, was, in his son's words, 'among the rapacious hell-hounds that growl in the kennel of justice'. A further connection between both these places and families is suggested by the death of a 'Mr James M'Clure, in Dumfries in 1814', who may be David Maclure's elder brother (baptized in Dailly, Ayrshire, 1725 – *IGI*):

> well known as the manager and superintendent of the assemblies and other public entertainment [at Dumfries] ... and a conspicuous promoter of the exertions

From: Moody, R. T. J., Buffetaut, E., Naish, D. & Martill, D. M. (eds) *Dinosaurs and Other Extinct Saurians: A Historical Perspective*. Geological Society, London, Special Publications, **343**, 31–47.
DOI: 10.1144/SP343.3 0305-8719/10/$15.00

so honourably made for the comfort of the widow and children of the Poet Burns.

(*GM*, **84**, (1), p. 524, May 1814)

This left David Maclure with a small, if forgotten, place in Burns history. Maclure, although evidently still well off, soon got 'into dire straits financially' (McVie 1935, p. 85) because of a banking crisis. His Ayr estates were sold in 1786 and he moved first to Glasgow and then to Liverpool (Doskey 1988, p. xvii). Here, by June 1794, David Maclure, or M'Clure, settled as a merchant at 20 James Street, Liverpool (see *Universal British Directory* – hereafter *UBD*, **3**, p. 677, 1794), where he died in 1799 (*Monthly Magazine*, **8**, p. 919, December 1799).

William Maclure (1763–1840)

The remaining Maclure family then moved to London, where Helen's brother, William, became a London merchant, trading with America, and who then became, in revolutionary times, an American citizen in 1796 (Morton 1841; Doskey 1988, p. xix). Such revolutionary ideas clearly later inspired his Hunter nephew, discussed here. Maclure, another trading merchant, was partly based in London, as partner in Miller, Hart and Co. This had been founded about 1784 and became Miller, Hart and Co. in 1790, in Throgmorton Street, City of London. By 1793 they had moved to Castle Court, Budge Row (*UBD*, 2nd edition, **1**, p. 230, 1793), London, just west of Hunter's Broad Street office. Maclure soon became sufficiently wealthy to give him time both to travel and to explore his burgeoning geological interests. The journals of his surviving European travels start in 1805 (Doskey 1988). We now know of his earlier days, and European movements, from his sad collaboration with Gregory Watt (1777–1804), son of the famous steam engineer James Watt (1736–1819) (Torrens 2006), when in 1801–1802 they explored Italian geology. This resulted in Watt's 'proto-geological' map of Italy of 1804. Maclure was later christened, in 1844 (Dean 1989, p. 549), 'father of American Geology' by Benjamin Silliman senior (1779–1864) for his geological work (Schneer 1981).

David Hunter

The Hunters, as we have seen, also migrated south to London, where David Hunter was based by 1794. He too became wealthy, establishing two homes; one in Bloomsbury, London and a second in nearby Blackheath. His main source of income was as a merchant. Joseph Farington (1747–1821 – *ODNB*), landscape painter and diarist, records connections with the Hunters between 1796 and 1811. The first was when Farington details David Hunter's dealings over a trading ship, *The Henry Addington*, in which Hunter had held shares since 1786, and over which he had suffered a considerable loss by 1798 (Farington 1978, Vol. 2, p. 515, 1979, Vol. 3, p. 1121). From 1798 to 1811 Farington, and his brother's children, became sufficiently friendly with the Hunters to dine, or stay, with them at their Blackheath home (Farington 1979, Vol. 3, pp. 1007 and 1060, 1979, Vol. 4, pp. 1233 and 1396). In September 1798 David Hunter discussed 'the vast commercial trade of Britain' with Farington, 'which accounts for the rise of price of Sugars etc, Coffee – so great is the demand for exportation that the markets at home are left unstocked' (Farington 1979, Vol. 3, p. 1060), implying that Hunter was particularly concerned in trading these.

David Hunter as London brewer, 1812–1822

The Griffin Brewery had been built in 1763 in Liquorpond Street, London. This became, through rebuilding in 1793–1795, among the largest in London and a pioneering enterprise in new mechanization, with new steam engine technology, by 1800: 'The brewery which became most dominated by new and independent wealth was Meux, Reid's Griffin Brewery' (Mathias 1959, p. 302). In 1797 there were five partners with a total capital of £220 000. But from 1801 'troubles broke out between the families which led to disaster' (Mathias 1959, p. 302). The collapse of the fraudulent partnership that controlled Meux, Reid forced this business into Chancery Court in 1809. Their brewery had been named after the Scot, Andrew Reid (*c.* 1751–1841, see *The Times*, 23 April 1841, p. 7, col. e – will proved in the Prerogative Court of Canterbury (hereafter PCC) 8 June 1841), and the Englishman, Henry Meux (1770–1841 – see *GM*, **16**, p. 203, August 1841 and *ODNB*, sub Meux family). This Court enforced its sale (*Monthly Magazine*, **27**, (1), p. 175, January 1809). It was then bought up by a rump of the old partnership, of Reids and Wigrams, together with a group of 15 new partners to provide extra capital (Corran 1981, p. 342).

Hunter may well have been one of these new 15. Certainly by 1812, until his death, he was a partner in this, now, Reid and Co. at the 'Meux brewery, a concern, which for magnitude, is scarcely equalled in the world' (*Monthly Magazine*, **27**, (1), p. 175, January 1809). The new firm succeeded by the accession of new capital from its new partners. By 1810 formidable amounts of extra capital were needed for the 'leases and loans to publicans to tie the trade to particular breweries' through tied houses. There were then 20 partners with a total capital of £530 000 and, by 1820, 16 partners with £480 000. The story is clearly complex. Hunter is named as a partner from 1812 until his death in 1822 (London Metropolitan Archives, O/245/005-007 and Centre for Buckinghamshire Studies D 117/16-18). He also held a share in the New Cross Alehouse, London.

Hunter's last known business involvement arose from the office at the old South Sea House, Broad Street, London, named in his will. This was then the major trading post for London merchants, as described in an essay by Charles Lamb (1775–1834 – *ODNB*), clerk there from 1792 to 1825, in his *Essays of Elia*. In 1817 *The Times* carried Hunter's advertisement asking 'all with any concerns in the ship *Tigris*, late in the East India Company's service to send him particulars' there (*The Times*, 25 January, p. 1, col. 2 and 28 January 1817, p. 1, col. 2). David Hunter died on 22 April 1822 (*GM*, **92** (1), p. 476, May 1822) at his home in Montague Street, beside the present British Museum, London. His will (PRO, PCC 11/1656), proved 30 April 1822, left money to two surviving sisters, and money for a ring to his 'friend and brother-in-law, William Maclure, late of Castle Court, Budge Row, but now resident in America . . . , as a mark of my esteem and regard'. Hunter would have continued to ask Maclure to remain a trustee and executor of this will:

> except that his absence from England might produce inconvenience to my other Trustees and Executors, but I shall continue him as one of the Guardians of my children and I entreat of him that he will continue his affectionate care and attention to them.

The will mentions Hunter's four daughters, but names only the eldest, Margaret, with whom he recommended their Guardians should 'place my younger children [including William Perceval] under her immediate superintendence and care'. William Maclure's journals name two more of these, Ann and Jessie (Doskey 1988, pp. 732–744). Jessie [i.e. Janet], second daughter, born February 1804 (*IGI*), reappears in 1836. David senior's partnership in the brewery, and his property in both Dumfriesshire and London, are mentioned in his will and he clearly died wealthy. His 'large and fine wine cellar' was sold in 1823 (*The Times*, 26 April, p. 4, col. 3 and 29 April, p. 4, col. 4).

Hunter children

David and Helen Hunter had at least 11 children, of whom the baptisms of 10, in London, Lewisham, Greenwich and Ayr, are known. The eldest, Margaret, was baptized in Bishopsgate, London on 11 February 1796 (*IGI*). She left a manuscript diary for January 1818–January 1819, which Mike Bishop kindly allowed me to study (see his www.personalia.co.uk/newstock website)[1]. It gives a fascinating glimpse of the Hunter family. Hunter's will, and Maclure's journals (Doskey 1988, pp. 733–744), only name the eldest son, David (1802–1878). This was the Rev. David Hunter (1801–1878), who went to Eton (1814–1817) and then Oxford (1819–1823) to become a clergyman (Foster 1887–1888, Vol. 2, p. 717; *The Times*, 7 October 1878, p. 1, col. 1). It was David junior who recommended on 2 September 1823, just after he had graduated with a B.A., that because his father had 'only left him £400 more per annum [as the eldest son] than the rest of the boys, . . . that all the [male] youngsters should [now] be sent to Eton to spend much money and gain bad habits of luxury and extravagance' (Doskey 1988, p. 733). Such bad habits may have had their own effects on William Perceval! But in the event William Perceval, who was the fourth surviving son (unnamed in Maclure's journals), was sent to London's Charterhouse School. We should also note that Perceval later preferred to use this name only (and to confuse us amid today's electronics, he often then, and since, wrongly became Percival).

Margaret's diary reveals their activities at both of their homes. These include reading, writing and accounts, visiting museums and art exhibitions, attending Drury Lane Theatre, playing music, with dining and social engagements, as well as attending church most Sundays at the 'Bedford Chapel', once famous in the evangelical movement of the Church of England when under the ministry of Rev. Richard Cecil (1748–1810 – *ODNB*). Her diary also shows her teaching the younger Hunter children in her care, whom she names as Helen, Perceval, George and Walter. The diary's entries give a fine flavour of the family's range of activities and circle of acquaintances: visits are recorded to the nearby British Museum, in January 1818 or, in February, from Doctor William Babington (1756–1833), physician and mineralogist, founder of the 1807 Geological Society of London (Lewis & Knell 2009). In March they visited the 'India House' and

[1]This is now held in the University of Pennsylvania's Rare Book and Manuscript Library. A copy will be deposited, with the author's research notes, at Oxford University's Museum of Natural History.

were 'much pleased'. This was the East India House in Leadenhall Street, home of the East India Company, which was demolished in 1862 when its fine collections were dispersed, most ending up in today's Victoria & Albert Museum. In July they went to Bullock's Museum, built up by the naturalist and antiquary William Bullock (*c*. 1773–1849), which between 1812 and 1819 was located in his specially built Egyptian Hall in Piccadilly (Costeloe 2008). Then, between August and October 1818, Margaret took the above brothers and sisters, plus Anne, to Malvern, where they indulged in country life. Finally, in October 1818, Margaret's diary notes 'My Father consulted Sir E. Home about himself'. Sir Everard Home (1756–1832 – *ODNB*) was a surgeon, as well as sergeant-surgeon to George III and palaeontologist to many of the vertebrate fossils being then uncovered in Britain.

William Perceval Hunter (1812–1878)

William Perceval Hunter (hereafter WPH), fourth son, was born on 11 May 1812 and baptized on 7 December 1813 at St Alphage Church, Greenwich, Kent (*IGI*) near Blackheath. In 1818 he is frequently mentioned in his sister Margaret's diary, who taught him reading and writing, until her marriage in June 1819. Her diary confirms the sadly different picture WPH was forced to paint in his last known letter of 12 April 1843, when 'for the space of now nearly fifteen months, Mr Wm Perceval Hunter has been prevented from attending theatres, concerts, music parties, been debarred all communication with the fair sex, balls etc – from travelling or visiting museums, picture galleries, or frequenting places of public amusement, instruction or resort to which he has from his earliest youth been addicted' (Geological Society of London archives – hereafter GSL – LR7/339). When William Maclure visited the Hunter family, in 1824, they were living at Walthamstow (Doskey 1988, p. 732). This was soon after he had become WPH's absent, and historically invisible, guardian, following WPH's father's death in 1822.

WPH and natural history

Inspired probably by these frequently recorded visits to museums, WPH soon took a great interest in natural history, with a special interest in geology, publishing books and papers across all these fields. WPH started whilst still at Charterhouse School, 'Irvine's House, from October 1827 to 1828 or 1829' (Arrowsmith 1974, p. 203), a long and enthusiastic correspondence on all aspects of natural history. This began in the November 1828 issue of John Claudius Loudon (1873–1843 – *ODNB*)'s *Magazine of Natural History* – hereafter *MNH*. His first was on botany, offering to list the 'most beautiful flowers which flourish at Leith Hill, Surrey' (*MNH*, **1**, p. 303, 1828). The next was on birds there (*MNH*, **2**, p. 208, 1829). Then followed one on a whale which had beached, and died, in February 1829 at Whitstable, Kent (*MNH*, **2**, pp. 197–198, 1829). Hunter now gave his address as 'Kingstone Rectory, near Canterbury'. The rector there was Rev. Thomas Bartlett (*c*. 1789–1872), M.A. Oxford 1813.

In March 1829 Hunter sent a short contribution on a tulip to another of Loudon's journals, *Gardener's Magazine* (**5**, p. 734, 1829) as from Epping Forest. Other notes followed, in *MNH*, on the alligator, a bird and the guinea pig, with a new query on where he could find memoirs of the lives of various naturalists, already including Felix Azara of Spain (1746–1821) (*MNH*, **2**, p. 402, 1829; **3**, pp. 192 and 447, 1830). By March 1830 WPH was back at the family home at Walthamstow, near London (*MNH*, **3**, p. 449, 1830). Then, in July 1830 he was admitted as a pensioner at Trinity College, Cambridge, and matriculated there at Michaelmas (Venn 1947, Vol. 3, p. 495).

On 30 September 1830 WPH wrote the first of his surviving manuscript letters. This was one to the zoologist William Swainson (1789–1855 – *ODNB*) in the Linnean Society archives, London. This noted that he intended to translate the two volumes of Azara's books on the Quadrupeds of Paraguay; but 'as I am not at present in any wise acquainted with ornithology, I must defer [his] three volumes of Birds till some future period'. Hunter now asked Swainson for help with his project.

But, first, Hunter hoped to accompany the author and traveller James Silk Buckingham (1786–1855 – *ODNB*) on a planned voyage around the world. This was to have been a government-sponsored voyage, away for 3 years, to travel out to India and then China, into the Japan seas and return via the Pacific Islands, around Cape Horn to England. Details are given in WPH's second letter to Swainson, dated 6 October 1830, when Hunter notes 'I am a complete tyro even in my most favourite (Mammalogy) branch of natural history, [as I] am totally unacquainted with Comparative Anatomy'. But Hunter would have been able to translate Azara, since 'Spanish is a language not generally known, but one with which I happened to be in some slight measure acquainted', perhaps as a legacy of his two parents' mercantile backgrounds, whether with America, or from connections with Liverpool? But a 17 October 1830 letter from zoologist William Jardine (1800–1874 – *ODNB*) to Swainson seems to imply that Swainson was already giving the impression that this Azara translation was to be his alone:

> I sincerely rejoice that you are to do Azara, it will make an excellent companion [to Jardine's edition of Alexander Wilson's *American Ornithology* published in 1832 (Jackson & Davis 2001, pp. 41–42)] & I should think the size well adopted for it. – if you announce Azara you are at liberty to mention that it will be of a like size and a comparison to Wilson and indeed [I] will be obliged by your doing so.
>
> (Swainson archive, Linnean Society)

Full details of Buckingham's planned voyage were given in the Prospectus that Hunter enclosed to Swainson (which has not survived). But an original broadsheet version does[2], listing the 'nearly 90 members of the Royal Institution [of London] who, on 22 July 1830, were selected from the earliest subscribers to this undertaking'. An original copy of the separate Prospectus of the same date (pp. 1–8, Octavo) survives among Dawson Turner's collections (in the British Library – hereafter BL – pressmark 1879.b.1, Vol. 1, f. 33). The sorry final outcome of this aborted project was recorded, along with the same reprinted Prospectus, in 1832 by Buckingham himself (1832, pp. 160–174). This voyage had come to a sudden end when the Royal Institution changed its mind about its support (see Archives of the Royal Institution 1971, Vol. 7, p. 361, 2 August 1830). This meant Buckingham was unable to find a suitable ship.

Hunter now transferred to Merton College, Oxford, where he matriculated in January 1832 (Foster 1888, Vol. 2, p. 718). From here he wrote to *MNH* in July about vultures and ducks (*MNH*, **6**, pp. 83–84 and 141–142, 1833). But Hunter never graduated from either university. He now became highly itinerant. WPH's wish to travel may have been associated with his 'family's propensity to hereditary consumption', or pulmonary tuberculosis, which William Maclure noted in 1824 (Doskey 1988, p. 732). By 1802 doctors were recommending that sufferers should seek out fresh air and exercise, which travel supplied (Torrens 2005, p. 18). As WPH himself later noted, in 1843, 'for the last twelve years of his life he has been in the habit of spending several months of every year in travelling on horseback, and on foot, amongst the mountains, for the good of his health and the acquirement of practical scientific knowledge' (GSL LR7/339).

By 1833 Hunter was listed, as 'Perceval Hunter', amongst members of the new British Association for the Advancement of Science (Anon. 1833, p. 118; Reports of the British Association 1833, 1–2, p. 616) of 'Leamington [Spa], Warwickshire'. In April 1833 came his first geological contribution, when he asked *MNH* if pitchstone was found in Scotland (*MNH*, **6**, pp. 191–192, 1833). In 1833 he joined the Société Géologique de France, as a life member, only 3 years after it had been founded. Between 1834 and early 1835, when listed by that Society as 'rentier à Paris', he was travelling through France and Spain. In Spain, in September 1834, he wrote about the salt of the mountain of Gern, Cardona, Spain (*MNH*, **7**, pp. 640–644, 1834) and was very rude about ignorant Spanish attitudes to naturalists like himself. By July 1835 Hunter was back in England living at Sandgate, just inside the Wealden outcrop, on the Kent coast, whence he wrote on the geographical range of the flamingo, which he had just seen in Spain and France, and on the Irish Greyhound (*MNH*, **8**, pp. 571–572, 1835, **9**, p. 156, 1836).

WPH and geology

Hunter's interests at Sandgate now understandably turned to geology. WPH had acquired a copy of William Fitton's 1833 *Geological Sketch of Hastings*[3]. He now wrote to *MNH* about the properties of stones that allowed some to weather better than others. He particular cited the sandrock of nearby Bodiam Castle, 9 miles NW of Winchelsea, Sussex (*MNH*, **9**, pp. 379–380, 1836). His essay aroused John Ruskin's (1819–1900 – *ODNB*) geological interests, who responded with a further discussion (Ruskin 1836, 1903, **1**, pp. 197–200). Hunter also wrote about the Isle of Sheppey and its abundant fossils (*MNH*, **9**, pp. 381–382, 1836), which drew a similar response from another new geological recruit, the Colchester stonemason John Brown (1780–1859 – *ODNB*). Brown is recorded as having taken up the study of geology 'about 1830', and so his interest had also been stimulated by WPH's article.

Hunter next took particular issue with claims about the rates of English cliff erosion, which Charles Lyell recorded in his *Principles of Geology* (*MNH*, **9**, pp. 381–382, 1836). His reference allows us to identify the source as Lyell's third edition (Lyell 1834, Vol. 2, p. 407). This discussed (as had Lyell's first edition, 1830, Vol. 1, p. 275) rates of erosion at Sheppey. The Church of

[2]A copy was reproduced in Henry Sotheran's 2007, *Travel and Exploration Catalogue*, item 290.

[3]Hunter's own copy, dated May 1835, survives in the Natural History Museum – hereafter NHM – library, London, pressmark 72 Aa O Hun.

Reculver at Minster, Lyell claimed, had been in the middle of the island 50 years before and he conjectured that 'the whole isle will be annihilated in about half a century' (*MNH*, **9**, p. 381, 1836). Hunter thought these figures too exaggerated. This was a subject Hunter returned to in his last work, published in Italy.

In July 1836 Hunter published, perhaps, his most significant geological periodical piece, on the 'Limestone Quarries and Petrifying Spring at Pounceford [today Poundsford, near Burwash] in Sussex; with Preliminary Remarks on the Wealden Rocks' (*MNH*, **8**, pp. 597–608, 1835 – dated Sandgate, 28 July 1835). These limestones are the Purbeck beds here (Howitt 1964). WPH's paper, quoting Fitton (1833, p. 30), pointed out how difficult it was to find outcrops in the interior of a cultivated county like Sussex:

> When, therefore, we meet with sections nearly 100 feet deep, such as those afforded by the vertical shafts sunk for extracting the shelly bivalve limestone at Pounceford, no opportunity should be omitted of examining and measuring the strata. [WPH had been induced to put these notes together] . . . from perceiving that [Gideon] Mantell, though he mentions the spring [Mantell 1833, p. 22], says very little about these beds, which appear to have been unknown to Dr. Fitton, who, speaking of the general structure of the country surrounding Brightling says, 'as there are here no coal beds to reward the labour and expense of accurate levelling and surveying, *it is impossible, at present, to give a correct section of the country*'.
>
> (Fitton 1833, p. 55)

WPH first discussed the stratigraphy and palaeontology of the Wealden beds here, down to these Purbeck beds, with a short outline of the surrounding country. He confirms, after Fitton, that the majority of the fossils of the Wealden beds here were freshwater. Hunter cited his own recent observations on the possible interplay of fresh with salt waters he had met with at the Albufuera, near Alcudia, on Majorca during his recent Iberian travels, and the effect on shells living there.

Of the newly discovered Wealden vertebrate animals, Hunter noted the *Megalosaurus* could have been 80 foot long, twice as large as Cuvier had estimated (following William Buckland); while the *Iguanodon* was yet more gigantic, but that not a single mammaliferous animal had yet been discovered, although reptilia were so well developed. Finally, Hunter described the working, and scale of operations, of these underground limestone quarries. He follows this with a detailed bed by bed description of the 'section at the vertical shaft south of Pounceford Farm', where the limestone beds were excavated for lime-burning. He gave exact measurements of 26 beds found in the vertical section of the southern shaft down to these mines. WPH carefully measured and collected these himself, giving names, within inverted commas, that were given him by the workmen (*MNH*, **8**, pp. 604–606, 1835). WPH's section was sufficiently useful to be quoted by Topley 40 years later (Topley 1875, pp. 39–41).

Hunter also noted his disagreement over Wealden palaeogeography from that noted by Lyell, despite calling his *Principles of Geology*:

> a work pronounced by men of all parties (for among geologists, to their shame be it spoken, party spirit runs as high as among politicians) to be the most eloquent, comprehensive, and truly philosophical outline of the science ever published in the English or any language.
>
> (MNH, **8**, p. 603, 1835)

Hunter agreed more with the views of George Poulett Scrope (1797–1876 – *ODNB*) as given in a recent review (Scrope 1835). Hunter was to return to a critical review of Lyell's *Principles of Geology* in his last, unfinished, book.

Hunter's first book

Hunter privately published his first, rare, book, entitled *Geological Notes* (Hunter 1835), although its contents are not entirely geological, 'printed for the author by William Tiffin' in Hythe and dedicated, on 27 July 1835, to Mantell[4] (Fig. 1).

Its frontispiece (Fig. 2) reproduces the *Penny Magazine's* illustration of 'Organic Remains Restored' from Volume 2, 100th issue, of 26 October 1833.

Hunter calls himself 'Member of the British Association for the Promotion [recte Advancement] of Science and the Société Géologique de France'. This book reprinted his geological articles on Wealden, Sheppey and Spanish rocks from *MNH*, but with additions. These comment both on the main two dinosaurs-to-be, *Megalosaurus* and *Iguanodon*, and on the marine saurian *Plesiosaurus*. It is worth examining these contributions, as they have escaped all notice. His reprinted articles from the *MNH* are:

- his Poundsford piece on Wealden Rocks (pp. 1–26);
- Spanish Salt (pp. 27–38);
- Sheppey (pp. 38–46);
- The Induration of Rocks (pp. 47–69);
- The Flamingo (pp. 71–74);
- Attacks on [Charles] Waterton (pp. 74–82).

[4]Copies survive at BL, British Geological Survey and NHM.

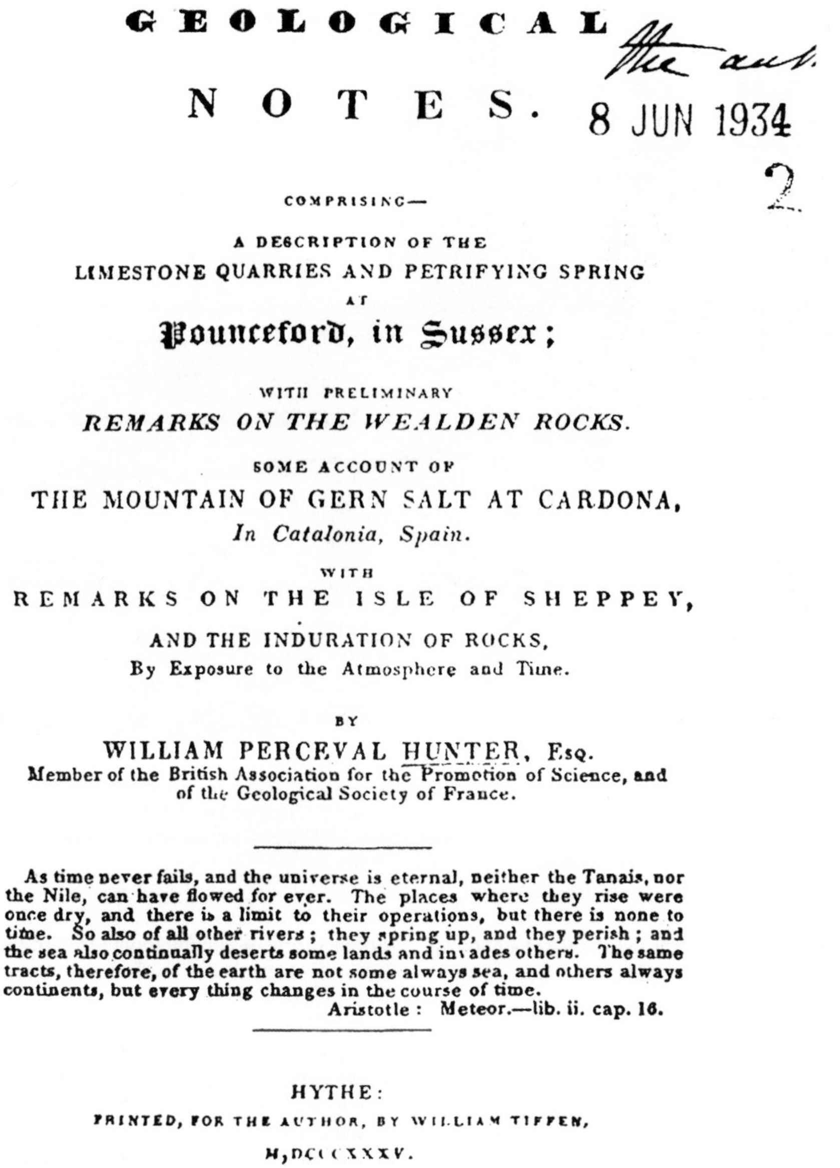

GEOLOGICAL NOTES.

COMPRISING—

A DESCRIPTION OF THE
LIMESTONE QUARRIES AND PETRIFYING SPRING
AT
Pounceford, in Sussex;

WITH PRELIMINARY
REMARKS ON THE WEALDEN ROCKS.

SOME ACCOUNT OF
THE MOUNTAIN OF GERN SALT AT CARDONA,
In Catalonia, Spain.

WITH
REMARKS ON THE ISLE OF SHEPPEY,
AND THE INDURATION OF ROCKS,
By Exposure to the Atmosphere and Time.

BY
WILLIAM PERCEVAL HUNTER, Esq.
Member of the British Association for the Promotion of Science, and of the Geological Society of France.

As time never fails, and the universe is eternal, neither the Tanais, nor the Nile, can have flowed for ever. The places where they rise were once dry, and there is a limit to their operations, but there is none to time. So also of all other rivers; they spring up, and they perish; and the sea also continually deserts some lands and invades others. The same tracts, therefore, of the earth are not some always sea, and others always continents, but every thing changes in the course of time.
Aristotle: Meteor.—lib. ii. cap. 16.

HYTHE:
PRINTED, FOR THE AUTHOR, BY WILLIAM TIFFEN,
M,DCCCXXXV.

Fig. 1. Title page of Hunter 1835.

Then follows the forgotten Appendix, in which WPH discusses

- *Plesiosaurus* (pp. 83–88);
- *Megalosaurus* (pp. 88–91);
- *Iguanodon* (pp. 91–97);
- Coprolites in Hastings Sand (pp. 97–100).

Eight very rough plates follow (p. 101) on: A–C, *Plesiosaurus*; D, *Hylaeosaurus*; E, *Iguana*; F, *Iguanodon*; G, *Megalosaurus*; and H, Pounceford Shells.

WPH's description of the *Plesiosaurus* acknowledges that our knowledge chiefly came from W. D. Conybeare's papers in *Transactions of the Geological Society of London*, from which he copied two plates. WPH had been amazed at the length of the neck, the immense number of vertebrae and the small size of the head in the type of *P. dolicodeirus*. He thought its 'curious paddles were formed with the express purpose of laughing to scorn the fanciful theories of some naturalists', a clear reference to the recently departed anatomist Sir Everard Home

Fig. 2. The *Penny Magazine's* illustration of 'Organic Remains Restored', which had appeared in Volume 2, in the 100th issue, of 26 October 1833 (author's collection). 1–6, Plants; 7, Dragon Fly; 8, Geometric Tortoise; 9, Megalosaurus; 10, Icthyosaurus; 11, Plesiosaurus; 12, Ammonitis; 13, Echinus; 14, Nautilus; 15, Cuttle Fish; 16, Encrinitis; 17, Bird-like bats (Ornithocephali).

(1756–1832 – *ODNB*), whom his father had known and consulted. Hunter thought:

> Such a strange compound of serpent, lizard, crocodile and bird was never before beheld. Had any of the ancient philosophers left us a description, or indeed had any writer at the commencement of the present century given us a drawing of this reptile, its existence would have been scouted, as incredible, – opposed to everything we knew of nature – an invention – a chimera – an idle dream – the mere coinage of some frenzied brain.
>
> (Hunter 1835, p. 84)

In his notes on the *Megalosaurus*, WPH quotes at some length the section from Job beginning 'Cans't thou draw out Leviathan with an hook' (Chapter 41) as providing a beautiful emblematical description of this animal and then quotes Georges Cuvier's description from *Ossements Fossiles*. He adds notes from Buckland and Mantell, and ends 'there can exist no reasonable doubt that the *Megalosaurus* was contemporary with the *Iguanodon*', a matter that had been much debated (Torrens 2011).

WPH's section on *Iguanodon* was also prefaced by a quotation from Job. He had been inspired by a recent paper by Hull's Thomas Thompson, which tried to ascertain what were the animals designated in the Scriptures by the names Leviathan and Behemoth (Thompson 1835). WPH next quotes from that sorely underused source, '*Griffith's Translation of Cuvier*' (i.e. Pidgeon 1830). WPH added that 'various bones of this animal have [now] been found also, in the Isle of Wight, and the Isle of Portland', quoting from Buckland's recently published paper, which was first read in December 1829 but only published in 1835 (Buckland 1835[5])

> The vertebrae of some bones found in the parish of Brook, near the South-west extremity of the iron-sand formation in the Isle of Wight, are as large as those of an elephant, and exceed in magnitude the vertebral

[5]Reprinted in Weishampel & White (2003), Chapter 10, pp. 120–125.

> dimensions of any other living animal, excepting the whale: they possess also that quadrangular form which Mr. Mantell has marked as characteristic of the vertebrae of the *Iguanodon*.
>
> (Hunter 1835, pp. 93–94)

Both of these references are very early notices of the dino-to-be-riches of the Isle of Wight. These bones:

> occur along a quarter of a mile of this shore, but most abundantly at a spot called Bull-face Ledge, near Brook Point, where the iron-stone is abundantly loaded with prostate trunks of fossil trees. Mr Vine's attention was attracted to these bones about a year ago [late 1828] by the fact of their being collected to be broken up for grotto-work.
>
> (Buckland 1835, p. 428)

The discovery of Brook as a future dino-locality is due to this equally forgotten James Vine (1774–1837), born in Portsea (*IGI*) but who moved to London, apparently, by 1793 as clock and watch maker in Charing Cross (*UBD*, 2nd edition, **1**, p. 319, 1793). Vine was elected MGS in April 1818 and served as the Geological Society's Treasurer in 1821–1822 (Woodward 1907, p. 298), when he donated 'specimens of gypsum hardened by heat' to the Society's museum. His later gift of 'bones of the *Iguanodon* from Brook, in the Isle of Wight', found late in 1828, came on 31 March 1830 (Moore *et al.* 1991, p. 140). Vine bought his second home, Puckaster Cottage, on the Undercliff, below Niton, at the southern tip of the Isle of Wight between 1818 and 1828, This had been his base while uncovering these future dino-riches and here Vine died on 10 July 1837 (*GM*, NS **8**, p. 212, August 1837).

Vine was clearly the original discoverer of this classic dino-locality. Indeed, as I have pointed out, the fused sacrum of *Iguanodon* found here some time later, when located by Richard Owen (1804–1892) in the museum of the socialist London wine merchant William Devonshire Saull (1784–1855 – ODNB), became the 'vital single specimen on which the characters of the Order Dinosauria were mainly founded'. It was thus the first ever dinosaur specimen to be diagnosed as such (Torrens 2011). So, in a real sense, the Isle of Wight should be regarded as the birthplace of the concept of the 'dinosaur'.

Hunter concluded his description of *Iguanodon* by pointing out the importance of the recently discovered Maidstone *Iguanodon* (Norman 1993). He noted that, although the first description of this by Mantell had appeared in July 1834 (Mantell 1834*a*), other early ones had appeared in Mantell's own catalogue of his museum from its third edition onwards (Mantell 1834*b*, pp. 24–28), and by Robert Bakewell in February 1835 (Bakewell 1835). The Maidstone *Iguanodon* had been uncovered thanks to William Harding Bensted (1802–1873), on whom Olinthus Vignoles (1891, pp. 560–566) provides new data.

Hunter's later geological work

Hunter next visited Dorset and described aspects of its geology in 'Rough Notes made during a Visit to the Freestone Quarries of the Isle of Portland on 25 August 1835' (*MNH*, **9**, pp. 97–101, 1836). This was written up during another, now Irish, visit dated 'Isle of Valentia, Kerry, Ireland, 7 December 1835'. His visit to Ireland was again written up, at least in part, in his 'Account of the Bursting of a Bog in the County of Antrim, Ireland on September 25 1835; with some preliminary Remarks on the Nature, Extent, Origin, etc of Peat' (*MNH*, **9**, pp. 251–261, 1836), dated Kenmare, Kerry, 28 December 1835. A copy of this Peat paper survives, heavily annotated by William Smith (1769–1839) back in Scarborough, Yorkshire, who noted, on page 251, 'I have found the following paper on Bogs & Peat, by my Mr H. so interesting that I am induced to make some [MSS] remarks on it'. This must imply that they had met by then, and got on well. The date of such a meeting must have been before November 1836 as another of Smith's annotations, on p. 255, is dated 'Wm. Smith, 6 Nov. 1836, Scarboro'[6]. Their meeting was at the 1836 BAAS Bristol meeting, which both Smith and WPH attended, and where they shared accommodation, confirmed by the record of 'Hunter P.: London [and] Dr. [William] Smith,: Newboro' Cottage, Scarborough, [both] at Bush Inn [Bristol]' (Anon. 1836).

On 26 February 1836 Hunter had been admitted to the Inner Temple, London, 'aged 23, of Merton College, Oxford' (from Admission Register, courtesy of Dr C. Rider, Inner Temple archivist). His last letter, of 1843, records 'how he had [since] been prevented from completing his terms in the law courts, from being called to the bar, going the circuits or attending to his legal business or studies as a special pleader, been in a word literally cut out of the land of the living and rendered to all intents and purposes for the time being civilly dead' (GSL LR 7/339). Because WPH was never able to get called to the Bar, that the Temple has no further data on him. Hunter was now living at The Albany in London (next to today's Geological

[6]This is in NHM Library, London. It came from the library of that museum's former Keeper of Botany, from 1871 to 1895, William Carruthers (1830–1922), FRS, FLS.

Society of London) and is listed here as an annual BAAS subscriber, in the previous year's 1835 list (Reports of the 5th Meeting, 1836, List p. 23). Hunter was then also admitted, as life member, to the Geological Society of London on 14 December 1836, recommended by geologist Roderick Murchison (1792–1871), astronomer Francis Baily (1774–1844) and palaeobotanist W[illiam] Hutton (1797–1860) of Newcastle on Tyne (application in GSL archives) – for all of whom see *ODNB*. WPH's surviving letter, dated 19 December, from this address (GSL LR 2/235) sends his admission fee of six guineas.

WPH now made several donations to the Geological Society: lithological specimens from Spain on 14 December 1836; Irish rocks and Herefordshire Pudding-stone on 5 April 1837[7]; and Scottish specimens on 19 April and 1 May 1837. Some of these last, Carboniferous plants, survive in British Geological Survey collections (Cleevley 1983, p. 159). His final gift to the Society was a bust, made from life, of William Smith, which was given on 13 June 1837[8], but which has sadly disappeared. Smith had had two busts made that year (Cox 1942, p. 36) but only the posthumous bust made in 1848 by Matthew Noble (1816–1876) of Hackness, preserved in the church outside which Smith lies buried in Northampton, seems to survive.

We should also recall, in the context of dinosaurs-to-be, how Smith had found large bones at Cuckfield in Sussex in 1809 during excavation of the local Ouse Navigation there (Phillips 1844, p. 64). As these could only be diagnosed as those of *Iguanodon* after 1825, they were then no more than large bones. They were of no use to Smith simply because they provided, as a unique discovery, no means whereby he could identify these strata with any others. They did not yet possess any correlative value.

Hunter's activities from 1837 onwards

The Natural History Museum holds a WPH letter, addressed to ornithologist John Gould (1804–1881 – *ODNB*) dated Albany [London] 30 June 1837 (NHM archives), asking him to get a bird skin that WPH had forwarded to him cured. This shows WPH still maintained his wide range of interests across natural history. This was confirmed when, in 1837, he became a Fellow of the Zoological Society of London. In their 1839 list he is of '3 Elm Court, Temple', his probable address after admission to the Inner Temple. The Zoological Society removed him from membership only in February 1864 and he is marked as 'dormant' in their records, with no address after 1839. The Geological Society equally have no further data on him, but he was only removed from their lists, as a result of the decision by the GSL Council, on 24 May 1893 'to remove those Fellows with no known addresses'. He would then have been 81. But this removal then misled cataloguers (led by B. B. Woodward) at the Natural History Museum Library into thinking Hunter had died in 1893 (Woodward 1904, Vol. 2, p. 894).

Hunter's Azara books

Late in 1837 Hunter's first book based on the work of Spanish military engineer Don Felix de Azara (1746–1821), who spent 1781–1801 exploring South America from Buenos Ayres to the Tropic of Capricorn (Beddall 1975, 1983), appeared in London. This Azara volume was Hunter's second book. It translated *Selections from the Natural History of the Quadrupeds of Paraguay and the River Plate* by de Azara (Hunter 1837). Hunter had written to Swainson about this work several years earlier, as we have seen. The flyleaf of Hunter's 1835 Geological Notes announced that he was then 'preparing for publication Azara's Natural History, in five volumes with notes and illustrations of the rarer species by W[illiam] Swainson'. In view of this, it is a mystery why Swainson, in his Cabinet Cyclopaedia entry of 1840 (Swainson 1840, pp. 117–120) fails to mention either of Hunter's translations of Azara, which had appeared in 1837 and 1838. Swainson, who was 'a difficult man to deal with' (Jackson & Davis 2001, p. 235), studiously avoided mentioning Hunter in his publications and no more is heard of their collaboration.

WPH's 1837 book carried the dedication: 'To John James Audubon, citizen of the United States, author of "The Birds of America" . . . , 30 June 1837'. Hunter must have met Audubon during the latter's British travels, some time between July 1826 and September 1828, since WPH had already applauded the zoological work of 'my talented friend' in May 1829 (*MNH*, **3**, p. 447, 1830). Hunter's first Azara book was published in London by Abraham John Valpy (1787–1854 – *ODNB*). Hunter gave a, now lost, copy to GSL on 13 December 1837. In the list of Life Members

[7]His manuscript letter, donating these, dated 'Albany, 11 March 1837', survives (in Geological Society archives, LR 3/54).

[8]His manuscript letter donating this bust 'of the father of English Geology . . . of Scarborough' survives (in Geological Society archives, LR 3/96).

who had attended the 1837 BAAS meeting in Liverpool that year Hunter's address is still given as 'Albany, London' (Reports of the 7th meeting, 1838, List, p. 9).

But WPH had now left London for Edinburgh. Here more of his translations of Azara followed in 1838 when Volume 1 of WPH's next translation (Hunter 1838) was published. Its appearance was announced in June 1838 (*GM*, NS **9**, p. 634), and it was briefly reviewed in *Tait's Edinburgh Magazine* (1838, p. 469). This was to have been in two volumes but the second, with its promised memoir on Azara, never appeared. Volume 1 was again dedicated to Audubon (1785–1851) and its preface is dated 'Edinburgh, 1 April 1838'.

Hunter in Italy; Florence 1839, Rome and Sicily 1840, and Venetia 1841

WPH's stay in Edinburgh must have been brief. By April 1839 he was living in Florence, Italy. Here the first parts of his fourth and last (again, unfinished) book, *An Enquiry into the Theory of actual Causes or Outlines of the Modern Changes of the Earth's surface being an Examination of Lyell's* Principles of Geology appeared. 'Part 1, Aquaeous Causes' (pp. 1–233) was published in 1839 in Florence by the firm founded by Guiseppe Molini (1772–1856), who was librarian of the Palatina Library, and a good English scholar (Molini 1858). The book's preface is signed W. P. H. and is clearly by Hunter. In this volume Hunter was now as rude about inadequate Florentine library facilities as he had been about Spanish attitudes to naturalists.

This is a scarce volume, published in parts and in sections, of which copies in the UK are only held at Glasgow University and NHM (both these of only 132 pages, which must comprise sections 1 and 2), and in more complete form in the Eyles collection, Bristol University. WPH also presented some part of this book, anonymously, to the Geological Society of London on 23 September 1839. This, which must have been part of Part 1, is missing. The unique Eyles copy is ex libris William Montagu (1771–1843), Duke of Manchester, subscriber to William Smith's 1815 *Map of the Strata*. This comprises a much longer 259 pages and, initially, seemed to give full details of its publication. But an additional part, still in its original wrappers, survives in Oxford's Hope Library[9] to prove this was not the case. It also shows the publishing history of this to have been more complex. It carries the signature of entomologist Frederick William Hope (1797–1862 – *ODNB*). It comprises only pages 235–259 and shows, first, that this was the first section of a 'Part 2, Igneous Causes' and, second, that this second Part was published Rome 1840 by 'Joseph Salviucci and Son', an equally reputed publisher there (Fig. 3). It indicates that WPH was in Rome by 1840, where Hope must have acquired this unique item and who was then also in Italy.

Hunter's Italian *Examination of Lyell's* Principles of Geology was dedicated to William Smith, in this deserved tribute:

> to whose original discoveries towards the close of the last century and Geological Map published in 1815, the Science of Geology owes its rise and rank as a Science, and is mainly indebted for its present promising State of Progression . . . as a slight tribute of respect and admiration from his Friend, the Author, Florence, Italy, 18 April 1839.

Smith produced his own, strange, attempt to disagree with Lyell's *Principles* in July 1835. Smith produced his for that year's BAAS meeting in Dublin (North 1927), when on 13 August he had been given his LL.D. degree at Trinity College. Hunter may have been inspired by Smith's attempt. Martin Rudwick has discussed the reactions to Lyell's *Principles* (Rudwick 2008), but without citing Hunter's completely forgotten attempt, which certainly deserves further analysis.

Return to Scotland

WPH last appeared in GSL lists in 1837 of 'Albany, London', having 'compounded for his annual subscription'. He is missing from their next 1839 list, clearly as he was in Italy. Hunter's movements after Rome were unclear. He certainly reappears in the 1841 GSL list, but with no address given, as the Society had clearly lost track of him. In Paris the Société Géologique had the same problem. Between 1844 and 1895 he was listed as 'of London'. Then his name disappears too, but he was never recorded as among their annual list of deceased members.

Some details of his European involvements in and after 1840 are given in three, repetitious, increasingly desperate and confused letters of 1842 and 1843, addressed to GSL, written after he had returned to Britain late in 1841. These are: (1) LR7/152, 22 June 1842; (2) LR7/153, 23 August 1842, [addressed to, and 'received from', Sir Henry de la Beche; and (3) LR7/339, 12 April 1843. These, quoted here, were 'written [while WPH was] compelled frequently to write by stealth and put his letters into the post unpaid'. All are written from Dalkeith, near

[9]Oxford University Museum of Natural History – press mark 1882.e.10 (1).

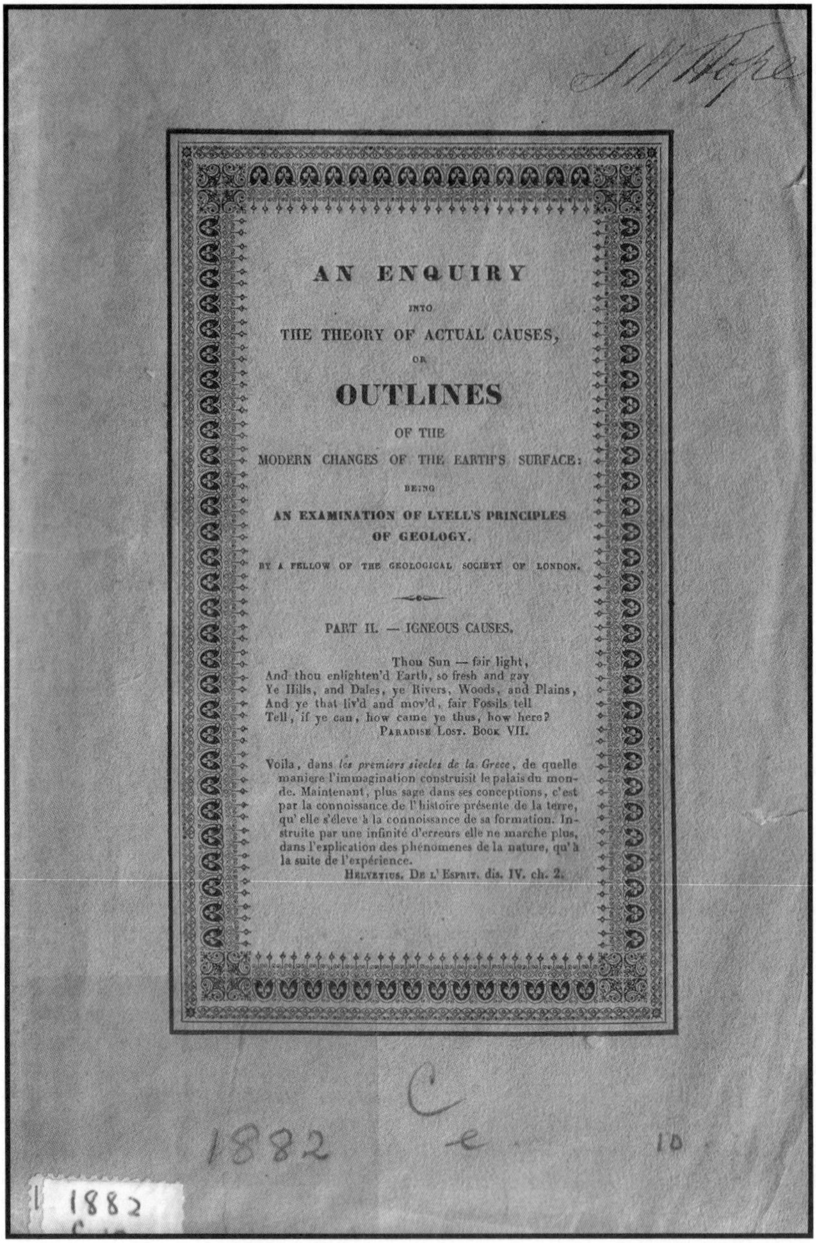

AN ENQUIRY

INTO

THE THEORY OF ACTUAL CAUSES,

OR

OUTLINES

OF THE

MODERN CHANGES OF THE EARTH'S SURFACE:

BEING

AN EXAMINATION OF LYELL'S PRINCIPLES OF GEOLOGY.

BY A FELLOW OF THE GEOLOGICAL SOCIETY OF LONDON.

PART II. — IGNEOUS CAUSES.

Thou Sun — fair light,
And thou enlighten'd Earth, so fresh and gay
Ye Hills, and Dales, ye Rivers, Woods, and Plains,
And ye that liv'd and mov'd, fair Fossils tell
Tell, if ye can, how came ye thus, how here?
PARADISE LOST. BOOK VII.

Voila, dans *les premiers siecles de la Grece*, de quelle maniere l'immagination construisit le palais du monde. Maintenant, plus sage dans ses conceptions, c'est par la connoissance de l'histoire présente de la terre, qu' elle s'éleve à la connoissance de sa formation. Instruite par une infinité d'erreurs elle ne marche plus, dans l'explication des phénomenes de la nature, qu' à la suite de l'expérience.
HELVETIUS. DE L'ESPRIT. dis. IV. ch. 2.

Fig. 3. Wrapper of Hunter (1840) 'Part 2, Igneous Causes'.

Edinburgh, and record how he had spent the $3\frac{1}{2}$ years previous to November 1841:

> Mr W. Perceval Hunter begs leave most respectfully to submit to them that, though unknown by any works or discoveries etc, to the leading members of the Geological World, he has for several years past been engaged in the study of practical geology, visiting the most remarkable places in his own island, Germany, Switzerland and Italy and Sicily, comparing them with the best accounts extant in French, English, Italian or Spanish and making notes on the spot with the view of preparing himself in later life for active original geological research in South America, or other countries, where, from their extent and the richness and variety of their geological wonders and the paucity of scientific

> visitants, so much remains to be done, that two years ago [1841] he spent several months on Mount Etna, making observations on the meteorology at the basic [illeg.] and the summit, collecting specimens.
>
> (LR 7/153)

He also noted that his 3 years in Italy and Sicily had involved the study of Roman Antiquities [LR 7/339]. In this last letter W. P. H. mentioned:

> having been most reluctantly compelled in 1841 to leave the Italian Peninsula, . . . of which he intended writing for a volume on *Outlines of the Geology of the Italian Peninsula*. Having more recently been molested in Switzerland, he had resolved on devoting his time and attention to a study of the geology of England and Wales and in hopes of procuring a restoration of unfettered liberty of study and action – he has ventured [to send? illeg] these pages to the attention of the Council [LR 7/339]. Mr Wm Perceval. Hunter . . . [had suffered] Metternichian and Jesuitic false persecutions which induced him most reluctantly, after a sojourn of three years spent in geological researches and the study of antiquities, to abandon the Italian peninsula [where he had last studied Venetian Volcanos there in summer 1841 – LR 7/339], and more recently Switzerland, where he had retreated in the hopes of securing a comfortable residence, where he might be protected from the intrusion and espionage of foreign police, with a view of devoting his attention to the study of Alpine Geology and secondly the still severer treatment he had received, after a fortnight's residence in November last [1841] in Edinburgh, in Dalkeith, having for the last nine months [since December 1841] been living under forcible restraint in solitary captivity in Dalkeith [LR7/153]. [He had suffered] in consequence of incessant espionage, finding not only himself seriously molested in his pursuits, but the scientific foreigners on whom he called, likewise subjected to annoyances, and having recently been subjected to nocturnal molestations of the most disagreeable character.
>
> [LR 7/152]

Klemens Wenzel, Prince von Metternich (1773–1859), the Austrian politician, had been actively forming political police forces throughout the Hapsburg Empire, which then included the province of Lombardo-Venetia in this period (Emerson 1960), and these may well have been spying on such a protestant, revolutionary Englishman as WPH. As one fellow-sufferer, the Italian patriot Guiseppe Mazzini (1805–1872 – *ODNB*), a near contemporary of Hunter, was exiled from Genoa in 1831, sentenced to death as a refugee in Switzerland in 1833, and came to England on expulsion from France and Switzerland in 1837. Here, at Metternich's request, George Hamilton-Gordon, fourth earl of Aberdeen (1784–1860), British Foreign Secretary 1841–1846 and later Prime Minister, opened letters addressed to Mazzini in 1844 to inform Austria about the patriotic republican movement he was planning for Italy.

WPH added 'that previous to coming [back] to Scotland he had been staying for a fortnight at Montbard in Burgundy'. Montband, 60 km NW of Dijon, was the birthplace of Georges-Louis Lelerc, Comte de Buffon (1707–1788) the famous naturalist. He had appealed for a memoir on Buffon in 1829 (*MNH*, **2**, p. 402, 1829). This suggests that he was continuing to take an interest in the lives of former natural historians.

WPH had returned to Edinburgh because:

> he had made up his mind to reside there for some months and publish the second and concluding volume of his translation of Azara's *Quadrupeds*, the volume of which he published in 1838 [Hunter 1838] in a supplement to which would have been a condensed account of the numerous fossil mammals discovered of late years in Paraguay and Buenos Ayres – he remained a fortnight . . . during [which] he wrote out, corrected and printed 15 pages of a *Treatise on Volcanos* [clearly another part of the second Igneous volume of his Italian publication] an elementary work on *Actual Causes* – 280 pages of which he printed for his amusement and instruction in Italy, with this additional printing of which in Edinburgh, when he was induced under false pretences to visit Dalkeith, where he has ever since been forcibly detained in solitary confinement and not only deprived of his usual exercise, [but] prevented from out of door geological studies, and subjected to continual insult, but owing to the regime he is subjected to [illeg.] utterly incapable of reading, writing & geological or natural historical study. Mr W. Perceval Hunter adds that not the slightest shadow of a foundation on the plea of ill health – the pretended, but most ridiculous plea, he is told will be put up as an excuse – exists for such imprisonment. Mr Hunter having spoken to several persons in Edinburgh who are ready to come forward and attest his perfect convalescence.

The last we hear of WPH, within natural science, is the advertisement in *The Times* (29 August 1842, p. 8, col. 1) re-offering Volume 1 of his book on *The Natural History of the Quadrupeds of Paraguay* (Hunter 1838) for sale, with news that 'the second volume, completing the Quadrupeds, is in the press and will be published immediately'. But this never appeared amid WPH's new troubles in Scotland.

Confinement in Dalkeith (December 1841 to at least 1851)

> Mr Wm Perceval Hunter hereby certifies that he has for upwards of fourteen months been living in solitary captivity by forcible detention in the house of a Dr Graham of Dalkeith, subject to the most [left blank] treatment, to the great injury of his health, constitution, of his intellect, character, and reputation and prospects in life.
>
> (LR 7/339)

In the 1851 census WPH was still living as a 'Gentleman', supposedly 'boarding' in this same Dalkeith High Street household of the Dalkeith-born and Edinburgh-trained surgeon and physician Charles William Montagu Scott Graham (1797–1877 – see *The Times*, 23 May 1877, p. 1, col. 1), who graduated with a M.D. from Edinburgh University in 1830. WPH had been kept here under forcible detention, under Graham's direct medical supervision, since December 1841, 'in a country in the immediate vicinity of which is little of geological interest, and [is] not permitted to make use of his hammer, his collections, etc and debarred the use of museums, libraries, as well as entirely cut off from all rational intercourse, being to all intents and purposes a person for the last nine months civilly dead (LR 7/153)'. WPH hoped by writing to the Geological Society they would be able to ensure his release from such confinement, in

> hopes that they may be induced to afford protection to a member of their Society, engaged for several years past in active geological study ... with a view to future original geological research in South America and the United states but forcibly prevented from his usual out of door studies ... There appearing to be an intention on the part of the authors of Mr W. Perceval Hunter's imprisonment to keep him in solitary captivity as long as possible, he feels himself compelled to make use of all means to procure his liberty, is in hopes that the fact need only be made known to the influential members of the Geological Society to have him enlarged [i.e. set at large].
> (LR 7/152)

WPH, as often with the mentally ill, was convinced there was nothing the matter with him. He

> believes his confinement to have been caused by foreigners, who have, on advice of Dr Munro – Professor of Anatomy in University of Edinburgh [Dr Alexander Munro (1773–1859) tertius, Professor of anatomy there, in a highly nepotic succession, 1817–1846 – *ODNB*] ... and a Dr Smith, proprietor of a lunatic asylum near Edinburgh [Dr John Smith (1798–1879) M.D. Edinburgh University 1823, thesis on 'De Insania' – see Tuke 1880), who had recently become manager of the private Saughton Hall Asylum, Edinburgh were] the ostensible agent[s] in Mr W.P.H's confinement, backed by ministerial or state connivance, from the belief of his intending to write a book upon the different governments of the Italian Peninsula, where he spent three years previous to his arrival in England, during which he possessed opportunities of seeing the country and visiting provinces etc – not generally known to British tourists, and for the purpose of preventing his composing any such work, at least while the memory of the places should be fresh in his mind, the humiliating regime which incapacitates him as above, stopped from thinking, or writing to any purpose, has been adopted.
> (LR 7/339)

This establishes that his confinement had been initiated from 'abroad by foreigners' and confirmed by Munro. The missing link is the fact that Munro had recently married, as his second wife, Janet (or Jessie) Hunter, WPH's elder sister, in 1836 (*The Times*, 23 July 1836, p. 7, col. 3).

This final letter has two last pages clearly added in much haste, although whether from WPH's then mental, or physical, state from 'being compelled frequently to write by stealth and [then] put his letters in the post unpaid [in secret]. W.P.H. is given to understand that he has been kept here by the Duke of Buccleuch on account of letters written respecting him in Italy by [words illeg], hired he supposes by the High Sheriff of this county, the Duke of B'. This Duke was Walter Francis Montagu-Douglas Scott (1806–1884 – *ODNB*) of Dalkeith House, among his many properties, and whose father Charles William Henry Montagu Scott shared many of the same four Christian names as Dr Graham, in some as yet unexplained connection.

Hunter's final years, 1841–1878

In the 1861 census Graham is still listed as living at Dalkeith, but now without boarders. WPH had at some time, after 1851 and before 1861, been placed in the more secure old Saughton Hall Asylum, on the western edge of Edinburgh, which long had famous gardens (Buxton 2007) (Fig. 4). This was then managed by the above Dr John Smith.

This had been set up as 'a private Lunatic Asylum exclusively designed for the reception of patients of the higher ranks' in the 1790s (Barfoot 2009, p. 66; http://archiver.rootsweb.com/th/read/MIDLOTHIAN/2005-03/1110225353).

As a private institution, records of admissions are less likely to have survived (none are in today's Lothian Health Services Archives). The resident physician at the probable time of Hunter's admission was Dr William Henry Lowe (1815–1900), born in Whitchurch, Shropshire, who shared WPH's interests in natural history. He had graduated with an M.D. from Edinburgh University in 1840 and became a Fellow of the Entomological Society of London in 1850 (Verrall 1901, p. xliii). He published two papers on local Lepidoptera in 1854–1857, in *Proceedings of the Edinburgh Physical Society*. In an interesting paper Finnegan has pointed out how in some Scottish asylums natural history was encouraged as an aid to better mental health (Finnegan 2008). This may have also been the case at Saughton. Lowe had left Saughton Hall by 1868 and died in August 1900 (*The Times*, 30 August 1900, p. 9. col. 2).

An extraordinary book that sheds light on this asylum at the very time WPH was there is the highly sarcastic 'farce' by Henry Justinian

Fig. 4. View of old Saughton Hall (Grant 1887, p. 320).

Newcome (1815–1905 – see *The Times*, 14 October 1905, p. 1, col. 1) entitled The Lunatic (Newcome 1861). This was a rebuttal of the idea that Newcome had 'excited himself into insanity in 1859', in a book dedicated to the 'proprietors of Saughton Hall, without permission'. In this the same Drs Lowe and Smith are frequently cited, the same two who were involved in confining Hunter. But, very unlike what happened to Hunter, as soon as Newcome was sent to another asylum, of 'a very different character, where he met with every possible kindness', he recovered. This was Brislington House, Bristol, asylum of the Quaker doctor brothers Francis Ker Fox (1804–1883) and Charles Joseph Fox (1806–1870), founded in 1794 for the 'humane treatment of the insane' (Lane 2001, pp. 105–107).

At Saughton Hall on 2 September 1878 at 9.30 a.m., Hunter, a 'Fund Holder' (i.e. of independent means), died aged 66 (Death Certificate, General Register Office, Edinburgh), from 'Fatty Desquamation of the heart – 5 Months, and Dropsy – 1 Month'. At the time of Hunter's death here the superintending physician was the Beverly-born Sir John Batty Tuke (1835–1913), M. D. Edinburgh 1836 (who had joined Smith and Lowe – see *British Medical Journal*, 18 October 1913, pp. 1045–1046). He was a pioneer in the treatment of mental illnesses, on which he wrote (see *British Medical Journal*, 31 July 1880, pp. 189–190) and lectured widely (in Edinburgh from 1875: see Comrie 1932, Vol. 2, p. 709). He was elected a Fellow of the Royal Society of Edinburgh in 1874 (Bennet *et al.* 1983). His attitude to mental illness is well expressed in his later article (see Tuke 1889). The man who signed WPH's death certificate was the later resident physician there, David Bower (1853–1929) (White 1929).

Hunter's sad end here has guaranteed him a forgotten life. The Geological Society had long since lost all trace of him and listed him among 'Addresses unknown' in 1872 (Hall 1872). WPH provides a fine example of how easily historically significant figures can escape the historians' net.

Grateful thanks are due to the following for their kind help: M. Barfoot (Edinburgh), M. Bishop (Newport), W. Cawthorne (London), G. Demarsily (Paris), G. Douglas (London), F. Driver (London), D. Finnegan (Belfast), A. Gardener and L. Brouard (Edinburgh), J. Gaudant (Paris), M. Lawley (Ludlow), A. Lum (London), S. Pierce (Wincanton – indefatigable), C. Rider (London), J. Sellick (London), M. Taylor (Edinburgh) and E. Vaccari (Insubria, Italy).

References

ANON. 1833. *Lithographed Signatures of the Members of the British Association for the Advancement of Science who met at Cambridge, June 1833.* Pitt Press, Cambridge.

ANON. 1836. *List of Members of the British Association for the Advancement of Science not residing in Bristol, enrolled at Bristol 27 August 1836.* Chilcott, Bristol (Bristol Ref. Lib. B 9713).

ARCHIVES OF THE ROYAL INSTITUTION 1971. *Minutes of Managers' Meetings, 1799–1900*, Volumes 1–13. Scolar Press, Menston.

ARROWSMITH, R. L. 1974. *Charterhouse Register 1769–1872*. Phillimore, Chichester.

BAKEWELL, R. 1835. On the Maidstone fossil skeleton, in the Museum of Gideon Mantell, LL.D. F.R.S., Brighton. *Magazine of Natural History*, **8**, 99–102.

BARFOOT, M. 2009. The 1815 Act to Regulate Madhouses in Scotland; a reinterpretation. *Medical History*, **53**, 57–76.

BEDDALL, B. G. 1975. 'Un Naturalista Original': Don Felix de Azara, 1746–1821. *Journal of the History of Biology*, **8**, 15–66.

BEDDALL, B. G. 1983. The isolated Spanish genius – myth or reality? Felix de Azara and the birds of Paraguay. *Journal of the History of Biology*, **16**, 225–258.

BENNET, F., BOYLE, A., HAYWARD, T. & HUNTER, L. 1983. *Scotland's Cultural Heritage, Volume 4, The Royal Society of Edinburgh, 100 Medical Fellows Elected 1841–1882*. University of Edinburgh, Edinburgh (unpaginated).

BUCKINGHAM, J. S. 1832. *Mr Buckingham's Defence of his Public and Private Character*. Blackwell, Sheffield (BL, pressmark 10864.aa.14).

BUCKLAND, W. 1835. On the discovery of the fossil bones of the Iguanodon, in the Iron Sand of the Wealden Formation in the Isle of Wight and in the Isle of Purbeck. *Transactions of the Geological Society of London*, Series 2, **3**, 425–432.

BUXTON, A. 2007. Saughton Gardens. *The Caledonian Gardener*, 7–10.

CLEEVLEY, R. J. 1983. *World Palaeontological Collections*. British Museum (Natural History), London.

COMRIE, J. D. 1932. *History of Scottish Medicine*, 2 volumes. Wellcome Historical Medical Museum, London.

CORRAN, T. H. 1981. James Deady, Henry Meux and the Griffin Brewery: fraud in an early-nineteenth-century business. *Business History*, **23**, 327–345.

COSTELOE, M. P. 2008. *William Bullock. Connoisseur and Virtuoso of the Egyptian Hall: Piccadilly to Mexico (1773–1849)*. HiPLAM, Bristol.

COX, L. R. 1942. New light on William Smith and his work. *Proceedings of the Yorkshire Geological Society*, **25**, 1–99.

DEAN, D. R. 1989. New light on William Maclure. *Annals of Science*, **46**, 549–574.

DOSKEY, J. S. 1988. *The European Journals of William Maclure [1805–1825]*. American Philosophical Society, Philadelphia, PA.

EMERSON, D. E. 1960. *Metternich and the Political Police: Security and Subversion in the Hapsburg Monarchy 1815–1830*. Martinus Nijhoff, The Hague.

FARINGTON, J. 1978–1984. *The Diary of Joseph Farington, Volumes 1–16*. Yale University Press for the Paul Mellon Centre for Studies in British Art, New Haven, CT.

FINNEGAN, D. A. 2008. 'An aid to mental health': natural history, alienists and therapeutics in Victorian Scotland. *Studies in the History and Philosophy of Biological and Biomedical Sciences*, **39**, 326–337.

FITTON, W. H. 1833. *A Geological Sketch of the Vicinity of Hastings*. Longmans, London.

FOSTER, J. 1887–1888. *Alumni Oxonienses, the Members of the University of Oxford, 1715–1886 ... Being the Matriculation Register of the University*, 4 volumes. Parkers, Oxford.

GRANT, J. 1887. *Cassell's Old and New Edinburgh*, Volume 3. Cassell & Co, London.

HALL, T. 1872. *A Topographical Index to the Fellows of the Geological Society of London*. Geological Society, London. World wide web address: http://jgslegacy.lyellcollection.org/cgi/.

HOWITT, F. 1964. Stratigraphy and structure of the Purbeck inliers of Sussex. *Quarterly Journal of the Geological Society of London*, **120**, 77–113.

HUNTER, W. P. 1835. *Geological Notes*. Tiffen, Hythe.

HUNTER, W. P. 1837. *Selections from the Natural History of the Quadrupeds of Paraguay and the River La Plata* .... A. J. Valpy, London.

HUNTER, W. P. 1838. *The Natural History of the Quadrupeds of Paraguay and the River La Plata, from the Spanish of De Azara, with a Memoir of the Author, a Physical Sketch of the Country and Numerous Notes*, Volume 1 [only]. A. & C. Black, Edinburgh.

HUNTER, W. P. 1840. *An Enquiry into the Theory of Actual Causes, or Outlines of the Modern Changes of the Earth's Surface being an Examination of Lyell's* Principles of Geology, *Part 2, Igneous Causes*. Joseph Salviucci and Son, Rome, 235–239.

JACKSON, C. E. & DAVIS, P. 2001. *Sir William Jardine: A Life in Natural History*. University Press, Leicester.

LANE, J. 2001. *A Social History of Medicine*. Routledge, London.

LEWIS, C. L. E. & KNELL, S. J. (eds) 2009. *The Making of the Geological Society of London*. Geological Society, London, Special Publications, **317**.

LYELL, C. 1834. *Principles of Geology*, 3rd edn, 4 volumes. John Murray, London.

MCVIE, J. 1935. The Lochlie Litigation. *Burns Chronicle*, **2**, 69–87.

MANTELL, G. A. 1833. *The Geology of the South-east of England*. Longman, London.

MANTELL, G. A. 1834*a*. Discovery of the Bones of the Iguanodon. *Edinburgh New Philosophical Journal*, **17**, (July), 200–201.

MANTELL, G. A. 1834*b*. *A Descriptive Catalogue of the Collection, Illustrative of Geology and Fossil Comparative Anatomy, in the Museum of ...*, 3rd edn. Relfe & Fletcher, London.

MATHIAS, P. 1959. *The Brewing Industry in England 1700–1830*. Cambridge University Press, Cambridge.

MOLINI, L. 1858. *Operette bibliografiche del cav. Guiseppe Molini*. Cellini, Firenze.

MOORE, D. T., THACKRAY, J. C. & MORGAN, D. L. 1991. A short history of the Museum of the Geological Society of London, 1807–1911. *Bulletin of the British Museum (Natural History) (Historical Series)*, **19**, 51–160.

MORTON, S. G. 1841. *Memoir of William Maclure, esq.* Collins, Philadelphia, PA.

NEWCOME, H. J. 1861. *The Lunatic: or English Clergymen and Scottish Doctors. An Autobiography*. Pownceby, London (Bodleian lib. 250.c.131(17)).

NORMAN, D. B. 1993. Gideon Mantell's 'Mantel-Piece': the earliest well preserved Ornithischian Dinosaur. *Modern Geology*, **18**, 225–245.

NORTH, F. J. 1927. Deductions from established facts in geology by Wm. Smith. *Geological Magazine*, **64**, 532–540.

PHILLIPS, J. 1844. *Memoirs of William Smith LL.D.* Murray, London.

PIDGEON, E. 1830. *The Fossil Remains of the Animal Kingdom*, Whitaker, Treacher & Co., London.

REPORTS OF THE BRITISH ASSOCIATION 1833–1838. Meetings 1–2 to 7. British Association for the Advancement of Science, London.

RUDWICK, M. J. S. 2008. *Worlds Before Adam. The Reconstruction of Geohistory in the Age of Reform.* University of Chicago Press, Chicago, IL.

RUSKIN, J. 1836. To what properties in nature is it owing that the stones in buildings... gradually become indurated. *Magazine of Natural History*, **9**, 488–490.

RUSKIN, J. 1903. *The Works of John Ruskin (Cook E. T. & Wedderburn A. eds)*, Volume 1. Allen, London.

SCHNEER, C. 1981. William Maclure's geological map of the United States. *Journal of Geological Education*, **29**, 241–245.

SCROPE, G. P. 1835. [Review of] Lyell's *Principles of Geology. Quarterly Review*, **53**, 406–448.

SWAINSON, W. 1840. *Natural History. Taxidermy, Bibliography and Biography.* Longman, London.

THOMPSON, T. 1835. An attempt to ascertain the animals designated in the scriptures by the names Leviathan and Behemoth. *Magazine of Natural History*, **8**, 193–197, 307–321.

TOPLEY, W. 1875. *Geology of the Weald.* HMSO, London.

TORRENS, H. S. 2005. The Moravian minister Rev. Henry Steinhauer (1782–1818); his work on fossil plants. *In*: BOWDEN, A. J., BUREK, C. V. & WILDING, R. (eds) *History of Palaeobotany: Selected Essays.* Geological Society, London, Special Publications, **241**, 13–28.

TORRENS, H. S. 2006. The geological work of Gregory Watt, his travels with William Maclure in Italy (1801–1802), and Watt's 'proto-geological' map of Italy (1804). *Geological Society of America, Special Paper*, **411**, 179–197.

TORRENS, H. S. 2011. Politics and palaeontology: Richard Owen and the invention of dinosaurs. *In*: FARLOW, J. O. & BRETT-SURMAN, M. K. (eds) *The Complete Dinosaur*, 2nd edn. Indiana University Press, Bloomington, IN (1st edn, 1997, pp. 175–190), in press.

TUKE, J. B. 1880. Dr John Smith. *Proceedings of the Royal Society of Edinburgh*, **10**, 353–354.

TUKE, J. B. 1889. Lunatics as patients, not prisoners. *Nineteenth Century*, **25**, 595–607.

VENN, J. 1940–1954. *Alumni Cantabrigienses, a Biographical List of all Known Students, Graduates and Holders of Office at the University of Cambridge, From the Earliest Times to 1900, Part 2, From 1752 to 1900*, 6 volumes. Cambridge University Press, Cambridge.

VERRALL, G. H. 1901. Obituary of Dr. W. H. Lowe. *Transactions of the Entomological Society of London*, **1900**, xliii.

VIGNOLES, O. J. 1891. Geological reminiscences. *Temple Bar*, **91**, 551–566.

WEISHAMPEL, D. B. & WHITE, N. M. 2003. *The Dinosaur Papers.* Smithsonian Press, Washington, DC.

WHITE, E. W. 1929. Obituary – David Bower. *Journal of Mental Science*, **75**, 832.

WOODWARD, B. B. (compiler) 1903–1940. *Catalogue of the Books, Manuscripts, Maps and Drawings in the British Museum, Natural History*, 8 volumes. British Museum, Natural History, London.

WOODWARD, H. B. 1907. *The History of the Geological Society of London.* Geological Society, London.

‘Old bones, dry subject’: the dinosaurs and pterosaur collected by Alfred Nicholson Leeds of Peterborough, England

LESLIE F. NOÈ[1]*, JEFF J. LISTON[2] & SANDRA D. CHAPMAN[3]

[1]*Thinktank, Birmingham Science Museum, Millennium Point, Curzon Street, Birmingham B4 7XG, UK; College of Life and Environmental Sciences, School of Geography, Earth and Environmental Science, University of Birmingham, Edgbaston, Birmingham B15 2TT, UK*

[2]*Thurso Street Research Facility, Hunterian Museum, University of Glasgow, 13 Thurso Street, Glasgow G11 6PE, UK; Division of Environmental & Evolutionary Biology, Faculty of BioMedical & Life Sciences, University of Glasgow, Glasgow G12 8QQ, UK*

[3]*Department of Palaeontology, The Natural History Museum, Cromwell Road, London SW7 5BD, UK*

**Corresponding author (e-mail: leslie.noe@thinktank.ac)*

Abstract: Alfred Nicholson Leeds, F.G.S., amassed one of the largest collections of fossil vertebrates from a single geological horizon anywhere in the world. The Leeds Collection is world famous for its large marine reptiles, but also includes the remains of a fine range of dinosaurs and a fragmentary pterosaur. The Leeds Collection ornithodirans were almost exclusively recovered from the Peterborough Member of the Oxford Clay Formation, with a single specimen of a sauropod derived from the underlying Kellaways Formation. The Leeds Collection includes the remains of at least 12 individual dinosaurs representing at least eight taxa (with other remains currently generically indeterminate) and a single fragmentary rhamphorhynchid pterosaur. Perhaps most intriguingly of all, in 1898 Alfred Leeds discovered a probable reptile egg, later attributed to a dinosaur. Each dinosaur and the pterosaur from the Leeds Collection is discussed, and, where known, details of the provenance, a brief history of research and pertinent archive material are included to provide the most comprehensive and up-to-date survey of the Leeds Collection ornithodirans to date.

Alfred Nicholson Leeds (1847–1917) was a gentleman farmer, amateur fossil collector and Fellow of the Geological Society of London who had a remarkable skill for collecting and piecing together fossils from the Jurassic Oxford Clay Formation around Peterborough (Smith Woodward 1917; Harker 1918; Bruce-Mitford & Harden 1956). Leeds lived at an auspicious time when brickworks were being opened up on an industrial scale, but when the clay was still being worked by hand, so fossils were frequently discovered (Harker 1918; Leeds 1956). These unique circumstances, together with Leeds’ personality as a born collector, combined to permit this one man, with the help of his brother and other members of his family, to bring together an unrivalled collection of fossil vertebrates (C.L.F. 1956; Swinton preface to Leeds 1956). Alfred Leeds never published on his collection, indeed his only published work was a short joint-authored article relating to a Geologists’ Association field trip and visit to his collection in 1897 (Leeds & Smith Woodward 1897). However, Leeds was a hospitable man, who encouraged interested laymen and scientists alike to engage with his ‘bones’ (Bruce-Mitford & Harden 1956; Leeds 1956), and many of the scientific greats of his day inspected, studied, referred to or published on his collection. These included: Harry Govier Seeley (1839–1909: Anon. 1909), John Whitaker Hulke (1830–1895: Anon. 1895), Henry Woodward (1832–1921: Anon. 1921), Othniel Charles Marsh (1831–1899: Woodward 1899), Richard Lydekker (1849–1915: Anon. 1915), Arthur Smith Woodward (1864–1944: Forster Cooper 1945), Friedrich von Huene (1875–1969: Leeds 1956, p. 92) and Charles William Andrews (1866–1924: Smith Woodward 1924).

The Leeds Collection contains numerous crocodiles, ichthyosaurs, plesiosaurs, pliosaurs, fish and invertebrates; what is less well known is that Leeds collected several genera and species of dinosaurs and fragmentary pterosaur remains (but see Ashworth 1911). Although terrestrial and volant reptiles were rare in the marine deposits around Peterborough (Leeds 1956), Alfred Leeds found dinosaur material ranging from isolated and incomplete elements, to substantially complete skeletal remains, a fragmentary pterosaur and a putative

From: Moody, R. T. J., Buffetaut, E., Naish, D. & Martill, D. M. (eds) *Dinosaurs and Other Extinct Saurians: A Historical Perspective*. Geological Society, London, Special Publications, **343**, 49–77.
DOI: 10.1144/SP343.4 0305-8719/10/$15.00

dinosaur egg. Both ornithischian and saurischian herbivores are represented in the Leeds Collection, but there are no remains of carnivorous dinosaurs; the pterosaur is one of a very few recovered from the Oxford Clay. Today, the Leeds Collection remains of international importance and is regularly consulted by researchers across a wide range of disciplines. The wealth of archive material associated with the fossilized remains has, unfortunately, been sadly neglected, and this contribution goes a small way towards rectifying this situation by exploring some of the history of the ornithodiran material contained within the Leeds Collection.

Leeds: Charles, Alfred and a collection of 'bones'

Alfred Nicholson Leeds was born at the family home of Eyebury, near Peterborough, on 9 March 1847 (Smith Woodward 1917). He was the youngest of eight children and the second surviving son of Edward Thurlow Leeds (1802–1851) and Eliza Mary Leeds (née Nicholson) (Leeds 1956). Alfred Leeds and his elder brother Charles Edward Leeds (1845–1912: Anon. 1912*b*) were both educated at Warwick Grammar School (Smith Woodward 1917; Leeds 1956), and in October 1865 Charles Leeds commenced study at Exeter College Oxford, where he attended the lectures of John Phillips (1800–1874: Anon. 1874), Professor of Geology (1856–1874). This contact acted as a spur for the older Leeds brother to explore the Oxford Clay deposits close to his home in Peterborough (Leeds 1956), and he was soon joined by his younger brother Alfred. Thus, the Leeds Collection had its beginnings.

Alfred Leeds worked with his brother Charles to collect and piece together the fossils found in the increasing numbers of newly opening brick pits around Peterborough (Smith Woodward 1917; Leeds 1956). Alfred Leeds had wanted to become a medical doctor (Smith Woodward 1917), but, with his older brother having elected to go to university, the responsibility for running the family farm at Eyebury (held in trust since his father's death in 1851; Leeds 1956) fell to the younger brother when he reached the age of 21. Charles Leeds, upon graduating from Oxford in 1868, spent time in Newark on Trent before studying to become a solicitor in Bury St Edmunds, taking his final exams in 1873; he then spent time working in Westminster and York (Leeds 1956). Hence, it seems likely that from about 1870 onwards the Leeds Collection was mostly or solely accumulated by Alfred Leeds. Nonetheless, Charles Leeds continued to take an active interest in the collection and his academic contacts meant that, for instance, it was the elder brother who invited Seeley to study the collection in 1874 and again in 1885 (Seeley 1874, 1889). Indeed, the lack of scientific interest in the collection following Seeley's 1874 visit was probably a result of Alfred's quiet work in selflessly accumulating fossils over the ensuing years for his own enjoyment and pleasure (Leeds 1956).

In 1875 Alfred Leeds married Mary Ferrier ('Ferry') Fergusson (1858–1922) in Glasgow (Liston 2006), and the couple had five sons (Fig. 1) (Leeds 1956), of which only the second, Edward Thurlow Leeds (1877–1955), took any real interest in Alfred Leeds' 'bones' (Bruce-Mitford & Harden 1956). As the Leeds family grew, so did the Leeds Collection and it inevitably came to the notice of the wider scientific community. This occurred in around 1885, following a letter from Charles Leeds to H. G. Seeley (Seeley 1889), which resulted in the first contacts with staff at the British Museum (Natural History) in London (BMNH, now the Natural History Museum (NHM), London), including Henry Woodward (Keeper of Geology) and J. W. Hulke, which grew into a life-long partnership between Alfred Leeds and Britain's national museum. In 1887 Charles Leeds left England for Matakana in New Zealand (Leeds 1956), never to return to the UK, and Alfred Leeds, assisted by his wife and sons, continued to collect, clean and mount newly excavated fossils (Smith Woodward 1917). The degree to which Mrs Leeds assisted in the processing of the bones is unknown (Leeds 1956), but it is likely to have been much underestimated. For instance, a watercolour painted by Margaret Croom Crewdson (Mary Leeds' sister), as an everyday scene at Eyebury, apparently shows Mary washing bones with her husband (Fig. 2). Another painting by Alfred Leeds' cousin William (later Sir William) Nicholson (1872–1949) dating from 1889 shows Alfred Leeds sitting in one of his two attic 'bone rooms' (Fig. 3) (Leeds 1956, frontispiece). Clearly working on Oxford Clay fossils was a daily occurrence and a normal part of life for the Leeds Family.

By 1888 the BMNH had made overtures to purchase Alfred Leeds' collection, although this appears to have initially been resisted (Anon. 1888). However, in 1890, Alfred Leeds consented to the sale, on the condition that the BMNH took the collection in its entirety (Leeds 1956). It is not clear whether the decision to sell was primarily precipitated to free up space for more material or because of the late Victorian agricultural depression (Fletcher 1961; Turner 1992), which was especially harsh around Peterborough in the 1880s (Perry 1972) and may have meant that Alfred Leeds was forced to consider alternative sources of income to farming. Either way, half of the money from the sale was sent to Charles Leeds in New Zealand (Leeds 1956). This does not appear to reflect of the amount of time Charles Leeds contributed to

Fig. 1. Alfred Nicholson Leeds and his family. (Left) Alfred Leeds and his wife Mary Fergusson Leeds in around 1875. (Right) The Leeds family in around 1906 showing Alfred Leeds (left), Mary Leeds (rear) and their five sons, left to right: Edward Thurlow Leeds (1877–1955), Alexander Andrew Fergusson ('Fergie') Leeds (1876–1913), Lewis Alfred Leeds (1883–1918), Keith Ferrier Newzam Leeds (1894–1974) (front) and Charles Herbert Leeds (1878–1954). Images © the Leeds family, reproduced with permission.

building up the collection (Leeds 1956), but could be interpreted as recognition by Alfred Leeds of the way Charles Leeds' efforts had brought the collection to the attention of experts and, thus, facilitated its sale.

Having sold one collection, Alfred Leeds continued collecting, and by 1893 the Leeds Collection was sufficiently well known and important for the Geological Society to award him one-half of that year's Lyell Fund, jointly with Miss Raisen (Anon. 1893). The sales of fossil material continued, including one group to the Dublin Science and Art Museum in November 1893 (Araújo *et al.* 2008) and through auction on 18 August 1896 (Chalmers-Hunt 1976). In March 1896 Leeds gave a public lecture in his local village hall, at which he was surprised at the positive response the audience had to what he referred to as his 'old bones' in such a 'dry subject' (lecture notes held by the Leeds family; letter dated 8 March 1896; BMNH ML DF100/30; full abbreviations given later). By now, Alfred Leeds' collection had gained an international reputation, but Leeds fossils only really began to spread across Europe when he was approached by Bernhard Stürtz in Bonn on the recommendation of Smith Woodward in October 1897 for the 'skull of a saurian' (Leeds 1939, plate 38). Leeds Collection material also reached North America through a gift to O. C. Marsh for the Yale Peabody Museum, after he visited Eyebury in October 1888 (letters to O. C. Marsh dated 3 and 4 September 1888, Yale University Library: Manuscripts and Archives; Leeds 1939, plate 57), and later by exchange between the BMNH and the American Museum of Natural History in New York. In around 1903 Alfred Leeds' son, E. T. Leeds, returned home from the Far East to recuperate from illness, and remained at home for the next 5 years assisting his father in his fossil collecting as well as undertaking archaeological work (Bruce-Mitford & Harden 1956). In 1912 the initiator of the Leeds Collection, Charles Leeds, died in Auckland, New Zealand aged 67 (Anon. 1912*a*, *b*).

Alfred Leeds continued collecting fossils despite his advancing age and economic depression. Additions to the collection were severely reduced by the Great War (1914–1918; now more usually referred to as the First World War or World War I) (letter from Alfred Leeds to W. R. Smellie, Assistant Curator of Geology, dated 18 September 1916; Hunterian Museum, uncatalogued), during which time many of the workmen went off to fight and a number of the Peterborough brick pits were closed (some to store munitions) or maintained at minimal production (Hillier 1981). However, even before this, the pits had begun to be mechanized, which much reduced the chances of acquiring fossil material, and the finds dwindled during this period (Leeds 1956). Having built up one of the most comprehensive collections of fossil vertebrates from a single geological horizon anywhere in the world, Alfred Leeds died from a heart attack at the age of 70 on 25 August 1917 (Smith Woodward 1917; Harker 1918). On 11 December 1918 Lewis

Fig. 2. Watercolour entitled 'Eyebury. "The Office"' showing Alfred Leeds (rear) at work on his 'bones' with Mary Leeds assisting. Painted by Margaret Croom Crewdson probably in the late 1870s or early 1880s. Image reproduced courtesy of and © the Leeds family.

Fig. 3. Painting of Alfred Leeds in 1889 sitting in one of his attic 'bone rooms' repairing fossils; note the three-legged table at which he works, the tray used for supporting specimens, the mounted specimens arranged around the walls and the large vertebra to the lower right (now part of R1984). From a painting by (Sir) William Nicholson, owned by Lewis Leeds, photography by Nicholas Hall. Image reproduced courtesy of Sue Hall (née Leeds) and © the Leeds family; previously figured (in black and white) as the frontispiece to Leeds (1956).

Ferrier Leeds, the only son of Alfred Leeds to show any real interest in farming, died suddenly of tuberculosis. In 1919 E. T. Leeds had to urgently dispose of the remains of his father's collection (with the majority going to the Hunterian Museum, University of Glasgow) in order to sell Eyebury (Leeds 1956). E. T. Leeds went on to become Keeper of the Ashmolean Museum in Oxford (1928–1945: Bruce-Mitford & Harden 1956; MacGregor 2001), and wrote a posthumously-published book on the Leeds Collection (Leeds 1956), an extended manuscript copy of which still resides with the Leeds family (Leeds 1939).

Brick pits and fossils

The Leeds Collection was largely derived from the Oxford Clay Formation, a predominantly argillaceous deposit of Callovian–lower Oxfordian age that crops out in England as an almost continuous strip from the Humber in the NE to Dorset on the south coast (Hudson *et al.* 1991). The formation has three major divisions, in ascending stratigraphic order: the Peterborough, Stewartby and Weymouth members (Martill & Hudson 1991). The deposits in the neighbourhood of Peterborough, from which the Leeds Collection was primarily derived, comprise the entire Peterborough and base of the overlying Stewartby members (Hudson & Martill 1994). These deposits were formed in a shallow epicontinental sea, under fully marine conditions with high organic productivity (Martill *et al.* 1994), and near enough to land to contain an abundance of fossil wood (Porter 1863). The Oxford Clay strata largely consists of fine-grained, organic-rich mudstones with a shaly fissility, and it is these properties that made the clay ideal for brick making (Hillier 1981).

The clays around Peterborough have long been utilized for making bricks (Hillier 1981). Initially, small excavations or 'borrow pits' were opened close to where the bricks were required (Leeds 1956; Hillier 1981). These small pits utilized the weathered surface clays or 'callow'. However, the removal of brick tax, the advent of the limited liability company, the coming of the railways, the discovery that the organic-rich clay was virtually 'self-firing', the development of the 'dry press' method of brick production (following the realization that the clays required no additional water) and the introduction of the Hoffmann kiln, all meant that from the 1860s brick making around Peterborough developed on an industrial scale (Fig. 4). Pits began to be dug into the deeper layers of the Oxford Clay (Hillier 1981), which was worked by hand (Fig. 5), each man wielding a 6 ft (almost 2 m) long, 36 lb (*c.* 16 kg) weight crowbar, to hew the clay in semi-circular 'amphitheatres' (Anon. 1924; Leeds 1956; Hillier 1981). The presence of fossilized remains, and especially of 'devils thunderbolts' (belemnites), caused the bricks to explode on firing, so the men extracted the fossils and were paid a bonus for a full 'bolt bucket'. An experienced 'clay-getter' could differentiate between the sound of a crowbar striking belemnites and bone, and Leeds would pay the men more for the bones than the pit owners would for the contents of their bolt buckets (Leeds 1956). Hence, when fossilized bones were found, notice would sometimes be sent to Eyebury (Leeds 1939), although the constant jarring of the crowbars on the clay above a specimen usually meant the bones were broken into many, often thousands, of fragments (Leeds 1956). In addition, Alfred Leeds would only be able to collect the bones exposed by the currently worked 'face' of the pit, and often had to wait weeks or even months for the rest of an animal to be revealed so as not to interrupt work in the pit (Smith Woodward 1917; Leeds 1956).

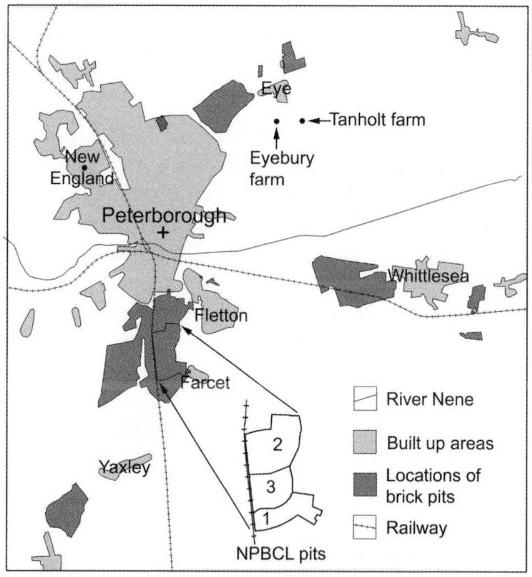

Fig. 4. The broad distribution of industrial brick pits around the city of Peterborough during the lifetime of Alfred Nicholson Leeds. Eyebury, the Leeds family home; Tanholt farm, location of one of the early pre-industrial pits visited by the Leeds brothers; and the villages surrounding the city known to have been sources of the Leeds Collection material are also indicated. The inset shows the distribution of the three New Peterborough Brick Company Limited (NPBCL) pits based on information contained on a contemporary 1:10 000 scale OS map. For more detailed information on pit distributions see Leeds (1956, figure facing p. 17) and Hillier (1981, pp. 84–96).

It was the relative abundance of fossils, both vertebrate and invertebrate, in the lower levels of the Oxford Clay around Peterborough (Martill 1986) (although vertebrate fossils were collected from the clays at all levels: Leeds 1956) that led to the development of the Leeds Collection. Fossils are extremely common, especially in the lower parts of the Oxford Clay, including abundant bivalves, ammonites, belemnites and gastropods, together with rarer scaphopods, brachiopods, cnidarians, bryozoans, annelids, cirripedes, echinoderms, crustaceans and nautiloids (Martill & Hudson 1991; Martill *et al.* 1994). However, it is the superb range and quality of preserved vertebrates – fish, marine reptiles, and rarer allochthonous dinosaurs and occasional pterosaurs (Andrews 1910, 1913; Smith Woodward 1891, 1895; Martill 1988) – for which the clays have become justifiably famous. Fossils had been collected from the Oxford Clay around Peterborough since before the Leeds Collection began (Porter 1861), but the opening up of the brick pits on an industrial scale provided an opportunity to recover specimens from the generally more productive deeper layers of the clay (C.L.F. 1956). The Leeds brothers would pay the workmen in the pits to inform them of fossil finds, which were, wherever possible, carefully extracted from the clay by the Leeds family, although numerous specimens were reconstructed from remains collected from the men's bolt buckets (Smith Woodward 1917; Leeds 1956). The whole Leeds family would then be involved in cleaning and washing the bones, and Alfred Leeds would spend hours piecing together the fragments (Smith Woodward 1917). Cleaning the bones acted as entertainment for Alfred Leeds and his family during the long winter evenings (Anon. 1888; Leeds 1956), at a time before the advent of radio, television or the cinema.

Sources and conventions

Numerous archive sources have been used to compile this review, including BMNH purchase and acquisition registers, letters, lists and manuscript catalogues. Additional material, including an extended draft manuscript (Leeds 1939) of E. T. Leeds' book on the Leeds Collection (Leeds 1956) and associated material, which includes insurance documents, correspondence, photographs and

Fig. 5. 'Clay getters' in a Peterborough brick pit, date unknown but probably around 1900. Note the metal crowbars for hewing the clay by hand, and the chute in the background down which the clay from higher in the pit was sent into wagons on the pit floor. Photograph courtesy of and © Whittlesea Museum.

an Eyebury visitors book, have been kindly made available to us by the Leeds family. Although all the dinosaur and pterosaur material found by Alfred Leeds went to the BMNH, no collection register for the dinosaurs exists, and a letter from Alfred Leeds to the Dublin Museum of Science and Art in 1896 appears to indicate that rigorous record-keeping for his collection did not come about until after 1893 (Araújo *et al.* 2008). As a result, few data as to exactly when and where the Leeds dinosaurs were obtained have been recorded; hence, much of the information has had to be gleaned from unpublished letters and other material. The exact dates of collection of the fossils are often unknown, with the source pits only rarely recorded (and even when noted, they are not always easy to interpret). The geological horizon is often simply cited as 'Fletton' or 'Peterborough', although parts of the collection, possibly including the dinosaurs, may have originated from the many villages surrounding the city, including New England, Fletton, Eye and Whittlesea (Fig. 5).

For the purposes of this contribution, the protocol established by Leeds (1956) has been followed. The collection up to about May 1890, and purchased in its entirety by the BMNH is referred to as the 'First Collection', and all of the material collected between about May 1890 and August 1917 is referred to as the 'Second Collection'. The entirety of the First and Second Collections is referred to as the 'Leeds Collection'. In the following sections on the Leeds Collection dinosaurs and pterosaur are divided by collection, and identified by month of arrival at the BMNH. All specimens reside in the Palaeontology Department of the Natural History Museum, London, Cromwell Road, London (BMNH) with numbers prefixed by 'R' for reptile. BMNH archive material is held in both the Palaeontological Library (BMNH PL) and the Main Library (BMNH ML). Other unpublished material referred to remains in the possession of the Leeds family.

A note on currency

Prior to decimalization on 14 February 1971, British 'old' money was divided into pounds (librae or l), shillings (solidi or s) and pence (denarii or d), often shortened to L.S.D. or l.s.d. There were 12 old pence (d) to the shilling (s), and 240d or 20s to the pound (L, l or £); hence one (old) pound three shillings and sixpence would be shown in the format £1-3-6, with values in full pounds simply shown as £250. Although it is notoriously difficult to compare historical with modern prices, £100 in 1900 would equate to *c.* £42 000 at 2007 prices based on average income (Anon. 2008). All prices paid for the Leeds Collection material are cited as the amount paid at the time and no conversions are attempted.

The dinosaurs and pterosaur in the First Collection

Alfred Leeds' First Collection, made up until about May 1890, was purchased in its entirety by the BMNH for £1500 and paid for in four instalments between 1890 and 1892 (Annual Purchases, BMNH ML DF 102/17 and DF 102/2). Alfred Leeds was keen that his collection was not 'cherry picked', which would have meant that he was left with the isolated, less attractive remains, as later occurred with the Second Collection (Leeds 1956). With the sale agreed, the whole of the First Collection was packed up over 3 weeks during the summer of 1890 and dispatched to the BMNH in London (Leeds 1956, p. 33). Within the First Collection there were the remains of four dinosaurs: two saurischians (both brachiosaurid sauropods) and two ornithischians (a stegosaur and a dryosaur), as well as the only pterosaur remains in the entire collection. Of particular use in establishing what dinosaur and other ornithodiran material was in the collection at this time are two notebooks compiled by Henry Woodward; one on the occasion of his first visit to Eyebury in September 1885, and the second produced between 8 and 12 May 1890 (both BMNH PL, uncat.). The latter visit dates are known as an Eyebury visitors' book was started in 1888, recording the length of stay of friends, family and the curious, which remains with the Leeds family. Woodward's 1890 notebook was apparently a list of material to be included in the BMNH sale. Other data sources utilized below include E. T. Leeds book (Leeds 1956), an extended manuscript including much unpublished information (Leeds 1939), as well as anecdotal comments made in various scientific publications by visitors to the Eyebury collection.

Brachiosaurid sauropod (R1984), acquired August 1890

R1984 (Fig. 6) consists of four large (*c.* 530 mm diameter) associated, anterior caudal vertebrae with neural spines and transverse processes attached (Smith Woodward 1905), which are currently considered to belong to an indeterminate brachiosaurid sauropod (Upchurch & Martin 2003). One of these vertebrae is present in the 1889 painting by William Nicholson, showing Alfred Leeds working at a table in one of the attic 'bone' rooms, lying on the floor in the lower right, propped up against a wall (Fig. 3) (Leeds 1956, frontispiece and p. 34). This composition was somewhat posed, as noted by Leeds (1956), as all four caudal vertebrae normally resided 'on a narrow ledge bordering the uppermost treads' of 'the steep, dark staircase to the Bone Room' (Leeds 1956, p. 34), making them the first specimens from the collection encountered by a visitor to the Eyebury attic prior to 1890.

The date and location from which the vertebrae were recovered is unrecorded, but they are considered to have been derived from the Lower Oxford Clay Formation (now called the Peterborough Member) (Martill 1988, p. 184). It is noteworthy that these vertebrae were one of the main prompts for Alfred Leeds to seek the advice of the authorities at the BMNH: Leeds took a tracing of one of the vertebrae to London with him, to seek help in identifying the animal from which it came (Leeds 1956). As Alfred Leeds recalled to his son in respect of that first interview with Henry Woodward, Henry Flower and J.W. Hulke, 'they didn't seem to bustle with their information' (Leeds 1956, p. 27). However, it was as a result of this meeting that Henry Woodward arranged a visit to see the entire collection of fossil material at Eyebury firsthand. The four vertebrae were ultimately acquired by the BMNH in August 1890 as part of the first instalment of the 1890 sale (Annual Purchases, BMNH ML DF102/2, p. 10) and the remains are mentioned in a number of items of archive material relating to the First Collection.

The R1984 vertebrae are mentioned in Henry Woodward's 1890 notebook (BMNH PL, uncat.) as 'four large vertebrae $10\frac{1}{2}$–12 inches [*c.* 265–305 mm] diameter, the largest 29 inches [735 mm] high'. They were first described, and one figured, by Smith Woodward (1905, p. 236, fig. 42) who assigned them to *Cetiosaurus leedsi*. The bones were later displayed together with R3078 (see below), an incomplete sauropod skeleton later recovered by Alfred Leeds (Leeds 1956, p. 38). Upchurch & Martin (2003, pp. 213–214) considered R1984 to be part of the holotype of *Cetiosaurus leedsi*; however, Smith Woodward (1905, p. 232) and Leeds (1956, p. 35) both indicate that the four R1984 vertebrae did not belong to the same individual as the R3078 *Cetiosaurus leedsi* [= *Cetiosauriscus stewarti*] remains described by Smith Woodward in 1905. The confusion seems to have arisen from the table of measurements given by Smith Woodward (1905, p. 243) where the R1984 material is incorrectly cited as belonging to R3078. However, for a number of reasons (given below) it can be categorically stated that there is no association between the holotype of *Cetiosauriscus stewarti* (R3078) and these four R1984 anterior caudal vertebrae.

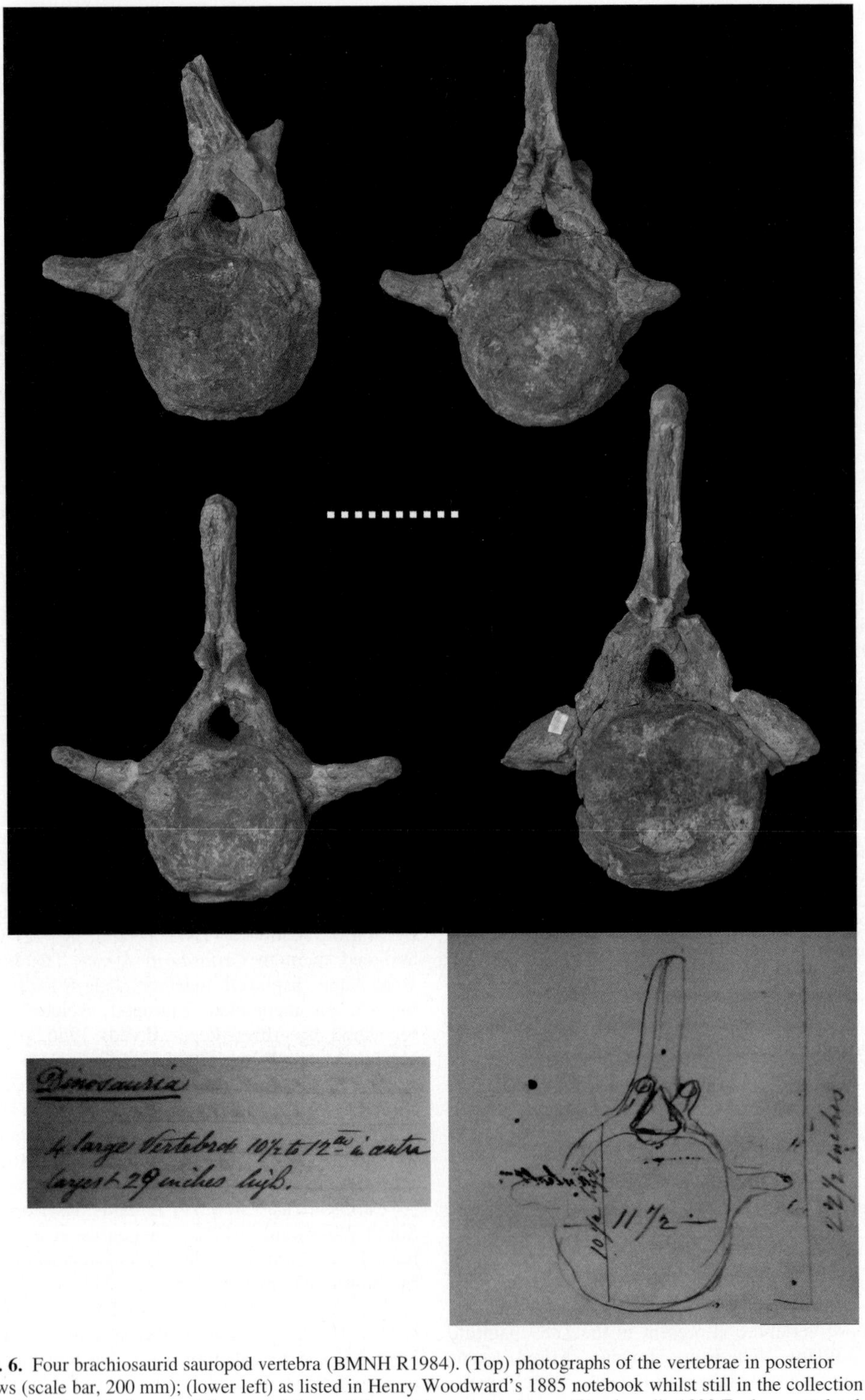

Fig. 6. Four brachiosaurid sauropod vertebra (BMNH R1984). (Top) photographs of the vertebrae in posterior views (scale bar, 200 mm); (lower left) as listed in Henry Woodward's 1885 notebook whilst still in the collection of Alfred Leeds at Eyebury; and (lower right) a vertebra as illustrated in Henry Woodward's 1890 Eyebury notebook. Photographs courtesy of Sandra Chapman (Image Resources, NHM), archive material © BMNH PL uncatalogued.

Ornithopsis leedsii *(R1985–1988), acquired May 1892*

The dinosaur remains with perhaps the strongest claim to have been the first discovered by the Leeds brothers are those of the sauropod *Ornithopsis leedsii* Hulke 1887 (Fig. 7), which Seeley recalled seeing when he visited the Leeds Collection in 1874 (Seeley 1889). They are also the oldest in another sense as, unusually for the Leeds Collection, this specimen was collected from below the Oxford Clay, in the underlying Kellaways Formation (Callomon 1968). The remains came from a well dug 36 ft (*c.* 11 m) down at a gasworks to the east of the city of Peterborough (Seeley 1889; Leeds 1956; Martill 1988), possibly the Great Northern Railway gasworks at 'New England' [UK NGR TF 178 010] (Fig. 4). The bones were found lying in a bedded sandy unit at the boundary of an underlying clay (Seeley 1889; Leeds 1956), but were noted by Henry Woodward in his September 1885 notebook as being in 'a dark very tenacious (hard)

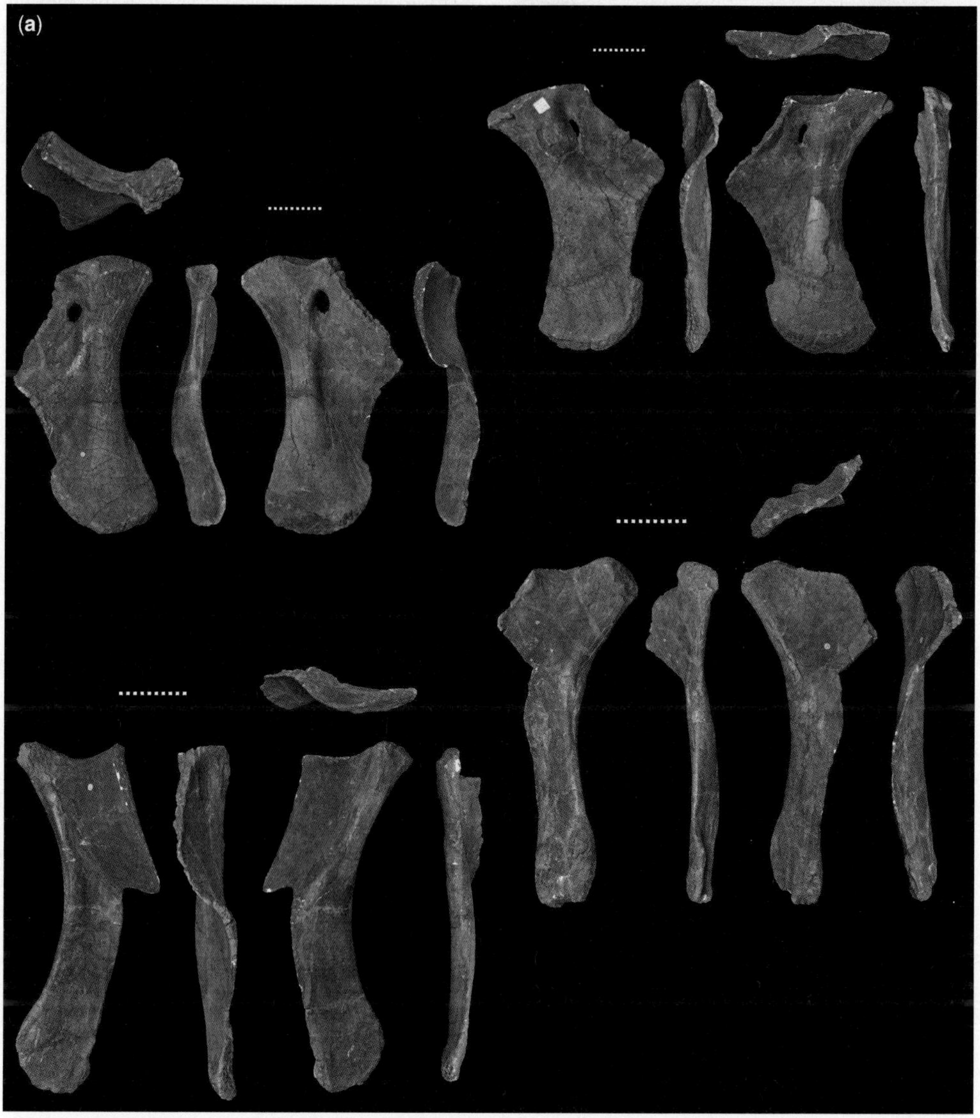

Fig. 7. (**a**) *Ornithopsis leedsi* (BMNH R1985–1988): (top left) left pubis, (top right) right pubis, (bottom left) left ischium and (bottom right) right ischium (all BMNH R1988) in standard views. Scale bars, 200 mm. Photographs courtesy of Sandra Chapman (Image Resources, NHM).

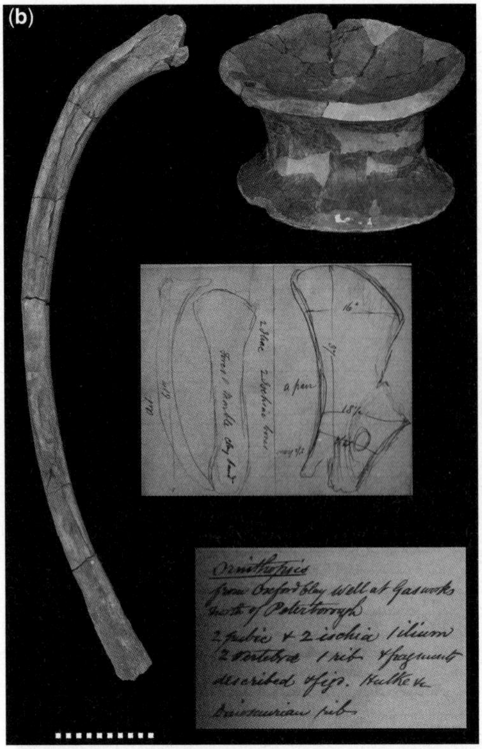

Fig. 7. (**b**) (*Continued*) *Ornithopsis leedsi* (BMNH R1985–1988): (left) rib (BMNH R1985), (top right) dorsal centrum (R1986), (middle right) the remains as sketched in Henry Woodward's 1885 notebook whilst still in the collection of Alfred Leeds at Eyebury and (bottom right) as listed in Henry Woodward's 1890 Eyebury notebook. Scale bar, 200 mm. Photographs courtesy of Sandra Chapman (Image Resources, NHM), archive material © BMNH PL uncatalogued.

dark green clay', which he referred to as the 'Forest Marble Clay Band' (BMNH PL, uncat.). Based on a sound knowledge of the local stratigraphy, Martill (1988, p. 172) considered the remains to almost certainly have been derived from the lower Callovian stage Kellaways Formation, at the boundary between the Kellaways Clay and the Kellaways Sand, in the *Macrocephalites macrocephalus* Biozone (although his accompanying table 1 suggests that the bones may have been derived from the overlying *Sigaloceras calloviense* Biozone).

When originally described, R1985–1988 consisted of four crushed and distorted dorsal centra with fragments of the neural arches and processes attached; portions of dorsal ribs, including one almost complete; both pubes and both ischia; a fragmentary and distorted right ilium; and a number of fragments too small for identification (Hulke 1887). In his 1885 notebook, Henry Woodward illustrated the remains of the 37 inch (*c*. 940 mm) × $18\frac{1}{2}$ inch (455 mm) pubis and the 61 inch (1.55 m) long rib of this animal, and on the following page notes 'vertebra 12″ [12 inches, *c*. 300 mm] diameter of *Cetiosaurus* belonging to pelvic bones', although this wording suggesting he saw only a single vertebra (BMNH PL uncat.). The remains of R1985–1988 currently held by the BMNH, as recorded by Upchurch & Martin (2003, p. 214), are: four portions of anterior thoracic ribs (R1985), two almost complete; a damaged dorsal centrum with large pleurocoels (R1986); two unidentified bones (R1987); a distorted and fragmentary ilium, a right pubis and both ischia (R1988); the remaining material presumably having decayed (see Seeley 1889). The BMNH specimen card for R1987 incorrectly records the specimen as 'fragments of the mounted skeleton' [i.e. R3078, see below], and is marked 'destroyed'. It is not clear from this whether there has been confusion between fragments of R3078 that have been destroyed, whether part or all of R1987 has been destroyed, or both. In addition, R1716, a plaster cast made in the BMNH in 1889 and recorded as '*Pelorosaurus leedsi* original in the Leeds Collection – imperfect lumbar vertebra' (S. Chapman pers. comm. 2009), is believed to be from one of the R1986 vertebrae (Martill 1988, p. 184). The *Ornithopsis leedsii* remains were purchased by the BMNH as part of the third instalment of the First Collection on 30 May 1892, together with the majority of the dinosaur material (Annual Purchases, BMNH ML DF100/2, p. 3). In addition to Henry Woodward's 1885 notebook, R1985–1988 is mentioned in several other items of archive material relating to the First Collection.

Seeley (1889) recalled seeing the *Ornithopsis* remains during a visit to Eyebury in 1874, whilst preparing a description of the plesiosaur *Muraenosaurus leedsi* (Seeley 1874). At that time a large rib, an ischium, part of a pubis and part of a dorsal centrum were visible, but the remains were still largely encased in a sandy matrix (although we note that this is different from the matrix described by Henry Woodward in his 1890 notebook, see earlier). In 1874 Seeley regarded the bones as belonging to the sauropod *Cetiosaurus* (as reported in Seeley 1889), based on remains described and figured by Phillips (1871). Some 11 years later, in around 1885, Charles Leeds compared the pelvis of the Leeds sauropod to that of the Kimmeridgian genus *Ornithopsis* in the BMNH, and considered the Peterborough remains to belong to the same taxon (Leeds 1956). Charles Leeds wrote to Seeley inviting him to Eyebury to describe the remains, but Seeley was busy in London and directed Charles Leeds to J. W. Hulke at the BMNH, who had already written several papers on *Ornithopsis* (Seeley 1889). Hence, Hulke's first visit to Eyebury was made in May 1886 (Hulke 1887) in the company of Henry Woodward (not Arthur Smith Woodward as stated by Martill 1988, p. 172). The published description of *Ornithopsis* followed a second visit by Hulke to the Leeds Collection in early 1887 when he returned with memoirs on sauropods by Marsh and Sir Richard Owen (Hulke 1887). The Leeds sauropod remains were considered sufficiently distinct by Hulke (1887) to be named as a new species of *Ornithopsis*: *Ornithopsis leedsii*. The remains of *O. leedsii* are therefore both chronologically and stratigraphically the oldest dinosaur remains in the Leeds Collection, and the first of a number of dinosaurs to be named after Alfred Leeds for his generosity in allowing scientific access to his collection (Hulke 1887). Following the initial description, part of the pelvis (R1988) was cited and figured by Seeley (1889), who improved the anatomical orientation and reconstruction of the elements; Alfred Leeds was present at the reading of Seeley's paper to the Geological Society, and agreed with this reinterpretation of the bones (discussion following Seeley 1889, p. 396).

There has been considerable confusion as to what constitutes the holotype of *Ornithopsis leedsii*. The material described by Hulke (1887) was the associated remains now R1985–1988, whereas Upchurch & Martin (2003, pp. 213 and 214) include the proximal caudal vertebrae R1984 (see above) as part of the holotype. However, E. T. Leeds records that the proximal caudals (R1984) and pelvic and other elements (R1985–1988) did not belong to the same individual (Leeds 1956, p. 35). In addition, the one remaining dorsal ('trunk' of Hulke 1887) vertebra of *Ornithopsis* preserves pleurocoels (Upchurch & Martin 2003, p. 214), and the least crushed of the four vertebrae in the original description had 'large chambers opening externally in the lateral aspect of the centrum' (Hulke 1887, p. 695), whereas the four anterior caudals (R1984), as noted by Smith Woodward (1905) and Upchurch & Martin (2003, p. 214), lack pleurocoels. The vertebrae noted by Hulke (1887) all lacked their neural arches, whereas at least some of the R1984 vertebrae are virtually complete (Smith Woodward 1905, fig. 42). Furthermore, the dimensions of the vertebrae recorded by Hulke (1887, p. 695) vary considerably from those given by Smith Woodward (1905, p. 243, listed under Text-fig. 42, and erroneously referred to R3078 in the caption above the table). All of these points clearly indicate that the four dorsal vertebrae described by Hulke (1887), three of which now appear to have been lost, do not equate to the four R1984 anterior caudals. Hence, these two sets of specimens must be considered to belong to different individuals, as observed by Leeds (1956). Thus, as correctly noted by Martill (1988, p. 184) and Martill & Clarke (1994, p. 13), the holotype of *Ornithopsis leedsii* is R1985–1988.

R1985–1988 was originally designated as the new species *Ornithopsis Leedsii* (Hulke 1887), but the specific name is often erroneously been cited as '*leedsi*' (Smith Woodward 1905; Martill 1988; Upchurch & Martin 2003). The reduction of the initial capital of '*Leedsii*' to lower case is valid (ICZN 1999, Article 32.5.2.5); however, the emendation from '*leedsii*' to '*leedsi*' is an incorrect subsequent spelling (ICZN 1999, Article 33.4). Hence, the name *Ornithopsis leedsii* Hulke, 1887 should stand, as used by Naish & Martill (2007). With respect to the generic name, R1985–1988 was originally assigned to *Ornithopsis*, although the striking similarity to *Cetiosaurus* was noted (Hulke 1887). During the subsequent reinterpretation of the pelvic material (Seeley 1889), the specimen was referred to *Ornithopsis* in the title of the paper, and as (*Ornithopsis*) (sic) in the text, although the similarity to *Cetiosaurus* was once again strongly indicated. Indeed, although the published paper does not explicitly refer the material to *Cetiosaurus*, it is clear from the published discussion that Seeley suggested the abandonment of *Ornithopsis* in favour of *Cetiosaurus* during his oral presentation, although Lydekker, and possibly others, did not agree with the proposed nomenclatural revision (see the discussion following Seeley 1889, pp. 396–397). Subsequently, during the description of a more complete sauropod (R3078, see later) Smith Woodward (1905) incorrectly noted that Hulke (1887) and Seeley (1889) had both referred the pelvic elements (i.e. R1988) to *Cetiosaurus*, and went on to describe all the Leeds sauropod material as a single taxon, *Cetiosaurus leedsi*. Upchurch & Martin (2003, pp. 213–214) described R1985–1988 under the name *Cetiosaurus*, whilst noting that *Cetiosaurus leedsi* was an indeterminate brachiosaurid and the name a *nomen dubium*. However, later in the same paper, the material was also referred to as '*Ornithopsis leedsi*' (sic) (Upchurch & Martin 2003, p. 229). However, at present R1985–1988 is usually referred to the genus *Ornithopsis* (e.g. Martill 1988; Naish & Martill 2007).

Lexovisaurus durobrivensis *(R1989–1992), acquired May 1892*

The stegosaurian ornithopod *Lexovisaurus durobrivensis* (Hulke 1887) Hoffstetter, 1957 (Fig. 8) was the second dinosaur to be described from the Leeds Collection, in part two of the paper describing

(a)

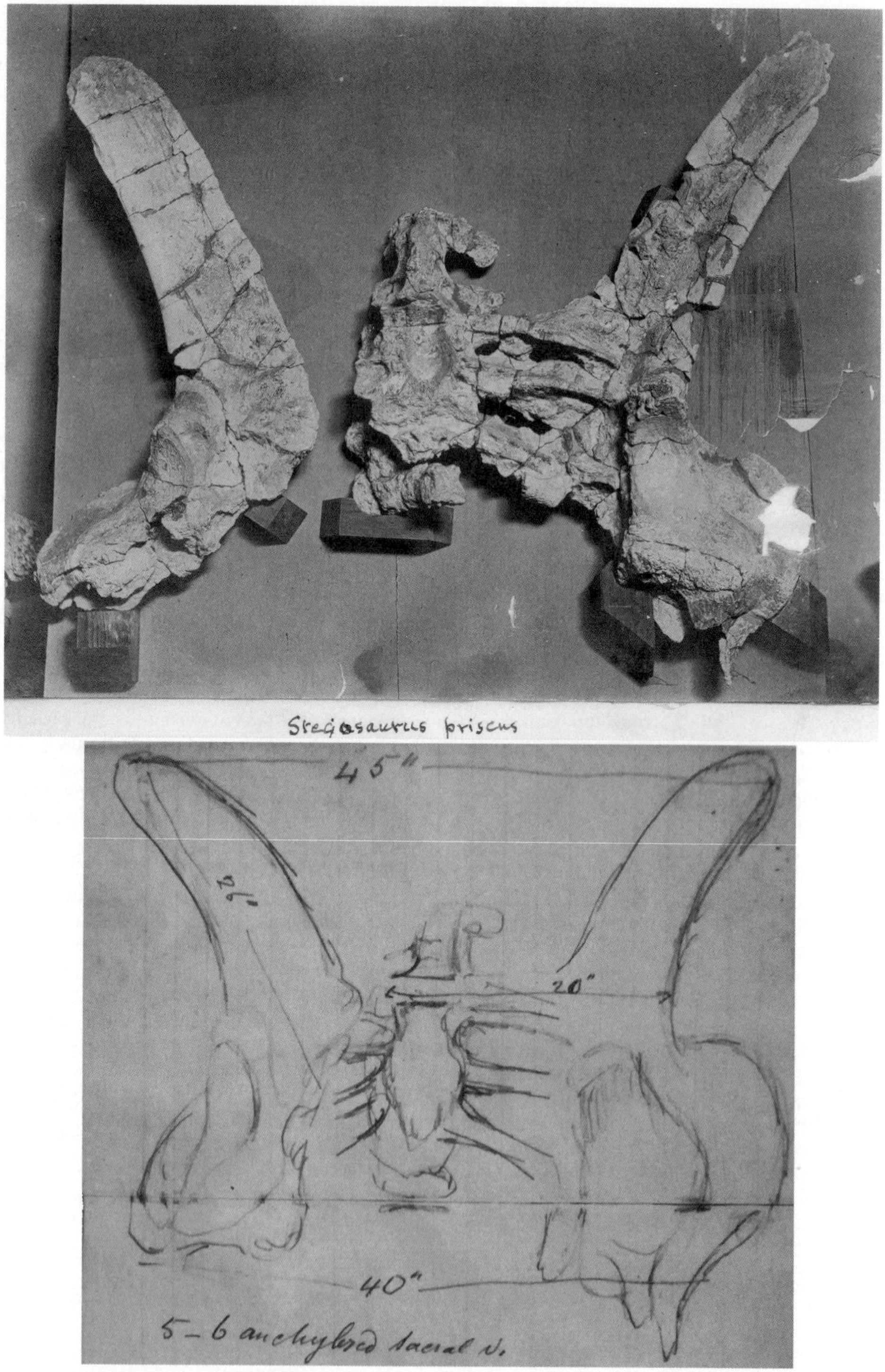

Fig. 8. (**a**) *Lexovisaurus durobrivensis* (BMNH R1989–1992): (top) photograph of the sacrum with both ilia (the future R1989) whilst still in the Leeds Collection at Eyebury, and (bottom) as illustrated in Henry Woodward's 1885 notebook. Photographs courtesy of Julian Leeds and the Leeds family, archive material © BMNH PL uncatalogued.

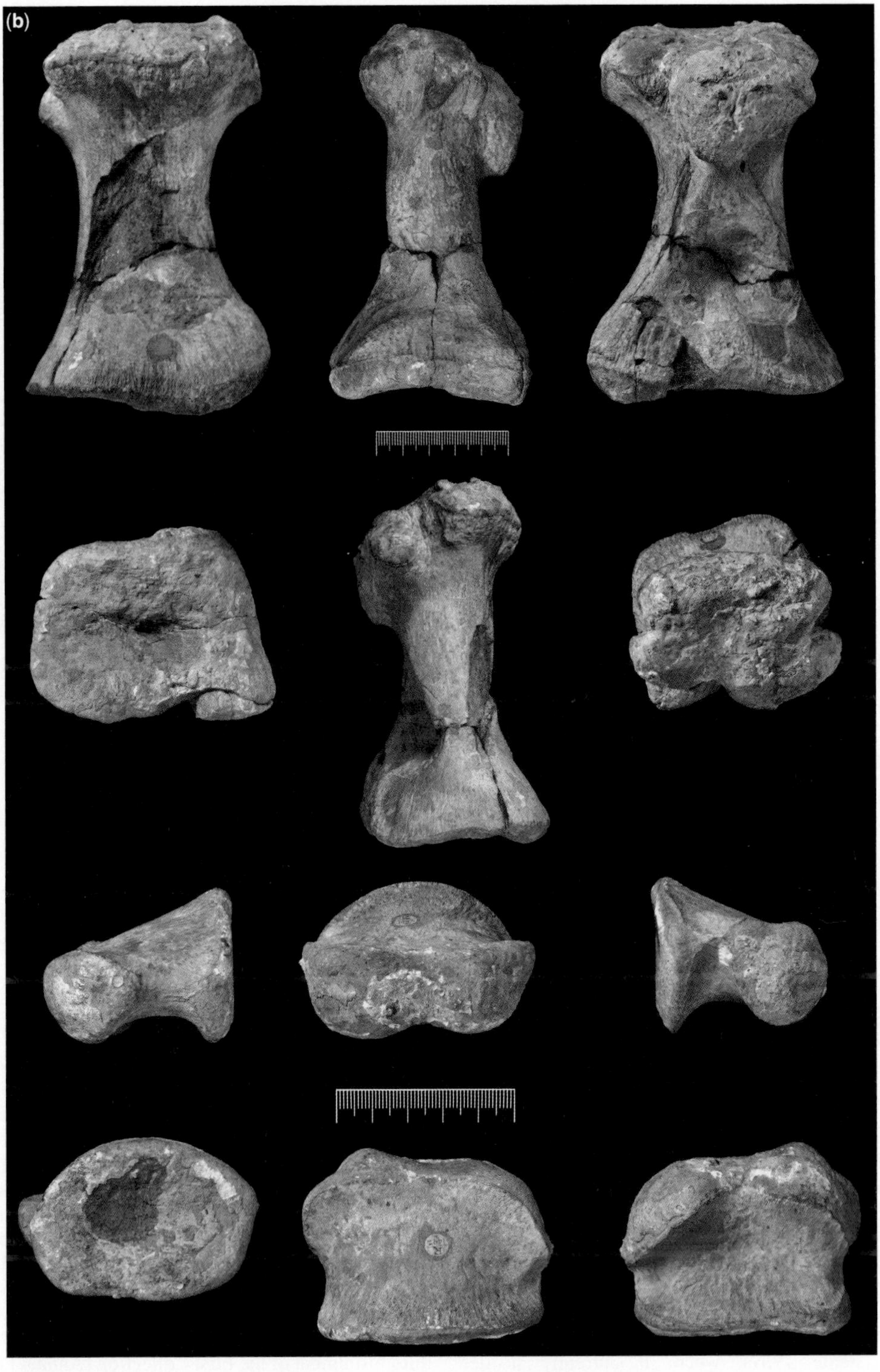

Fig. 8. (*Continued*) (**b**) *Lexovisaurus durobrivensis* (BMNH R1989–1992): (top) metapodial (R1992) and (bottom) phalangeal (R1992a) in six standard views. Scale bars, 200 mm. Photographs courtesy of Sandra Chapman (Image Resources, NHM).

(c)

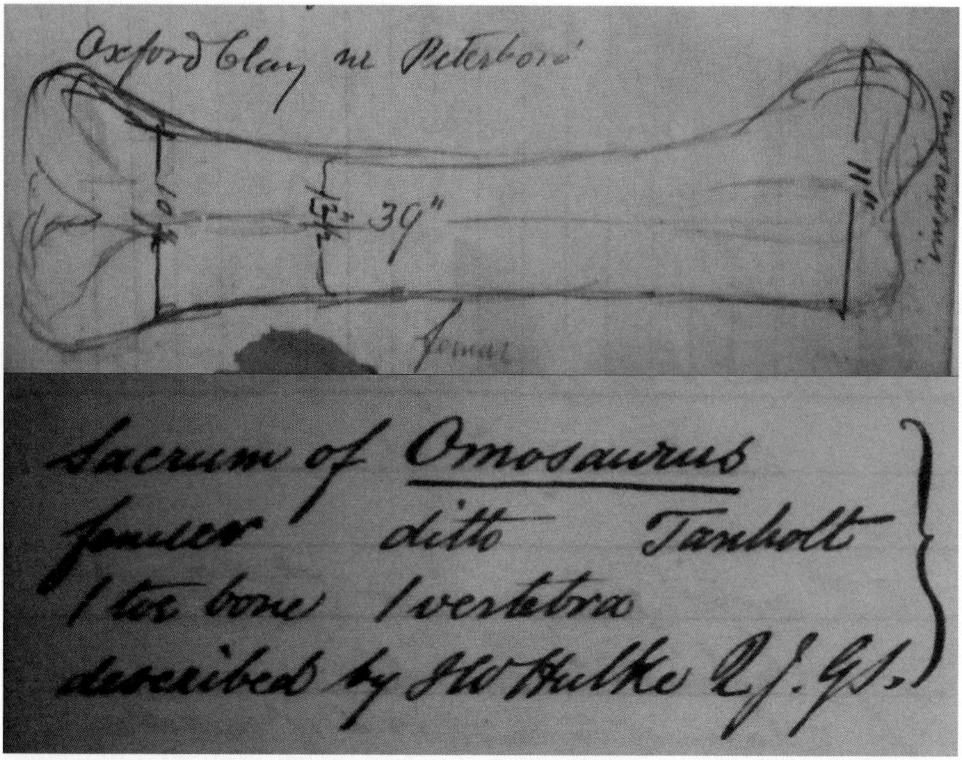

Fig. 8. (*Continued*) (**c**) *Lexovisaurus durobrivensis* (BMNH R1989–1992): (top) the left femur (now R1991) as sketched in Henry Woodward's 1885 notebook and (bottom) the material as listed in Henry Woodward's 1890 Eyebury notebook. Archive material © BMNH PL uncatalogued.

Ornithopsis leedsii (R1985–1988, see earlier). R1989–1992 comprises a caudal vertebra and parts of two other (probably lumbar) vertebrae (R1990), a sacrum with both ilia (R1989), a left femur 1 m long (R1991), a metapodial (R1992) and a phalangeal (R1992a) interpreted as from the outer side of the left pes, together with many fragments (Hulke 1887). The specimen was originally referred to the Kimmeridgian genus *Omosaurus* (Hulke 1887), partly due to confusion between the Kimmeridge and Oxford Clay formations. The specimen was given the new name *Omosaurus durobrivensis* Hulke, 1887, after a Roman settlement located to the west of the city of Peterborough. Later, Marsh informed Lydekker that the name *Omosaurus* was preoccupied by Leidy in 1856 for a phytosaur (Naish & Martill 2008), and Lydekker proposed that the generic name *Stegosaurus* should be used instead (Lydekker 1888). R1989–1992 was later transferred to the genus *Lexovisaurus* (Hoffstetter 1957), where it currently resides as *Lexovisaurus durobrivensis*. The 45 inch (*c.* 1.14 m) span pelvis, and the 39 inch (990 mm) long femur of the future R1989–1992 were sketched by Henry Woodward in his 1885 notebook (BMNH PL, uncat.). The specimen was purchased by the BMNH as part of the third instalment of the First Collection on 30 May 1892 (Annual Purchases, BMNH ML DF102/2, p. 3).

In addition to the material noted above, several large plates of bone from the same locality as R1989–1992 were described as the dermal armour assumed to be present along the back of *Omosaurus* (Hulke 1887), as in the genus *Stegosaurus*. These elements of supposed dermal armour were later recognized by Marsh, when visiting Eyebury with Henry Woodward on 22 August 1888, as belonging to a gigantic fish (Leeds 1956). These bony plates, part of BMNH P.6921, are now known to have been derived from the giant pachycormid fish *Leedsichthys* (Smith Woodward 1889*a*) (Liston 2004; Liston & Noè 2004). The bones represent part of the skull roof of this large osteichthyan (Liston 2008), which were purchased as part of the third instalment of the First Collection (Annual Purchases, BMNH ML DF102/2, pp. 3–4). Within a week of Marsh's pronouncement on these bones, Arthur Smith Woodward, the BMNH fossil fish expert, visited Eyebury and produced a description of the fish that was published the following year (Smith Woodward 1889*a–c*, 1890).

Hulke (1887) described *Omosaurus*, as well as *Ornithopsis* (see above), as having been derived from the Kimmeridge Clay Formation. However, the Kimmeridge Clay does not crop out in the Peterborough brick pits nor in the immediate neighbourhood of Peterborough (Martill 1988, p. 172), and the Leeds brothers are not known to have collected beyond the surface outcrop of the Oxford Clay. Indeed, the horizon and location are inferred to have been the Peterborough Member of the Oxford Clay Formation, middle Callovian stage, most probably the *Kosmoceras jason* Biozone of Peterborough (Martill 1988, p. 181). However in his May 1890 notebook Henry Woodward indicates that the remains were collected from a pit at Tanholt (BMNH PL, uncat.). The excavation at Tanholt was not an industrial brick pit, and was only worked locally for bricks in the early days of the Leeds Collection (Leeds 1956, pp. 55–56). The Tanholt pit, which lies south of the Eye fault, could be higher in the Peterborough Member succession, perhaps top *Erymnoceras coronatum* or even lower *Peltoceras athleta* Biozone (D. M. Martill pers. comm. 2009). Hence, it is possible that this specimen was found earlier than R1985–1988, currently the earliest known dinosaur from the Leeds Collection.

R1984, R1985–1988 and R1989–1992 (see earlier) are the only three specimens that can be confirmed to have been in the Leeds Collection as of September 1885, according to Henry Woodward's notebook (BMNH PL, uncat.). While it is possible that other specimens were present but not noticed or noted during that first surprising visit for Henry Woodward, it seems more likely that the other specimens, which first appear in Woodward's May 1890 notebook (BMNH PL, uncat.) and are considered immediately below, were discovered and collected some time after September 1885.

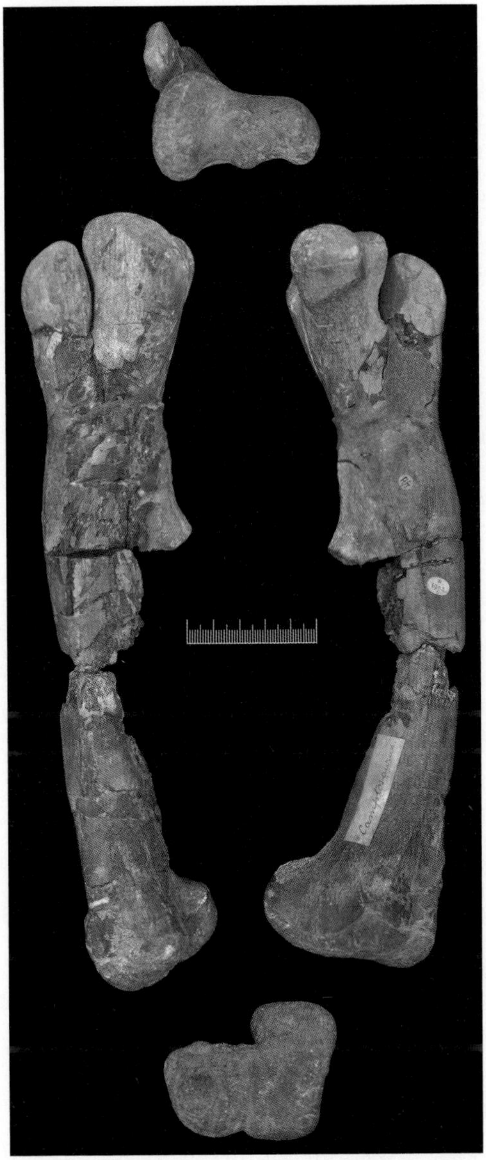

Fig. 9. *Callovosaurus leedsi* (BMNH R1993) isolated left femur in four standard views. Scale bar, 200 mm. Photographs courtesy of Sandra Chapman (Image Resources, NHM).

Callovosaurus leedsi *(R1993), acquired May 1892*

R1993 (Fig. 9), the holotype of *Callovosaurus leedsi* (Lydekker 1889; Galton 1980*a*), is an isolated left femur (noted as R1933, a right femur *in errore* by Martill 1988, pp. 172 and 182) some 480 mm in length. The limb bone was originally described as the new species *Camptosaurus leedsi* Lydekker, 1889, and was subsequently considered to be the oldest known example of an iguanodontian dinosaur (Naish & Martill 2008). However, as R1993 is based on an isolated and possibly non-diagnostic element, *Callovosaurus leedsi* was considered a *nomen dubium* (Naish & Martill 2007, 2008), but of possible value as a 'metataxon' (Naish and Martill 2007, p. 506), although *nomen dubia*, and hence 'metataxa' based on them, have no validity under the prevailing ICZN rules (ICZN 1999). In contrast, it has recently been proposed that *Callovosaurus* is not only a valid taxon, but also represents the earliest known dryosaurid (Ruiz-Omeñaca *et al.* 2007), as noted by Naish & Martill (2008).

Few collection or locality data are recorded for *Callovosaurus* R1993, other than 'Oxford Clay,

Fletton', although the specimen was probably derived from the middle Callovian stage, *Kosmoceras jason* Biozone of the Peterborough Member of the Oxford Clay Formation (Martill 1988, p. 183; Martill & Clarke 1994, p. 8). R1993 was purchased by the BMNH on 30 May 1892 (Annual Purchases, BMNH ML DF102/2, p. 3), with the specimen listed in several items of archive material relating to the First Collection.

Rhamphorhynchid *pterosaur (R1995), acquired May 1892*

R1995 (Fig. 10) constitutes the only pterosaur material in the Leeds Collection. It consists of three wing bones, a complete right ulna 100 mm in length, and broken left and right humeri (Martill 1988, p. 178), which have been referred to *Rhamphorhynchus* sp. (Wellnhofer 1978; Martill 1991). These bones were noted as '3 bones of *Pterodactylus*' in Woodward's 1890 notebook (BMNH PL, uncat.), and recorded as '3 specimens of *Pterodactylus*, sp. nov.? belonging to one individual only' in a list of the First Collection material in the hand of Henry Woodward dating from 1890 (BMNH PL, uncat.). These bones have also been noted by a number of authors and referred to the genus *Rhamphorhynchus* (Andrews 1912; Leeds 1956; Martill 1988); however, they are non-diagnostic and are best considered to belong to an indeterminate rhamphorhynchid pterosaur (Unwin 1996). Although consistently noted as three bones, there are currently four parts registered in the BMNH under R1995. R1995 was purchased on 30 May 1892 (Annual Purchases, BMNH ML DF 102/2, p. 3), together with the majority of the dinosaur bones from the First Collection.

Dinosaurs from the Second Collection

The BMNH's share of the Second Collection was purchased in 16 instalments between October 1892 and June 1920 for a total of £2187 (Annual Purchases, BMNH ML DF 102/2). The majority of these purchases included at least some dinosaur material, with the first payment coming before the First Collection had been completely paid for. The last payment was made to Alfred Leeds widow in 1920, although this purchase did not include dinosaur material, so far as is known. The Second Collection dinosaurs consist of at least eight individuals and six taxa including three families of sauropod, a nodosaur and a stegosaur, together with four generically unidentified bones and a putative reptile egg, later suggested as possibly dinosaurian (Swinton 1950). The Second Collection dinosaurs were acquired by the BMNH as they were found, cleaned and repaired by Alfred Leeds, so there is little ambiguity about their order of excavation. Hence, the numbers in the accession register generally reflect the order of discovery, so in the following section these finds are discussed in the sequence in which they were numbered by the BMNH.

Fig. 10. (**a**) An indeterminate rhamphorhynchid pterosaur (long considered '*Pterodactylus*' sp. or '*Rhamphorhynchus*' sp.) (BMNH R1995), right ulna in six standard views. Scale bar, 50 mm. Photographs courtesy of Sandra Chapman (Image Resources, NHM).

Diplodocid sauropod (R1967), acquired October 1892

R1967 (Fig. 11) is the whiplash-like tail of a diplodocid sauropod consisting of 10 distal caudal vertebrae (Smith Woodward 1905). The exact date

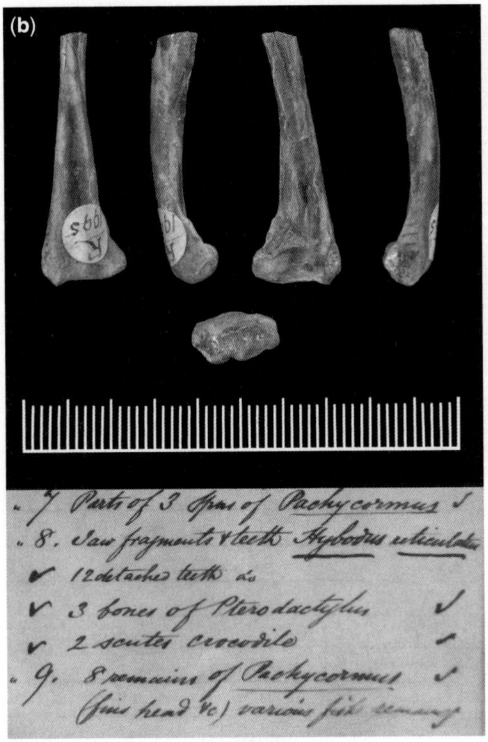

Fig. 10. (*Continued*) (**b**) An indeterminate rhamphorhynchid pterosaur (long considered '*Pterodactylus*' sp. or '*Rhamphorhynchus*' sp.) (BMNH R1995): (top) incomplete humerus in five standard views (scale bar, 50 mm) and (bottom) the three pterosaur bones as listed (amongst fish material) in Henry Woodward's 1890 Eyebury notebook. Photographs courtesy of Sandra Chapman (Image Resources, NHM), archive material © BMNH PL uncatalogued.

and location of discovery of R1967 are not known, although the bones are likely to have been derived from the middle Callovian stage *Kosmoceras jason* Biozone of the Peterborough Member of the Oxford Clay Formation (Martill 1988). The R1967 tail appears to have been acquired by the BMNH in October 1892 as part of the first purchase from the Second Collection. The bones were described as 'unnamed $10\frac{1}{2}$ vertebrae' and were purchased for £1-0-0 (Annual Purchases, BMNH ML DF102/2, p. 10).

The first published mention of R1967 is most probably the bones referred to as 'some long, terminal caudal vertebrae' (Seeley, discussion following Lydekker 1893, p. 287), which Seeley suggests may be part of the same animal (presumably meaning the same taxon, rather than the same individual) as the holotype of *Sarcolestes leedsi* Lydekker, 1893 (R2682, see later). The vertebrae were later described in detail, and one of the bones figured, by Smith Woodward (1905, p. 238, fig. 45) who assigned the tail to *Cetiosaurus leedsi* as evidence of the diplodocid nature of the genus (see R1985–1988 above and R3078 below). Smith Woodward (1905) also noted that the R1967 caudal vertebrae had been broken in two places during life and that they had subsequently healed. However, Smith Woodward (1905) did not describe the bones as proximal caudal vertebrae (*contra* Martill 1988, p. 183, presumably referring to R1984, see earlier) or suggest that the tail belonged to the same specimen as R3078. Hence, there is no evidence that '*Cetiosauriscus* does possess a whiplash tail, as in other diplodocids' (Upchurch 1995, p. 381). Presumably the confusion has arisen, once again, because in the table of measurements for the *Cetiosaurus leedsi* material (R3078) in which Smith Woodward (1905, p. 243) incorrectly cites all the figured vertebrae as belonging to R3078. However, as clearly stated earlier in the same paper (Smith Woodward 1905, p. 232), there is no association between the (now) holotype of *Cetiosauriscus stewarti* (R3078), the four anterior caudal vertebrae (R1984) and the R1967 whiplash tail, all of which belong to different individual sauropods. Hence, as the material comes from three different individuals, and includes no overlapping elements, it is possible that these three sets of remains represent two (Martill 1988, p. 184) or even three distinct sauropod taxa.

Sarcolestes leedsi *(R2682), acquired October 1895*

R2682, the nodosaurid ankylosaur *Sarcolestes leedsi* Lydekker, 1893 was described based on an incomplete left mandible and an attached dermal scute (Fig. 12). No collection or locality data are known, but the specimen is considered to have been derived from the middle Callovian stage *Kosmoceras jason* Biozone of the Peterborough Member of the Oxford Clay Formation of Fletton or Peterborough (Martill 1988, p. 182). Unusually, the description of this jaw does not seem to have followed a visit to Leeds' Collection by Lydekker, who only appears in the Eyebury visitors' book once (during June 1888) prior to the agreement to purchase the First Collection. It seems instead that the specimen was brought to Lydekker at South Kensington by Alfred Leeds, for the BMNH Department of Geology visitors' book records that Leeds visited three times in 1892: from the 28 to 29 March; on the 4 June; and on the 17 October (BMNH ML DF108/3). Any of these three visits could have been an opportunity for the specimen to be dropped off for examination and description at the BMNH (and, presumably, picked up again). R2682 was purchased on 1 November 1895,

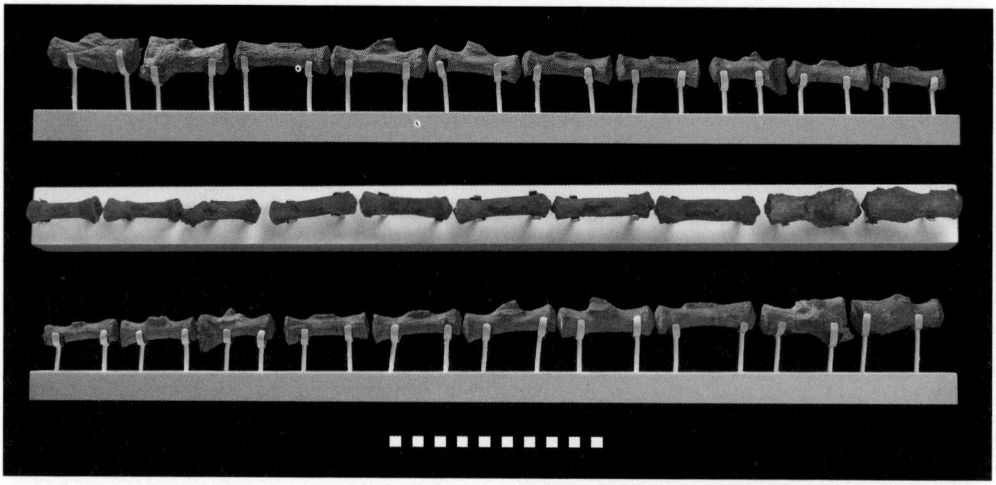

Fig. 11. Whiplash tail of a diplodocid sauropod (BMNH R1967) mounted and consisting of 10 caudal vertebrae; note the pathology where the tail was broken in life, as noted by Woodward (1905). Scale bar, 200 mm. Photographs courtesy of Sandra Chapman (Image Resources, NHM).

although the individual purchase price is not recorded (Annual Purchases, BMNH ML DF102/2, p. 40).

Sarcolestes, the 'flesh robber' (Martill & Clarke 1994), was first described as a new taxon of carnivorous dinosaur (Lydekker 1893) based on misidentification of the dermal element as a serrated theropod tooth. In the discussion following presentation of the original paper, Seeley suggested that *Sarcolestes* may not represent a new genus. Seeley suggested *Sarcolestes* might be related to the stegosaurid *Omosaurus*, based on a perceived association with some elongate caudal vertebrae (presumably the sauropod R1967, see earlier) in Mr Leeds' Collection (Seeley, discussion following Lydekker 1889). However, *Sarcolestes leedsi* is currently considered a valid taxon of ankylosaur (Galton 1980*b*, *c*, 1983; Naish & Martill 2008).

Two dinosaur limb bones (R2854 and R2855), acquired August 1896

Two isolated dinosaurian elements (Fig. 13) are: a tibia R2854 probably belonging to a thyreophoran (either a stegosaur or an ankylosaur); and an ulna R2855 belonging to a sauropod (independent identifications made by Paul Barrett (BMNH) pers. comm. 2009 and JJL). It is not known if these two bones were found together; however, it is clear they cannot belong to the same individual. The two bones were purchased on 4 August 1896, although the individual purchase prices are not recorded (Annual Purchases, BMNH ML DF102/2, p. 50). Both elements await formal description.

Camarasaurid sauropod (R3777), acquired November 1897

Three dinosaur teeth (Fig. 14), R3777 (referred to as R3377 *in errore* by Martill 1988, p. 183; Martill & Clarke 1994, p. 12), have been considered to belong to a camarasaurid sauropod (Martill 1988). The R3777 teeth have long been thought of as associated with the (now) holotype of *Cetiosauriscus stewarti* (R3078, see below) (Leeds 1956; Martill 1988, p. 183), and were used as evidence that more of the skeleton of R3078 lay below the clay of the New Peterborough Brick Company No. 1 pit (Leeds 1956, p. 38). However, as the R3777 teeth were purchased in 1897, prior to the discovery of the partial skeleton of R3078 (see below) in May 1898, it can be conclusively stated that there is no link between these two specimens (as correctly deduced by Martill 1988, p. 183; Martill & Clarke 1994; Naish & Martill 2007). The teeth were sold to the BMNH on 17 November 1897 for a purchase price of £5-0-0 (Annual Purchases, BMNH ML DF102/2, p. 64) and displayed together with the skeleton of R3078 in 1903 (Anon. 1903*b*; Leeds 1956).

'Egg of saurian' (R2903), acquired 1898

This putative egg of a dinosaur (Fig. 15) is an unusual specimen as, although records indicate that it was collected from the Oxford Clay around Peterborough (Leeds 1956), there is no mention of it in the purchase registers for 1898, the year it was received and noted in the BMNH accession

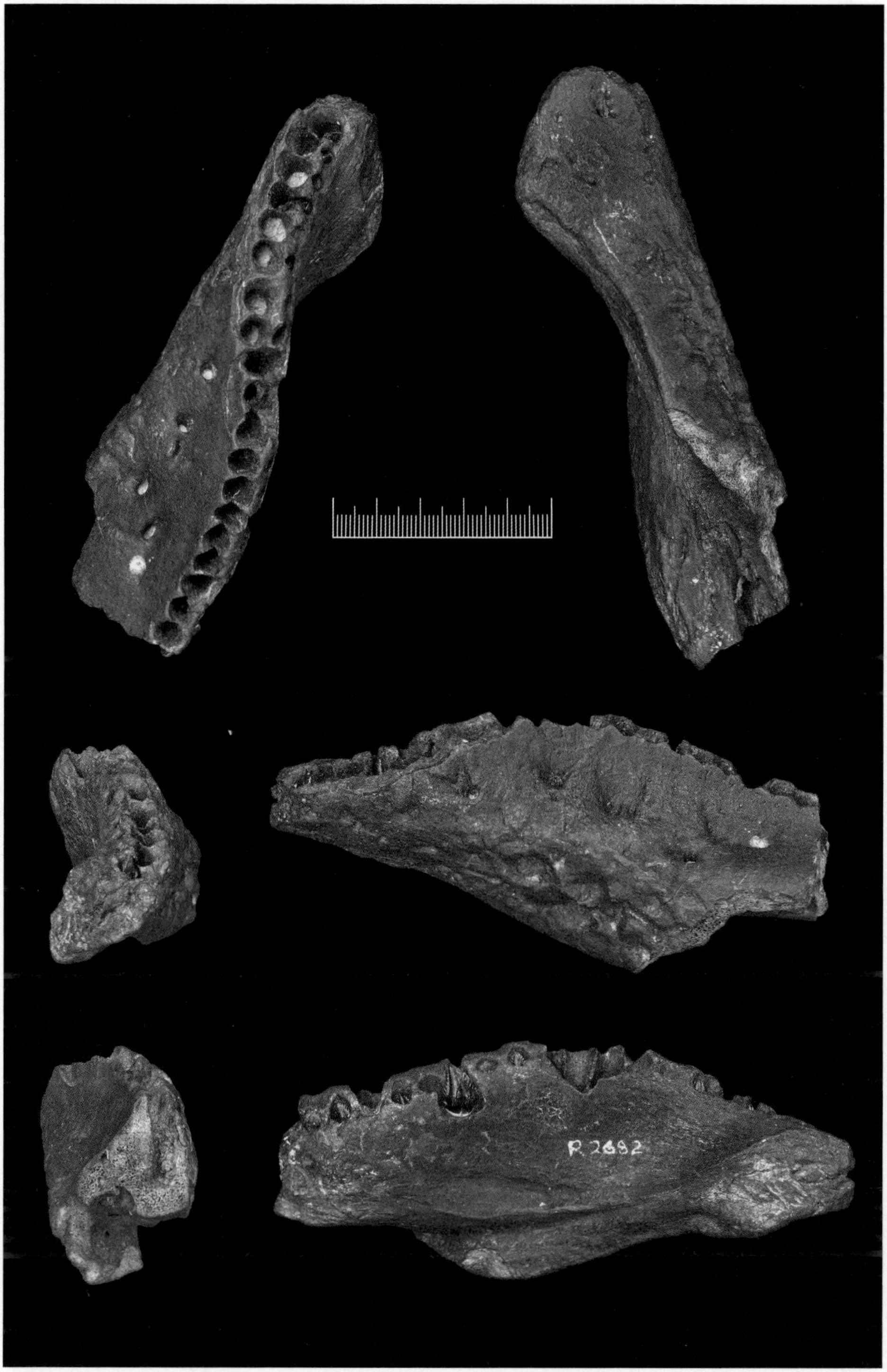

Fig. 12. Fragment of jaw of the nodosaurian ankylosaur *Sarcolestes leedsi* (BMNH R2682) in six standard views. Scale bar, 50 mm. Photographs courtesy of Sandra Chapman (Image Resources, NHM).

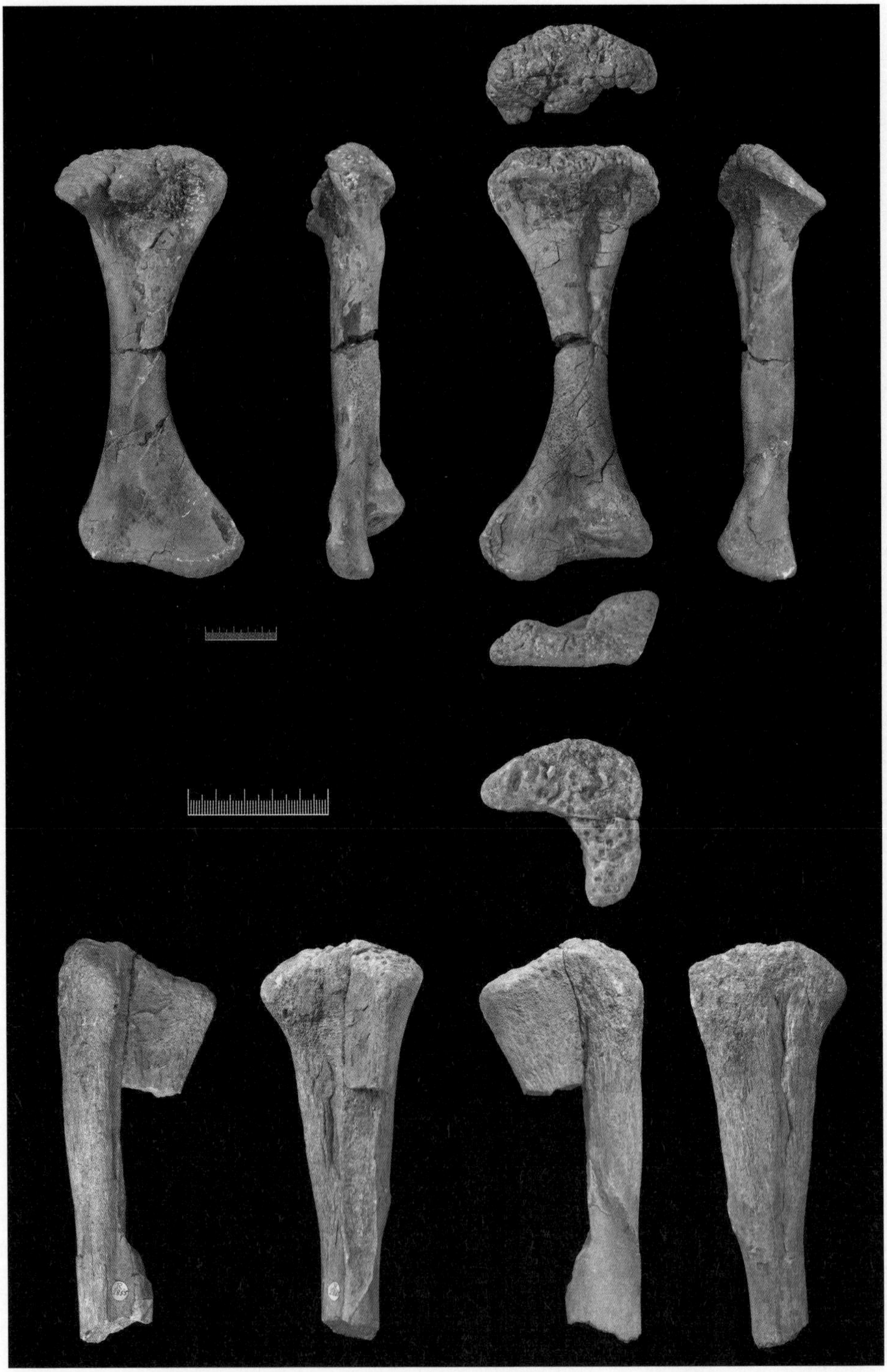

Fig. 13. Two isolated dinosaurian limb bones: (top) a probable thyreophoran tibia (BMNH R2854) and (bottom) a sauropod ulna (BMNH R2855) in standard views. Scale bars, 50 mm. Identifications made independently by P. Barrett (BMNH) and J. J. Liston. Photographs courtesy of Sandra Chapman (Image Resources, NHM).

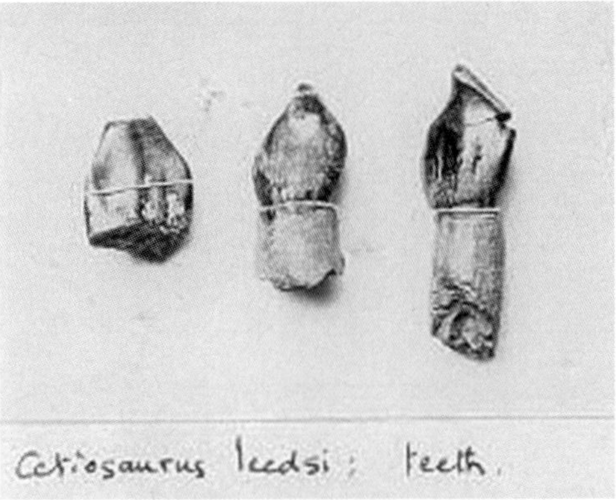

Fig. 14. Three isolated teeth of a diplodocid sauropod (BMNH R3777), labelled as '*Cetiosaurus leedsi*' following the description of Woodward (1905), images from Leeds (1939). Photograph reproduced courtesy of and © Julian Leeds and the Leeds family.

register as the 'egg of a saurian'. When Roy Chapman Andrews Third Asiatic Expedition in 1922 announced the discovery of dinosaur eggs in the Gobi Desert, *The Sphere* published a somewhat dismissive article, noting this as nothing new, given that a reptile egg had been discovered in England many years before (Anon. 1923*a*). In 1950, in response to the announcement of yet more dinosaur egg discoveries in Tanganyika (now Tanzania), Swinton declared in the *Illustrated London News* that the Oxford Clay egg might have been laid by an 'amphibious dinosaur' (Swinton 1950). Although initially noted in early reviews of fossil eggs (e.g. van Straelen 1928), it seems to have subsequently fallen into disrepute and been ignored in subsequent reviews for almost 80 years (e.g. Mikhailov 1997). Fragments of ammonite shell adhering to one surface of the putative egg may have made the specimen superficially resemble a limestone nodule around a mollusc, common in the Oxford Clay. Recent X-ray diffraction (XRD), scanning electron microscopy (SEM) and computerized tomography (CT) work has demonstrated that it may, indeed, be a fossil egg (Chapman & Liston 2008), and work is ongoing on this enigmatic and intriguing specimen.

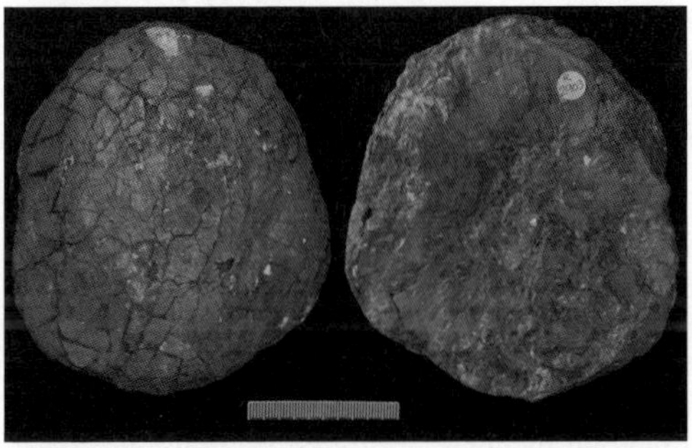

Fig. 15. Putative dinosaur egg (BMNH R2903) from the Leeds Collection. Note the cracked, shell-like texture on the left, and the ammonite impression on the right. Photographs courtesy of Sandra Chapman (Image Resources, NHM).

'Mr Leeds' Dinosaur': Cetiosauriscus stewarti *(R3078), acquired February 1899*

Perhaps the most important, and by far the most spectacular, dinosaur find made by Alfred Leeds was the closely associated remains of a single individual of the sauropod *Cetiosauriscus stewarti* (Charig 1980), BMNH R3078 (Fig. 16). The remains consist of much of the proximal region of the tail, part of the pelvis, the left hind-limb and right fore-limb (Smith Woodward 1905). These remains were originally described as belonging to *Cetiosaurus leedsi* together with the diplodocid tail (R1967), and the brachiosaurid vertebrae and other material (R1984, and R1985–1988) noted earlier. von Huene (1927) placed R3078 in the cetiosaurid subfamily Cardiodontidae, giving it a new genus name of *Cetiosauriscus* as he felt that the limbs and vertebrae of this specimen had proportions different enough from *Cetiosaurus* to warrant a new name. Charig (1980) opined that R3078 could not be assigned to the same taxon as R1985–1988 because the ilia were so badly preserved in both specimens and as such renamed *Cetiosauriscus leedsi* to become *Cetiosauriscus stewarti*, designating R3078 the type species of the genus *Cetiosauriscus* (Charig 1993). Although confusion over the specimens and names required submission to the International Commission on Zoological Nomenclature. Currently, the specimen has been recognized as a eusauropod (Heathcote & Upchurch 2003) and probably represents a mamenchisaurid (Naish & Martill 2007).

Discovery and mounting. The future R3078 was discovered in May 1898 in the Oxford Clay Formation, probably the middle Callovian stage *Kosmoceras jason* Biozone (Martill 1988, table 1; although possibly the *Erymnoceras coronatum* Biozone, p. 184). The specimen was recovered from the Fletton area to the south of Peterborough and to the east of the Great Northern Railway in a New Peterborough Brick Company Limited (NPBCL) pit. The forerunner of the NPBCL was the Peterborough Brick Company Limited, incorporated in July 1896, and owned by George and Arthur James Keeble (local farmers and entrepreneurs) and the McDougall family (flour grinders of Manchester) (Hillier

Fig. 16. The incomplete skeleton of *Cetiosauriscus stewarti* (BMNH R3078) mounted prior to display in around 1903. Photographed in the BMNH, and reproduced courtesy of the Leeds family, with layout by J. J. Liston. Note the similarity of this photograph to the drawing of the skeleton in Woodward (1905); previously figured in Anon. (1924) and Naish & Martill (2008).

1981). This company was set up with 45 acres of farm land acquired from the Keebles at a cost of £5300, but early in 1897 the land was sold, together with another 200 acre site to the north, to the newly formed NPBCL, which had a total start up capital of £150 000 and was owned by the same people (Anon. 1897*a–c*; Hillier 1981). During 1897 three NPBCL pits (numbered 1–3) began working the Oxford Clay for brick manufacture, strung out from north to south along the east of the railway line (Fig. 4) (see also Leeds 1956, figure facing p. 17; Hillier 1981, pp. 84–96 detailed distribution of the pits).

The pit from which R3078 was recovered is usually cited as NPBCL pit No. 1 (following Leeds 1956, pp. 18 and 36). The order of the pits from north to south along the railway line is given as 3, 1 and 2 in a letter from E. T. Leeds dated 28 June 1914 (BMNH ML 100/58 unnumbered). In his letter, E. T. Leeds is clear that pit No. 1 was the middle of the three, but is uncertain as to the position of the other two. However, this numbering of the NPBCL pits is in contradiction to the contemporary UK OS 1:10 000 map for the area, which indicates the pits were numbered 2, 3 and 1 from north to south (Fig. 5, inset). The distinction is an important one as Leeds (1956, p. 18) recalls that the number of vertebrate finds in the Oxford Clay to the east of the railway diminished southwards. A letter from Alfred Leeds dated 25 January 1907 (BMNH ML DF100/41/253a) gives the position of the pit face and the buildings in the pit, and this most closely matches the mapped buildings for the northernmost of the three pits. Hence, assuming the OS mapping is accurate and correctly numbers the pits, it appears R3078 was recovered from the northernmost of the three NPBCL pits, which was yard No. 2. As the pits were only opened in 1897, it is likely that these sauropod remains were recovered at a relatively early stage in the life of the pit.

The NPBCL sauropod remains were taken to Eyebury, the Leeds family home, to be cleaned and repaired. E. T. Leeds records that he was met by his father on returning to Peterborough from the University of Cambridge for the summer vacation with the words 'I've got a little work for you' (Leeds 1956, p. 36). For the whole of the summer father and son spent many hours cleaning and reconstructing the remains. In mid-August Henry Woodward visited Eyebury from the BMNH to produce a life-size drawing of the remains to present to the British Association for the Advancement of Science Meeting to be held in Bristol, although the presentation appears to have been made to the meeting by C. W. Andrews (Andrews 1899). Following the meeting, Henry Woodward returned to Eyebury with O. C. Marsh on 17 August 1898. Marsh considered the sauropod remains to belong to, or be closely allied with, the American genus *Diplodocus* (Leeds 1956, p. 38). Around this time, *The Times* of London carried an article on this new 'monster', declaring it to have been at least '50 feet long' (based on a cutting held by the Leeds family, although the exact date of publication has yet to be established).

On 21 February 1899 Alfred Leeds offered the sauropod remains to the BMNH for the princely sum of £250. Leeds listed the elements he had recovered and indicated that the price included the stoppage of work at the pit 'for days', the men's wages, as well as his and his son's work for nearly 12 months (BMNH PL, uncat.). However, it is worth noting that the 12 months' work, referred to by Alfred Leeds and cited in Leeds (1956), is not strictly accurate. The discovery of the sauropod was made in May 1898 and the offer of sale occurred in February 1899, which is at most 10 months, and during this time E. T. Leeds had commenced his third year of undergraduate study at the University of Cambridge, beginning in the autumn of 1898. However, it is possible that Mrs Leeds, and possibly Leeds' other sons, had spent significant amounts of time working on the remains. Henry Woodward, Keeper of Geology at the BMNH, 'had great pleasure' (BMNH PL, uncat.) in recommending to the Trustees of the BMNH that the remains be purchased. His arguments for the acquisition of the specimen included those put forward by Leeds, but in addition he noted Alfred Leeds' time in making numerous trips to the pit, that Marsh would have carried off the remains to America had Leeds not considered that the BMNH should have first refusal and that more remains would be sought if or when the area in which the discovery was made was further opened up (BMNH PL, uncat.). Clearly Alfred Leeds believed more of the animal was present, still hidden beneath the clay of the pit. The discontinuous nature of the remains (forelimb unconnected to the hindlimb and tail) may also have suggested further remains lay undiscovered nearby.

The purchase of the Leeds' sauropod was considered and sanctioned by the BMNH Trustees on 25 February 1899. At the same time five other collections, including chalk fishes, microscope slides and bryozoa, were offered to the museum (BMNH PL uncat.). The total cost of these collections was £357-14-10, of which £275 was requested for Alfred Leeds' specimens, £250 for the dinosaur, and £25 for the tail and other remains of the giant pachycormid fish *Leedsichthys* (BMNH P.10000; Liston & Noè 2004), which gives an indication of the relative value placed on the dinosaur remains. The purchase was completed on 17 March 1899, and described as 'a considerable part of the skeleton of a gigantic land reptile from the Oxford Clay near Peterborough probably related to *Diplodocus*' (Annual Purchases, BMNH ML DF 102/2, p. 79). Subsequently, Alfred Leeds wrote to Henry Woodward thanking him for 'getting my little account through the directors' (BMNH PL uncat.). Hence, in 1899, Alfred Leeds' sauropod was considered to be of immense scientific and cultural value. It was the largest and most complete sauropod discovered in the UK, and is only now equalled in completeness by the Rutland sauropod discovered in 1967 (Upchurch & Martin 2002).

In 1903 the mounting of the Leeds dinosaur was nearing completion, leading to questions as to how it had been found. In a letter, dated 3 February 1903, Alfred Leeds indicated that the 26 caudals of R3078 had not all been found in a row together (BMNH ML DF 100/35/95). The skeleton finally went on display in the BMNH during April 1903 (Anon. 1903*a–c*), although at least one report (Anon. 1903*c*) confused R3078 with the *Ornithopsis* remains R1985–1988 (see earlier) described by Hulke in 1887. The display of 'Mr Leeds dinosaur' occurred just prior to the arrival and display of the American *Diplodocus* skeleton, which went on display in February 1905 (Snell & Tucker 2003, p. 33). The bones of the Leeds dinosaur were displayed with the four brachiosaurid vertebrae (R1984) from the First Collection and the three camarasaurid teeth (R3777) collected by Alfred Leeds the year before (Anon. 1903*b*). Some time later, a full description of the remains appeared in print (Smith Woodward 1905), and it is worth noting the similarity of Text-figure 39 therein to a photograph of the mounted skeleton taken in the BMNH just prior to public display in 1903 (Fig. 16) (see also Anon. 1924; Naish & Martill 2007, fig. 4a).

The search for more remains. Although it is clear that Alfred Leeds thought more of the dinosaur was present in the pit (see above), E. T. Leeds records that his father did not think that there was much chance of recovering more of the animal (Leeds 1956). Nonetheless, by 1906 the BMNH was keen to take Leeds up on his offer to find the remainder of the animal. According to Leeds (1956), Mr Henry Knipe of Tanholt near Eyebury (a keen amateur palaeontologist) provided funds to the BMNH to search for further remains of the dinosaur. However, Alfred Leeds' letters refer to a Mr Go(o)dman (Leeds spelling is variable) as providing the money, and at present the exact source of the funds for this dig remains unresolved. On 10 October 1906 Alfred Leeds wrote to the BMNH indicating he had met that day with the owner of the NPBCL pit, and had agreed where the excavation should take place, where the spoil was to be deposited and that he could have two men that were surplus to requirements at the pit (BMNH ML DF100/41/231). Leeds indicates his initial enthusiasm and hope that the enterprise will succeed by writing on 12 October 'would Mr Goodman like to see any bones in the ground before we remove them?' (BMNH ML DF100/41/232). By 2 November Leeds wrote that the men had dug two large holes where the bones might have been expected to be found, but that no bone had been forthcoming, although they would link the excavations in the hope of finding further remains (BMNH ML DF100/41/233). By 13 November, Leeds writes that 'there is no hope of finding more of the dinosaur, and that Mr Goodman's money has been spent in vain' (BMNH ML DF100/41/234).

In a letter dated 26 November 1906, Alfred Leeds indicates the rate of pay for the workmen and gives some idea of the amount of work that was undertaken to try and find more of the dinosaur (BMNH ML DF100/41/235a). The men were initially paid 6d per cubic yard (*c.* 0.75 m^3) of clay removed, but Leeds was soon required to pay them by the hour as the digging progressed and barrowing of the spoil increased. At the end of the months' work Leeds calculated that the men had earned something over £9-10-0, and rounded this up to £10-0-0, saying that the men were very grateful for the extra shillings. At 6d per cubic yard, this would represent some 350 cubic yards (*c.* 265 m^3) of clay removed by two men in a month – and, although this is undoubtedly an overestimate, it gives some idea of just how much work could be achieved in digging out the sticky Oxford Clay, with two good men, a pair of 6 ft, 6 cwt (hundredweight) crowbars and a wheelbarrow. The two men had undoubtedly earned every penny of the money they were paid for their work that month. On 25 January 1907 Leeds wrote once again, presumably in response to a request from the BMNH, to indicate where the work had taken place in relation to the original find. Leeds indicated the positions of the pit face and works buildings, and added that there was no chance of finding further remains of the sauropod (BMNH ML DF100/41/253a).

Lexovisaurus durobrivensis *(R3167), acquired January 1904*

The remains of a second specimen of the stegosaurine stegosaur *Lexovisaurus durobrivensis* (Hulke 1887) Hoffstetter, 1957 (Fig. 17) were purchased by the BMNH on 25 January 1904, although the sale price is not recorded (Annual Purchases, BMNH ML DF100/2, p. 122). The remains consisted of: 26 vertebrae (two anterior cervicals including the axis, nine dorsals or fragments thereof and 15 caudals); a cervical rib; four dorsal ribs (three left and one right); fragments of chevrons; a right humerus and ulna; a left femur, tibia, fibula, carpal, astragalus and calcaneum; fragments

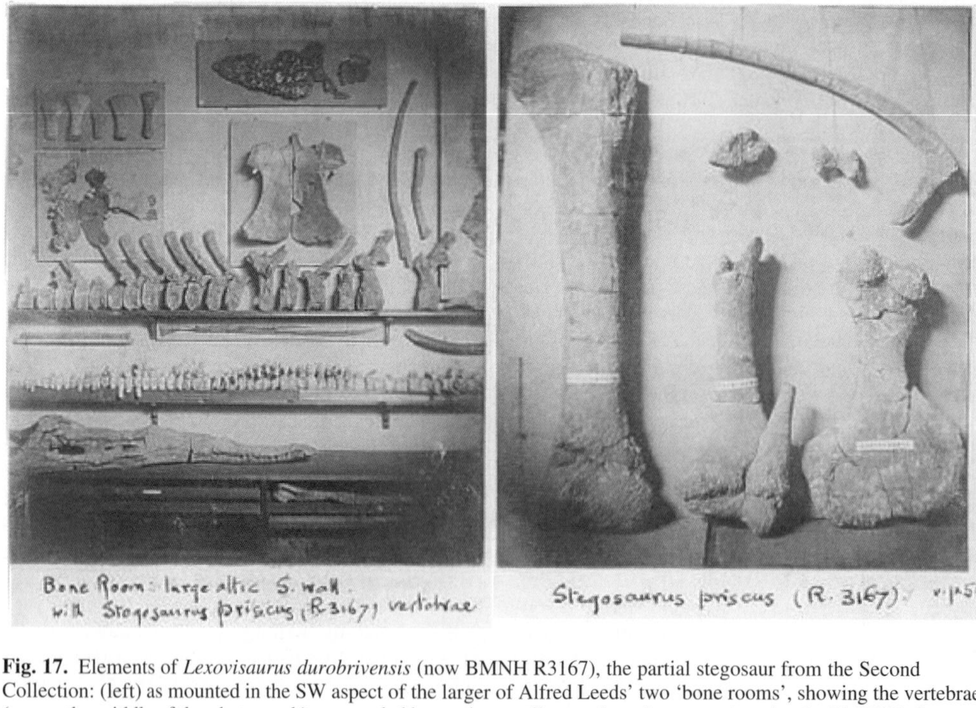

Fig. 17. Elements of *Lexovisaurus durobrivensis* (now BMNH R3167), the partial stegosaur from the Second Collection: (left) as mounted in the SW aspect of the larger of Alfred Leeds' two 'bone rooms', showing the vertebrae (across the middle of the photograph) surrounded by marine reptile remains prior to purchase by the BMNH in January 1904; and (right) various elements including, from left to right, the conjoined tibia and fibula, scapula (below), and two fragments and a dorsal rib (above). Photographs reproduced courtesy of and © the Leeds family.

of both ilia, parts of both pubes and ischia; and elements of the dermal armour (Nopcsa 1911*b*). The specimen is recorded as having been found in the Oxford Clay of Fletton, Peterborough (Nopcsa 1911*a*), and is considered to most likely have been derived from the middle Callovian stage, *Kosmoceras jason* Biozone of the Peterborough Member of the Oxford Clay Formation (Martill 1988, p. 181). R3167 was originally described under the name *Stegosaurus priscus* (Nopcsa 1911*a*, *b*), and was incorrectly referred to as R1989–1992 by Leeds (1956, p. 38). *Lexovisaurus durobrivensis* is a valid taxon and was most recently reviewed by Galton (1985; see also Naish & Martill 2008).

On 15 December 1901 Alfred Leeds wrote to Woodward (although it is not clear whether this was Henry Woodward, who was about to retire, or Arthur Smith Woodward, but probably the former) stating that he had found the remains of a *Stegosaurus* the previous month (BMNH ML DF 100/32/68a). Leeds is somewhat perplexed as to why the remains are so imperfect, as he had excavated the skeleton himself. In the same letter Leeds asks if *Stegosaurus* has been found in this country previously, presumably not considering his former stegosaurian find (R1989–1992, see earlier) as belonging to the same genus. In his next letter, Leeds makes it clear he was unaware of the stegosaur remains described by von Huene and held in the Woodwardian (now Sedgwick) Museum in Cambridge (von Huene 1901). Leeds notes that von Huene had been misled, as had Hulke (1887) when describing the first Leeds stegosaur many years before, and criticizes the authorities in Cambridge who had mixed up stegosaur and *Leedsichthys* material (BMNH ML DF 100/32/69). On 2 February 1902 Leeds once again wrote to (presumably Smith) Woodward asking which lots of bones Henry Woodward wanted, as B. Stürtz was planning a visit on the 10th of the month (BMNH ML DF 100/33/87). The letter is annotated with 'crocodile and dinosaur', the latter presumably referring to R3167.

An undated list shows the bones offered for sale as '1 humerus (very short and broad), 1 scapula, 1 ulna, 1 femur, 1 tibia and broken fibula (attached), 2 part[s] of 2 iliac bones, 2 portions of 2 ischia, 1 phalange, 1 tarsal bone, 21 vertebrae, 4 perfect ribs, 2 caudal spines, portions of dorsal spines (30)' (BMNH ML DF 100/33/88a). The '30' at the end of the list appears to be the offer price in pounds for the stegosaur material. Another letter written by Alfred Leeds on 15 February 1903 (BMNH ML DF 100/35/96b) indicates he has discovered further fragmentary remains of the stegosaur, including a fragment of the pubis and two cervical vertebrae, of which Leeds includes some sketches. The totality of R3167 was eventually sold for £50-0-0, as recorded in a letter dated 17 March 1904 (BMNH ML DF 100/36/357b), and this coincides well with the purchase register which shows a sale of £130 for this dinosaur, two crocodiles, a pliosaur and the head of a fish (BMNH ML DF102/2, p.122).

'Cetiosaur' rib (R3706), acquired July 1909

R3706 is regarded as an isolated dinosaur rib, belonging to a cetiosaurian dinosaur, although the specimen (Fig. 18) may belong to a large pliosaur (H. Ketchum pers. comm. 2008). This is probably the rib reported as having been put on display in the BMNH in 1923 and noted as 'of the gigantic dinosaur, *Cetiosaurus leedsi*' and 'six feet in length, and [. . .] remarkable for its slenderness'

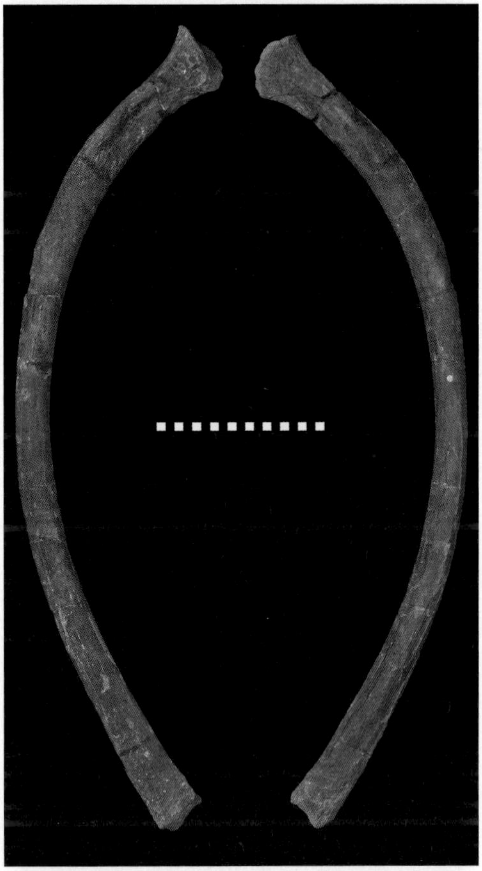

Fig. 18. Undescribed sauropod rib (BMNH R3706) in anterior and posterior views; however, note that this bone has recently been considered to belong to a large pliosaur (H. Ketchum (BMNH) pers. comm.). Scale bar, 200 mm. Photographs courtesy of Sandra Chapman (Image Resources, NHM).

Fig. 19. Two isolated dinosaur bones: (left) an indeterminate dinosaur rib, possibly belonging to a sauropod (BMNH R4060) (scale bar, 200 mm) and (right) a sauropod phalanx (BMNH R4061) in various views (scale bar, 50 mm). Identifications made independently by P. Barrett (BMNH) and D. Naish (University of Portsmouth). Photographs courtesy of Sandra Chapman (Image Resources, NHM).

(Anon. 1923*b*). The bone was purchased on 28 July 1909 for £5-0-0 (Annual Purchases, BMNH ML DF 102/2, p. 172), and has yet to be formally described.

Dinosaur rib (R4060) and ungual phalange (R4061), acquired January 1914

Two isolated dinosaurian elements, a rib (R4060) and an ungual phalange (R4061) were the last dinosaur remains discovered by Alfred Leeds (Fig. 19). The R4060 rib is Dinosauria indet., but possibly Sauropoda and R4061, a pedal ungual phalange with proximal articulating surface, is also Sauropoda indet. (independent identifications made by P. Barrett (BMNH) and D. Naish (University of Portsmouth) pers. comms 2009). The two bones were purchased on 26 July 1914 for £5-0-0 and are listed as 'Rib and ungual phalange of dinosaur' (Annual Purchases, BMNH ML DF 102/2, p. 216). It is not clear whether the two specimens came from the same locality and therefore belong to the same individual or not. These elements have not been formally described and no further archive material is known relating to these two bones

Summary and conclusions

The Leeds Collection is of outstanding international importance. The collection was initiated by Charles Leeds whilst at the University of Oxford following the influence of John Phillips. However, it was Charles Leeds' younger brother, Alfred – later with the help of his wife and sons – to whom the vast majority of the collection can be attributed. Alfred Leeds worked for almost 50 years (between about 1870 and 1917) amassing a collection of fossil vertebrates of unparalleled importance in the annals of UK palaeontology.

The Leeds Collection was almost exclusively derived from the Oxford Clay Formation in the neighbourhood of Peterborough. The Oxford Clay has yielded a fantastic variety of fossil vertebrates, most famously the fabulously preserved marine reptiles and the giant pachycormid fish *Leedsichthys problematicus*. However, the Leeds Collection also includes the remains of at least 12 dinosaurs, belonging to a minimum of eight taxa including: six sauropods (a mamenchisaurid, a diplodocid, a camarasaurid, a cetiosaurid and two brachiosaurids) and three ornithischians (a stegosaur, a nodosaur and a dryosaur), as well as the fragmentary remains of a rhamphorhynchid pterosaur. The Leeds Collection also contains the only remains attributed to a reptilian egg known from the formation.

Alfred Leeds' dinosaurs, although lacking detailed provenance data, provide a tantalizing snapshot into the variety of ornithodirans living on the islands scattered across the western European archipelago during uppermost Middle Jurassic times. The remains include the oldest known ornithopod, the UK's second most complete sauropod and the earliest reported putative dinosaur egg. Although the material is often fragmentary, the Leeds collection of dinosaurs and pterosaur represent an invaluable resource for researchers today and offers a fascinating window into the UK and Europe's Jurassic terrestrial and volant fauna. In addition to the superb fossil material, underutilized archive material from a range of sources is continuing to add new dimensions to our understanding of this rich palaeontological resource.

Our grateful thanks go to numerous people, principal amongst these are: The Leeds family, especially: Julian, Lewis, Rosie and Sue; M. Mitchell, Caudle Design for assistance with data transfer; A. Milner, P. Barrett, S. Chapman, H. Ketchum, P. Tucker, C. Goche, J. Hatton and S. Snell (BMNH); K. Ingham and I. Rolfe (formerly of the Hunterian Museum); J. Heathcote and P. Upchurch (UCL); the late P. Dawn; and M. Howgate. We also thank the staff and volunteers at: the National Museum of Wales, Liverpool University, Liverpool Museum, Kendal Museum, Hunterian Museum, Whittlesea Museum and numerous other institutions; M. Evans (New Walk Museum, Leicester); G. Wass (Peterborough Museum); D. Norman and M. Dorling (Sedgwick Museum, Cambridge); E. Tilly and S. Humbert (Departmental Library, Cambridge); D. Martill (Portsmouth); M. Forthuber (Braunschweig); and M. Maisch (Tübingen). We extend our grateful thanks to everyone not named here who has contributed in large and small ways to our ongoing understanding of Alfred Nicholson Leeds, his life, family and collection of Oxford Clay fossil vertebrates. Special thanks to D. Martill who provided a thorough and thoughtful review of the original manuscript that significantly improved this contribution.

References

ANDREWS, C. W. 1899. On some dinosaurian remains from the Oxford Clay of Northampton [title only]. *Report of the British Association for the Advancement of Science*, **68**, 883.

ANDREWS, C. W. 1910. *A Descriptive Catalogue of the Marine Reptiles of the Oxford Clay – Based on the Leeds Collection in the British Museum (Natural History), London, Part I.* British Museum (Natural History), London.

ANDREWS, C. W. 1912. The fossil reptiles of the Oxford Clay. *Ealing Natural History and Microscopial Society Transactions*, 1911-**1**, 6–8.

ANDREWS, C. W. 1913. *A Descriptive Catalogue of the Marine Reptiles of the Oxford Clay – Based on the Leeds Collection in the British Museum (Natural History), London, Part II.* British Museum (Natural History), London.

ANON. 1874. Professor Phillips. *Geological Magazine*, **11**, 240.

ANON. 1888. A palæontological museum. *Peterborough and Huntingdonshire Standard*, Saturday, 7 April 1888 – supplement, 2.

ANON. 1893. Mr. Leeds – (awarded Lyell Geological Fund). *Quarterly Journal of the Geological Society of London*, **49**, 43–44.

ANON. 1895. John Whitaker Hulke, F.R.S., President of the Royal College of Surgeons of England; Foreign Secretary of the Geological Society of London. *Geological Magazine*, **32**, 189–192.

ANON. 1897*a*. The New Peterborough Brick Company (Limited). Incorporated under the Companies acts, 1862 to 1890. *The Peterborough Advertiser*, Saturday, 6 March 1897, 3.

ANON. 1897*b*. Important development of the Peterboro' brick enterprise, 5,200 shares offered to the public. *The Peterborough Advertiser*, Satuday, 6 March 1897, 6.

ANON. 1897*c*. The brickyard enterprise in Huntingdonshire, statutory meeting of the New Peterborough Brick Company. *The Peterborough Advertiser*, Saturday, 10 July 1897, 7.

ANON. 1903*a*. A sixty-foot reptile. The Cetiosaurus leedsi, South Kensington's new resident. *Daily Graphic*, London, **54**, no. 4153, Saturday, 11 April 1903, 149.

ANON. 1903*b*. Recent progress in zoological science. *Illustrated London News*, London, 18 April 1903, 574.

ANON. 1903*c*. [A UNIQUE specimen]. *Nature*, **67**, 617.

ANON. 1909. Professor H. G. Seeley, F.R.S., F.L.S., F.G.S., F.Z.S., F.R.G.S., Fellow of King's College, London [obituary]. *Geological Magazine*, **46**, 93–94.

ANON. 1912*a*. [The death is announced of Mr. Charles Edward Leeds]. *Nature*, **89**, 118.

ANON. 1912*b*. Charles Edward Leeds, M.A., Exeter College, Oxford. *Geological Magazine*, **49**, 287.

ANON. 1915. Obituary. Richard Lydekker, B.A. (Camb.), F.R.S., F.G.S., F.Z.S., J. P. Herts. *Geological Magazine*, **52**, 238–240.

ANON. 1921. Obituary. Henry Woodward. *Geological Magazine*, **58**, 481–484.

ANON. 1923*a*. A fossil reptile's egg unearthed in England. *The Sphere*, London, 17 November 1923, 196.

ANON. 1923*b*. [A WELL-PRESERVED rib of the gigantic dinosaur, *Cetiosaurus leedsi*]. *Nature*, **111**, 509.

ANON. 1924. *Bricks Without Straw*. Hicks & Co., Old Fletton.

ANON. 2008. World wide web address: http://www.measuringworth.com/ukcompare/. Date accessed 27 August 2008.

ARAÚJO, R., SMITH, A. S. & LISTON, J. 2008. The Alfred Leeds fossil vertebrate collection of the National Museum of Ireland – Natural History. *Irish Journal of Earth Sciences*, **26**, 17–32.

ASHWORTH, J. H. 1911. Zoology at the British Association. *Nature*, **88**, 23–27.

BRUCE-MITFORD, R. L. S. & HARDEN, D. B. 1956. Edward Thurlow Leeds 1877–1955. *In*: HARDEN, D. B. (ed.) *Dark-age Britain*. Methuen, London.

CALLOMON, J. H. 1968. The Kellaway Beds and the Oxford Clay. *In*: SYLVESTER-BRADLEY, P. C. & FORD, T. D. (eds) *The Geology of the East Midlands*. Leicester University Press, Leicester.

CHALMERS-HUNT, J. M. 1976. *Natural History Auctions 1700–1972, A Register of Sales in the British Isles*. Sotherby Park Bernet Publications, London.

CHAPMAN, S. D. & LISTON, J. J. 2008. Immortal Clay II: a first for Alfred Leeds – but is it a reptile egg? [poster abstract]. *In*: MOODY, R., BUFFETAUT, E., MARTILL, D. M. & NAISH, D. (eds) *Dinosaurs (and Other Extinct Saurians) A Historical Perspective. Abstracts Booklet*. Geological Society, London, 59.

CHARIG, A. J. 1980. A diplodocid sauropod from the Lower Cretaceous of England. *In*: JACOBS, L. L. (ed.) *Aspects of Vertebrate History, Essays in Honour of E. H. Colbert*. Museum of Northern Arizona Press, Flagstaff, AZ, 231–244.

CHARIG, A. J. 1993. Case 1876. *Cetiosauriscus* von Huene, 1927 (Reptilia, Sauropodomorpha): proposed designation of *C. stewarti* Charig, 1980 as the type species. *Bulletin of Zoological Nomenclature*, **50**, 282–283.

C.L.F. 1956. The Leeds Collection of fossil reptiles – review. *Geological Magazine*, **93**, 440.

FLETCHER, T. W. 1961. Lancashire livestock farming during the great depression. *Agricultural History Review*, **9**, 17–42.

FORSTER COOPER, C. 1945. Arthur Smith Woodward 1864–1944. *Obituary Notices of Fellows of The Royal Society*, **5**, 79–112.

GALTON, P. M. 1980*a*. European Jurassic ornithopod dinosaurs of the families Hypsilophodontidae and Camptosauridae. *Neues Jahrbuch für Geologie und Paläeontologie, Abhandlungen*, **16**, 73–95.

GALTON, P. M. 1980*b*. *Priodontognathus phillipsii* (Seeley), and ankylosaurian dinosaur from the Upper Jurassic (or possibly Lower Cretaceous) of England. *Neues Jahrbuch für Geologie und Paläeontologie, Monatchefte*, **1980**, 477–489.

GALTON, P. M. 1980*c*. Armoured dinosaurs (Ornithischia: Ankylosauria) from the Middle and Upper Jurassic of England. *Geobios*, **13**, 825–837.

GALTON, P. M. 1983. *Sarcolestes leedsi* Lydekker, an ankylosaurian dinosaur from the Middle Jurassic of England. *Neues Jahrbuch für Geologie und Paläeontologie, Monatchefte*, **1983**, 141–155.

GALTON, P. M. 1985. British plated dinosaurs (Ornithischia, Stegosauridae). *Journal of Vertebrate Paleontology*, **5**, 211–254.

HARKER, A. 1918. Alfred Nicholson Leeds. *Quarterly Journal of the Geological Society, London*, **74**, lxi.

HEATHCOTE, J. & UPCHURCH, P. 2003. The relationships of *Cetiosauriscus stewarti* (Dinosauria; Sauropoda): implications for sauropod phylogeny [abstract]. *Journal of Vertebrate Paleontology*, **23**, 60A.

HILLIER, R. 1981. *Clay That Burns, A History of the Fletton Brick Industry*. London Brick Company, London, 100.

HOFFSTETTER, R. 1957. Quelques observations sur les stegosaurines. *Bulletin de Muséum National d'Histoire Naturelle*, **29**, 537–547.

HUDSON, J. D. & MARTILL, D. M. 1994. The Peterborough Member (Callovian, Middle Jurassic) of the Oxford Clay Formation at Peterborough, UK. *Journal of the Geological Society, London*, **151**, 113–124.

HUDSON, J. D., MARTILL, D. M. & PAGE, K. N. 1991. Introduction. *In*: MARTILL, D. M. & HUDSON, J. D. (eds) *Fossils of the Oxford Clay*. The Palaeontological Association, London, 11–14.

HULKE, J. W. 1887. Note on some dinosaurian remains in the collection of A. Leeds, Esq., of Eyebury, Northamptonshire. *Quarterly Journal of the Geological Society, London*, **43**, 695–702.

ICZN 1999. *International Code of Zoological Nomenclature*, 4th edn. The International Commission on Zoological Nomenclature, c/o The Natural History Museum, London.

LEEDS, A. N. & SMITH WOODWARD, A. 1897. Excursion to Peterborough. *Proceedings of the Geologists' Association*, **15**, 188–193.

LEEDS, E. T. 1939. *Eyebury and the Leeds Collection*. Manuscript.

LEEDS, E. T. 1956. *The Leeds Collection of Fossil Reptiles From the Oxford Clay of Peterborough*. BM(NH) and Basil Blackwell, Oxford.

LISTON, J. 2006. From Glasgow to the Star Pit and Stuttgart: a short journey around the world's longest fish. *Glasgow Naturalist*, **24**, 59–71.

LISTON, J. 2008. A review of the characters of the edentulous pachycormiforms *Leedsichthys*, *Asthenocormus* and *Martillichthys* nov. gen. *In*: ARRATIA, G., SCHULTZE, H.-P. & WILSON, M. V. H. (eds) *Mesozoic Fishes 4 – Homology and Phylogeny*. Dr. Friedrich Pfeil, München, Germany, 181–198.

LISTON, J. J. 2004. An overview of the pachycormiform *Leedsichthys*. *In*: ARRATIA, G. & TINTORI, A. (eds) *Mesozoic Fishes 3 – Systematics, Paleoenvironments and Biodiversity*. Dr. Friedrich Pfeil, München, Germany, 379–390.

LISTON, J. J. & NOÈ, L. F. 2004. The tail of the Jurassic fish *Leedsichthys problematicus* (Osteichthyes: Actinopterygii) collected by Alfred Nicholson Leeds – an example of the importance of historical records in palaeontology. *Archives of Natural History*, **30**, 236–252.

LYDEKKER, R. 1888. British Museum catalogue of fossil Reptilia, and papers on the enaliosaurians. *Geological Magazine*, **25**, 451–453.

LYDEKKER, R. 1889. On the remains and affinities of five genera of Mesozoic reptiles. *Quarterly Journal of the Geological Society, London*, **45**, 41–59.

LYDEKKER, R. 1893. On the jaw of a new carnivorous dinosaur from the Oxford Clay of Peterborough. *Quarterly Journal of the Geological Society, London*, **49**, 284–287.

MACGREGOR, A. 2001. Leeds, Edward Thurlow (1877–1955). *In*: MÜLLER, R. (ed.) *Reallexikon der Germanischen Altertumskunde*. Walter de Gruyter, Berlin, 191–194.

MARTILL, D. M. 1986. The stratigraphic distribution and preservation of fossil vertebrates in the Oxford Clay of England. *Mercian Geologist*, **10**, 161–186.

MARTILL, D. M. 1988. A review of the terrestrial vertebrate fossils of the Oxford Clay (Callovian–Oxfordian) of England. *Mercian Geologist*, **11**, 171–190.

MARTILL, D. M. 1991. Terrestrial reptiles. *In*: MARTILL, D. M. & HUDSON, J. D. (eds) *Fossils of the Oxford Clay*. The Palaeontological Association, London, 244–248.

MARTILL, D. M. & CLARKE, M. 1994. *Dinosaurs of the East Midlands*. Department of Geology, University of Leicester, Leicester, 1–16.

MARTILL, D. M. & HUDSON, J. D. (eds) 1991. *Fossils of the Oxford Clay*. The Palaeontological Association, London, 286.

MARTILL, D. M., TAYLOR, M. A. & DUFF, K. L. 1994. The trophic structure of the biota of the Peterborough Member, Oxford Clay Formation (Jurassic), UK. *Journal of the Geological Society, London*, **151**, 173–194.

MIKHAILOV, K. E. 1997. Fossil and recent eggshell in amniotic vertebrates: fine structure, comparative morphology and classification. *Special Papers in Palaeontology*, **56**, 1–80.

NAISH, D. & MARTILL, D. M. 2007. Dinosaurs of Great Britain and the role of the Geological Society of London in their discovery: basal Dinosauria and Saurischia. *Journal of the Geological Society, London*, **164**, 493–510.

NAISH, D. & MARTILL, D. M. 2008. Dinosaurs of Great Britain and the role of the Geological Society of London in their discovery: Ornithischia. *Journal of the Geological Society, London*, **165**, 613–623.

NOPCSA, F. 1911*a*. Notes on British dinosaurs. Part IV: *Stegosaurus priscus* sp. nov. *Geological Magazine*, **48**, 109–115.

NOPCSA, F. 1911*b*. Notes on British dinosaurs. Part IV: *Stegosaurus priscus* sp. nov. [continuation]. *Geological Magazine*, **48**, 145–153.

PERRY, P. J. 1972. Where was the 'great agricultural depression'? A geography of agricultural bankruptcy in late Victorian England and Wales. *Agricultural History Review*, **20**, 30–45.

PHILLIPS, J. 1871. *Geology of Oxford and the Valley of the Thames*. Clarendon Press, Oxford.

PORTER, H. 1861. *The Geology of Peterborough and its Vicinity*. T. Chadwell, Peterborough.

PORTER, H. 1863. On the occurrence of large quantities of fossil wood in the Oxford Clay, near Peterborough [abstract]. *Quarterly Journal of the Geological Society, London*, **19**, 317–318.

RUIZ-OMEÑACA, J. L., PEREDA-SUBERBIOLA, X. & GALTON, P. M. 2007. *Callovosaurus leedsi*, the earliest dryosaurid dinosaur (Ornithischia: Euornithopoda) from the Middle Jurassic of England. *In*: CARPENTER, K. (ed.) *Horns and Beaks: Ceratopsian and Ornithopod Dinosaurs*. Indiana University Press, Bloomington, IN, 3–16.

SEELEY, H. G. 1874. On *Muraenosaurus leedsii*, a plesiosaurian from the Oxford Clay, part I. *Quarterly Journal of the Geological Society, London*, **30**, 197–208.

SEELEY, H. G. 1889. Note on the pelvis of *Ornithopsis*. *Quarterly Journal of the Geological Society, London*, **45**, 391–397.

SMITH WOODWARD, A. 1889*a*. On the palaeontology of sturgeons. *Proceedings of the Geologists' Association*, **11**, 24.

SMITH WOODWARD, A. 1889*b*. Notes on some new and little-known British Jurassic fishes. *Annals and Magazine of Natural History*, **6**, 405.

SMITH WOODWARD, A. 1889*c*. Preliminary notes on some new and little-known British Jurassic fishes. *Geological Magazine*, **26**, 448–455.

SMITH WOODWARD, A. 1890. Notes on some new and little-known British Jurassic fishes. *Report of the British Association for the Advance of Science*, **59**, 585–586.

SMITH WOODWARD, A. 1905. On parts of the skeleton of *Cetiosaurus leedsi*, a sauropodous dinosaur from the Oxford Clay of Peterborough. *Proceedings of the Zoological Society, London*, **1**, 232–243.

SMITH WOODWARD, A. 1917. Obituary. Alfred Nicholson Leeds, F.G.S. *Geological Magazine*, **54**, 478–480.

SMITH WOODWARD, A. 1924. Charles William Andrews (obituary). *Geological Magazine*, **61**, 479–480.

SMITH WOODWARD, A. S. 1891. *Catalogue of Fossil Fishes in the British Museum (Natural History), Part II*. British Museum (Natural History), London.

SMITH WOODWARD, A. S. 1895. *Catalogue of Fossil Fishes in the British Museum (Natural History), Part III*. British Museum (Natural History), London.

SNELL, S. & TUCKER, P. 2003. *Life Through a Lens: Photographs From the Natural History Museum 1880–1950*. The Natural History Museum, London.

SWINTON, W. E. 1950. Fossil eggs from Tanganyika. *The Illustrated London News*, London, 30 December 1950, 1082–1083.

TURNER, M. 1992. Output and prices in UK agriculture, 1867–1914, and the great agricultural depression reconsidered. *Agricultural History Review*, **40**, 38–51.

UNWIN, D. M. 1996. The fossil record of middle Jurassic pterosaurs. *In*: MORALES, M. (ed.) *The Continental Jurassic*. Museum of Northern Arizona, Flagstaff, AZ, 291–304.

UPCHURCH, P. 1995. The evolutionary history of sauropod dinosaurs. *Philosophical Transactions of the Royal Society of London B*, **349**, 365–390.

UPCHURCH, P. & MARTIN, J. 2002. The Rutland *Cetiosaurus*: the anatomy and relationships of a Middle Jurassic British sauropod dinosaur. *Palaeontology*, **45**, 1049–1074.

UPCHURCH, P. & MARTIN, J. 2003. The anatomy and taxonomy of *Cetiosaurus* (Saurischia, Sauropoda) from the Middle Jurassic of England. *Journal of Vertebrate Paleontology*, **23**, 208–231.

VAN STRAELEN, V. 1928. Les oeufs de reptiles fossiles. *Palaeobiologica (Vienna)*, **1**, 295–312.

VON HUENE, F. 1901. Notizen aus dem Woodwardian-Museum in Cambridge. *Centralblatt für Mineralogie, Geologie und Paläontologie*, **23**, 715–719.

VON HUENE, F. 1927. Short review of the present knowledge of the Sauropoda. *Memoirs of the Queensland Museum*, **9**, 121–126.

WELLNHOFER, P. 1978. *Pterosauria*. Gustav Fischer Verlag, Stuttgart, New York.

WOODWARD, H. 1899. Othniel Charles Marsh. *Geological Magazine*, **35**, 237–240.

Life and ideas of Giovanni Capellini (1833–1922): a palaeontological revolution in Italy

FEDERICO FANTI

Alma Mater Studiorum, Università di Bologna, Dipartimento di Scienze della Terra e Geologico-Ambientali, Via Zamboni 67, 40126 Bologna, Italy
(e-mail: federico.fanti@unibo.it)

Abstract: During the nineteenth century Europe and then America were the focal points for major advances in the study of palaeontology and the great, often acrimonious, debate on evolutionary theory. Natural history was one of the great educational disciplines of the day and those involved were part of an educated elite who practised as medics, clergymen, chemists and anatomists. Some were shy and retiring, others forceful even bombastic, sometimes evil by intent. Many were driven by fame and it was their wish to discover the best, the biggest and the most important specimens they could get their hands on. Others were great orators who could defend a cause; some were the first of many who became diligent and careful in the collection and storage of material or brilliant field scientists who taught us the importance of observation, data gathering and interpretation of sedimentary successions worldwide. Being considered worthy of joining such an elite social, scientific circle was an immense tribute to their contribution to the natural sciences. It was an honour denied William Smith who lacked the educational background of the middle classes of the time, but given in abundance to the Italian scientist Giovanni Capellini who was born into an upper middle-class Italian family and who received a classic ecclesiastical training before venturing into the natural sciences.

Supplementary material: A list of selected publications by Giovanni Capellini (1858–1907) is available at http://www.geolsoc.org.uk/SUP18417.

Giovanni Capellini (1833–1922) (Fig. 1) dedicated his entire life to the study the natural sciences. He was a polyglot, a pioneering anthropologist and ardent collector; Capellini stands as a unique touchstone not only for geologists, but also for all those who deal with research and publication within the natural sciences. From the outset, his teaching and research activities, although rooted in his country, were planned and carried out in the European arena. He was fully aware that if progress was to be made in subjects such as geology and palaeontology it was dependent on international correlation and comparison, through the exchange of knowledge and experience. He was somewhat inimitable in his endeavour to establish unique relationships with other European researchers and institutions, and in 1863 he set out to cross the Atlantic and visit the New World. This visit was a privilege reserved for very few of his contemporaries, and proved invaluable to Capellini as a scientist and teacher.

Capellini was ahead of his time and he was to influence the education of many generations to come. In 1861 he was the first to separate out palaeontology (his specialist subject) from geology, not only in taught courses but also in the museum and in the organization of the collection storage, curation and display. Most significantly, he was the first Italian scientist to recognize the important role that dinosaurs occupied as a fundamental and extremely powerful tool through which he could demonstrate the emergent principles of Evolution and Actualism.

The vast heritage of scripts and scientific materials left by Giovanni Capellini are proof that he was unquestionably one of the most significant personages in the history of geology and palaeontology. Even now, his work is a formidable source of inspiration and motivation for those who deal with research, collection and publication in palaeontology. Detailed field notes and beautiful freehand drawings, together with accurate and exhaustive descriptions, characterize his work. As do pioneering methods for the storage, curation and display of museum collections and exhibitions. These are but a few of Capellini's innovative contributions to scientific methodology.

Giovanni Capellini was unquestionably a self-taught man: he came from a middle-class family in La Spezia (Liguria, NW Italy) which encouraged him to follow a career as a musician and secondarily an ecclesiastic life. However, he was to leave the priory where he served in 1854, at the age of 21, on the death of his father. From then on he had to support himself and his family, and he variously worked as a bookbinder, tutor at a college in La Spezia and as a repairer of mechanical devices.

From: Moody, R. T. J., Buffetaut, E., Naish, D. & Martill, D. M. (eds) *Dinosaurs and Other Extinct Saurians: A Historical Perspective*. Geological Society, London, Special Publications, **343**, 79–87.
DOI: 10.1144/SP343.5 0305-8719/10/$15.00

Fig. 1. Professor Giovanni Capellini standing with the exquisitely preserved skull of the whale *Aulocetus sammarinensis*, recovered in the Republic of San Marino in 1897.

Thanks to his interests in natural history and his training in self-denial, Capellini managed to attend university in Pisa where he had the opportunity to demonstrate both his academic ability and personal skills. Capellini, in fact, was a brilliant and agreeable person, who rapidly gained recognition, funding, letters of introduction, promotion and honours from various institutions and academies. While still a student in Pisa, he was elected as corresponding member of the German Society of Naturalists of Halle. After obtaining his first degree in Pisa in 1857, Capellini began his career as a field geologist, focusing primarily on the Apuan Alps, which are famed for their high-quality marble. By the age of 27, his name had spread far and wide, and he was honoured by a visit from Charles Lyell (1797–1875). Such was his status among natural scientists that he was the one to introduce Lyell (to his professorial mentors) rather than they to him.

Unlike the vast majority of his Italian colleagues, Capellini yearned to extend his studies in natural history beyond Italy, and in the early years of his career (1858–1860) he sought to establish long-lasting personal and scientific relationships with leading scientists of the day, including geologists, zoologists and archaeologists, throughout Europe. His travels took him first to Switzerland, France, England and Germany, and later to Romania, Turkey, Belgium, Denmark, Sweden, Greece and Hungary. In particular (1858–1859), he started a long-standing friendship with one of the characters that would do most to influence his career and education. His new friend was none other than Louis Agassiz (1807–1873), the first scientist to propose that the Earth had been subject to glaciations and who was an ardent critic of the Deluge as the mechanism to explain the occurrence of fossils.

It is during this critical period of his life that Capellini witnessed the development of science in the academies of Europe in an age of innovative theories and major discoveries. These developments would exert a strong influence in terms of his understanding of both geology and palaeontology. Above all were the innovative works and ideas of Charles Lyell, Richard Owen (1804–1892), Louis Agassiz and Thomas Huxley (1825–1895), together with the voyage of the *Beagle* and the publication of '*On the Origin of Species*' in 1859. The exhibition of the first life-sized models of extinct reptiles at the Crystal Palace in 1854 and the discovery of extraordinary fossils in Europe (e.g. *Archaeopteryx* in 1860) and North America further enthused his cause.

This was a period of intense travel during which Capellini began to develop his firm conviction that the detailed illustrations of outcrops, fossils and other materials were essential in order to enhance the accumulation of data and theoretical interpretation. His diaries and field notes (Fig. 2) are rich in accurate and exhaustive descriptions of hundreds of localities, which are illustrated by exquisite freehand drawings of outcrops and fossils. Travel reinforced Capellini's intention to create a geological museum designed not only to store type and comparative specimens of fossils and rocks, but also to become a place for debate and the exchange of knowledge and personal experience. Capellini's scripts show how readily he changed his *forma mentis*, thanks unquestionably to stimulating debates and correspondence with friends and colleagues from other countries: from mere description to direct comparison, from local to global, and from geology to palaeontology as separate disciplines to the birth of palaeobiogeography.

It was at home in Italy where he first became conscious of the similarities and possible correlations between coeval strata and fossil assemblages from different geographical areas worldwide. This was fundamental in order to properly understand the mode and tempo of geological change and biological (including human) evolution. Of paramount importance, Capellini realized the need for common and worldwide-accepted rules tying the geological mapping to standard material stored in museums. This unique vision was focal to the introduction of

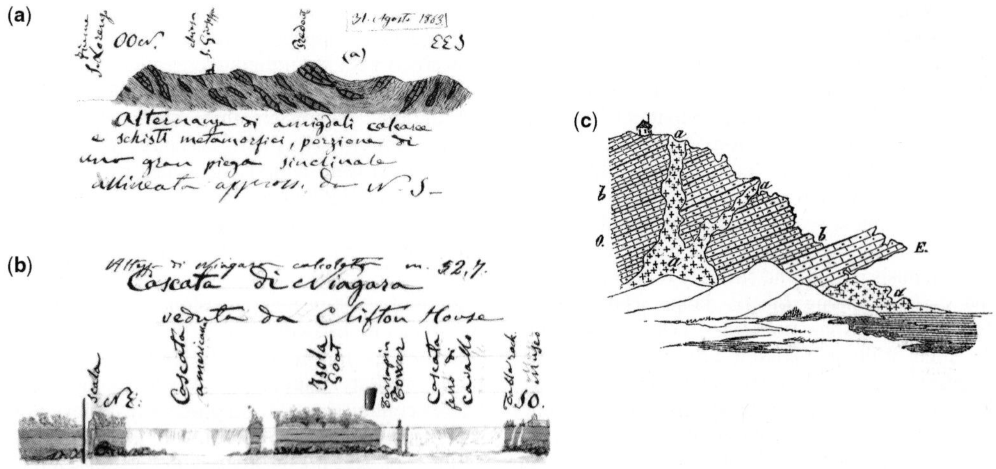

Fig. 2. Freehand sketches that Capellini made during his journey in North America. (**a**) Geological section along the St Laurence estuary; (**b**) the Niagara Falls as seen from Clifton House in summer 1863; and (**c**) Louis Agassiz used to call the magnificent cliffs facing the Atlantic near his house at Nahant 'my Aquarium'. Capellini was accompanied by Agassiz on a visit to the nearby 'Pulpit Rock', which he sketched on his personal notes.

Capellini's innovative methods for museum collections and exhibitions. Later, as the revolutionary theories of Lyell, Agassiz and Darwin spread through the major scientific institutions of Europe, Capellini was one of their more enthusiastic and active supporters.

In 1859, at the age of 26, Giovanni Capellini was elected as professor in Genoa and the following year appointed by the Government in the person of Minister Terenzio Mamiani (1799–1885) as a full Professor of Geology and Mineralogy at the University of Bologna. In the first half of the nineteenth century Zoology, Mineralogy and Geology were taught in Italy at university as a single subject course, usually under the inclusive name of 'Natural History'. From 1861 onwards Capellini taught each subject as a separate discipline. His notes of that time include the following statement:

> I will not fully follow neither Catastrophists nor Uniformists, giving above all relevance to Palaeontology as a discipline, also developing the idea of Geology in connection with the progresses that will follow Lamarck's theories, and for the great impulse that they would receive from the immortal Charles Darwin.

As a result of his involvement in the new concepts of the natural sciences, Capellini became a member of a small elite of European scientists that wanted to travel to the New World to study on a broader scale the 'relationships between the past and the present'. Besides, he also wanted to collect and describe specimens that could be added to his 'Theatre of Nature'. Correspondence, meetings and discussions with Agassiz and Lyell inspired his will to travel and explore.

In January 1863 Capellini received an invitation from his French friend Professor Jules Marcou (1824–1898) (who had moved to Cambridge, Massachusetts, USA, to work with Agassiz) to join him on an expedition along the Missouri River in Iowa and Nebraska. After almost 7 months of planning, Capellini left Bologna. He was to travel via Liverpool, but en route he stopped first in Paris, where he received letters of introduction and advice to extend his journey to Canada from Baron De-Verneuil. In London he had arranged to see the fossil of *Archaeopteryx lithographica* recovered from the Jurassic limestone of Pappenheim. In his notes Capellini expressed his personal interest in this unique specimen suggesting that:

> ... the fossil – whose reptilian and bird characters are equal – reveals us one of those transitional terms that Palaeontology will allow us to discover, many of which will be even more atypical and attractive.

On 8 August 1863, Capellini sailed for the New World: his travel took him first to eastern Canada where, after a short stop in Terranova, he acquired a collection of molluscs in Halifax (Nova Scotia). From there he moved on to Boston where his friend Agassiz, one of the most active supporters of his expedition to North America, not only hosted him in his home but also provided a storage place for the samples collected by Capellini during his visit to North America. Agassiz also offered to pay for their transportation from Boston to New York at the end of his journey. During his short stay in Boston, Agassiz showed Capellini his zoological laboratory, named *The Aquarium*

(Fig. 2), and the Museum of Comparative Zoology at Harvard College.

Capellini left Boston to start a long continental journey across Canada and the United States with main stops in Quebec City, Montreal, Niagara, Detroit, Chicago, Burlington, Nebraska, Omaha City, Sioux City, New York, Albany, St Louis, Philadelphia, Washington, Pittsburgh and Schoharie. His tireless search for new material to study and discuss with colleagues led him to meet important scientists who would strongly influence his life and career. Among others, James Hall (1811–1898), John Strong Newberry (1822–1892) and Sir John William Dawson (1820–1899) would, together with Capellini, become members of the Founding Commettee of the International Geological Congress. It is also important to note that these and many other 'old friends' and colleagues of Capellini not only allowed him to visit and study in detail the collections in their care, but also were pleased to contribute material from their palaeontological, geological and natural history collections to his future museum.

From his notes and meticulous illustrations recorded in several diaries, it emerges that Capellini had an enthusiastic approach to all aspects of Nature. He collected and described extinct and extant birds, mammals, reptiles, fish and plants, and recorded hundreds of geological sections and rock samples. Interestingly, Capellini was also a passionate anthropologist and large sections of his diaries on the North American expedition were devoted to detailed descriptions of the Omaha, Sioux and Ponka tribes. During his stay in the Black Bird Hills of Nebraska, he became a friend of the Omaha Chieftain Ne-hi-ga-kuh, and was introduced to the traditions, lifestyle and history of his tribe. As always, Capellini recorded the happenings of the everyday life of the natives, together with their history and the economics, social science and social interactions among Native Americans, which are now of great value to historians.

In November 1863, after 5 months and more than 7000 km of journeying across North America (all accomplished despite the ongoing civil war), Capellini had gained knowledge that was the privilege of very few of his contemporaries.

Capellini the teacher and curator

After his return to the University in Bologna, Professor Capellini set out to impart this knowledge to his students, colleagues and a more wide-ranging audience. First of all, Capellini worked on a radical, and extraordinarily novel, reorganization of his classes. The first part of the course, 25 lectures, was dedicated to Geology, with an overall introduction to geomorphology, stratigraphy, and the major sedimentary, igneous and metamorphic rocks; the subsequent component consisting of 12 lectures, concerned with stratigraphic concepts, and a comprehensive introduction to Palaeontology, and the 'stratigraphic characters that can be inferred by fossils' (Fig. 3). The final 17 lectures (of a total of 50 lectures) were entirely dedicated to 'Historical Geology' or 'Geological Chronology'. Each lecture was organized in order to elucidate a specific period of Earth history (such as Cambrian, Silurian, Jurassic, etc.), with the essential support of the large amount of geological and palaeontological data and specimens he had collected on his travels. For his courses Capellini prepared detailed notes from his studies in Italy, Europe and North America, with figures commissioned from professional illustrators (Fig. 4); he also made great use of the remarkable number of specimens housed in the museum in Bologna, which had reached a total of half a million under his supervision.

His new teaching methods had the specific aim of encouraging a scientific approach based on the association of fossils and rocks, this allowing Capellini to introduce and promote the two principles of Evolution and Actualism.

Besides teaching, Capellini laid the groundwork for a second 'revolution' within the academic system in Bologna and Italy at large. The revolution was based on a new approach to museum collections and exhibitions. First of all, albeit a logical consequence to Capellini's association with the spread of Darwinian theories across Europe, he set about the reorganization of the incomparable collections of the Natural History Museum in Bologna. As with his university courses, the collections were split between zoology, mineralogy, geology and palaeontology. In addition, his desire to relate theory with material evidence induced Capellini to continually add to the collections in the museum in Bologna with magnificent specimens from all over the world.

Apart from a multitude of fossil plants, invertebrates and vertebrates (including terrestrial and marine reptiles, fish, birds, whales, sirenids, elephants and bears), he acquired primates, including hominids, that could better document the relationships between extinct and extant organisms. Significantly, primates had not been placed on exhibition in any Italian museum until Capellini expressed his support for Darwin's theories on evolution. After 1871, when Capellini hosted the *Fifth International Congress on Prehistoric Anthropology and Archaeology* in Bologna, the exhibition of hominid specimens became the norm in museum exhibits. For the museum in Bologna, Capellini acquired casts of *Oreopithecus bambolii* (Miocene, Mt Bamboli, Italy), *Dryopithecus fontani* (Miocene, Sansan, France) and *Mesopithecus pentelici* (upper

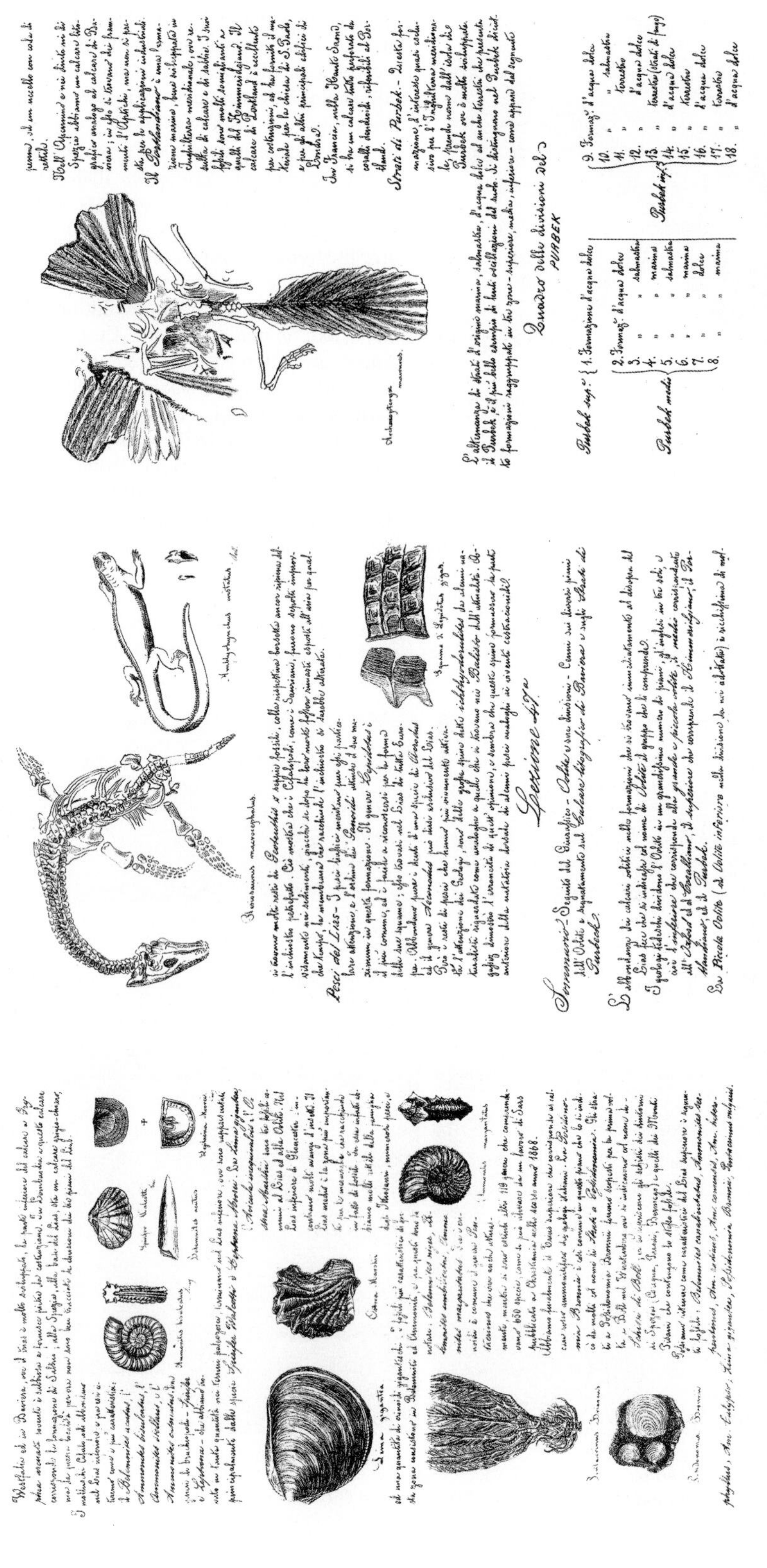

Fig. 3. Notes written by Giovanni Capellini for his 1868–1869 course. In these lectures on Jurassic deposits, Capellini discussed strata and the most significant fossils (including dinosaurs) known from several coeval European localities, thus introducing a palaeobiogeographical approach to his students.

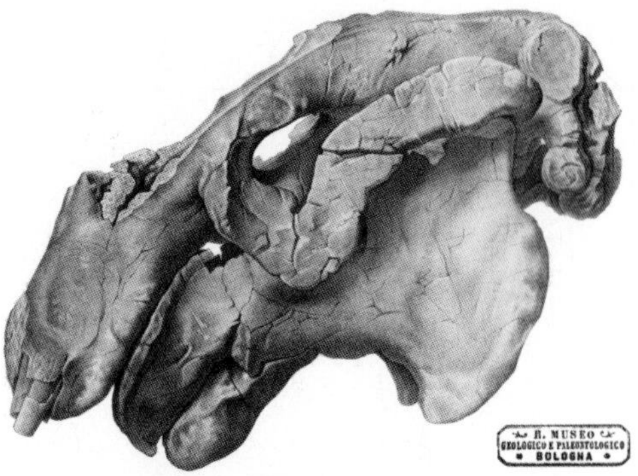

Fig. 4. Freehand illustration of the exquisitely preserved skull of *Felsinotherium forestii* (now subjective synonym of *Metaxytherium subapenninum*) described by Capellini in 1871.

Miocene, Pikermi, Greece). He also managed to acquire, for the main vertebrate hall in the museum, a complete skeleton of *Scelidotherium capellinii* and a giant *Glyptodon* from Argentina. This was not by chance: as these creatures were reported by Charles Darwin himself during his first visit to Patagonia on board the *Beagle*. Placed in the museum they served as obvious reminders to colleagues still sceptical or adverse to the Darwinian principles of evolution (Fig. 5).

Capellini also expressed a particular interest in another group of vertebrates that was creating a real revolution among geologists and naturalists: dinosaurs. He was the first person in Italy to recognize the tremendous potential of dinosaurs and other extinct reptiles to support and promote the most important principles of evolution. His highly respected reputation among European and North American scientists ensured that the museum acquired a variety of specimens, photographs, illustrations and models. His scientific standing also came into play in 1877 when the 38 skeletons of *Iguanodon* were recovered from a coal mine in Bernissart (Belgium). Capellini was well known to the Belgians and immediately started to negotiate with Luis De Pauw (the collection manager of the Museum in Brussels) an agreement to display original specimens and casts of the new dinosaur in Bologna. Thanks to his position and persistence over the years the permanent exhibitions in the

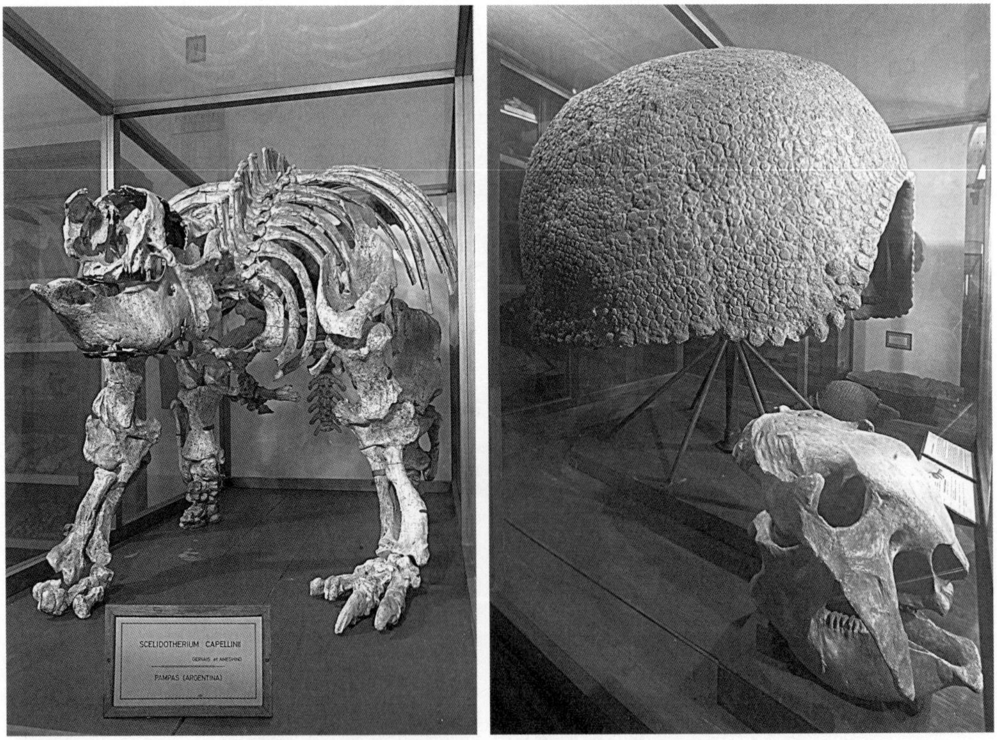

Fig. 5. The giant *Scelidotherium capellinii* (left) and *Glyptodon* (right) from the Pliocene–Pleistocene deposits of Patagonia were donated by Florentino Ameghino (1854–1911) to Giovanni Capellini for his permanent exhibition in the museum.

museum in Bologna were enriched with magnificent specimens, including the following list of saurians.

1. **Dinosaurs:**
   Compsognathus longipes (Kelheim, Germany – replica)
   Megalosaurus (replica of Crystal Palace dinosaur sculpture)
   Tyrannosaurus rex (pictures and plates of the restoration made by H. F. Osborne for the American Museum of Natural History)
   Allosaurus fragilis (pictures and plates of the restoration made by H. F. Osborne for the American Museum of Natural History)
   Apatosaurus excelsus (pictures and plates of the restoration made by H. F. Osborne for the American Museum of Natural History)
   Diplodocus carnegiei (Como Bluff, Wyoming, USA – replica)
   Iguanodon bernissartensis (Bernissart, Belgium – photographs, plates, low relief)
   Iguanodon (replica of Crystal Palace dinosaur sculpture).

2. **Marine reptiles:**
   Pliosaurus brachydeirus (Wiltshire, UK – replicas)
   Plesiosaurus latispinus (Dampicourt, France – replicas)
   Plesiosaurus neocomiensis (Sainte Croix, France – replica)
   Plesiosaurus (replica of Crystal Palace dinosaur sculpture)
   Ichthyosaurus intermedius (Dorset, UK – replica)
   Ichthyosaurus tenuirostris (Olzmaden, Germany – replica)
   Ichthyosaurus acutirostris (Olzmaden, Germany – replica)
   Ichtyosaurus (replica of Crystal Palace dinosaur sculpture)
   Stenopterygius quadriscissus (Olzmaden, Germany – replicas)
   Mosasaurus missouriensis (Nebraska, USA – replica).

3. **Pterosaurs:**
   Pterodactylus longirostris (Solnhofen, Germany – replica)
   Rhamphorhynchus munsteri (Solnhofen, Eichstatt, Germany – replicas).

Capellini's international reputation and personal skills in the management of meetings and the scientific committees was recognized as early as 1861, when he organized the 43rd session of the Sociéte Suisse des Sciences Naturelles. In 1865 he became the founder of the International Congress of Anthropology and pre-Historical Archaeology that he personally hosted in Bologna in 1871.

Capellini and the world of geology

In 1874 he was one of the first to propose an International Congress on Geology, which actually came about in 1878 and took place in Paris (Ellenberger 1978; Vai 2003). Finally, in 1881, Capellini's work received international recognition during the Second International Geological Congress hosted in the renewed halls of the museum (Fig. 6). The second IGC (Vai 2004*a*), as proposed by Thomas Sterry Hunt (1826–1892) (who was incidentally the first scientist to link climate change to the concentration of carbon dioxide in the atmosphere), was unanimously assigned to Bologna. Capellini being given the difficult task of promoting the cause for a common terminology in geology. The meeting attracted more than 200 participants from 22 countries outside Italy. They were welcomed by Giovanni Capellini, as chairman of the Congress.

By 1888, when Bologna celebrated the eighth centennial of its university, the museum boasted the largest geological and palaeontological collections in Europe, and the fact that it occupied an eminent position in scientific, academic and cultural leadership. On this occasion Capellini invited a delegation from the National Academy of Sciences (America) under O. C. Marsh (President) to attend. Marsh was delighted to receive the invitation from such 'a distinguished colleague', and personally prepared and shipped to Italy several charts showing various restorations of extinct animals, including dinosaurs with the note:

> ... designed to be framed, and exhibited in the museum, lecture room, or laboratory of your institution.

At the turn of the century, after more than 40 years of travels and the acquisition of materials, Capellini was proud to be director of the Museum of Geology and Palaeontology (that now bears his name) that housed extraordinary specimens from all over the world, including various species of dinosaurs.

His personal efforts culminated in the exhibition in 1909 of the complete skeleton of *Diplodocus carnegiei* donated by Andrew Carnegie himself, in the main hall of the museum in Bologna in 1909. The magnificent plaster cast arrived in Italy shortly after other copies had enriched the collections of London (1905), Berlin and Paris (1908). The gift of the cast elevated Bologna to the rank of a major

Fig. 6. Delegate group photograph taken during the Second International Geological Congress hosted in Bologna in 1881. Giovanni Capellini, convener of the congress is seated sixth from the left in the front row.

European capital city. The choice of Bologna, instead of Rome or Milan, was in recognition of the importance of Capellini's work, and his influence on the education of new generations through a change in teaching methods and a revolution in the management and display of museum collections and galleries. Thanks to the well-established links with many European and North American institutions, Capellini and his ideas became a point of reference within the scientific elite: today, *c.* 30 000 of Capellini's letters clearly indicate how extensive his public relations were. Furthermore, through his personal dedication to a holistic understanding of the natural sciences he gained the respect and friendship of several European kings and queens, including the Italian Royal Savoia family, Christian IX of Denmark, Oskar II of Sweden and Leopold of Belgium.

Apart from his skills as a manager and communicator, Giovanni Capellini was also an excellent researcher and scientist. During his life he published *c.* 250 papers in both Italian and European scientific journals, including studies on geology, palaeontology, anthropology and biogeography. His early geological publications include studies carried out near his home town, La Spezia, and thereafter near Bologna: his publications also list more than 70 geological papers based on innovative studies and the production of detailed maps. He also contributed to the first comprehensive geological map of Italy commissioned by King Vittorio Emanuele II in 1873, and was an active member of the International Commission for the Unification of Geological Nomenclature. It should also be noted that Capellini together with Quintino Sella (1827–1884) and Felice Giordano (1825–1892), on the occasion of the Second International Geological Congress (Bologna 1881), laid the ground rules for the establishment of the Italian Geological Society.

His most significant palaeontological works reflect his personal interest in mammals, particularly whales, dolphins and sirenids: between 1858 and 1878 Giovanni Capellini published 15 scientific papers on fossil whales, including a remarkable study in which he compares a specimen recovered near Taranto (southern Italy) with extinct and extant whales from northern Italy, Belgium and New Zealand. Later palaeontological studies include detailed descriptions of birds (*Aepyornis*), whales and killer whales (*Aulocetus sammarinensis*, *Balaena montalionis*, *Idiocetus guicciardinii*, *Pachyacanthus*, *Orca citoniensis*), sirenids (*Metaxytherium rovistai*, *Felsinotherium forestii*), elephants (*Mastodon avernensis*), bears (*Ursus spelaeus*) marine turtles (*Protosphargis veronensis*) and crocodiles (*Tomistoma calaritanus*, *Tomistoma lyceensis*). Furthermore, Capellini published two studies on the marine reptile *Ichthyosaurus campylodon* found in association with cicadee remains in the Cretaceous Argille Scagliose deposits of northern Italy (see the list of his publications available as Supplementary Publication SUP18417) that had previously been identified as an Eocene gavialid (*Gavialis mutinensis*). He also wrote two definitive papers on *Protosphargis veronensis* (Capellini) (see Supplementary Publication SUP18417) found in the Upper Cretaceous near Sant'Anna di Alfaedo in Valpolicella.

It is finally worth mentioning that Capellini also published several studies on fossil plants, notably the Cretaceous cycads (Bennettitaleans, *Raumeria masseiana*, *Cycadeoidea intermedia*, *C. etrusca*, *C. capelliniana* and *C. ferrettiana*).

Capellini furthered his personal interest in anthropology by participating in all the major international congresses dedicated to this topic, including those hosted in Copenhagen (1869), Stockholm (1875), Budapest (1876) and Paris (1905), and by publishing several studies depicting the everyday life of the first hominid from the Pliocene in northern Italy.

When he retired from his position as a professor in 1911, several of his students who were by then successful geologists and palaeontologists in their own right resolved to continue Capellini's work and to pass on his revolutionary ideas. His last relevant publications are dated 1915, when he was 82. The long list of countries that decorated Capellini with honours during his life include Italy, Greece, France, Portugal, Brazil, Sweden, Denmark and the Ottoman Empire.

Giovanni Capellini died 7 years later on 28 May 1922. He had possessed unquestionable academic and political skills. He served as a Senator in Rome from 4 December 1890 and was for 7 years a permanent member of the Royal Academy of Sciences. His vast knowledge of the natural sciences and his passion for his work made him one of the most influential scientists of his time. It was because of Capellini's work that Evolution and Actualism became widespread within the scientific academies in Italy; his dedication to innovative methods brought him fame and recognition. Capellini can be considered ahead of his time, and not only in his home country but worldwide. He led the way with the implementation of new methods dealing with the storage and curation of science materials, and with his devotion to the standardization of geological and palaeontological terminology. In so doing, Capellini taught his students the importance of biostratigraphical correlations based on standardized geological maps and fossil association. He was a pioneer in a discipline that is now seen as the basis of many research projects combining both geology and palaeontology: palaeobiogeography.

Conclusions

This paper pays homage to the life of Giovanni Capellini and his dedication to the fascinating disciplines of geology and palaeontology. To many he had almost saintly qualities, but it should be noted that to many contemporaries he was seen to be overconfident, overambitious, arrogant and a genius (*outside the family*) (Corsi 2003). Although he published a large number of scientific publications, the deepest insights into his life and ideas come from specific sentences written in personal diaries, notes and epistolary correspondence. A large collection of his handwritten notes are located in the archives of the Museum of Geology and Palaeontology Giovanni Capellini in Bologna, and in the library of the Department of Earth and Geoenvironmental Sciences and the Archiginnasio Library in Bologna. Capellini's diaries related to his 1863 journey in North America were published by Vai (2004*b*).

Over 30 000 handwritten letters are also stored in various archives, with letters between Capellini and Sir Archibald Geike (1835–1924) between 1886 and 1904 stored in The Edinburgh University Library Special Collections Division. Readers can also find important information on Capellini's life, professional career and international travels in the publications listed in the Supplementary Publication.

I am greatly indebted to Dr G. Ciarmadori and Dr M. Tolomelli for innumerable enlightening discussions at every stage of this work. Many thanks are also extended to Professor G. Battista Vai, Dr C. Sarti, Dr F. Gerali, Professor R. Moody and Dr E. Buffetaut, whose help greatly improved this manuscript.

References

Ellenberger, F. 1978. *The First International Geological Congress (1878)*. Available online at: http://www.iugs.org/PDF/1st%20IGC.pdf.

Corsi, P. 2003. The Italian Geological Survey: the early history of a divided community. *In*: Vai, G. B. & Cavazza, W. (eds) *Four Centuries of the Word 'Geology': Ulisse Aldrovandi 1603 in Bologna*. Minerva Edizioni, Bologna, 255–279. Available on-line at: pcorsi@history.ox.ac.uk.

Vai, G. B. 2003. Giovanni Capellini and the origin of the International Geological Congress. *In*: Vai, G. B. & Cavazza, W. (eds) *Four Centuries of the Word 'Geology': Ulisse Aldrovandi 1603 in Bologna*. Minerva Edizioni, Bologna, 301–315.

Vai, G. B. 2004*a*. The Second International Geological Congress, Bologna, 1881. *Episodes*, **27**, 13–20.

Vai, G. B. 2004*b*. *Giovanni Capellini: Ricordi di un Viaggio Scientifico nell'America Settentrionale nel 1863. [Giovanni Capellini: Memories of a Scientific Journey in North America in 1863.]* Arnaldo Forni Editore, Bologna.

Alan Jack Charig (1927–1997): an overview of his academic accomplishments and role in the world of fossil reptile research

RICHARD T. J. MOODY[1]* & DARREN NAISH[2]

[1]*School of Geology and Earth Sciences, Kingston University, Penrhyn Road, Kingston Surrey KT1 2EE, UK*

[2]*School of Earth & Environmental Sciences, Burnaby Building, Burnaby Road, University of Portsmouth, Portsmouth PO1 3QL, UK*

**Corresponding author (e-mail: rtj.moody@virgin.net)*

Abstract: Alan Jack Charig was Curator of Fossil Amphibians, Reptiles and Birds at the British Museum (Natural History) from 1961 to 1987. We here review his academic accomplishments and the impact of his work within vertebrate palaeontology. His position gave him considerable influence in the discussion of emerging theories and in how vertebrate palaeontology was portrayed to the public. His main areas of scientific interest included biogeography and faunal provinces, the evolution of an erect gait in archosaurs, the systematics and diversity of Triassic proterosuchians, erythrosuchians and their relatives, and the origin of dinosaurs. Besides Triassic archosaurs, ornithischian, theropod and sauropodomorph dinosaurs, he published on gastropods, amphisbaenians and plesiosaurs. While he did produce some lasting contributions to the literature, it is telling that he failed to publish the specimen-based analyses he apparently planned to, despite citations of 'in press' manuscripts. Between the 1970s and 1990s Alan opposed or offered alternatives to many emerging theories and schools of thought. He is best described as 'conservative' in terms of his views on palaeontological controversies and his opinions would not conform with those favoured by the majority of palaeontologists today. He was highly critical of the concept of dinosaur monophyly, the dinosaurian origin of birds, of the division of archosaurs into a crocodilian and bird-dinosaur clade, and of cladistics. Several of his papers are ICZN (International Commission on Zoological Nomenclature) submissions, published in order to clear up taxonomic problems, and they served to bring nomenclatural stability. Contradicting views exist of him as a scientist and a popularist. He has, not without contradiction, been described as intellectually arrogant, most clubbable, humorous, charming, an academic snob, political and meticulous. His lasting fame, however, is that very few of us live to be referred to as the 'Carl Sagan of the BBC' or have the good fortune to describe a dinosaur as important as *Baryonyx*.

Alan Jack Charig (1927–1997) (Fig. 1) was born of Jewish–Ukranian parents. He was educated at Haberdashers' Aske's Boys' School (Cox 1997) and was considered academically outstanding even in his earliest days of secondary education (R.C.H. Old Haberdashers Obits). Prior to joining the then British Museum (Natural History) he studied zoology at Emanuel College Cambridge and interrupted his degree to serve his National Service; first in The Royal Armoured Corps and then as an interpreter in the Russian Section of the British Army of Occupation in Germany. On leaving the forces he returned to Cambridge to complete his degree in Natural Sciences and to study for a PhD under Rex Parrington (1905–1981). Alan and A. W. ('Fuzz') Crompton were the first two students to work with Parrington.

Alan's 1956 PhD thesis was titled 'New Triassic archosaurs from Tanganyika, including *Mandasuchus* and *Teleocrater*'. He subsequently mentioned these taxa – particularly *Mandasuchus* – in many of his publications and an 'in press' manuscript supposedly describing them (titled 'Preliminary note on the archosaurs in the Manda Formation (Middle Trias) of Tanzania', and cited as if appearing in a 1967 edition of *Palaeontology*) was cited in Appleby *et al.* (1967), the Reptilia chapter of the Geological Society of London's (GSL's) compendium *The Fossil Record* (Fig. 2). According to the latter article, *Mandasuchus* was a member of Prestosuchidae, a group noted by Appleby *et al.* (1967, p. 46) as being 'probably ancestral to sauropodomorphs'. We discuss the possible significance of this proposed phylogenetic significance later on. *Teleocrater* was regarded as representing a new 'family', Teleocrateridae Charig, 1967 (Appleby *et al.* 1967, p. 46). Another taxon planned for the 1967 *Palaeontology* article – *Nyasasaurus cromptoni* – was also mentioned in Appleby *et al.* (1967). Although classified as a thecodontosaurid

From: Moody, R. T. J., Buffetaut, E., Naish, D. & Martill, D. M. (eds) *Dinosaurs and Other Extinct Saurians: A Historical Perspective*. Geological Society, London, Special Publications, **343**, 89–109.
DOI: 10.1144/SP343.6 0305-8719/10/$15.00

Fig. 1. Alan J. Charig in 1977. Photograph © NHM.

sauropodomorph, Appleby *et al.* (1967, p. 712) noted that it 'might still be a prestosuchid pseudosuchian'. This again highlighted the fact that Alan regarded 'pseudosuchian thecodonts' and sauropodomorph dinosaurs as close allies. Finally, Appleby *et al.* (1967) included mention of another Manda Formation taxon, *Hypselorhachis mirabilis*: this was attributed to 'Charig 1966' (presumably another reference to the planned 1967 *Palaeontology* article) and suggested to be ancestral to Spinosauridae. Subsequent authors identified *Hypselorhachis* as a close relative of *Ctenosauriscus koeneni*, a poorly known archosaur with tall neural spines (Krebs 1969, 1976; Nesbitt 2003, 2005). The same 'Preliminary note' article was also cited as 'in press' in Charig & Reig (1970). Alas, Alan never did publish proper descriptions of these taxa and they have persisted in the literature as *nomina nuda*. As we will see, Alan was to claim on numerous additional occasions that his descriptive work had progressed further than it actually had.

After receiving his doctorate, Alan briefly lectured in zoology at Kumasi College (then Gold Coast, now Ghana) in 1955 and 1956. During this time he visited Timbuctu, Mali, in a Morris Minor, and later told of the time he saw lions in the Sahara.

In 1957 Alan joined the staff of the Palaeontology Department of the British Museum (Natural History) and initially worked in the Mollusca Section, publishing a paper on the gastropod *Thatcheria* in 1963, well after he had been transferred to Fossil Reptiles in 1961. It would appear, somewhat strangely, that the museum hierarchy had a policy of placing people outside their own speciality, as Bill Swinton (1900–1994) (who preceded Alan) initially worked on mammals before transferring to Fossil Amphibians, Reptiles and Birds. Swinton worked at the British Museum

Fig. 2. Maurice Wilson's reconstruction of the Manda Formation archosaur *Mandasuchus*, as published in the Brooke Bond *Prehistoric Animals* tea cards set.

(Natural History) from 1934 to 1961 and, like Alan, was skilled at portraying the wonders of dinosaurs to a dedicated audience. Similarly, Swinton's extracurricular activities were frowned upon by a conservative management. By the time Swinton had left for Canada and Alan had become Curator of Fossil Amphibians, Reptiles and Birds, Cyril Walker had also been moved to the section (via the library) to work alongside Barney Newman as technical officer.

During the quarter century he worked as Curator of Amphibians, Reptiles and Birds at the museum, Alan became the 'face' of palaeontology in the UK and was responsible for the popularization of dinosaurs throughout the 1970s. Alan was married in 1955 to Marianne Jacoby, his soul mate. He often said that she played a major role in his success, and he was very proud of their two sons and daughter. When he retired from the museum in 1987, Marianne was very poorly; she died later that same year.

His contributions to his science

In a career spanning four decades, Alan published on dinosaur origins and evolution, on the changing fortunes of Triassic tetrapod groups, and on the systematics and classification of non-dinosaurian archosaurs, the 'thecodonts'. He was also involved in descriptive work on exciting new specimens and taxa, some of which were the subject of great debate and of popular interest. He published on evolution, the fossil record and on the philosophy of cladistics. While several of his descriptive papers continue to be widely cited, many of his theoretical proposals have not stood the test of time.

One of Alan's earliest published works was his 1962 description of the early ornithischian *Heterodontosaurus tucki* from South Africa, published with Crompton (Crompton & Charig 1962). Fragments of similar dinosaurs had been known since 1911 (it is now known that both *Geranosaurus* Broom 1911 and *Lycorhinus* Haughton 1924 represent close relatives of *Heterodontosaurus*), but the discovery of a near-complete skull and lower jaw showed that these dinosaurs were remarkable heterodont ornithischians with prominent caniniform fangs. Alan was involved in work on the enigmatic heterodontosaurids later on in his career (Charig & Crompton 1974; Santa Luca *et al.* 1976), but a planned monographic collaboration on *Heterodontosaurus* with Crompton was never completed. 1962 also saw the publication of a brief article, co-authored with Barney Newman, on dinosaur tracks from the Purbeck Limestone (Charig & Newman 1962).

In 1963 Alan published a large study of the Indo-pacific gastropods belonging to the genus *Thatcheria* Angas 1877 (this is an extant taxon but fossil species from the Miocene and Pliocene have been referred to it by various authors). Therein he named the new species *T. vitiensis* from the Pliocene of Fiji (Charig 1963).

Together with John Attridge and Crompton, Alan published 'On the origin of the sauropods and the classification of the Saurischia' in 1965 (Charig *et al.* 1965). The genesis of this paper was a presentation that Alan had given during the Palaeontological Association meeting at Bristol in 1961, although subsequent discoveries had caused him to modify several of his original conclusions. Incorporating a review of ideas on sauropodomorph evolution and classification, the paper is of historical interest to students of the Dinosauria in including the first mention of the 'Blikana dinosaur', later named *Blikanasaurus cromptoni* by Galton & Van Heerden (1985). Charig *et al.* (1965) stated that this dinosaur was described 'in press' by Crompton & Wapenaar, but, again, this manuscript never saw publication. Some of the contentions made in this paper repeated those made later on in Alan's work: it was argued, for example, that 'the anatomy of sauropods affords no suggestion that their ancestors were bipedal; the arguments generally advanced for the fundamentally bipedal nature of the archosaur stock will not bear critical examination' (Charig *et al.* 1965, p. 204). While it was admitted by Charig *et al.* (1965) that various 'prosauropod' lineages were at least partially bipedal, it was argued that such forms were divergent offshoots from a lineage of 'quadrupedal creatures which lay on or near the main sauropodomorph line' (Charig *et al.* 1965, p. 205), the evidence for which was wanting due to preservational bias. Phylogenetic arguments that invoke the existence of hypothetical taxa are, to put it mildly, suspect. The phylogenetic hypothesis that Charig *et al.* (1965) objected to (that bipedal sauropodomorphs were ancestral to the quadrupedal sauropods, and that the earliest sauropodomorphs inherited their bipedality from older bipedal saurischians and bipedal 'pseudosuchians') was later supported by the discovery of the bipedal non-dinosaurian archosaurs *Lagosuchus* and *Lagerpeton* (Romer 1971, 1972; Bonaparte 1975). In contrast, the hypothesis of persistent quadrupedality in the sauropodomorph lineage did not win much support: as discussed below, it seems that the Tanzanian archosaurs described by Alan in his PhD thesis were integral to his ideas about persistent quadrupedality in early dinosaurs. As new discoveries eroded the potential significance of his discoveries, it is possible that Alan lost momentum in his plans to describe them.

By 1970 Alan had (together with Osvaldo A. Reig of the Universidad Central de Venezuela) published his first academic contribution on Triassic non-dinosaurian archosaurs: a review of the proterosuchians (Charig & Reig 1970). A lengthy, thorough and well-illustrated paper, it included a huge amount of information and concluded that all members of this group (which are not presently regarded as forming a clade) could be grouped into two 'families': Proterosuchidae and Erythrosuchidae. Another review of proterosuchians appeared in 1976 (see later).

In 1971 Alan published 'Faunal provinces on land', a review concentrating on the distribution of Permo-Triassic reptiles and on what this distribution might mean (Charig 1971). Mostly overlooked are his suggestions that *Tyrannosaurus* and *Tarbosaurus* might be congeneric (a concept that would be revisited by many palaeontologists, and one that remains the source of disagreement today), and his statement that Bakker's theory about endothermy in dinosaurs and pterosaurs is 'certainly worthy of consideration' (Charig 1971, p. 126). Also in 1971, Alan worked with John Horell in producing a brief report on the Fletton plesiosaur (Charig & Horell 1971). Excavated in 1970 and presented to the British Museum (Natural History) by Sir Ronald Stewart of the London Brick Company, this was a specimen of *Cryptoclidus eurymerus* described by Charig & Horell (1971, p. 39) as 'probably the best plesiosaur skeleton discovered since the days of the Leeds Collection'. Given this claim, it is fitting that the specimen was visited *in situ* by delegates from the Symposium of Vertebrate Palaeontology and Comparative Anatomy, held in 1970 in Cambridge, including A. S. Romer and his wife, and F. R. Parrington. The Fletton plesiosaur (NHMUK R8621) did become an important specimen of *Cryptoclidus eurymerus*, being both figured and discussed in Brown's (1981) comprehensive monograph on the taxon. Stewart would later be honoured by Alan in the naming of a new Jurassic sauropod.

Alan became well known for promoting the view that dinosaurs differed from other archosaurs by way of their erect-legged gait and in 1972 published an influential article on this subject titled 'The evolution of the archosaur pelvis and hind-limb: an explanation in functional terms' (Charig 1972). This was Alan's contribution to Parrington's festschrift volume. Romer (1956) had stated that thecodonts displayed a tendency towards being bipedal and other workers (e.g. Colbert 1962) assumed that bipedality had arisen early on in the history of the Archosauria, with quadrupedal forms being secondarily quadrupedal. As discussed above in connection with Charig *et al.* (1965), Alan argued against this and stated in several publications that no such trend was apparent. He also argued that crocodilians and *Mandasuchus*-like archosaurs exhibited a 'semi-improved' stance that was intermediate between the sprawling stance of typical reptiles and the 'fully improved' stance of dinosaurs. Based on what was known about Triassic archosaurs, it was assumed that all early archosaurs had complex, crocodile-like ankles, but if this was correct, and if dinosaurs had descended from such forms, then dinosaur ancestors (with simple, hinge-like ankles) had undergone simplification of the ankle joint. Krebs (1965) argued for this in his description of the rauisuchian *Ticinosuchus* (thought at the time to be close to the ancestry of dinosaurs). The alternative possibility was that dinosaurs had not descended from forms with crocodile-like ankles at all. Alan remained non-committal on this debate (indeed, he can be charged with remaining non-committal on several areas of disagreement!) but saw the merits of a theoretical dinosaur ancestor that lacked a crocodile-like ankle (Charig 1972, p. 152). Non-dinosaurian archosaurs with simple, hinge-like ankles were later described (Romer 1971, 1972; Bonaparte 1975): rather than being primitive for archosaurs as a whole, it now seems that the crocodile-style ankle is unique to the clade that includes crocodilians and their relatives. Indeed, Alan's view that *Mandasuchus*-like archosaurs with a 'semi-improved' stance might be ancestral to 'fully improved' dinosaurs could only be maintained if there was a close phylogenetic affinity between these groups, and as evidence accrued it became clear to most workers that this was not the case.

In 1967 and 1969 Björn Kurtén proposed that the Cenozoic radiation of mammalian 'Orders' was driven by continental fragmentation, and that the large number of mammalian 'Orders' was directly related to the fact that, by the Cenozoic, there were several continents. In contrast, Kurtén proposed that the lower number of continents present during the Mesozoic has resulted in a lower number of reptilian 'Orders'. Alan took issue with this hypothesis, arguing in 1973 that 'ordinal variety' is not necessarily a reliable indicator of adaptive radiation (Charig 1973). Perhaps ironically (given Alan's objections to cladistics), arguments over the usefulness of Linnaean categories like 'Orders' demonstrate the danger of assuming that such ranks are real. As reported in their 1974 paper on heterodontosaurids (Charig & Crompton 1974), Alan and Fuzz Crompton had by now made substantial progress on a detailed description of the skull of *Heterodontosaurus tucki*, citing 'The Triassic ornithischian *Heterodontosaurus tucki*: skull, dentition and systematic relationships' as 'in press' for *Annals of the South African Museum*, and writing 'The *Heterodontosaurus* holotype has now been completely developed and the detailed description of its skull (Charig & Crompton, in press) is likely to make it the most completely described dinosaur skull in existence' (Charig & Crompton 1974, p. 170). The paper never appeared and, again, it was not the last time that Alan would claim to have completed a major work that, in reality, was not as ready to appear as he had stated. During the late 1970s and possibly earlier, Alan planned to redescribe the type material of the Lower Jurassic pterosaur *Dimorphodon macronyx*, originally described by Buckland in the 1830s and monographed by Owen in 1870 (see Martill 2010). Kevin Padian discussed these plans with Alan when visiting the BM(NH) in 1978 and 1979; Alan planned to have the material acid prepared and hoped to work on it in his retirement (K. Padian pers. comm. 2009). These plans never came to fruition.

In 1974 Robert Bakker and Peter Galton published the claim that Dinosauria was a monophyletic group deserving of 'Class' status (Bakker & Galton 1974). They argued that Triassic dinosaurs exhibited a number of features not seen in other archosaurs, hence indicating descent from a single common ancestor. While Dinosauria had been regarded as a natural group during the nineteenth century and by several workers of the early twentieth century, this view was generally regarded as incorrect by the 1960s. 'Dinosaur' was, instead, a term used for two or even three distinct archosaur groups that had descended from different 'thecodontian' ancestors. Alan disagreed with Bakker & Galton's new arguments for monophyly, arguing that the characters supposedly shared by dinosaurs and not present in other archosaurs were either non-existent or erroneous, and that the two major dinosaur groups (saurischians and ornithischians) were more different than Bakker and Galton had admitted (Charig 1976*a*). His main conclusion seemed to be, however, that Bakker and Galton's suggestion of 'Class' status for Dinosauria was premature and would prove impractical for a community used to a 'Class Aves' (Aves would, of course, be included in 'Class Dinosauria' if Bakker and Galton were correct). This is a rather irrelevant criticism in that it was surely the least important implication of Bakker and Galton's argument, and Alan's objections to the proposed monophyly of Dinosauria appear unsatisfactory to modern eyes. Alan also provided a detailed discussion of Bakker's idea that predator–prey ratios might be informative in determining physiology, but concluded that 'dinosaurs may well have been at least partly endothermic' (Charig 1976*a*, p. 96). He returned to these subjects later on. Incidentally, Alan was able to begin preparation of his response to Bakker & Galton (1974) long before its publication because he had obtained a copy of the article about a year beforehand. This explained how Alfred Romer, who had died in 1973, had been able to comment on an article that was itself critiquing another not published until 1974 (Charig 1976*a*, p. 102).

Also in 1976, Alan published with Hans-Dieter Sues the Proterosuchia volume of the *Handbuch der Paläoherpetologie* series (the same volume included Alan's historical review of Thecodontia: Charig 1976*b*). An introductory note inserted by the publisher explains how Hans-Dieter and Alan were both given the Proterosuchia section to do, and that 'this confusion led to the unfortunate situation, that neither author knew that the other was preparing an independent contribution' (Charig & Sues 1976, p. 11). On learning that their work was duplicated, they agreed to share authorship, but with Alan's more complete text being the version that saw publication. In addition to providing a diagnosis for each included taxon, this review also provides such data as holotype numbers and precise stratigraphic information. It might be assumed that this level of detail is provided across a series of volumes entitled *Handbuch der Paläoherpetologie*, as indeed it should be, but in fact some of the other contributions in the series (e.g. Steel 1969, 1970) are extremely superficial. 1976 also saw the publication (with Albert P. Santa Luca and Fuzz Crompton) of the first brief report on a new complete *Heterodontosaurus tucki* specimen (Santa Luca *et al.* 1976).

Alan's work on dinosaurs continued in 1980 when his contribution to the Colbert festschrift volume was published. Therein, he described a distinctive 'sled-shaped' sauropod chevron from the Wessex Formation of the Isle of Wight (Charig 1980*a*). Thought at the time to belong to a diplodocid (its identity has since been challenged (Upchurch 1998; Naish & Martill 2001) due to new ideas on the distribution of 'sled-shaped chevrons' within Sauropoda), it was suggested by Alan to provide biogeographical evidence linking the Lower Cretaceous dinosaur fauna of Britain with that of Upper Jurassic North America. Alan was highly critical of Peter Galton's suggestions that fossils from the Jurassic and Cretaceous of Europe and North America might provide evidence for biogeographical connections between these areas. Alan also used this paper to indulge in some required nomenclatural action, and showed that von Huene had erred in giving the name *Cetiosauriscus leedsii* to an Oxford Clay sauropod first described by Woodward (1905). Because Woodward's specimen was not the type specimen for the species, it required a new species name, so Alan named it *Cetiosauriscus stewarti* (Charig 1980*a*). The specific name honours Sir Ronald Stewart (see earlier).

Alan was of the opinion that the erect-legged gait of dinosaurs made them competitively superior to other Mesozoic terrestrial tetrapods, and that key anatomical innovations allowed dinosaurs to rise to success and to replace other archosaurs and synapsids as the dominant terrestrial animals of the Mesozoic (Charig 1980*b*). This view was popular at the time and was integral to Alan's work on dinosaur origins and success. Benton (1983) showed that the data did not support this view and that dinosaurs had not risen rapidly to success, but had instead remained rare and low in diversity until their competitors had been removed by mass extinction events: essentially, dinosaurs seemed to be 'victors by default'. The idea that dinosaurs were 'special' compared to other archosaurs was also to be challenged as it would eventually be shown that the erect gaits thought by Alan and colleagues to be unique to dinosaurs were more widespread among archosaurs. Again, Alan's cherished hypothesis about the evolution of 'semi-improved' and 'fully improved' archosaurs was under attack.

The 1980s saw some of Alan's most significant scientific publications, with both the discovery of the Lower Cretaceous English theropod *Baryonyx* and the famous forgery charge against *Archaeopteryx* occupying his research time. He continued to write about more philosophical issues, however, and in 1981 published 'Cladistics: a different point of view' in *Biologist* (Charig 1981). He followed this with a lengthy paper in 1982: 'Systematics in biology: a fundamental comparison of some major schools of thought', in which he argued that paraphyletic groups – while not permitted in Hennigian systematics – are practical, and hence should be retained (Charig 1982*a*). On cladistics, Alan sometimes sided in debate with the more idiosyncratic Beverly Halstead (1933–1992) and so drew the wrath of committed cladist Colin Patterson (1933–1998), a colleague at the BM(NH) who worked on fossil fish.

In 'Problems in dinosaur phylogeny: a reasoned approach to their attempted resolution', Alan drew attention to the limits of the information then available on early dinosaurs. He continued to argue that proposals of dinosaur monophyly were problematical, that good shared characters uniting dinosaurs to the exclusion of other archosaurs were weak and that more convincing ones would be needed to make a more robust case. He implied that all three major dinosaur groups might have separate origins, and he remained non-committal on avian origins (Charig 1982*b*). By now such views were very much behind the times, and Alan's complaints failed to win adherents. The hypotheses of dinosaur monophyly, of a division of Archosauria into a crocodilian clade and bird-dinosaur clade, and of the theropod ancestry of birds were already better supported than the rather vague alternative proposals, and became increasingly so in the years that followed. Indeed, what makes Alan particularly interesting is that he was among the last of the 'old guard'; in the face of substantial opposition, he tried to maintain the status quo of the pre-cladistic era.

In 1985 Alan published 'Analysis of the several problems associated with *Archaeopteryx*' in Hecht *et al.*'s *The Beginnings of Birds*. This was a cursory contribution, but included comments on how the term Aves should be limited and defined (Charig 1985). Ironically (given Alan's views on cladistics), his proposal that the name Aves be formally restricted to 'the clade that is demarcated from its antecedents by the appearance of the evolutionary novelty 'feathers'' (p. 26) has recently been noted as a phylogenetic apomorphy-based definition for Aves (Senter 2005). Alan's non-committal stance on bird origins seems peculiar (given that he was an archosaur specialist); in his various discussions of the subject he generally cited both non-dinosaurian and dinosaurian origin hypotheses as if they were equally worthy, and at times he even seemed hostile to the idea that birds might be derived theropods (e.g. Charig 1979, p. 140). Rather than holding a strong opinion on this subject himself, it seems that Alan was influenced by the fact that his colleagues (such as Alick Walker and John Ostrom) held divergent views. Again, Alan can perhaps be charged with trying to maintain the status quo. Alternatively, Alan's sense of fair play and gentlemanly behaviour may have seemed more important to him than resolving the debate, and his discussions of avian origins seem more concerned with the overarching philosophy than the raw palaeontological data.

A far more noteworthy contribution on *Archaeopteryx* was to appear in 1986 when Fred Hoyle and Chandra Wickramasinghe's claims that the London *Archaeopteryx* must be a fake demanded a response. Together with Frank Greenaway, Angela Milner, Cyril Walker and Peter Whybrow, Alan published a demonstration of the non-fraudulent nature of the London *Archaeopteryx* in *Science* (Charig *et al.* 1986). We discuss this episode further later.

Perhaps Alan's most significant contribution was his work, co-authored with Angela Milner, on a remarkable new theropod that had been discovered by amateur collector William Walker in 1983. Preliminary information on this animal had been presented at the Dinosaur Systematics Symposium, held at the Tyrrell Museum of Palaeontology in June 1986, and so surprising was the combination of features present in this new animal that there was apparently some discussion of the possibility that it might represent a late-surviving rauisuchian or an aberrant crocodilian rather than a theropod. Already, however, some workers (specifically P. Taquet) had begun to compare the Surrey dinosaur with *Spinosaurus* (Dodson 1987). Published in *Nature* in 1986, *Baryonyx walkeri* was hailed as an entirely new kind of theropod deserving of its own 'family', Baryonychidae (Charig & Milner 1986). The final monographic description of *Baryonyx* was published in *Bulletin of the Natural History Museum, Geology Series* (Charig & Milner 1997). Of all Alan's technical publications, this monograph is arguably the one that has stood the test of time, and it remains widely cited in the dinosaur literature.

Like so many scientists who specialize on dinosaurs, Alan sometimes published comments on the Cretaceous–Tertiary (K–T) boundary and its associated extinction event. In 1989 he published 'The Cretaceous–Tertiary boundary and the last of the dinosaurs' (Charig 1989). While the notion of a global cataclysm caused by a bolide impact (Alvarez *et al.* 1980) had become popular by this time, Alan's perspective might, again, be regarded as 'conservative' or 'traditional': he argued that stratigraphical correlations worldwide were not good enough for scientists to be confident that a synchronized mass global dieing had occurred, and he considered it plausible that non-avian dinosaurs in some regions had survived beyond the end of the Cretaceous. Some of Alan's thoughts on this issue had previously been announced at meetings: he mentioned (Charig 1989, p. 388) an 'unpublished paper' presented at the Lyell Meeting of the Geological Society of London, and a 1987 talk on the subject given at the Palaeontological Association meeting 'Catastrophes and the history of life'. In contrast to the majority of his colleagues, Alan sometimes drew attention to the minority opinion that non-avian dinosaurs might not have gone extinct at all, but that mystery animals such as the Congolese mokele-mbembe might be surviving dinosaurs; in Charig (1989, p. 392), he cited two pro-mokele-mbembe articles and mentioned the mokele-mbembe-hunting research expeditions led by Chicago University cryptozoologist and biochemist Roy Mackal. However, Alan was by no means sympathetic to these suggestions.

During the 1990s Alan's academic work focused on dinosaurs, although research on Triassic archosaurs and other reptiles continued in the background. The decade began with the publication of a substantially delayed paper, co-authored with Carl Gans, on two new fossil amphisbaenians ('worm lizards') collected from the Lower Miocene of Rusinga Island, Lake Victoria, Kenya (Charig & Gans 1990). These represented two new taxa, *Listromycter leakeyi* and *Lophocranion rusingense*, both of which had been collected by L. S. B. Leakey in 1947 and sent to the British Museum (Natural History) in 1950. With a skull estimated at 36 mm long when complete, *Listromycter leakeyi* remains the largest known amphisbaenian.

1990 also saw the appearance of Alan's paper (co-authored with Angela Milner) on the affinities of *Baryonyx walkeri*. Published within *Dinosaur Systematics: Approaches and Perspectives* (edited by Kenneth Carpenter and Philip Currie), Charig & Milner (1990) provided a critique of Gauthier's recently published phylogenetic analysis of theropods (Gauthier 1986), and responded to recent claims from Paul (1988) and Buffetaut (1989) that *Baryonyx* might be a spinosaurid. Buffetaut (1989) noted that *Baryonyx* and *Spinosaurus* both possessed long-rooted teeth that were subrounded in cross-section and emerged from circular (rather than rectangular) alveoli, a vertical expansion at the tip of the dentary, and enlarged third and fourth dentary teeth. Charig & Milner (1990, p. 133) concluded that the characters shared by the two taxa did 'suggest a phylogenetic relationship between them' and, hence, agreed with Buffetaut somewhat, but they felt that the differences, rather than the similarities, carried more weight. This phenetic approach may have been favoured by Alan because it emphasized the apparent uniqueness of *Baryonyx*, and the fact that any conclusions on the morphology of *Spinosaurus* were based on lost material (Stromer's original *Spinosaurus* specimens had been destroyed during World War II) may, in Alan's view, have weakened the case. Ultimately, however, suggestions of an affinity between *Baryonyx* and *Spinosaurus* were to prove correct.

Relatively little known is that Owen's holotype for the armoured ornithischian *Scelidosaurus* is not the quadrupedal animal represented by a near-complete skeleton (specimen NHMUK R1111), but a knee joint and other fragments now known to belong to a theropod, as had been established by Newman (1968) (see also Charig 1972, p. 139). In order to officially associate the generic name with the armoured ornithischian, Charig & Newman (1992) made NHMUK R1111 the neotype. Of incidental interest is that a full monograph on *Scelidosaurus* was noted at this time as being under preparation: in a comment similar to that made earlier about unpublished work on *Heterodontosaurus*, Charig & Newman (1992) wrote 'When the osteology of *Scelidosaurus* is eventually published it will be better known than that of almost any other dinosaur, and considerably better known than that of many extant reptiles' (pp. 281–282). Once again, Alan never completed his work on this taxon. In another act of nomenclatural tidying, Alan completed the work he had started in his 1980 sauropod paper by petitioning the ICZN to make the sauropod *Cetiosauriscus stewarti* the type species of *Cetiosauriscus* (Charig 1993*a*).

In response to the increasing number of cladograms depicting the evolutionary relationships of archosaurs (or archosauriforms) that were appearing during the 1980s and 1990s, Alan argued that there was little or, indeed, no evidence for progress, and that there seemed to be no indication of a consensus (Charig 1993*b*). Despite the flurry of new work produced by various authors, Alan argued that 'the recent analyses have told us **nothing** [emphasis in original] that we did not know thirty-five years ago' (Charig 1993*b*, p. 55). This rather pessimistic perspective stood in marked contrast to Benton's (1984) claim of a 'radical new consensus' and solicited a comprehensive response from Gower & Wilkinson (1996). While certain practices employed by some workers (e.g. the naming of groups whose phylogenetic reality remained doubtful) were, undeniably, worthy of the criticism that Alan heaped upon them, strong evidence for a 'current consensus' could, indeed, be found (Gower & Wilkinson 1996). One interpretation of Alan's response to this work is that it further undermined his proposal, discussed earlier, that *Mandasuchus*-like archosaurs with a 'semi-improved' stance were in some way ancestral to the 'fully improved' dinosaurs. While a new generation of workers was promoting the view that tree-based thinking and a quest for shared derived characters had begun to resolve archosaur phylogeny, Alan still seemed reluctant to change his views and appeared staunchly 'traditional'. Alan's 1993 paper on archosaur phylogeny was yet another in which he alluded to a manuscript that was never to appear: when discussing new phylogenetic work on ornithischians, he described how comparative work (presented at the Palaeontological Association meeting of 1987) had shown 'only one significant improvement over the phylogenetic tree given by Romer in 1956 in his *Osteology of the Reptiles*' (Charig 1993*b*, p. 45). The resulting manuscript, planned for *Palaeontology*, was titled 'A review of cladistic methods of phylogeny reconstruction and classification, as applied to the ornithischian dinosaurs'.

Alan's last paper was published posthumously, and was another nomenclatural paper published in the ICZN Bulletin (Charig & Chapman 1998). It is somewhat fitting that this article presented a new solution to a problem afflicting the nomenclature of one of the very earliest named dinosaurs: *Iguanodon*. While *Iguanodon* had become well known for its Belgian representative (*I. bernissartensis*, named in 1881) and for *I. atherfieldensis* from the Isle of Wight (named in 1925, and recently renamed *Mantellisaurus atherfieldensis*: Paul 2007), Mantell's original material – named *Iguanodon anglicum* (later changed to *I. anglicus*) in 1829 – consisted of non-diagnostic teeth discovered in the Grinstead Clay Formation (of middle Valanginian age) of the Hastings Beds Group. *Iguanodon* was therefore a *nomen dubium*, and action was needed if the name were to be preserved. Charig & Chapman (1998) argued that *I. bernissartensis* should be made the type species for the genus. There are two perspectives on this decision. One is that it may have been inappropriate given that the large, robust taxon *I. bernissartensis* (which may be as young as Barremian–Aptian in age) is, apparently, a very different animal from whichever taxon is represented by the Grinstead Clay Formation remains (Naish & Martill 2008; Paul 2008). A second is that, given the relatively early discovery of *I. bernissartensis*, its good representation in collections and the literature, and its frequent use as 'examplar' for the genus, making *I. bernissartensis* the type species was the most sensible course of action. Because the latter decision was supported by the majority of palaeontologists who expressed an interest, it was officially accepted by the ICZN in 2000.

Research expeditions

Alan took part in several collecting expeditions both during and prior to his time at the BM(NH), some of which resulted in the recovery of significant specimens. Cox (1997) recorded that Alan was a member of a joint expedition with London University in 1963 to Zambia (then northern Rhodesia) and Tanzania (Fig. 3). This expedition lasted for 4 months and collected five tons of material. In 1966–1967 Alan took part in the Joint BM(NH), University of London and South African Museum expedition to Basutoland (Lesotho) (Figs 4 & 5). The field team included John Attridge (Birkbeck College, University of London), Peter Whybrow (BM(NH)), Ionie Rudner (South African Museum) and Alan Charig. These expeditions resulted in some significant discoveries, including material of the Triassic mammal *Megazostrodon*, later worked on by Fuzz Crompton and Farrish Jenkins (Crompton & Jenkins 1968), anomodonts later studied by Barry Cox (Cox 1969), and prosauropod material later studied by Paul Sereno (Sereno 1991).

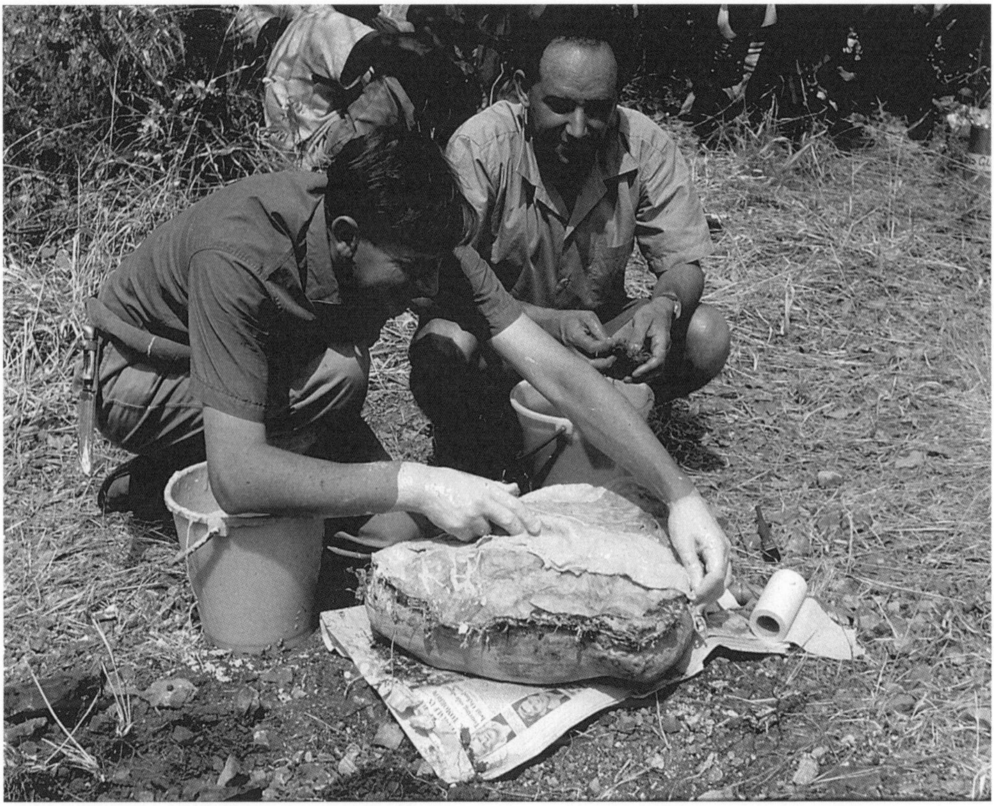

Fig. 3. 1963 Joint BMNH–University of London expedition to northern Rhodesia (Zambia) and Tanganyika (Tanzania). John Attridge (Birkbeck College, University of London) and Alan Charig completing a plaster jacket around the skull of the thecodontian '*Pallisteria*' from the Early Triassic, Tanzania. Photograph © H. W. Ball.

Fig. 4. 1967 Joint BMNH–University of London and South African Museum expedition to Basutoland (Lesotho). The field team included, from left to right: John Attridge (Birkbeck College, University of London), Peter Whybrow (BMNH), Ionie Rudner (South African Museum) and Alan Charig. Photograph © NHM.

Fig. 5. 1967 Joint BMNH–University of London and South African Museum expedition to Lesotho. Excavation of prosauropod material in the Late Triassic–Early Jurassic Red Beds near Pokane. From left to right: Peter Whybrow (BMNH), Ionie Rudner (South African Museum) and Alan Charig. Photograph © NHM.

Other specimens collected on these trips have yet to be described and are the subject of current research (A. Milner pers. comm. 2009).

In 1978 the Joint BM(NH), University of London and Queensland Museum expedition to Queensland, Australia, took place. Alan was accompanied by John Attridge, Barry Cox (King's College), David Norman (then at Queen Mary College) and Cyril Walker (Figs 6 & 7). Fossil herrings, representing the oldest known members of the group known at the time, were discovered on this expedition and were due to be described by Colin Patterson: these were never published, however (A. Milner pers. comm. 2009), and an older member of the group, *Spratticeps gaultinus*, was later reported in any case (Patterson 1970). A Lower Cretaceous ichthyosaur (Wade 1984) was also discovered.

Alan was proud of his first visit to China in 1979 as a guest of the British Council and vividly described some of the meals he ate during his visit. He published an article in *Biologist* magazine that was as much about his personal recollections of China and its people as about its palaeontological wealth (Charig 1980*c*). He was to return in 1982 as a leading member of a BM(NH) and Institute of Vertebrate Palaeontology and Palaeoanthroplogy, China (IVPP) expedition to Sichuan Province (Figs 8 & 9). The party included Dong Zhi-Ming, Li Jin-Ling, Sun Ai-ling, Ron Croucher and Angela Milner. Work was undertaken in the Upper Jurassic Upper Shaximaio Formation of Wang Cang County in Sichuan, and sauropod and stegosaur material was collected.

Popularization and the public

Like Bill Swinton before him, Alan was the dinosaur expert at the BM(NH) and was the great popularizer of his day, writing several semi-popular books that were highly praised for bringing a substantial amount of new information to the public. In 1970 Alan wrote the text for the Brooke Bond Picture Cards series *Prehistoric Animals* (Fig. 10). While this seems trivial, it had a significant impact on young people and their interest in prehistoric animals. Featuring art by Maurice Wilson and cover art by Michael Bell, it included an illustration of *Mandasuchus* and one of the earliest life restorations of *Deinonychus*. Because the work included some brief text on *Mandasuchus* it has jokingly been said that it is the only fossil reptile defined on the basis of a tea card (C. Walker pers. comm. 2009). As noted earlier, the name *Mandasuchus* had been used earlier on in the technical literature (e.g. Appleby *et al.* 1967), but published data remained scant.

In 1975 Alan published *Before the Ark* (with C. M. B. Horsfield), a book written to accompany

Fig. 6. 1978 Joint BMNH–University of London and Queensland Museum expedition to Queensland, Australia. Excavation of an ichthyosaur skeleton in Early Cretaceous beds. From left to right: John Attridge (Birkbeck College, University of London), Cyril Walker (BMNH), Barry Cox (King's College, London), Alan Bartholomai (Director, Queensland Museum) and Alan Charig. Photograph © NHM.

Fig. 7. Joint BMNH–University of London and Queensland Museum expedition to Queensland, Australia. Alan Charig and John Attridge (Birkbeck College, University of London) cataloguing finds in camp. In the background are Dave Norman (far left, then at Queen Mary College, University of London) and Cyril Walker (BMNH). Photograph © NHM.

Fig. 8. 1982 BMNH and IVPP expedition to the Upper Jurassic, Sichuan Province, People's Republic of China. Among others from left to right: (5th) Sun Ai-lin, (6th) Alan Charig, (7th) Li Jin-ling, (8th) Dong Zhi-ming, (9th) Angela Milner and (11th) Ron Croucher. Photograph © Angela Milner.

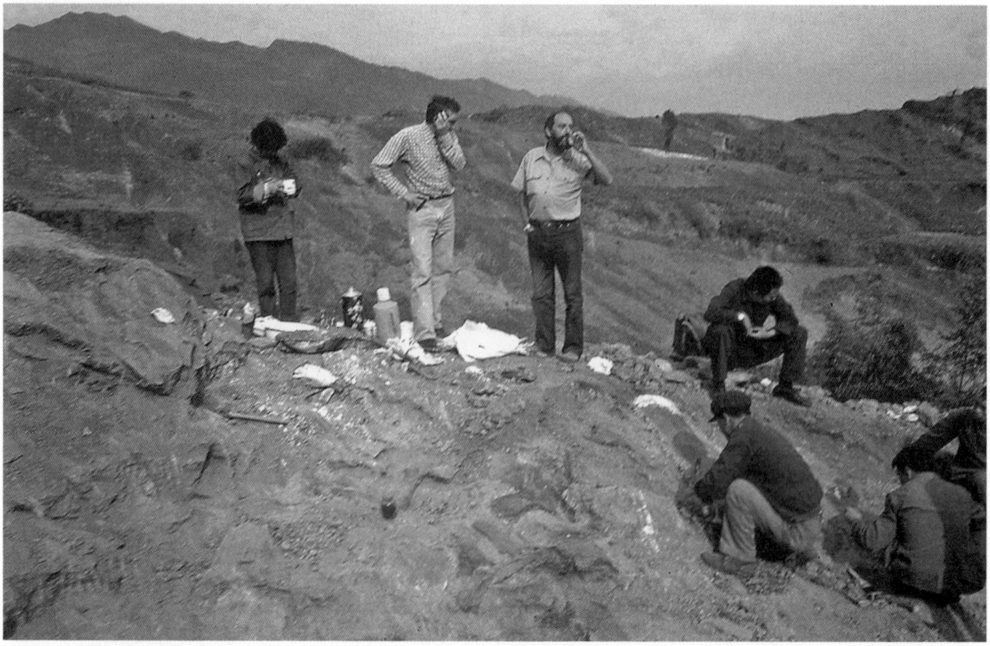

Fig. 9. 1982 BMNH and IVPP expedition to the Upper Jurassic, Sichuan Province, People's Republic of China. Li Jin-Ling, Ron Croucher and Alan Charig at the field site in the Upper Shaximaio Formation, Wang Cang. Photograph © Angela Milner.

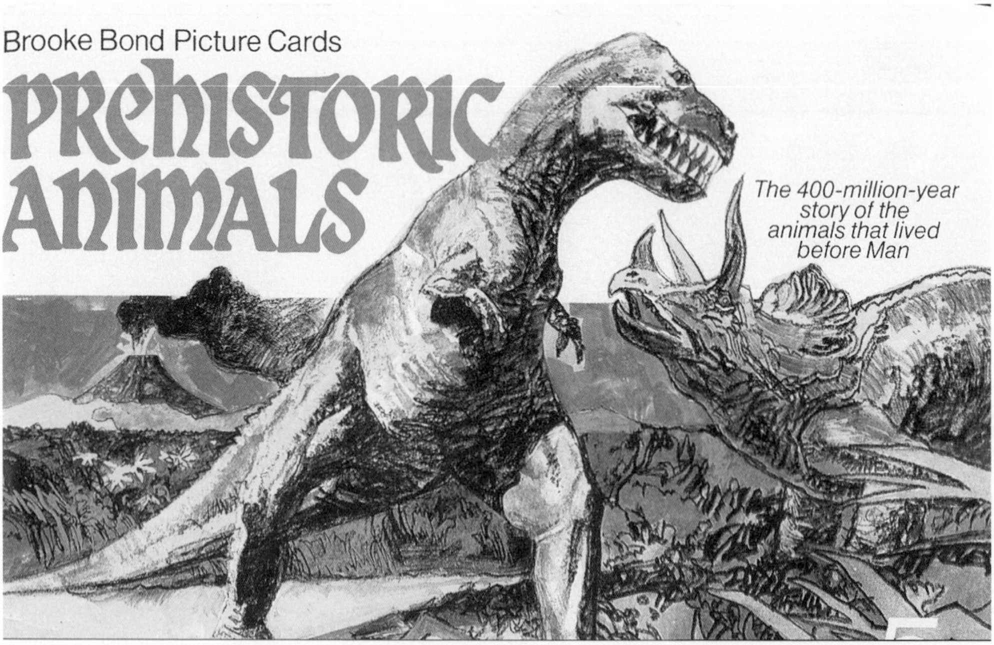

Fig. 10. Alan wrote several books that were highly praised for bringing a substantial amount of new information to the public. In 1970 Alan wrote the text for the Brooke Bond Picture Cards series *Prehistoric Animals*, which had a significant impact on young people and their interest in prehistoric animals. Featuring art by Maurice Wilson, it included an illustration of *Mandasuchus* and one of the earliest life restorations of *Deinonychus*.

a 10-part TV series of the same name that Alan presented (Fig. 11).

His best-known book, and one which saw several reprintings as well as translation into several languages, was his 1979 *A New Look at the Dinosaurs*. Aimed at interested lay-people and illustrated with excellent photographs, line drawings and colour plates, the volume included some entirely new data. Examples include photographs of a tiny juvenile of the South American sauropodomorph *Mussaurus*, one of its first appearances in print (the specimens were described by Bonaparte & Vince 1979). Alan's scepticism towards the idea that birds might be theropods was apparent. The volume included double-page coloured scenes produced by Peter Snowball, and including dinosaurs of different faunal assemblages (including the Morrison Formation, Wealden Supergroup and Hell Creek Formation). These paintings were reproduced by the BM(NH) as postcards and as large posters for children, and were still available for sale in the museum as late as the 1990s.

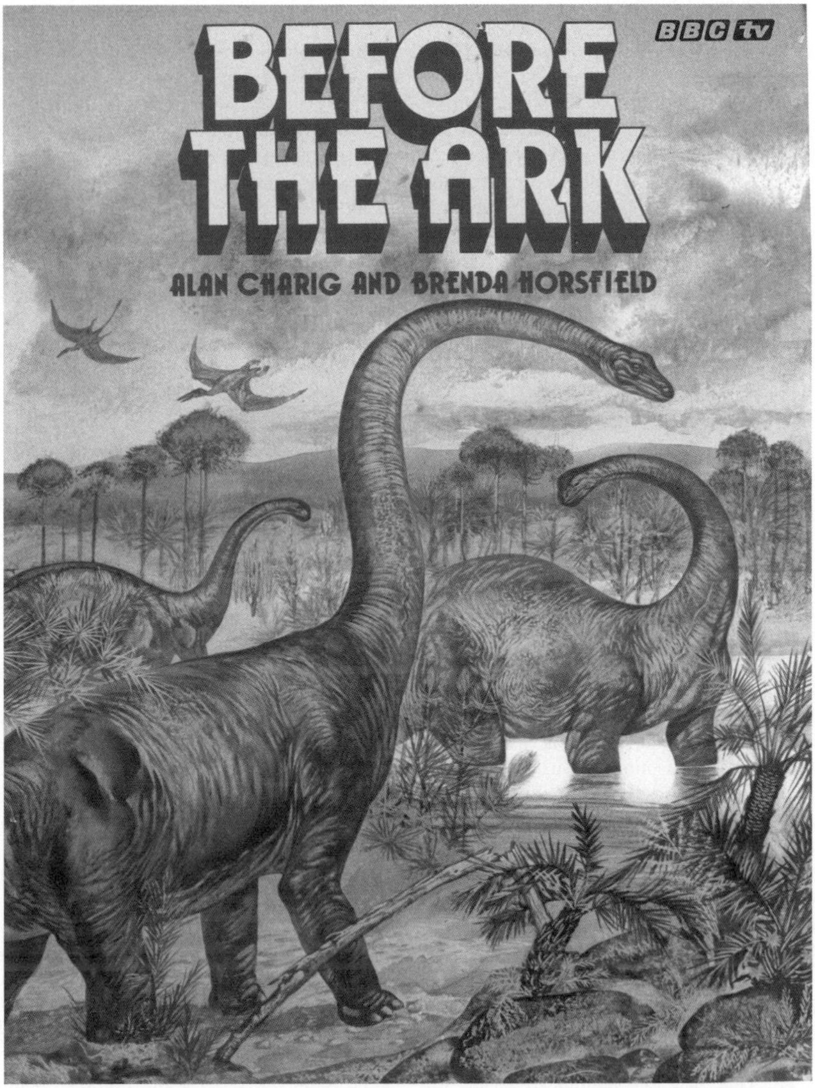

Fig. 11. In 1975 Alan Charig published *Before the Ark* with Brenda Horsfield. The book was written to accompany a 10-part TV series that Alan presented. His best-known book, and one which saw several reprintings, was his 1979 *A New Look at the Dinosaurs.*

The 1986 announcement of *Baryonyx walkeri* proved to be an area of enormous interest to the media and the public. Nicknamed 'Claws' by journalists (in reference to the fictional shark 'Jaws'), both *Baryonyx* and its discoverer (William Walker) were featured widely in the national and international newspapers, and even formed the focus of a BBC television documentary broadcast in February 1987 (Milner & Croucher 1987).

Alan was soon to be featured in the media again, but this time for controversial reasons: namely, Sir Fred Hoyle and Professor Chandra Wickramasinghe's bizarre claim of 1986 that the London *Archaeopteryx* must be a forgery, and one that had been made in the 1860s and later covered up by the staff at the BM(NH). The technical paper that Alan and colleagues published as a response (Charig *et al.* 1986) refuted in detail all of the evidence alleged to support the claim. Stating at the outset that they 'reject this forgery hypothesis unequivocally' (p. 623), the authors pointed to the many methodological and philosophical problems inherent to the idea, showing time and again how the supposedly suspicious details raised by Hoyle and Wickramasinghe could not be taken as evidence of forgery, but were instead genuine geological features or artefacts resulting from decades of preparation (Charig *et al.* 1986). The '*Archaeopteryx* is a forgery' idea remains popular among creationists and those on the lunatic fringe, but even they fail to appreciate the bizarre logic behind Hoyle and Wickramasinghe's argument. As explained in their book, *Archaeopteryx The Primordial Bird: A Case of Fossil Forgery*, Hoyle and Wickramasinghe sought to show that *Archaeopteryx* was faked because it proved an obstacle to their idea that dinosaurs and other Mesozoic vertebrates had been transmogrified by bacterial storms that had rained down on the Cretaceous world from outer space, grafting new genetic information onto the animals, and causing them to change into the birds and mammals of the Cenozoic (Hoyle & Wickramasinghe 1986). As a pre-Cenozoic bird, *Archaeopteryx* did not fit and had to be explained away (Hoyle and Wickramasinghe were generally unaware of other pre-Cenozoic birds, and ignored Mesozoic mammals entirely). Had this entertaining scenario been presented to the public at the same time as the '*Archaeopteryx* is a forgery' claim, it is doubtful whether it would have been taken as seriously as it was in some circles. A short popular book produced to accompany an exhibition about the charges, titled *The Feathers Fly!*, was produced by the museum. David Norman (1987) described how annoyed Alan was 'at having to waste his time with such refutations', but noted that 'they fed on many of his scientific attributes: notably a keen eye for detail and a constantly questioning, almost nagging persistence, for information and ultimate 'proof''.

Alan also wrote short sections on fossil reptiles for various popular or semi-popular books including the *The Collins Atlas of Animal Evolution* (1986) and *The Encyclopaedia of Reptiles and Amphibians* (1986).

Remembering Alan

As Curator of Fossil Amphibians, Reptiles and Birds, Alan was, of course, encountered by most active researchers in these fields. He was always reported to be extremely kind and helpful, making many suggestions that were to assist his colleagues in their pursuit of palaeontology. Alan also played a major role in social events of the UK palaeontological community and was an eminent member of the Tetrapods Club, an unofficial group that met up for occasional meals. The meetings and meals organized by this body were, apparently, unforgettable. A walrus baculum (rumoured to have been passed down from Thomas Huxley) was used as a sceptre by the chair.

However, Alan's relationships with other members of the Department of Palaeontology were sometimes strained. Barney Newman was a disciple of Bill Swinton but found it difficult to work with Alan as his new section head. Barney was larger than life and 'one of the museum's distinguished topers' (Fortey 2008); Alan was not! During his latter years at the museum, Bill Swinton gave Barney the task of writing letters on behalf of the section. Barney wrote them and signed them! When Alan took over, Barney asked him if this arrangement was satisfactory: in reply, Alan said that Barney could continue to write them, but that he would sign them. The explosive response was 'You sign em', you write 'em'. Barney's paper on the stance and gait of *Tyrannosaurus rex* (Newman 1970) did nothing to improve relations between the two. The *T. rex* specimen (the type of the junior synonym *Dynamosaurus imperiosus*, sold to the BM(NH) in 1960) was mounted in the museum's old dinosaur gallery in a rather 'modern' pose: that is, with its body and tail near-horizontal and its tail well up off the ground. It is generally assumed that Barney wanted to depict the animal in a dynamic, modern pose, and he said as much in his technical paper (Newman 1970). In fact, Alan revealed all by writing that the specimen 'was mounted with its body in a far too horizontal position: this was done because it would otherwise have been too tall for the Gallery. Newman, who made the mount, has attempted to rationalise this (1970) by stating that the posture was much more bird-like than is suggested by earlier mounts'

(Charig 1972, p. 137). Ultimately, Barney accepted a museum post in South Africa; his wife Margaret Lambert Newman survives him and is known as the illustrator of several books by Björn Kurtén.

People who have memories of Alan note that:

> Alan had a clinical mind and an outstanding memory which enabled him to 'pick the bones' out of other people's arguments.
>
> Cyril Walker

> He had the annoying habit of re-correcting his corrections until he had almost returned to the original text. He could also destroy your confidence by suddenly falling into a deep sleep whilst reading your thesis or manuscript.
>
> Dick Moody

> He will probably be best remembered for his involvement in the discovery and description of one of the most extraordinary dinosaurs to have been discovered on these shores: the curious fish-eating, gaff-clawed, *Baryonyx walkeri*. This dinosaur skeleton, now on display in the dinosaur gallery of the Natural History Museum, was discovered in a clay pit just south of London in the early 1980s. One of the most extraordinary facts about this dinosaur, apart from its remarkable diet, is that it was discovered in rocks that have been explored for well over 200 years – during which time not the slightest inkling of its existence had been gained; this is perhaps a salutary lesson for all we fossil researchers. It is gratifying, to himself and his memory, that the long-awaited monograph on *Baryonyx* was published just before he died.
>
> David Norman (1997)

> He was also unstinting in his efforts to popularise his area of interest and research through public lecturing tours both in this country and abroad; in this area he too was a consummate expert, bringing to his lectures not only his breadth and depth of knowledge, but also a delightful facility for the anecdote or happy (some times positively hilarious) reminiscence which showed him to be a scientist with a very humane side. Alan's public face was what he considered to be a necessary adjunct to his scientific rôle within a museum which prided itself on its scientific reputation and its public accessibility. Such public and (in a sense) private rôles are not always easy bed-fellows and there were times when the tension between these two facets of his life caused some difficulties during his career.
>
> David Norman (1997)

> Above all Alan Charig was a charming, witty, kindly, savagely critical, blinkered, biased, and at times absolutely infuriating man – so how could you do anything other than like the man. Who of us that knew him can ever forget those damned phone calls? How much he must have underpinned the profitability of the telecommunications industry, I shudder to think. Alan is gone now, he has left a hole by departing, but he has enriched us in many ways by what he left behind and he will be missed.
>
> David Norman (1997)

> When, as a fledgling palaeontologist, I first visited the fossil reptile collection of what was then the BM(NH), he was very friendly and made me feel at home. He even invited me to a meeting of the Tetrapods Club, and suggested that I should attend the SVPCA later that year. This was a suggestion I definitely followed, and I have missed very few since then (it must have been in 1976) and have organised a few of them myself.
>
> Eric Buffetaut

In all – Alan Charig was a fascinating character: he was good company and was always ready with a tale or joke. He was – in the language of dining clubs – most 'clubbable' and thoroughly enjoyed his evenings at the Tetrapods and the Geological Society Dining Club.

Conclusions

For four decades Alan Charig produced research on dinosaurs and other fossil archosaurs, and also contributed to knowledge on plesiosaurs, molluscs and other groups. A large number of popular articles and technical papers kept his name in the journals and helped promote the role of the BM(NH)–NHM in the global research community. Similarly, his popular books brought research on dinosaurs and their world to a huge audience. His research on new taxa, most notably *Heterodontosaurus* and especially *Baryonyx*, resulted in important publications that remain highly regarded.

However, he was definitely guilty of sitting on certain projects that were never to see fruition, even after decades of work: among them the planned descriptions of *Heterodontosaurus*, *Scelidosaurus* and *Dimorphodon*, and on his Tanzanian Triassic taxa. In fact, despite his many references to on-going work and in press manuscripts, his list of notable publications is short and it is difficult not to conclude that he avoided writing about specimens if he could! In recent years, renewed interest in archosaur morphology and phylogeny has resulted in progress on his planned projects, much of which has been carried out by Alan's academic 'descendants': *Heterodontosaurus* and *Scelidosaurus* are currently under study by David Norman, and the *Dimorphodon* holotype was studied by Sarah Sangster for her PhD thesis (Sangster 2001, 2003). Kitty Thomas studied *Mandasuchus* for the purposes of her PhD thesis (Thomas 2004); Sterling Nesbitt and Paul Barrett are currently working on *Nyasasaurus* and other Tanzanian material; and *Hypselorhachis* has been re-examined by Richard Butler and colleagues, and does, indeed, appear to be a ctenosauriscid (Butler *et al.* 2009).

During his research career Alan was strongly associated with his ideas on the evolution of archosaur gaits and on the changing fortunes of the different Mesozoic tetrapod groups. Ultimately, however, his arguments on these subjects were unconvincing and have been mostly falsified. The hypothesis that dinosaurs evolved from quadrupedal, crocodilian-like 'pseudosuchian thecodonts' with a 'semi-improved' stance proved incorrect, both because fossils intermediate between quadrupedal crocodile-line archosaurs and early dinosaurs were never discovered, because such animals were later shown to belong to distinct lineages, and because other finds (such as *Lagosuchus*) indicated an evolutionary history for dinosaurs somewhat different from that Alan envisaged. It is tempting to suggest that the increasing realization that his theoretical model was at odds with the evidence explains, in part, Alan's failure to publish on his Manda Formation taxa, as he stated in the popular literature that they would somehow be of special relevance to the subject of stance and gait in archosaur evolution. However, his excessive sense of perfectionism contributed to his slow progress on these projects, and he stated on occasion that he was saving some of this planned work for retirement.

Alan remained a conservative voice throughout the years of the 'dinosaur renaissance', resisting arguments proposing monophyly of Dinosauria and of the dinosaurian origin of birds. Ultimately, his position on these issues (which have not been supported by recent research) have meant that much of his work is now ignored and regarded as being primarily historical in interest. Alan's position on archosaur phylogeny as a whole – that a division of Archosauria into a bird-dinosaur clade and a crocodile clade was suspect, and that no significant progress had been made since the 1960s – also stands in marked contrast to the views of virtually all current workers. Similarly, his objections to cladistics did little to slow the revolution in 'tree-based thinking' and few working systematists agree with his view that paraphyletic groups and Linnaean ranks should be retained. In a sense, Alan could be regarded as one of the last members of the 'old school': he did not embrace or popularize the views promoted by the 'dinosaur renaissance' nor by the cladistic movement, and he gave no indication of giving up on the views that would have been regarded as mainstream in the 1950s and early 1960s.

One could argue that Alan's role as a popularizer of dinosaurs and palaeontology was inevitable given his professional position, and that the books, popular articles and television appearances that he was involved in are not therefore a consequence of any great skill as a communicator. Indeed, some colleagues are of this opinion. However, as Dave Norman (1987) stated, Alan was unstinting in his efforts as a communicator of science; he excelled as an extremely thorough reviewer of other people's work, and he was highly skilled at combining an enormous breadth of knowledge with a very 'human side', sometimes presenting anecdotes and reminiscences that were amusing and even downright hilarious.

Many people provided anecdotes, comments and information that contributed to this article. We are especially grateful to C. Walker (1939–2009), A. Milner, D. Norman and E. Buffetaut for discussion and data. P. Forey (via A. Milner) provided information on Colin Patterson's fossil herrings. A. Milner and D. Martill are thanked for their careful reviews of the manuscript. We also extend sincere thanks to K. Padian, P. Barrett, R. Butler, S. Nesbitt and H.-D. Sues for providing information and for sharing unpublished data.

Appendix: The scientific works of A. J. Charig

This list is given in chronological order.

Charig, A. J. 1956. *New Triassic Archosaurs from Tanganyika, Including* Mandasuchus *and* Teleocrater. PhD dissertation, University of Cambridge.

Charig, A. J. 1957. New Triassic archosaurs from Tanganyika including *Mandasuchus* and *Teleocrater*. *Abstracts and Dissertations of the University of Cambridge*, **1955–56**, 28–29.

Charig, A. J. 1960. Dr G. H. Francis [obituary]. *Nature*, **187**, 284–285.

Crompton, A. W. & Charig, A. J. 1962. A new ornithischian from the Upper Triassic of South Africa. *Nature*, **196**, 1074–1077.

Charig, A. J. & Newman, B. H. 1962. Footprints in the Purbeck. *New Scientist*, **14**, 234–235.

Charig, A. J. 1963. The gastropod genus *Thatcheria* and its relationships. *Bulletin of the British Museum (Natural History), Geology*, **7**, 257–297.

Charig, A. J. 1963. Stratigraphical nomenclature in the Songea Series of Tanganyika. *Records of the Geological Survey of Tanganyika*, **10**, 47–53.

Attridge, J., Ball, H. W., Charig, A. J. & Cox, C. B. 1964. The British Museum (Natural History)–University of London Joint Palaeontological Expedition to northern Rhodesia and Tanganyika, 1963. *Nature*, **201**, 445–449.

Charig, A. J., Attridge, J. & Crompton, A .W. 1965. On the origin of the sauropods and the classification of the Saurischia. *Proceedings of the Linnean Society, London*, **176**, 197–221.

Charig, A. J. 1965. Stance and gait in the archosaur reptiles. *Liaison Reports of the Commonwealth Geological Liaison Office*, **86**, 18–19 (Abstract).

Charig, A. J. 1966. Stance and gait in the archosaur reptiles. *Advancements in Science, London*, **22**, 537 (Abstract).

Charig, A. J. 1966. The role of vertebrate palaeontology in modern biology. *Biology and Human Affairs*, **32**, 31–41.

CHARIG, A. J. 1966. Yu. A. Orlov [obituary]. *Nature*, **212**, 460.

CHARIG, A. J. 1967. Subclass Archosauria. *In*: HARLAND, W. B., HOLLAND, C. H. ET AL. (eds) *The Fossil Record*. Geological Society, London, Special Publications, **2**, 708–718, 725–731.

CHARIG, A. J. 1967. A new Triassic mammal skull from Lesotho. *Biology and Human Affairs*, **32**, 19 [Incorrectly titled 'mammoth skull'!].

ATTRIDGE, J. & CHARIG, A. J. 1967. Crisis in evolution: the Stormberg Series. *Science Journal*, **3**, 48–54.

ATTRIDGE, J. & CHARIG, A. J. 1967. Sediments and skulls. *New Scientist*, **35**, 260.

CHARIG, A. J. & REIG, O. A. 1970. The classification of the Proterosuchia. *Biological Journal of the Linnean Society*, **2**, 125–171.

CHARIG, A. J. 1970. New names for two species of *Viviparus*. *Annales Musée Royal d'Afrique Centrale, 8, Sciences Géologique*, **67**, 79–80.

CHARIG, A. J. & HORELL, J. 1971. The Fletton plesiosaur, 1970. *Report of the Huntingdon Flora and Fauna Society*, **23**, 37–40.

CHARIG, A. J. 1971. *Prehistoric Animals*. Brooke Bond, London.

CHARIG, A. J. 1971. Faunal provinces on land: evidence based on the distribution of fossil tetrapods, with especial reference to the reptiles of the Permian and Mesozoic. *In*: MIDDLEMISS, F. A., RAWSON, P. F. & NEWALL, G. (eds) *Faunal Provinces in Space and Time: Proceedings of the 17th International University Geological Congress Held in Queen Mary College (University of London) – 17, 18, 19 December 1969*. Seel House Press, Liverpool, 111–128.

CHARIG, A. J. 1971. Archosauria; Eosuchia; Euryapsida; Lepidosauria; Ornithischia; Reptilia; Rhynchocephalia; Saurischia. *In*: LAPEDES, D. N. (ed. in Chief) *McGraw-Hill Year Book Encyclopedia of Science and Technology*. McGraw-Hill, New York, **1**, 570–571, one text-fig.; **5**, 33, two text-figs; **5**, 134–135, one text-fig.; **7**, 534, three text-figs; **9**, 471; **11**, 510–512, six text-figs; **11**, 589; **12**, 58–59.

CHARIG, A. J. 1972. The evolution of the archosaur pelvis and hind-limb: an explanation in functional terms. *In*: JOYSEY, K. A. & KEMP, T. S. (eds) *Studies in Vertebrate Evolution*. Oliver & Boyd, Edinburgh, 121–155.

CHARIG, A. J. 1973. Jurassic and Cretaceous dinosaurs. *In*: HALLAM, A. (ed.) *Atlas of Palaeobiogeography*. Elsevier, Amsterdam, 339–352.

CHARIG, A. J. 1973. Kurten's theory of ordinal variety and the number of the continents. *In*: TARLING, D. H. & RUNCORN, S. K. (eds) *Implications of Continental Drift to the Earth Sciences*, Volume 1. Academic Press, London, 231–245.

CHARIG, A. J. 1973. Competition between therapsids and archosaurs during the Triassic period: a review and synthesis of current theories. *In*: *Third International Gondwana Symposium*. Australian Academy of Science, Canberra, 58.

CHARIG, A. J. & CROMPTON, A. W. 1974. The alleged synonymy of *Lycorhinus* and *Heterodontosaurus*. *Annals of the South African Museum*, **64**, 167–189.

CHARIG, A. J. & HORSFIELD, C. M. B. 1975. *Before the Ark*. British Broadcasting Corporation, London.

CHARIG, A. J. 1976. Archosauria. *In*: CHARIG, A. J., KREBS, B., SUES, H.-D. & WESTPHAL, F. (eds) *Thecodontia. Handbuch der Paläoherpetologie*, Volume 13. Gustav Fischer, Stuttgart, 1–6.

CHARIG, A. J. 1976. Thecodontia. *In*: CHARIG, A. J., KREBS, B., SUES, H.-D. & WESTPHAL, F. *Thecodontia. Handbuch der Paläoherpetologie*, Volume 13, Gustav Fischer, Stuttgart, 7–10.

CHARIG, A. J. & SUES, H.-D. 1976. Suborder Proterosuchia Broom 1906b. *In*: CHARIG, A. J., KREBS, B., SUES, H.-D. & WESTPHAL, F. (eds) *Thecodontia. Handbuch der Paläoherpetologie*, Volume 13. *Thecodontia*. Gustav Fischer, Stuttgart, 11–39.

CHARIG, A. J., KREBS, B., SUES, H.-D. & WESTPHAL, F. (eds) 1976. *Thecodontia (Handbuch der Paläoherpetologie*, Volume 13. Gustav Fischer, Stuttgart.

CHARIG, A. J. 1976. 'Dinosaur monophyly and a new class of vertebrates': a critical review. *In*: BELLAIRS, A. D'A. & COX, C. B. (eds) *Morphology and Biology of Reptiles*. Academic Press, London, 66–104.

SANTA LUCA, A. P., CROMPTON, A. W. & CHARIG, A. J. 1976. A complete skeleton of the Late Triassic ornithischian *Heterodontosaurus tucki*. *Nature*, **264**, 324–328.

CHARIG, A. J. 1977. 'The hot-blooded dinosaurs: a revolution in palaeontology': an extended review. *Journal of Natural History*, **11**, 114–116.

CHARIG, A. J. 1978. Reptiles into birds. *Spectrum*, **155**, 2–4.

CHARIG, A. J. 1979. *A New Look at the Dinosaurs*. Heinemann, London, and the British Museum (Natural History), London.

CHARIG, A. J. 1979. Eggs; Gobi Desert; Karroo system; Lithographic stone; Lizards; Mosasaurs; Phytosaurs; Pseudosuchians; Rhynchocephalians; Snakes; Thecodontians; Wealden series. *In*: STEEL, R. & HARVEY, A. P. (eds) *The Encyclopaedia of Prehistoric Life*. Mitchell Beazley, London, 70, 92, 108–109, 115, 116–117, 133, 160, 172, 182–183, 195, 202–203, 210.

CHARIG, A. J. 1980. A diplodocid sauropod from the Lower Cretaceous of England. *In*: JACOBS, L. L. (ed.) *Aspects of Vertebrate History, Essays in Honour of E. H. Colbert*. Museum of Northern Arizona Press, Flagstaff, AZ, 231–244.

CHARIG, A. J. 1980. Differentiation of lineages among Mesozoic tetrapods. *Mémoires de la société géologique de France* (N.S.), **139**, 207–210.

CHARIG, A. J. 1980. 'A cold look at the warm-blooded dinosaurs': an extended review. *Palaeontological Association Circular*, **101**, 8–10.

CHARIG, A. J. 1980. A palaeontologist visits China. *Biologist*, **27**, 137–139.

CHARIG, A. J. 1980. Euryapsida. *In*: *McGraw-Hill Encyclopedia of Science and Technology*. McGraw-Hill, New York.
CHARIG, A. J. 1981. Cladistics: a different point of view. *Biologist*, **28**, 19–20.
CHARIG, A. J. 1982. Problems in dinosaur phylogeny: a reasoned approach to their attempted resolution. *In*: BUFFETAUT, E., JANVIER, P., RAGE, J.-C. & TASSY, P. (eds) *Phylogénie et paléobiogéographie: livre jubilaire en l'honneur de R. Hoffstetter Géobios*, Mémoire Spécial, **6**, 91–104.
CHARIG, A. J. 1982. The origin of bird flight. *Aspects*, **1982**, 10–13.
CHARIG, A. J. 1982. Cladistics: a different point of view. *In*: MAYNARD SMITH, J. (ed.) *Evolution Now: A Century after Darwin*. Macmillan, London (Nature, in association with *Nature*), 121–124.
CHARIG, A. J. 1982. *Dinosaurier: Rätselhafte Riesen der Urzeit*. Hoffmann & Campe, Hamburg.
CHARIG, A. J. 1982. Systematics in biology: a fundamental comparison of some major schools of thought. *In*: JOYSEY, K. A. & FRIDAY, A. E. (eds) *Problems of Phylogenetic Reconstruction*. Academic Press, London, 363–440.
CHARIG, A. J. 1983. Bones of contention. *Biologist*, **30**, 64.
CHARIG, A. J. 1983. *A New Look at the Dinosaurs* (amended reprint). British Museum (Natural History), London (in association with Heinemann).
CHARIG, A. J. 1983. Not the end of the dinosaurs. *Nature*, **304**, 472.
CHARIG, A. J. 1983. Dinosaur myths and misconceptions. *Teaching Science*, **1**, 66–70.
CHARIG, A. J. 1983. Comments on Felsenstein, J.: Statistical inference of phylogenies. *Journal of the Royal Statistical Society (A)*, **146**, 268–269.
CHARIG, A. J. 1984. The Triassic explosion in tetrapod evolution and the origin of dinosaurs. *The Linnean*, **1**, 19–20 (Abstract).
CHARIG, A. J. & MILNER, A. C. 1984. Digging up dragons in China. *Britain–China*, **25**, 4–5.
CHARIG, A. J. 1984. Competition between therapsids and archosaurs during the Triassic period: a review and synthesis of current theories. *In*: FERGUSON, M. W. J. (ed.) *The Structure, Development and Evolution of Reptiles: Essays in Honour of Professor Angus d'Albini Bellairs (Symposia of the Zoological Society of London, Volume 52)*. Academic Press, London, 597–628.
CHARIG, A. J. 1985. Analysis of the several problems associated with *Archaeopteryx*. *In*: HECHT, M. K., OSTROM, J. H., VIOHL, G. & WELLNHOFER, P. (eds) *The Beginnings of Birds – Proceedings of the International Archaeopteryx Conference, Eichstätt* 1984. Jura Museum, Eichstätt, 21–30.
CHARIG, A. J. 1985. Is *Archaeopteryx* a forgery? *Biologist*, **32**, 122–123.
CHARIG, A. J. 1985. *La verdadera historia de los dinosaurios*. Salvat, Barcelona.
CHARIG, A. J. 1986. Dinosaurs and other 'prehistoric monsters': the age of reptiles. *In*: HALLIDAY, T. R. & ADLER, K. (eds) *The Encyclopaedia of Reptiles and Amphibians*. George Allen & Unwin, London (Facts on File), 68–69.
CHARIG, A. J., GREENAWAY, F., MILNER, A. C., WALKER, C. A. & WHYBROW, P. J. 1986. *Archaeopteryx* is not a forgery. *Science*, **232**, 622–626.
CHARIG, A. J. & HALLAM, A. 1986. Early Mesozoic life. *In*: BERRY, R. J. & HALLAM, A. (eds) *The Collins Encyclopedia of Animal Evolution*. Collins, London, 22–27.
CHARIG, A. J. 1986. Bringing Nature into order: principles of animal classification. *In*: BERRY, R. J. & HALLAM, A. (eds) *The Collins Encyclopedia of Animal Evolution*. Collins, London, 62–63.
CHARIG, A. J. 1986. The first bird. *Anima*, Tokyo, **9**, 14–20 (in Japanese).
CHARIG, A. J. 1986. *Archaeopteryx* matters. Letter to *The Daily Telegraph* (no. 40845, 17 October), 20.
CHARIG, A. J. 1986. Unnatural selection [review of book: Archaeopteryx, the primordial bird: a case of fossil forgery" by Hoyle & Wickramasingh]. *The Times Literary Supplement*, (**4361**), 31 October, 1213.
CHARIG, A. J., GREENAWAY, F., MILNER, A. C., WALKER, C. A. & WHYBROW, P. J. 1986. The *Archaeopteryx* is not a forgery. *Petroleum Review*, **40**, 40–42.
CHARIG, A. J. & MILNER, A. C. 1986. *Baryonyx*, a remarkable new theropod dinosaur. *Nature*, **324**, 359–361.
CHARIG, A. J. 1987. *A New Look at the Dinosaurs*. Dobutsu-Sha, Tokyo (Japanese translation).
MILNER, A. C. & CROUCHER, R. 1987. *'Claws', A Great New British Dinosaur*. British Museum (Natural History), London (in association with A. J. CHARIG).
CHARIG, A. J. 1987. Dinosaurs from China (at the National Museum of Wales). *Geology Today*, **3**, 186–189.
CHARIG, A. J. 1988. *A New Look at the Dinosaurs*. British Museum (Natural History), London.
CHARIG, A. J. 1989. The ethics of buying and selling fossils. *Biologist*, **36**, 75–77.
CHARIG, A. J. 1989. Preface [obituary on Maurice Wilson], p. 7. *In*: ANDREWS, P. J. & STRINGER, C. B. (eds) *Human Evolution: An Illustrated Guide*. British Museum (Natural History), London.
CHARIG, A. J. 1989. The Cretaceous–Tertiary boundary and the last of the dinosaurs. *In*: CHALONER, W. G. & HALLAM, A. (eds) *Evolution and Extinction. Philosophical Transactions of the Royal Society of London (B)*, **325**, 387–400.
CHARIG, A. J. 1990. Evolutionary systematics. *In*: BRIGGS, D. E. G. & CROWTHER, P. R. (eds) *Palaeobiology: A Synthesis*. Blackwell Scientific, Oxford, 434–437.
CHARIG, A. J. & GANS, C. 1990. Two new amphisbaenians from the Lower Miocene of Kenya. *Bulletin of the British Museum of Natural History (Geology)*, **46**, 19–36.
CHARIG, A. J. & MILNER, A. C. 1990. The systematic position of *Baryonyx walkeri* in the light of Gauthier's

reclassification of the theropoda. *In*: CARPENTER, K. & CURRIE, P. J. (eds) *Dinosaur Systematics: Approaches and Perspectives*. Cambridge University Press, Cambridge, 127–140.

CHARIG, A. J. 1990. Francis Rex Parrington, 20 February 1905–17 April 1981. *Biographical Memoirs of Fellows of the Royal Society of London*, **36**, 359–378.

COLBERT, E. H., CHARIG, A. J., DODSON, P., GILLETTE, D. D., OSTROM, J. H. & WEISHAMPEL, D. 1992. Case 2840. *Coelurus bauri* Cope, 1887 (currently *Coelophysis bauri*; Reptilia, Saurischia): proposed replacement of the lectotype by a neotype. *Bulletin of Zoological Nomenclature*, **49**, 276–279.

CHARIG, A. J. & NEWMAN, B. H. 1992. *Scelidosaurus harrisonii* Owen, 1861 (Reptilia, Ornithischia): proposed replacement of inappropriate lectotype. *Bulletin of Zoological Nomenclature*, **49**, 280–283.

CHARIG, A. J. 1993. Disaster theories of dinosaur extinction. *Modern Geology*, **18**, (Halstead Memorial Volume), 299–318.

CHARIG, A. J. 1993. Case 1876. *Cetiosauriscus* von Huene, 1927 (Reptilia, Sauropodomorpha): proposed designation of *C. stewarti* Charig, 1980 as the type species. *Bulletin of Zoological Nomenclature*, **50**, 282–283.

CHARIG, A. J. 1993. Recently proposed phylogenetic analyses of the Triassic Archosauria: a critical comparison and evaluation, facilitated by a simple technique for the modification of conflicting dendrograms. *Paleontologia Lombarda della Società Italiana di Scienze Naturali e del Museo Civico di Storia Naturale di Milano*, Nuova serie, **2**, 45–62.

CHARIG, A. J. 1994. William Elgin Swinton [obituary]. *The Independent*, 28 June. Online at: http:/www.independent.co.uk/news/people/obituary-professor-william-swinton-1425671.html.

CHARIG, A. J. 1995. Geoffey Adams (1926–1995) [obituary]. *The Daily Telegraph*, 22 February.

CHARIG, A. J. 1995. Disaster theories of dinosaur extinction. *In*: SARJEANT, W. A. S. (ed.) *Vertebrate Fossils and the Evolution of Scientific Concepts*. Gordon & Breach, 309–328.

CHARIG, A. J. 1996. Dinosaurs. *In*: DASCH, E. J. (ed. in Chief) *Macmillan Encyclopedia of Earth Sciences*, Volume 1. Simon & Schuster Macmillan, New York, 159–164.

CHARIG, A. J. 1996. Dinosaurs for grown-ups [review of book: *The Evolution and Extinction of the Dinosaurs*, by Fastovsky & Weishampel]. *Nature*, **381**, 569–570.

CHARIG, A. J. 1996. Dinosaurs for grown-ups (review of Fastovsky & Weishampel). *Nature*, **381**, 569–570.

CHARIG, A. J. & MILNER, A. C. 1997. *Baryonyx walkeri*, a fish-eating dinosaur from the Wealden of Surrey. *Bulletin of the Natural History Museum*, **53**, 11–70.

CHARIG, A. J. & CHAPMAN, S. D. 1998. *Iguanodon* Mantell, 1825 (Reptilia, Ornithischia): proposed designation of *Iguanodon bernissartensis* Boulenger in Beneden, 1881 as the type species, and proposed designation of a lectotype. *Bulletin of Zoological Nomenclature*, **55**, 99–104.

References

ALVAREZ, W., ALVAREZ, L. W., ASARO, F. & MICHEL, H. V. 1980. Extraterrestrial cause for the Cretaceous–Tertiary extinction. *Science*, **208**, 1095–1108.

APPLEBY, R. M., CHARIG, A. J., COX, C. B., KERMACK, K. A. & TARLO, L. B. H. 1967. Reptilia. *In*: HARLAND, W. B., HOLLAND, C. H. *ET AL*. (eds) *The Fossil Record*. Geological Society, London.

BAKKER, R. T. & GALTON, P. M. 1974. Dinosaur monophyly and a new class of vertebrates. *Nature*, **248**, 168–172.

BENTON, M. J. 1983. Dinosaur success in the Triassic: a noncompetitive ecological model. *The Quarterly Review of Biology*, **58**, 29–55.

BENTON, M. J. 1984. Consensus on archosaurs. *Nature*, **312**, 599.

BONAPARTE, J. 1975. New materials of *Lagosuchus talampayensis* Romer (Thecodontia–Pseudosuchia) and its significance in the origin of the Saurischia, Lower Chanarian, Middle Triassic of Argentina. *Acta Geologica Lilloana*, **13**, 5–90.

BONAPARTE, J. & VINCE, M. 1979. El hallazgo del primer nido de dinosurios Triasicos, (Saurischia, Prosauropoda), Triasico Superior de Patagonia, Argentina. *Ameghiniana*, **16**, 173–182.

BROWN, D. S. 1981. The English Upper Jurassic Plesiosauroidea (Reptilia) and a review of the phylogeny and classification of the Plesiosauria. *Bulletin of the British Museum of Natural History (Geology Series)*, **35**, 253–347.

BUFFETAUT, E. 1989. New remains of the enigmatic dinosaur *Spinosaurus* from the Cretaceous of Morocco and the affinities between *Spinosaurus* and *Baryonyx*. *Neues Jahrbuch für Geologie und Paläontologie, Monatshefte*, **1989**, 79–87.

BUTLER, R. J., BARRETT, P. M., ABEL, R. L. & GOWER, D. J. 2009. A possible ctenosauriscid archosaur from the Middle Triassic Manda Beds of Tanzania. *Journal of Vertebrate Paleontology*, **29**, 1022–1031.

CHARIG, A. J. 1963. The gastropod genus *Thatcheria* and its relationships. *Bulletin of the British Museum (Natural History), Geology*, **7**, 257–297.

CHARIG, A. J. 1971. Faunal provinces on land: evidence based on the distribution of fossil tetrapods, with especial reference to the reptiles of the Permian and Mesozoic. *In*: MIDDLEMISS, F. A., RAWSON, P. F. & NEWALL, G. (eds) *Faunal Provinces in Space and Time: Proceedings of the 17th International University Geological Congress Held in Queen Mary College (University of London) – 17, 18, 19 December 1969*. Seel House Press, Liverpool, 111–128.

CHARIG, A. J. 1972. The evolution of the archosaur pelvis and hind-limb: an explanation in functional terms. *In*: JOYSEY, K. A. & KEMP, T. S. (eds) *Studies in Vertebrate Evolution*. Oliver & Boyd, Edinburgh, 121–155.

CHARIG, A. J. 1973. Kurten's theory of ordinal variety and the number of the continents. *In*: TARLING, D. H. &

Runcorn, S. K. (eds) *Implications of Continental Drift to the Earth Sciences*, Volume 1. Academic Press, London, 231–245.

Charig, A. J. 1976*a*. 'Dinosaur monophyly and a new class of vertebrates': a critical review. *In*: Bellairs, A. d'A. & Cox, C. B. (eds) *Morphology and Biology of Reptiles*. Academic Press, London, 66–104.

Charig, A. J. 1976*b*. Thecodontia. *In*: *Handbuch der Paläoherpetologie, Teil 13, Thecodontia*. Gustav Fischer, Stuttgart, 7–10.

Charig, A. J. 1979. *A New Look at the Dinosaurs*. Heinemann, London, and British Museum (Natural History), London.

Charig, A. J. 1980*a*. A diplodocid sauropod from the Lower Cretaceous of England. *In*: Jacobs, L. L. (ed.) *Aspects of Vertebrate History, Essays in Honour of E. H. Colbert*. Museum of Northern Arizona Press, Flagstaff, AZ, 231–244.

Charig, A. J. 1980*b*. Differentiation of lineages among Mesozoic tetrapods. *Mémoires de la société géologique de France (N.S.)*, **139**, 207–210.

Charig, A. J. 1980*c*. A palaeontologist visits China. *Biologist*, **27**, 137–139.

Charig, A. J. 1981. Cladistics: a different point of view. *Biologist*, **28**, 19–20.

Charig, A. J. 1982*a*. Systematics in biology: a fundamental comparison of some major schools of thought. *In*: Joysey, K. A. & Friday, A. E. (eds) *Problems of Phylogenetic Reconstruction*. Academic Press, London, 363–440.

Charig, A. J. 1982*b*. Problems in dinosaur phylogeny: a reasoned approach to their attempted resolution. *Geobios*, Mémoire Spécial, **6**, 113–126.

Charig, A. J. 1985. Analysis of the several problems associated with *Archaeopteryx*. *In*: Hecht, M. K., Ostrom, J. H., Viohl, G. & Wellnhofer, P. (eds) *The Beginnings of Birds – Proceedings of the International Archaeopteryx Conference, Eichstätt 1984*. Jura Museum, Eichstätt, 21–30.

Charig, A. J. 1987. Report of exhibition of Chinese dinosaurs. *Geology Today*, **3**, 187–189.

Charig, A. J. 1988. *A New Look at the Dinosaurs*. British Museum (Natural History), London.

Charig, A. J. 1989. The Cretaceous–Tertiary boundary and the last of the dinosaurs. *Philosophical Transactions of the Royal Society of London B*, **325**, 387–400.

Charig, A. J. 1993*a*. Case 1876. *Cetiosauriscus* von Huene, 1927 (Reptilia, Sauropodomorpha): proposed designation of *C. stewarti* Charig, 1980 as the type species. *Bulletin of Zoological Nomenclature*, **50**, 282–283.

Charig, A. J. 1993*b*. Recently proposed phylogenetic analyses of the Triassic Archosauria: a critical comparison and evaluation, facilitated by a simple technique for the modification of conflicting dendrograms. *Paleontologia Lombarda della Società Italiana di Scienze Naturali e del Museo Civico di Storia Naturale di Milano*, Nuova serie, **2**, 45–62.

Charig, A. J. & Chapman, S. D. 1998. *Iguanodon* Mantell, 1825 (Reptilia, Ornithischia): proposed designation of *Iguanodon bernissartensis* Boulenger in Beneden, 1881 as the type species, and proposed designation of a lectotype. *Bulletin of Zoological Nomenclature*, **55**, 99–104.

Charig, A. J. & Crompton, A. W. 1974. The alleged synonymy of *Lycorhinus* and *Heterodontosaurus*. *Annals of the South African Museum*, **64**, 167–189.

Charig, A. J. & Gans, C. 1990. Two new amphisbaenians from the Lower Miocene of Kenya. *Bulletin of the British Museum of Natural History (Geology)*, **46**, 19–36.

Charig, A. J. & Horell, J. 1971. The Fletton plesiosaur, 1970. *Report of the Huntingdon Flora and Fauna Society*, **23**, 37–40.

Charig, A. J. & Milner, A. C. 1986. *Baryonyx*, a remarkable new theropod dinosaur. *Nature*, **324**, 359–361.

Charig, A. J. & Milner, A. C. 1990. The systematic position of *Baryonyx walkeri* in the light of Gauthier's reclassification of the theropoda. *In*: Carpenter, K. & Currie, P. J. (eds) *Dinosaur Systematics: Approaches and Perspectives*. Cambridge University Press, Cambridge, 127–140.

Charig, A. J. & Milner, A. C. 1997. *Baryonyx walkeri*, a fish-eating dinosaur from the Wealden of Surrey. *Bulletin of the Natural History Museum*, **53**, 11–70.

Charig, A. J. & Newman, B. H. 1962. Footprints in the Purbeck. *New Scientist*, **14**, 234–235.

Charig, A. J. & Newman, B. H. 1992. *Scelidosaurus harrisonii* Owen, 1861 (Reptilia, Ornithischia): proposed replacement of inappropriate lectotype. *Bulletin of Zoological Nomenclature*, **49**, 280–283.

Charig, A. J. & Reig, O. A. 1970. The classification of the Proterosuchia. *Biological Journal of the Linnean Society*, **2**, 125–171.

Charig, A. J. & Sues, H.-D. 1976. Suborder Proterosuchia Broom 1906b. *In*: *Handbuch der Paläoherpetologie, Teil 13, Thecodontia*. Gustav Fischer, Stuttgart, 11–39.

Charig, A. J., Attridge, J. & Crompton, A. W. 1965. On the origin of the sauropods and the classification of the Saurischia. *Proceedings of the Linnean Society, London*, **176**, 197–221.

Charig, A. J., Greenaway, F., Milner, A. C., Walker, C. A. & Whybrow, P. J. 1986. *Archaeopteryx* is not a forgery. *Science*, **232**, 622–626.

Colbert, E. H. 1962. *Dinosaurs: Their Discovery and Their World*. Hutchinson, London.

Colbert, E. H., Charig, A. J., Dodson, P., Gillette, D. D., Ostrom, J. H. & Weishampel, D. 1992. *Coelurus bauri* Cope, 1887 (currently *Coelophysis bauri*; Reptilia, Saurischia): proposed replacement by a neotype. *Bulletin of Zoological Nomenclature*, **49**, 276–279.

Cox, C. B. 1969. Two new dicynodonts from the Triassic Ntawere Formation, Zambia. *Bulletin of the British Museum (Natural History) Geology*, **17**, 257–294.

Cox, C. B. 1997. Obituary: Alan Charig: *The Independent* (London), 13 August.

Crompton, A. W. & Charig, A. J. 1962. A new ornithischian from the Upper Triassic of South Africa. *Nature*, **196**, 1074–1077.

Crompton, A. W. & Jenkins, F. A. 1968. Molar occlusion in late Triassic mammals. *Biological Reviews of the Cambridge Philosophical Society*, **43**, 427–458.

Dodson, P. 1987. Review. Dinosaur systematics symposium, Tyrell Museum of Palaeontology, Drumheller,

Alberta, June 2–5, 1986. *Journal of Vertebrate Paleontology*, **7**, 106–108.

FORTEY, R. 2008. *Dry Store Room No. 1. The Secret Life of the Natural Hitory Museum*. HarperPress, London.

GALTON, P. M. & VAN HEERDEN, J. 1985. Partial hindlimb of *Blikanasaurus cromptoni* n. gen and n. sp., representing a new family of prosauropod dinosaurs from the Upper Triassic of South Africa. *Geobios*, **18**, 509–516.

GAUTHIER, J. 1986. Saurischian monophyly and the origin of birds. *Memoirs of the California Academy of Science*, **8**, 1–55.

GOWER, D. J. & WILKINSON, M. 1996. Is there any consensus on basal archosaur phylogeny? *Proceedings of the Royal Society of London B*, **263**, 1399–1406.

HOYLE, F. & WICKRAMASINGHE, C. 1986. *Archaeopteryx The Primordial Bird: A Case of Fossil Forgery*. Christopher Davies, Swansea.

KREBS, B. 1965. Die Triasfauna der Tessiner Kalkalpen. XIX. *Ticinosuchus ferox* nov. gen. nov. sp. *Schweizerische Paläontologische Abhandlungen*, **81**, 1–140.

KREBS, B. 1969. *Ctenosauriscus koeneni* (v. Huene), die Pseudosuchia und die Buntsandstein-Reptilien. *Eclogae Geologicae Helveticiae*, **62**, 697–714.

KREBS, B. 1976. Pseudosuchia. *In*: CHARIG, A. J., KREBS, B., SUES, H.-D. & WESTPHAL, F. (eds) *Thecodontia, Handbuch der Paläoherpetologie, 13*. Gustav Fisher, Stuttgart.

MARTILL, D. M. 2010. The early history of pterosour discovery in Great Britain. *In*: MOODY, R. T. J., BUFFETAUT, E., NAISH, D. & MARTILL, D. M. (eds) *Dinosaurs and Other Extinct Saurians: A Historical Perspective*. Geological Society, London, Special Publications, **343**, 287–311.

MILNER, A. C. & CROUCHER, R. 1987. *'Claws': The Story (so far) of a Great British Dinosaur*, Baryonyx walkeri. British Museum (Natural History), London.

NAISH, D. & MARTILL, D. M. 2001. Saurischian dinosaurs 1: Sauropods. *In*: MARTILL, D. M. & NAISH, D. (eds) *Dinosaurs of the Isle of Wight*. The Palaeontological Association, London, 185–241.

NAISH, D. & MARTILL, D. M. 2008. Dinosaurs of Great Britain and the role of the Geological Society of London in their discovery: Ornithischia. *Journal of the Geological Society, London*, **165**, 613–623.

NESBITT, S. J. 2003. *Arizonasaurus* and its implications for archosaur divergence. *Proceedings of the Royal Society, London B*, **270**, (Suppl.), S234–S237.

NESBITT, S. J. 2005. The osteology of the pseudosuchian *Arizonasaurus babbitti*. *Historical Biology*, **17**, 19–47.

NEWMAN, B. H. 1968. The Jurassic dinosaur *Scelidosaurus harrisoni*, Owen. *Palaeontology*, **11**, 40–43.

NEWMAN, B. H. 1970. Stance and gait in the flesh-eating *Tyrannosaurus*. *Biological Journal of the Linnean Society*, **2**, 119–123.

NORMAN, D. B. 1997. The dinosaur man: obituary of Alan J. Charig. *The Guardian*, 8 August.

PATTERSON, C. 1970. A clupeomorph fish from the Gault (Lower Cretaceous). *Zoological Journal of the Linnean Society*, **49**, 161–182.

PAUL, G. S. 1988. *Predatory Dinosaurs of the World*. Simon & Schuster, New York.

PAUL, G. S. 2007. Turning the old into the new: a separate genus for the gracile iguanodont from the Wealden of England. *In*: CARPENTER, K. (ed.) *Horns and Beaks: Ceratopsian and Ornithopod Dinosaurs*. Indiana University Press, Bloomington, IN, 69–77.

PAUL, G. S. 2008. A revised taxonomy of the iguanodont dinosaur genera and species. *Cretaceous Research*, **29**, 192–216.

ROMER, A. S. 1956. *Osteology of the Reptiles*. University of Chicago Press, Chicago, IL.

ROMER, A. S. 1971. The Chañares (Argentina) Triassic reptile fauna. X. Two new but incompletely known long-limbed pseudosuchians. *Breviora*, **378**, 1–10.

ROMER, A. S. 1972. The Chañares (Argentina) Triassic reptile fauna. XV. Further remains of the thecodonts *Lagerpeton* and *Lagosuchus*. *Breviora*, **394**, 1–7.

SANGSTER, S. 2001. Anatomy, functional morphology and systematics of *Dimorphodon*. *In*: *Two Hundred Years of Pterosaurs, A Symposium on the Anatomy, Evolution, Palaeobiology and Environments of Mesozoic Flying Reptiles*. *Strata*, Série 1, **11**, 87–88.

SANGSTER, S. 2003. *The Anatomy, Functional Morphology and Systematics of* Dimorphodon macronyx *(Diapsida: Pterosauria)*. PhD dissertation, University of Cambridge.

SANTA LUCA, A. P., CROMPTON, A. W. & CHARIG, A. J. 1976. A complete skeleton of the Late Triassic ornithischian *Heterodontosaurus tucki*. *Nature*, **264**, 324–328.

SENTER, P. 2005. Phylogenetic taxonomy and the names of the major archosaurian (Reptilia) clades. *PaleoBios*, **25**, 1–7.

SERENO, P. 1991. *Lesothosaurus*, 'Fabrosaurids', and the early evolution of Ornithischia. *Journal of Vertebrate Paleontology*, **11**, 168–197.

STEEL, R. 1969. *Handbuch der Paläoherpetologie. Part 15. Ornithischia*. Gustav Fischer, Stuttgart.

STEEL, R. 1970. *Handbuch der Paläoherpetologie. Part 14. Saurischia*. Gustav Fischer, Stuttgart.

THOMAS, K. M. 2004. *Rauisuchian Relationships and the Evolution of the Archosaur Hind Limb*. PhD thesis, Gonville and Caius College, Cambridge and The Natural History Museum, London.

UPCHURCH, P. 1998. The phylogenetic relationships of sauropod dinosaurs. *Zoological Journal of the Linnean Society*, **124**, 43–103.

WADE, M. 1984. *Platypterygius australis*, an Australian Cretaceous ichthyosaur. *Lethaia*, **17**, 99–113.

WOODWARD, A. S. 1905. On parts of the skeleton of *Cetiosaurus leedsi*, a sauropodous dinosaur from the Oxford Clay of Peterborough. *Proceedings of the Zoological Society of London*, **1905**, 232–243.

Forgotten women in an extinct saurian (man's) world

SUSAN TURNER[1]*, CYNTHIA V. BUREK[2] & RICHARD T. J. MOODY[3]

[1]*Monash University Geosciences, Victoria 3800, & Queensland Museum, Geosciences, 122 Gerler Road, Hendra, Queensland 4011, Australia*

[2]*Centre for Science Communication, University of Chester, Parkgate Road, Chester CH1 4BJ, UK*

[3]*Faculty of Science, Kingston University, Penrhyn Road, Kingston KT1 2EE, UK*

**Corresponding author: (e-mail: paleodeadfish@yahoo.com)*

Abstract: Despite dinosaurs becoming significant 'icons' in our culture, few women have made major contributions to the study of fossil vertebrates, especially reptilian taxonomy, by specializing in the dinosaurs and related 'saurians'. Most who were involved over the first 150 years were not professional palaeontologists but instead wives, daughters and pure (and usually unpaid) amateurs. Here we salute some 40 of them, showing how some kept alive childhood dreams and others fell into the subject involuntarily. As usual nineteenth-century female practitioners are virtually unknown in this area except for one icon, Dorset girl Mary Anning of Lyme Regis, who significantly contributed to the palaeontology. Only in the early twentieth century did women such as Tilly Edinger conduct research with an evolutionary agenda. Before the modern post-1960s era, beginning with Mignon Talbot, few were scientists or conducting research; others such as Mary Ann Woodhouse, Arabella Buckley, the Woodward sisters, Nelda Wright were artists, photographers and/or writers, scientifically illustrating and/or popularizing dinosaurs. Like many other women, they often battled to get from first base to job, appear fleetingly in the literature then disappear; or exist as anonymous presences behind eminent men. In contrast, the modern era offers better prospects for those wanting to pursue dinosaurs and their relatives, even if it means volunteering for a dino dig, watching a live 'Time team'-type dinosaur dig on TV or entering the Big Virtual Saurian World now on the Internet. This paper considers the problems and highlights the achievements of the oft-forgotten women.

Supplementary material: Additional references and list of books and publications by or about deceased women related to 'saurians', including these mentioned in the text, are available at http://www.geolsoc.org.uk/SUP18419.

When asked to give a review of the proposed content of this book in 2008, vertebrate palaeontologist Don Brinkman wrote:

> In terms of balance, one aspect of history that is notably absent is any mention of women. I realize that this is in part a reflection of the history of the times.

Well, maybe more than that. Why are there so few women involved in dinosaur land?

When it comes to modern-day children, probably as many little girls as little boys get hooked on dinosaurs. What happens then? When does this interest wane? Do girls just grow up? These days, women in general equal or often outnumber men in undergraduate Earth Science courses at university but then, as the authors of a recent in-depth study of women's role in geology (Burek & Higgs 2007*a*) found, the change normally occurs post-BSc or PhD, when there are no jobs and little funding in most parts of the world (cf. Torrens 1993). The USA is one exception where more opportunities present young women with grants, fellowships, internships to gain a foothold and then a job. In fact, the first scientific paper on a saurian written by a woman came from America (Talbot 1911), and this trend is reflected in the majority of now practicing vertebrate palaeontologists who work on 'saurians' being women employed professionally in that country.

Although the acceptance of dinosaurs was slow in coming (e.g. *West of England Conservative* in Torrens 1993), a few women early on were 'into fossils' and we explore their lives here. Dinosaurs per se, however, were not defined scientifically until 1842 (Torrens 1993) (Fig. 1) and we see no professional (paid) woman vertebrate palaeontologists working on them until the post-World War II era, and then in the Communist world. However, the dinosaurs, although central to our story, are also a vehicle for the larger, more interesting and

From: MOODY, R. T. J., BUFFETAUT, E., NAISH, D. & MARTILL, D. M. (eds) *Dinosaurs and Other Extinct Saurians: A Historical Perspective*. Geological Society, London, Special Publications, **343**, 111–153.
DOI: 10.1144/SP343.7 0305-8719/10/$15.00

Fig. 1. (**a**) 150th anniversary poster commemorating Owen's coining of the term 'Dinosauria' in 1841, created for the 1991 British Association meeting in Plymouth by courtesy and © J. Halstead (from Sargeant 1993; the date refuted by Torrens 1993); (**b**) the artist Jenny Middleton Halstead at Lyme Regis *c.* 1970 (photograph by S. Turner).

important story about the struggle to understand the meaning of fossils and what they tell us about prehistory, and we look at the role that women have played in this unfolding saga. Interestingly, Spielberg's film '*Jurassic Park*' also drew heavily on the work of women, using Halstead & Halstead's (1983) reconstructions of *Velociraptor* and Thulborn & Wade's (1984) unique dinosaur stampede. In our era of the twenty-first century, the significance for children is important here, because women as educators, whether mothers or teachers, help them to come to terms with the big questions of mortality, extinction and sheer size (e.g. Strader & Rinker 1989; Stemmler 2006). As Haste (1993) discussed, dinosaurs have become not only de rigeur for children but a supreme metaphor that permeates our world with images that focus our minds on all sorts of subjects from politics, pollution, climate change, extinction and even gender 'issues'. Most interesting in recent decades has been the astonishing increase in dinosaur lore aimed at children. One of us (S. Turner) as a young girl became 'hooked' on dinosaurs, after she read Ned Colbert's (1951) book. Like many young kids around the world, she grappled with the 'big words' of the scientific names and began to understand what 'vertebrate' and 'palaeontology' really meant – not just dinosaurs but fish, mammoths, giant sea-going reptiles, strange bird-like *Archaeopteryx*, even to our own ancestors. It is worth noting that 'Extinction has never been a barrier for children's imaginations, especially when it comes to magnificent prehistoric beasts like the dinosaurs' (www.busheymuseum.org); Curator David Wharlow was excited as he put the finishing touches to that museum's 'The Age of the Dinosaurs' exhibition at the end of 2008: 'We have a two-metre long *Stegosaurus* and lots of interactives', he enthused; 'There are teeth, bones, skeletons, fossils and models – including one of a baby *T. rex* in a nest. Children can work out the dinosaur family tree, look at different eggs and take part in a dino dig'.

But why did and why do women get involved with dinosaurs? Perhaps it is just continuing child-like curiosity. Certainly, the late eighteenth and early nineteenth centuries saw the beginnings of natural history 'crazes' (especially in Britain) that brought many young women into scientific pursuit (Allen 1976; Barber 1980; Creese & Creese 1994; Burek 2009*a*); 'Every lady has her *Outlines of Geology* – her bag and her hammer; and no drawing room is considered complete in its furniture, which has not its little cabinet and museum' (C. P. N. Wilton 1828 quoted in Mayer 2009, p. 205). Then the giant reptilian dinosaurs and other giant marine saurians began to be unearthed, many of the first by women, including the iconic Mary Anning (Fig. 2a) of Lyme Regis (Fowles 1991; Ticknell 1996; Taquet 2003) and her contemporaries (see below), some no more than a name; such as Miss Orless (unknown), English collector of reptiles (Cleevely 1983, p. 220), or Miss Lucy Oakes (Okes) and Miss Spekes, who hunted fossils with Mary Anning and Miss Pinney (see later; Goodhue 2004; J. Stacey pers. comm. 2008). And just like children today (e.g. *National Geographic* dinosaur issue 1993), these early young women could 'own' such work; they had not yet been told that digging up saurians and getting dirty was not fit for ladies. However, 'ladies' in higher social echelons could not get involved in the scientific debates then underway, especially in the fledgling Geological Society of London (GSL), founded from a gentlemen's dining club in 1807; 'ladies' might be allowed a visit but they did not 'fight', whereas the men often did in heated discussions (Thackray 1999). Anning again, as one of the few 'lower-class' women did have freedom to 'fight' and argue with the men and held her own with Henry Thomas De la Beche (1796–1855), the Bucklands, the Murchisons and others, gaining their respect if not always the necessary funds she needed to survive in her enforced profession (e.g. Pierce 2006).

Pioneer collectors

Mary Anning

Born in Lyme Regis, Mary Ann Anning (1799–1846) first learned to collect fossils around 1810 as a child, working alongside her cabinet-maker father Richard and her brother Joseph (e.g. Taylor & Torrens 1995), remaining a spinster all her life. She was often alone in all weathers with only her dog for companion (Fig. 2b). 'Fate' seemed to have made her exactly the right person at the right place and time to pioneer the emerging science of palaeontology. The unstable cliffs and stealthy sea made the task dangerous but after her father died, probably of tuberculosis, the sale of fossils sustained the family. Although circumstances were straightened, as Richard died leaving debts of £120 and at times they were in arrears with the rates, the family continued to receive parish funds until 1816 (J. Stacey pers. comm. 2009). After her father's death and her brother's apprenticeship, Mary continued in the fossil collecting and preparation business with her lesser-known mother, Mary (1764–1842) known as Molly (Cadbury 2000); see the letter from 'Fossil Shop'-owner Mrs Anning to Charles Konig in London negotiating over prices (Rolfe *et al.* 1988, text-fig. 4). In 1817 they met Lieutenant-Colonel Thomas Birch, a well-to-do fossil collector who became a supporter

Fig. 2. (**a**) Line drawing of Mary Anning reproduced from *Heroine of Lyme Regis. The Story of Mary Anning, the Celebrated Geologist of Lyme* by H. A. Forde. Image courtesy of the British Library Board. (**b**) Anning's dog Tray, from a sketch done by Anning, found in the Pinney papers (modified from Pierce 2006); (**c**) Mary's hammer (Image from R. T. J. Moody); (**d**) Mary Anning's gravestone in St Michael's church, Lyme Regis (Image from R. T. J. Moody).

of the family. He attributed major discoveries in the area to them, and arranged to sell his personal collection of fossils for the family's benefit.

Locally, Mary junior's fame started as an infant when she survived a lightning strike that killed the three adults around her; 'She had been a dull child before, but after this accident became lively and intelligent, and grew up so' (Roberts 1834). Anning did not get to collect dinosaurs per se but was a pioneer reptilian vertebrate palaeontologist as well as a dealer, mostly self-taught and therefore an (informed) amateur; she found many a 'first' and, as an amateur, corresponded with the upcoming (male) geologists of the day. In 1811, aged 12, she caught the public's attention when she (or probably her brother Joseph) unearthed first the head and later the skeleton of a 'fish lizard', 'sea-dragon', *Ichthyosaurus* or ichthyosaur (see Roberts 1834; Howe *et al.* 1981; Torrens 1993, fig. 3, 2008); although earlier ones had been found by the Philpots (q.v.). Later (1823) Mary found the first plesiosaur – *Plesiosaurus dolichodeirus* – with its extraordinary long neck (a 'sea monster' more recently associated, albeit erroneously, with the 'Loch Ness Monster'), a second specimen of which was bought on behalf of Cuvier by Constant Prévost who paid £10 gifted by the Muséum National d'Histoire Naturelle, Paris (MNHN) (Taquet 2003; Vincent & Taquet 2010). Taquet (2003) also noted that she actually bought the second specimen from 'sailors' for £3. She then unearthed the first specimen of a flying reptile, a pterodactyl, to be named in Britain – *Dimorphodon macronyx* – a frightening 'flying dragon' with hand claws and teeth (see cartoon in Torrens 1993, fig. 4). (The first pterosaur was found in France by Cosimo Collini (1727–1806) in 1784 (D. Martill pers. comm. www.pterosaur.co.uk/, accessed 2009)). Another specimen sold by Bullock in 1820 was the first (claimed) *Ichthyosaurus*, described by Sir Everhard Home in 1814 (but see Rolfe *et al.* 1988; Chevalier 2009). In spite of this, her many discoveries were announced to the world by men including the irrepressible William Buckland (1784–1856) and De La Beche, who often received the credit. Conybeare and Phillips sadly failed to send the Annings a copy of their (1822) book when published (Goodhue 2002, 2004). De la Beche, however, did use her finds as inspiration for his 1830 cartoon *Duria Antiquior*, copies of which were sold for her benefit (Rudwick 1992; Weishampel & White 2003).

As Torrens (1993, 1995) has emphasized, Mary Anning's discoveries of remarkable, complete and, then, inexplicable fossils were enormously important in kick-starting an unprecedented public interest. Many of the more intimate comments on Mary, however, are drawn from the writings of Anna Maria Pinney (1812–1861) (Lang 1954). Mary left school aged 11, after her father died, with a basic primary education; Pinney inferred (Lang 1954) that Mary helped in the household of Mrs Stock of the Great House in Broad Street (possibly a doctor's wife) in her early teens; this lady being the person who lent or gave Mary her first geology book, which she evidently had no trouble reading (J. Stacey pers. comm. 2009). Her father equipped her with her first hammer (Fig. 2c). Even so, against the odds, because she was relatively uneducated and poor, the wrong sex, in the wrong class and even the wrong religion (Burek 2001*a*, 2003), Mary, unlike any other woman, has been recognized for her endeavours on fossil saurians, being noted as a 'Dorset Worthy' (Curle 1963), 'St Georgina of Lyme Regis', a 'Princess of Palaeontology', a 'Helen to the geologists', a 'Pythoness' (prophetess), a 'geological Lioness' of fossils (Pierce 2006) and 'the greatest fossilist the world ever knew' (Torrens 1995). Mary never married (see Chevalier 2009 for one scenario) but her faithful companion in the field for many years was her trusted and trained dog (possibly called 'Tray', a common dog name in Victorian times, or 'Thursday' (Pinney papers: J. Stacey pers. comm. 2009) that was immortalized in the famous painting. Mary left us a sketch of him (Fig. 2b). Sadly, Tray was killed in a landslip before her eyes (Pierce 2006). Mary died a slower death over a 2-year period from incurable breast cancer (Fig. 2d).

Miss Pinney was herself a caring and philanthropic soul, well educated with a sharp mind and a strong religious conviction who came to have a very good understanding of Mary's moods and temperament. She was the daughter of a wealthy merchant and land-owning family from Somerton Erleigh, Dorset; William Pinney, her brother, was elected first MP for Lyme Regis and Charmouth in 1832; her journal was part published by W. D. Lang in 1954. The following quotes say much about Mary and her closeness to Anna Maria as well as the topics they discussed:

> She glories in being afraid of no one and in saying everything she pleases

and

> To think that life shall never have an end quite fills the mind, but to think of God without a beginning is more than a created being can comprehend.
>
> (Miss Anna Maria Pinney papers)

Mary could hold her own in intense scientific debates about what her giant bones were and what they meant, and so later in life was sorely disappointed that her contributions were not properly acknowledged. Nor had she been immortalized by the naming of any after her (although Louis Agassiz (1807–1873) did name a fossil fish for her – *Acrodus anningiae*); her reptilian fossils were described by contemporaries and named after other prominent men in the field. Her Jurassic saurians, especially plesiosaurs, grace the Natural History Museum (NHM) walls in London but her name is not there. Mary did impress with her intellectual mastery of anatomy; for example, Lady Harriet Silvester (unknown), widow of the Recorder of the City of London, who visited Anning in 1824 recorded in her diary that Mary:

> had made herself so thoroughly acquainted with the science that the moment she finds any bones she knows to what tribe they belong... by reading and application she has arrived to that greater degree of knowledge as to be in the habit of writing and talking with professors and other clever men on the subject, and they all acknowledge that she understands more of the science than anyone else in this kingdom.
>
> (Quoted in Torrens 1995)

At least the men, notably Buckland and De la Beche, raised a stipend at the British Association for the Advancement of Science meeting in Dublin 1835 to help her, and they did make her an Honorary GSL Member some months before her premature death (e.g. W. D. Lang 1936; Lambrecht *et al.* 1938; Sarjeant 1978–1987, Suppl. I, p. 1683, Suppl. II, p. 252, Suppl. III, pp. 433–434; Burek 2009*b*). In 1999 the bicentenary of her birth was celebrated in Lyme Regis with a conference held in her honour, and a new spate of books about her were published. Mary Anning has attracted many epithets and is now an icon. There are copious books on dinosaurs in which she appears, many written by women often for children (e.g. Trenchard 1999, who noted that Mary was thinking along the same lines as Darwin; Arnold 2007) and so we cannot say she is actually forgotten but the details of the hardship of her life and her scientific endeavours have only come to light slowly and more recently (e.g. Pierce 2006; Torrens 2008; Chevalier 2009). The recognition she sought is finally coming (e.g. Vincent & Taquet 2010). At the time, however, Mary did know a measure of 'fame'; during a visit from the King of Saxony she proudly noted that she was 'well-known throughout the whole Europe'. A pair of nineteenth-century nodding china figures from Germany (Meissen?), made some time after 1861 and reckoned to be of Anning and a male companion, either De la Beche or brother Joseph, were donated by an American to the Philpot Museum in the 1990s (M. Taylor pers. comm. 1997). This fame continues as a survey of public knowledge of women scientists throughout Europe showed that Mary Anning was the only female geologist cited and often that was not by name but by description 'the dinosaur women from Lyme Regis' (Burek & Higgs 2007*a*). Pierce in her (2006) biography on Mary Anning and her 'primeval monsters' redresses the imbalance of Mary's treatment. It is her mother, however, who made this ultimate salute:

> The most famous female fossilist. She is a history and a mystery.

Elizabeth, Margaret and Mary Philpot

After his marriage, the brother of the three surviving Philpot sisters settled them at Morley Cottage in Lyme Regis. Miss Elizabeth (1780–1857), the better known of the three as a fossil collector, Miss Margaret (1786–1845) and Miss Mary (1777–1838) were middle-class gentry, well educated but somewhat impoverished. All were active, pioneer collectors (Edmonds 1978) but it was Elizabeth who collected and meticulously cared for and presented her own collection, specializing in fossil fish in which she became an expert, sought out by Louis Agassiz. Unlike Mary, she had no need to sell her specimens. Their collections became the foundation for the Philpot Museum, Lyme Regis (Edmonds 1978).

The Philpots were patrons, friends and collaborators of Mary Anning, working on finding Dorset coast Jurassic reptiles, but Elizabeth is viewed as her 'lifetime companion' and main collaborator. The relationship between the two women from very different backgrounds but with a common devotion has been explored in the novel *Remarkable Creatures* by Tracey Chevalier (2009).

'Miss Congrieve'

Miss Congreve or Congrieve was an English fossil hunter in the 1820s linked with the Misses Philpot and Mary Anning; but not a great deal is known about her (Revd Tom Goodhue, H-net list 1995) and there might even be two collecting sisters, Mary (1745–1823) and Sarah (1737–1836) Congreve (R. Oudans pers. comm. 2009). *The Mirror of Literature, Amusement & Instruction* (Saturday, 25 July 1829, No. 382, price 2d) noted Bristol geologist George Cumberland's (1829) praise that:

> the world would to this day have remained ignorant of the treasures England possessed, but for the patient labours of three female pioneers in this service, viz. Mary Anning, a dealer; Miss Congrieve and Miss Philpots (sic), residents, who for years have been collecting and preserving these bodies from the wreck of the coast; the two last without any other view than the gratification of laudable curiosity, and who with unequalled liberality, communicated their collections to every man of science that visited the place; and it is to liberal minds like theirs and Miss Bennet's (sic) of Wiltshire that we owe the first rescuing of these natural gems from the spoilers.
>
> (Quoted in Brande's Journal http://www.gutenberg.org/files/11462/11462-8.txt)

Torrens (in litt. to T. Goodhue, 18 April 1996) believes that, unlike the Philpots, Miss Congrieve and perhaps her sister primarily collected fossils found by others rather than unearthing fossils themselves. Conybeare and De la Beche were well acquainted with at least one 'Miss Congreve', as witnessed by Conybeare's letters to the latter in 1821 (84.20G.D.297 dated 16 December and 84.20G.D.299, National Museum of Wales (NMW)) in which he describes examining an ichthyosaur head in 'Miss Congreve's' possession (Goodhue 2004). Conybeare also sent 'Miss Congreve' six scientific papers via De la Beche in the same year (NMW letters op. cit.).

Etheldred Benett

Miss Etheldred Benett (1776–1845), probably the first woman geologist (Torrens *et al.* 2000, Table 1), was born and bred in Wiltshire, UK, the daughter of a local squire (Torrens 1985). She spent much of her life in Norton Bavant near Warminster at the family country home, Norton House (Cleevely 1998). Her upbringing was somewhat formal, presumably by governesses, and she was correct by manner. Throughout her life she was subject to illness and became almost housebound later in life. When she was able to travel she spent a month each year in London and spent time at Weymouth. At some point she took to fossil collecting.

Her collection was built up of material collected by herself and fossils purchased from other collectors (Laming & Laming 2007). She had a very good eye as a collector but, unlike many of the age, was capable of using fossils to correlate the formations she collected from, effectively employing the method of William Smith (1789–1839). She sent her sections to the Geological Society in 1813 (Burek 2009*a*) and, as Cleevely (1998) notes, 'Her knowledge of the formations occurring in Wiltshire was used by Greenough in compiling his (1819) *Geological Map of England & Wales*, subsequently published as an appendix to the third volume of *The History of Modern Wiltshire* by R. C. Hoare in 1831'. Miss Benett became renowned among the evergrowing community of geologists and natural scientists, and developed a particular friendship and professional relationship with Gideon Mantell (1790–1852), who named a sponge *Ventriculites Benettiae* after her and wrote in 1822 that she was a:

> lady of great talent and indefatigable research to whom I am under infinite obligations for many valuable communications on scientific subjects.
>
> (*Fossils of the South Downs*, p. 177)

She in turn was robust when he suggested she should visit Portland whilst in Weymouth stating that a:

> lady going into the quarries is a signal for the men begging money for beer, and the few times I have been there I never got a specimen worth bringing home. All my Portland fossils have been purchased in Weymouth!
>
> (Mantell letter dated 2 November 1835)

Cleevely (1998) also notes that she was not averse to reprimanding her old friend Mantell:

> Pray allow me to remark that you have lately taken to spelling my Christian name 'Ethelred', whereas it is Etheldred as above.
>
> (Benett in litt., in a postscript 4 November 1842)

Miss Benett's letters are housed in the Mantell archive in the Turnbull Library, Wellington, New Zealand, and Cleevely (1998) records that data exist to prove that her collection contained teeth of *Iguanodon*, which he suggests could be missing types (see Mary Ann Woodhouse later). More detailed insights into the life of Etheldred Benett are given by Spamer *et al.* (1989), Nash (1990), Creese & Creese (1994), and Burek (2001*b*, 2004).

Mary Hone Smith

Mrs M. H. Smith (1784–1866) was possibly born in Stepney, London. She was an amateur collector who had continued contact with the learned geological community of the day. Mary was married to William Hugh Smith who died in 1838, prior to her move to first Sussex Place and then Mayo House in Tunbridge Wells, Kent. She devoted considerable time to the acquisition of a magnificent collection of local Cretaceous fossils. Like Miss Benett, she was known to purchase material from quarrymen and exchanged with other collectors. She also collected her own material from chalk quarries; some of her fossil reptiles were figured by Dixon and Owen (catalogue in NHM, purchased 1878) (Cleevely 1983). Cleevely (1983) listed fossils also in the Brighton and Nottingham museums, and in the Institute of Geological Sciences (IGS) (ex-GSL).

Gideon Mantell was well acquainted with Mrs Smith (Mantell 1832, pp. 98–108). In 1842, when he was living at Chester Square, Pimlico, Mantell wrote:

> Visit to Tunbridge' Called on Mrs Smith and inspected some beautiful and rare fossils from the Kentish chalk.
>
> (Mantell's Journal p. 158 – 13 June: Curwen 1940)

and on November 23 1845:

> Mrs Smith of Tunbridge Wells left for my inspection a beautiful specimen in chalk of 30–40 vertebrae with ribs, and jaws and teeth of a small lizard, allied to the *Agama*; such a beauty! and from Kent.
>
> (Mantell's Journal p. 198: Curwen 1940)

Mary was listed as blind in the 1861 census and died at the age of 82 in 1866. After her death her collections passed to her daughter, the first Mrs Bishop of Bramcote, Nottingham, who unfortunately died young. Her successor, the second Mrs Bishop, sold much of the collection to the British Museum (Natural History), London (BMNH), whereas Mr Bishop bequeathed material to Nottingham Museum in 1877 (Cleevely 1983). A small cabinet was retained by the second Mrs Bishop. Sadly, no one specific specimen from Mary Smith's collection exists in the Brighton Museum (J. Cooper pers. comm. 2009).

Two Harriets – Holland and Hutton

Harriett 'Sophia' Holland (1835–1908) (Fig. 3a) was the eldest daughter of Edward Holland (1806–1875), Lord of the Manor of Dumbleton and well-known agriculturalist, and his first wife Sophia (1813–1851) (see *www.dumbletonvillage.co.uk/Buildings/StPetersChurch*). Their home, Harescombe Hall, was built of hand-worked Cotswold Stone from the local Temple Guiting quarries. Dumbleton Hill is an outlier of the Cotswold escarpment, with limestone partially covering heavy Lias Clay that plagued her father's ploughmen. Sophia married Crompton Hutton (1822–1910) on 25 July 1865 (Torrens 1978). She collected excellent material from the Jurassic Inferior Oolite, and her hobby and enthusiasm encouraged her daughter Harriet Mary (1873–1937) to continue her work as a committed geologist (Anon. 1938). The Harriet Sophia Holland collection passed on her death to the Cheltenham Museum (Woodward 1911).

Before her death in 1937, Harriet 'Mary' Hutton (Fig. 3b) became one of the rare breed of women who were early Fellows of the Geological Society (FGSs) (Burek 2009*b*). By February 1922 there were only 21 female Fellows and Hutton's later fellowship can still be regarded as a major achievement. In 1931 she expressed the wish to divide her collection amongst several museums, with *Steneosaurus* and other saurians passing to Gloucester Museum (Torrens 1978).

Sophia was also the maternal grandmother of Beatrix Potter (Lear 2007) and was also related to the author Mrs Gaskell, who in turn was acquainted with the Bronte sisters. Beatrix visited her cousins Mary and Caroline at Harescombe Hall several times in the 1890s and developed an interest in fossils herself after collecting at the nearby quarry at Huddington Hill (Gardiner 2000).

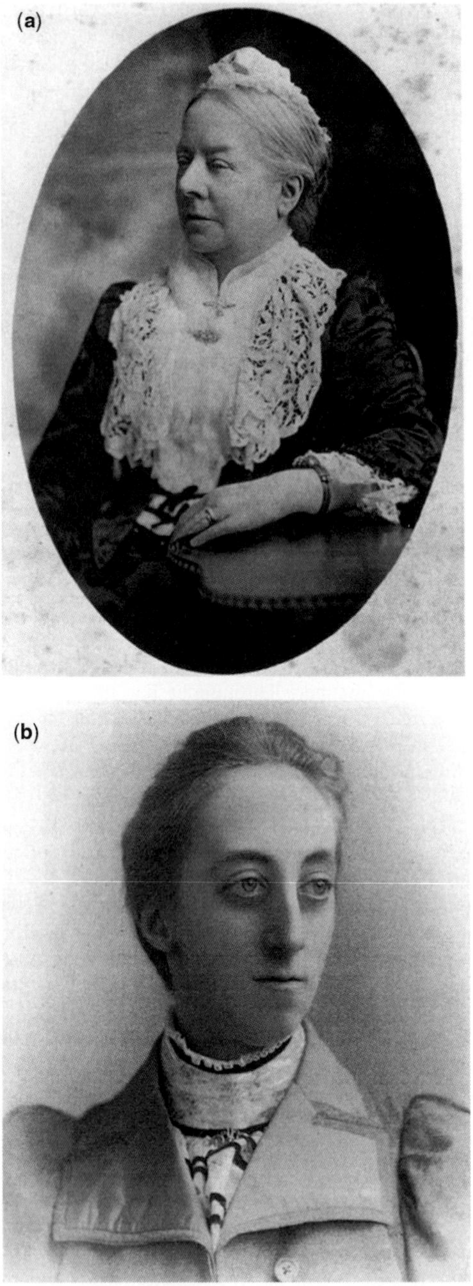

Fig. 3. (**a**) Nineteenth century collectors Sophia Holland; and (**b**) her daughter Harriet Mary Hunt (Copyright the Linnaean Society).

Ruth Mason

Like Mary Anning, Ruth Mason (1913–1990) was a young girl when she made a major find of saurian fossils. When only 7 years old, Ruth found a huge dinosaur bone bed on her family's Harding County ranch, near Faith, South Dakota, USA. Since then, tens of thousands of Cretaceous dinosaur fossils have been recovered from the 'Ruth Mason Quarry', including the duck-billed, plant-eating

Edmontosaurus annectens and *Tyrannosaurus rex* teeth. (See http://thunderbutte.blogspot.com/2009/06/dinosaur-bones for more details on the dinosaurs of Thunder Butte.)

Unsung heroines – wives and partners

Other wives, daughters and female relatives have played important roles in the forefront of saurian research; some only get a brief mention such as Mrs Townsend, who gave Stonesfield Slate reptiles to the Natural History Museum London (Cleevely 1983). Those described in this section were invariably skilled or talented in their own right. Some lived in times when wives existed in the background but by the late nineteenth century, women had cast off many of the enforced inhibition of previous generations, and lived full and spirited lives as equal partners.

Mary Morland

Mary Morland (1797–1857), an accomplished illustrator, became Mrs William Buckland in late 1825 after they met in a coach and she was sitting opposite him reading Cuvier (Cadbury 2000). She went on to illustrate her husband's papers (Kölbl-Ebert 1997; Burek & Higgs 2007*b*), notably in Buckland's (1824) *Megalosaurus* paper with her sublime plates (see also Weishampel & Wright 2003, pp. 56–59).

Rupke (1983, p. 7) stated 'His (Buckland's) prose, corrected by his wife, Mary Morland, was very fine indeed . . .'. She also illustrated for Cuvier (J. Stacey pers. comm.), Conybeare and Waterhouse Hawkins, who used Mrs B's drawings for the Bridgewater Treatise to assist his reconstructions (Gordon 1894, p. 198). She died a year after her husband.

Mary Ann Woodhouse

Mary Woodhouse (1795–1869), better known as Mrs Gideon Mantell (Curwen 1940), for whom we have two pictures (Fig. 4a, c), was the daughter of George Edward Woodhouse of Maida Hill, Paddington, London and mother Mary Ann (surname unknown). In May 1816, when she was sick at Lewes, Sussex, she met and later married (as a minor) Mantell, her father's doctor, a man 5 years older than herself (Edmonds 1979). Gideon Mantell (1790–1852) became a successful doctor in Lewes and an amateur geologist in his spare time (Curwen 1940); the chance to work as a professional geologist was not at first within his financial means.

Initially, Mary shared his interest in fossils and was happy to accompany her husband on his geological forays whenever there was a chance of collecting. Indeed, she is known for finding the first *Iguanodon* teeth (Fig. 4b) in the summer of 1822 when she was 27, in the coarse Wealden conglomerate at Whiteman's Green, Cuckfield, in Tilgate Forest during a walk while her husband was visiting a patient, which Mantell at first endorsed but recanted after they separated. This story has often been popularized (e.g. Edmonds 1979; Cadbury 2000) but recent doubt has been poured on the somewhat romanticized claim both on her involvement and the date (Dean 1999) with the suggestion that the Mantells probably bought the first teeth off local quarrymen (Naish 2009).

Nevertheless, Mary helped Mantell intensely between 1818 and 1822, illustrating his (1822) local book on *The Fossils of the South Downs* – producing over 364 fine lithographs from her husband's drawings. Many of the 42 plates engraved by Mrs Mantell contain multiple drawings (Fig. 4b); her skill in lithography improved from the first attempts, with the later plates being much better (Spokes 1927). Ethelred Benett commented to Mantell that with a little practice Mary's sketching would be 'stronger and bolder . . . all that is wanting to make them a great ornament to your work' (Burek 2001*b*). Professor Benjamin Silliman (1779–1864) of Yale College also acknowledged the quality of her engraving, and used them in his lectures:

> As a husband and an admirer of the fairer as well as the better part of our race, I was happy also to do honor to Mrs. Mantell's important agency in those discoveries: and to the illustrations of them by her pencil and graver, which have made Sussex not less renowned in modern times for its natural than in ancient days it was for its civil history.
>
> (Quoted from a letter to Mantell that was quoted in Spokes 1927)

Mantell was very proud of his wife's work but there is no evidence that she contributed to Mantell's second book of Tilgate Forest fossils (Spokes 1927).

Gideon Mantell corresponded and visited with many famous geologists, including Murchison, Buckland and Lyell:

> During the summer Mrs. Woodhouse, Mr. Lyell, Dr. Fitton, Sir Richard Phillips etc. have visited me and most of the gentry and nobility have called to inspect my collection. My work appears to have been well received both in this country and on the Continent.
>
> (Journal of Gideon Mantell 1822 in Curwen 1940)

Sometimes wives accompanied but Mary Mantell was rarely in attendance, as when Mantell went to the GSL (Thackray 1999) and attended a meeting in Cambridge in 1833, and met up with Buckland and Murchison and their wives Mary and Charlotte (Spokes 1927). The Mantells were not as wealthy as

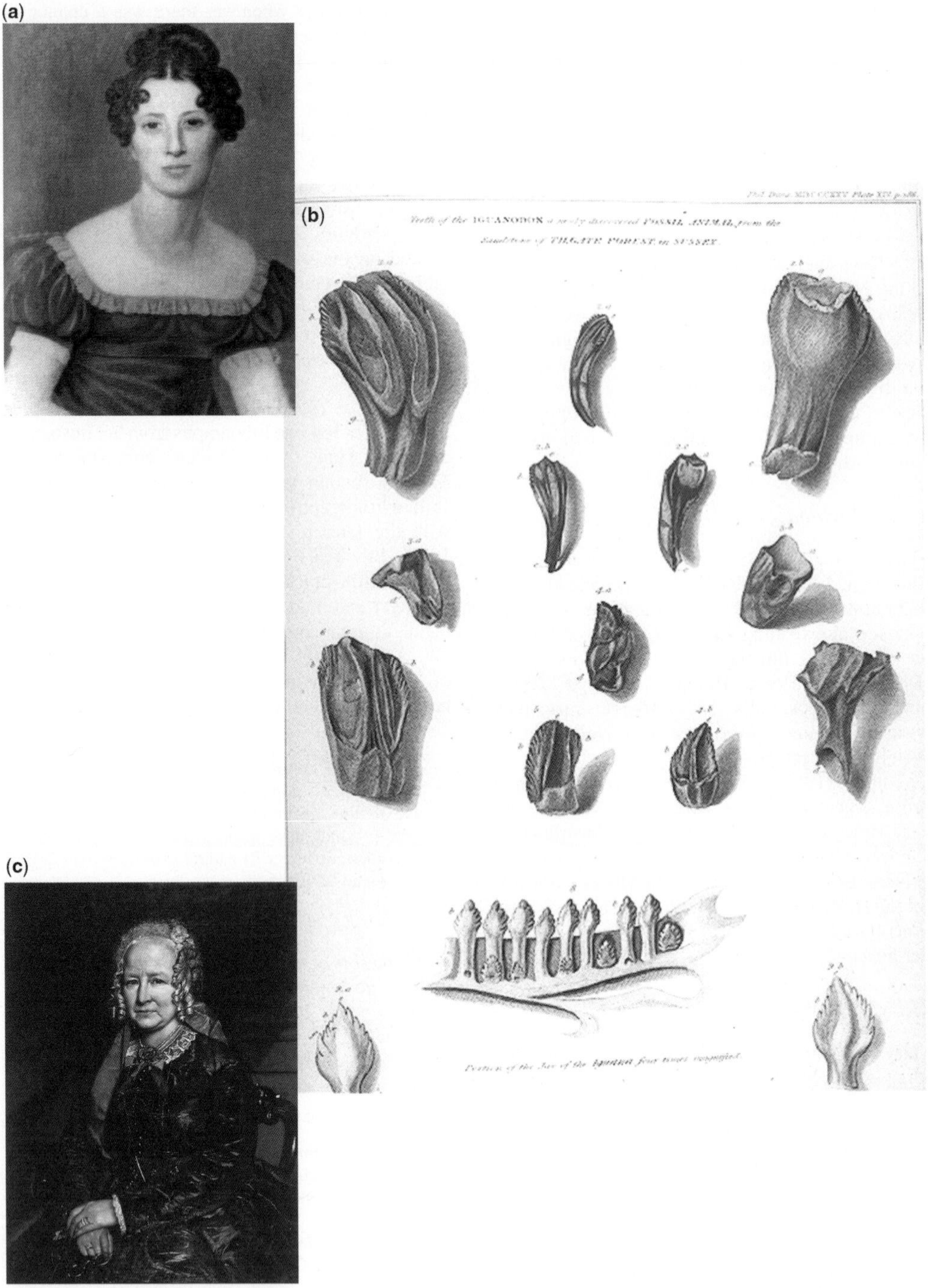

Fig. 4. (**a**) Mary Ann Woodhouse; (**b**) her drawings of the *Iguanodon* teeth; (**c**) Mrs Mantell in old age, a portrait in oils probably taken by or sent to her son Walter to remember her by (courtesy of Turnbull Library, Wellington, New Zealand).

the other 'geological' families, and money for non-essentials and numerous servants was lacking, which might explain Mary Ann's absence. In later years in London, Gideon maintained a reasonable household and a medical assistant (Anon. 1975).

Gradually Mary Ann perceived herself becoming sidelined by family responsibilities and illness both within herself, by her own and her husband's family. The illness and weakness of her third child must have been a significant trial. She felt her new house in Brighton was just a meeting house and museum, with endless visitors passing through and, although Gideon Mantell tried to limit this to 2 days a month, there were frequent infringements 'to the great annoyance of Mrs. Mantell and the discomposure of my domestic arrangements' (letter from Mantell to Silliman quoted in Spokes 1927). Thus, at the age of 45, worn out from the birth of four children and the move to a house that was effectively a museum, and with her husband mostly abandoning her for his first love of geology and his obsession with fossils instead of his livelihood, she left him in 1839. Was she, like the first Mrs Agassiz, not only a victim of overwork but also of a husband with undiagnosed mental problems (bipolar or Asperger's?), for both Gideon and Louis Agassiz (Tharp 1959) shared this obsessional behaviour, not unusual in 'focused' palaeontologists.

Mantell was disappointed in his wife and her attitude but perhaps this was through his own fault (Curwen 1940). He had married a young girl and, although he had tried at the beginning to include her in his work, as time went on his tremendous work ethic, lack of financial security and determination to succeed alienated what could have been a useful and fulfilling assistant to share his love of fossils. A quote from his journal following the breakup effectively sums this up:

> There was a time when my poor wife felt deep interest in my pursuits, and was proud of my success, but of late years that feeling had passed away and she was annoyed rather than gratified by my devotion to science.
>
> (From Mantell's Journal 1840 in Curwen 1940)

With children no longer dependent, Mary Mantell left with the housekeeper Hannah Brook, moving to Exeter. At that time divorce was not common and effectively Mary Ann Mantell gave up legal control of both her property and her children, then 21, 19, 17 and 12 years old. Except for brief visits in 1840 to the funeral of their second daughter, Hannah Matilda, and in 1850 to Chester Square, London, there is no evidence that she was with her husband again. He wrote in 1849:

> I am ... downright savage in mind from the conduct of my wife ... it is 8 years since my better 1/2 left me: ask Mr. Gell if I may not now be divorced? – (no fee, mind)
>
> (Quoted from Mantell's Journal in Curwen 1940, p. 141)

Divorce Act changes did not come into effect until 18 years later (1857), so the children remained with their father as was customary. Mary was still in Exeter in 1851 at the time of the census, living in a house run for ladies in the Parish of St Sidwell. This area is respectable but not well off; the property fronts onto the main Honiton Road whereas the back is close to Bridewell prison and the hospital. She is listed as the 55-year-old wife of a surgeon, living alone with no servants. Her neighbours were the widow of a navy captain and the householder. When Gideon Mantell died in 1852 from an opium overdose (no doubt related to extreme health problems from an accidental spinal injury in 1841: Spokes 1927, 1929), he had not acknowledged his wife at all and left her nothing in his will. The last we hear of her is of her youngest son visiting her in Cambridge in 1853; she died 16 years later a relatively old woman in her early 70s (Fig. 4c).

Thus, Mary Ann Mantell's role in saurian research is as a wife-assistant to her husband in collecting, illustrating and engraving. This not insignificant contribution serves to illustrate the roles played by many of the women of this period (cf. Burek & Higgs 2007*b*; Turner 2007).

Caroline Amelia Clift

Caroline Amelia (1801–1873) was the only daughter of William Clift FRS (1775–1849), Conservator of the Museum of the Royal College of Surgeons of England, and Caroline Harriet Pope (1775–1849). Her family was well placed in the elite intellectual and emergent scientific society of the day. She married young Lancastrian Richard Owen (1804–1892) on his birthday on 20 July 1835 at the New St Pancras Church, London. They had been engaged for 8 years since 1827, the same year he had become Assistant Conservator to her father. In 1837 she gave birth to their only child William, who committed suicide in 1886 aged 48, perhaps because of his father's 'lamentable coldness of the heart' (http://www.aim25.ac.uk/cats/9/6887.htm accessed December 2009); this, conversely, despite his affectionate early correspondence with mother and son 'Will' (Rupke 1994).

Caroline was self-taught in comparative anatomy and in her use of several languages, and if nothing else could have listened to the oft-difficult Owen with understanding and perhaps translated for him through his long but often acrimonious career; she once arrived home to find the carcass of a dead rhinoceros in her front hallway and encouraged Richard to smoke cigars to rid their house of smells (Rupke 1994). Whether she shared her husband's religious views and anti-evolutionist stance is unknown. She did try to illustrate for him but the 'appalling' Owen was not satisfied (Barber 1980). Caroline Owen died on 7 May 1873 at her last home, Sheen Lodge, Richmond Park, the gift of Her Majesty Queen Victoria to Owen in 1852.

Orra White Hitchcock

On the other side of the Atlantic, Orra L. White (1796–1863) became the wife of pioneer dinosaur worker Edward Hitchcock (1793–1864) in 1821. She was an illustrator as well as an excellent scientist, and in 1841 provided some of the first scientific illustrations of Mesozoic dinosaur footprints both in the United States and the world and became the first woman recognized for her work in American palaeontology (Aldrich 1982).

Orra was the daughter of Jarab White, who farmed near Amherst, Massachusetts, and from a very young age exhibited an interest in the visual arts and natural sciences and learned to draw from private tutors. Her name means 'pray' in Latin. Interestingly, Jarab believed in women's education and sent his favourite child to boarding school where she excelled in Greek, Latin, art, natural sciences, maths and astronomy; Orra then chose to become a teacher of exact sciences and fine arts at the private, coeducational Congregational Deerfield Academy, during which time she met Edward around the end of 1813. He later held the posts of Professor of Natural Science and Geology and President at Amherst College, and became an eminent scientist, beginning the study of Mesozoic footprints; Orra accompanied him on many of his geology and botany expeditions in Massachusetts, including the famous Connecticut Valley. She was an orthodox Christian, a firm believer in the sanctity of family and so gave up her career to become a pastor's wife. Their marriage produced eight children, six of whom lived past infancy, two of whom also graduated from Amherst becoming geologists; one, Edward 'Doc' Hitchcock, named one of the earliest dinosaurs discovered in America. Orra also got involved in the local community in her spare time!

Orra illustrated some of Edward Hitchcock's earliest geological papers, in the *American Journal of Science* in the 1820s, but was especially productive in drawing for his reports on the geology of the state of Massachusetts. Her plates for the state survey included fossils and scenes showing geological features and celebrating the New England landscape. She also created oversize paintings for use in her husband's classes, one life-size *Iguanodon* being 23 m long. Edward paid her due acknowledgement in his *The Religion of Geology and its Connected Sciences* (1851) and noted that in their joint work she had created 232 plates and over 1000 woodcuts! She continued to create works of art until she was involved in an accident in 1855, and was unable to continue. Succumbing to pneumonia she predeceased her husband (Marché 1991).

Although Orra deplored the notion of women geologists ('a shame for cows and women to be treated thus'), the Hitchcocks nonetheless encouraged the inclusion of science in the curriculum of the all-female school founded by their student and long-time friend, Mary Lyon, which eventually became Mount Holyoke College (Aldrich & Leviton 2001).

Yvette Borup

Better known as the wife of Roy Chapman Andrews (1884–1960), whom she had married in 1914 in Ossining, New York, Yvette (unknown) was undoubtedly long-suffering. On one of their forays into Mongolia she was attacked by feral black, corpse-eating dogs (Lavas 1993, p. 45). She was photographer and illustrator on several of Chapman Andrews' early expeditions, and is named as co-author in several editions of *Camps and Trails in China: A Narrative of Exploration, Adventure and Sport in Little-Known China*. These expeditions led to the famous first-known dinosaur eggs and nest discoveries in 1923, triggered by an unknown Mongolian woman who daily brought Andrews 'handfuls of eggshell fragments' that she traded for empty tin cans! (Lavas 1993, p. 47).

Yvette's father was Colonel Henry Borup (1853–1916), who was widely known in military circles and served as a Military Attaché in Paris and Petrograd. He was a also a member of Military Intelligence. Her brother, George, accompanied Peary on his journey to the North Pole but died at the age of 27 in 1912 – by drowning in Long Island Sound. The family name has Scandinavian roots. Yvette was educated at the Kaiserin Auguste Institute, Germany and was a close friend of Emperor Wilhelm's daughter the Duchess of Brunswick. The Andrews had two sons but were divorced in 1930 in Paris on the grounds of his desertion (*Time* magazine, 13 April 1931); it was later revealed that their second child Roy junior, the author of *Castles of Morea*, was not Roy's son.

Mrs Barnum Brown – the first

Barnum's first wife Marion Raymond Brown (1877–1910) died of scarlet fever soon after giving birth to their only child, Frances R. Brown, in 1910.

Marion, graduated from Wells College with a degree in biology and took her Masters at Colombia; before teaching biology at Erasmus High in Brooklyn. She accompanied Barnum in the field in 1904 but sadly her journal – '*A Log Book of the Bug Hunters*' – was never published.

(L. Dingus pers. comm. 2009)

Lilian MacLaughlin – Mrs Barnum Brown the second

Lilian Brown (née MacLaughlin) (1887–1971), American wife of palaeontologist Barnum Brown (1873–1963), was affectionately known as 'Pixie'.

Lilian did publish books on their travels – the iconic '*I Married a Dinosaur*' (Brown 1951) (Fig. 5a); '*Bring 'Em Back Petrified*' in 1958; and one more on Greece (D. Spalding pers. comm.) – but in following Barnum to seek fossils in India, Burma, Guatemala, she didn't really get her hands dirty but did see a fair bit of the world and wrote their stories, publicising his work. Brown and Lilian married in 1922 in Calcutta, India, where she was ostensibly on a world tour with an aunt.

> The more likely scenario was that she, like others before her, had decided that Barnum was the husband she wanted, and if he would not come after her, she would go after him, even if it meant crossing a couple of continents.
>
> (Roland T. Bird 1985)

Lonely, and as Frances (Brown 1987) states, 'ripe for the plucking' more than a decade after Marion's death, Brown rushed to meet Lilian in Calcutta 'and quickly decided to make her his wife'. Lilian, no doubt, expected to be whisked away on a romantic Oriental honeymoon, but as his daughter relates, 'Barnum was not youthfully starry-eyed and glowing over this marriage' as was clear from his choice of activities for the nuptial reception: 'The bride and groom spent the afternoon of their wedding day in the chairs of the only two English dentists in Calcutta. To Barnum this was just a routine practicality' (Brown 1987; Dingus & Norell 2007). In his preface of Lilian's (1951) book, Roy Chapman Andrews recommended her 'acute sense of humour, which was infectious. On their first visit to his American Museum of Natural History (AMNH), Barnum said 'Pixie, how'd you like to go on a dinosaur dig in Wyoming?'. He hesitated. 'Of course, it would mean postponing our honeymoon – but – '. She was game, and answered 'When do we start?' (Fig. 5b).

Lilian quickly adapted, helping to collect and keep records in the field for her husband. Health risks were rampant: in the lowlands of Burma, Brown contracted malaria, but Lilian saved his life with round-the-clock nursing. Their marriage lasted until Brown's death in 1963, probably because Lilian possessed a streak of independence almost as wide as her husband's. After their wedding, she set off on her own to Kashmir for a solitary honeymoon, and, catching the eye of an eminent maharaja, she was lavishly entertained and permitted to interact with his harem – an honour not previously bestowed upon any westerner (Dingus & Norell 2007).

Ruth Romer

Ruth Romer (née Hibbard 1901–1992) was born in Ithaca, New York, and was a graduate of the University of Missouri, who studied also at the University of Chicago and Bryn Mawr. When Alfred Sherwood Romer (1884–1973) went to Chicago in 1923 he encountered Ruth, working as a labour statistician. They became friends, fell in love, and by the autumn were married in Columbia, Missouri, where Ruth's father was a University of Missouri professor. It was a fortunate and a happy marriage, and she complemented Al in all he did. They moved to Cambridge when Al joined the Harvard faculty in 1934; Ruth was the devoted wife (having three children) and acknowledged power behind Al's Museum of Comparative Zoology, Harvard (MCZ) throne; who, according to Margaret Colbert 'was always very brave and confident... she kept all the tiresome details away from him' (Elliott 2000). Ruth looked after many a student on the way (K. Carpenter pers. comm. March 2009), one of us (S. Turner) included. She accompanied him on his research trips far and wide (Fig. 5c). Al wrote that Ruth:

> furnished my transportation and day after day picked me up, footsore and weary, after a long trek across the cow pastures.
>
> (A. S. Romer, 27 November 1974 *Breviora*, No. 427)

Margaret Matthew

Margaret Colbert (née Matthew) (1911–2007) was born in Brooklyn, New York. She represents a palaeontological dynasty being the daughter of vertebrate palaeontologist William Diller Matthew (1871–1930) and an unconventional, free-spirited mother Kate Matthew (née Lee) (1876–1955) who he married in 1905; Kate specialized in needlework and dressmaking (Colbert 1992; Elliot 2000). Margaret was also granddaughter of George Frederick Matthew (1837–1923) of New Brunswick, Canada, and was named after birth-control pioneer Margaret Sanger (Colbert 1992). Margaret trained as an artist at the California College of Arts, beginning her career at the AMNH in New York city drawing fossil bones; there she met, and later married noted palaeontologist Edwin (Ned) Colbert (1905–2001); they had five boys, and

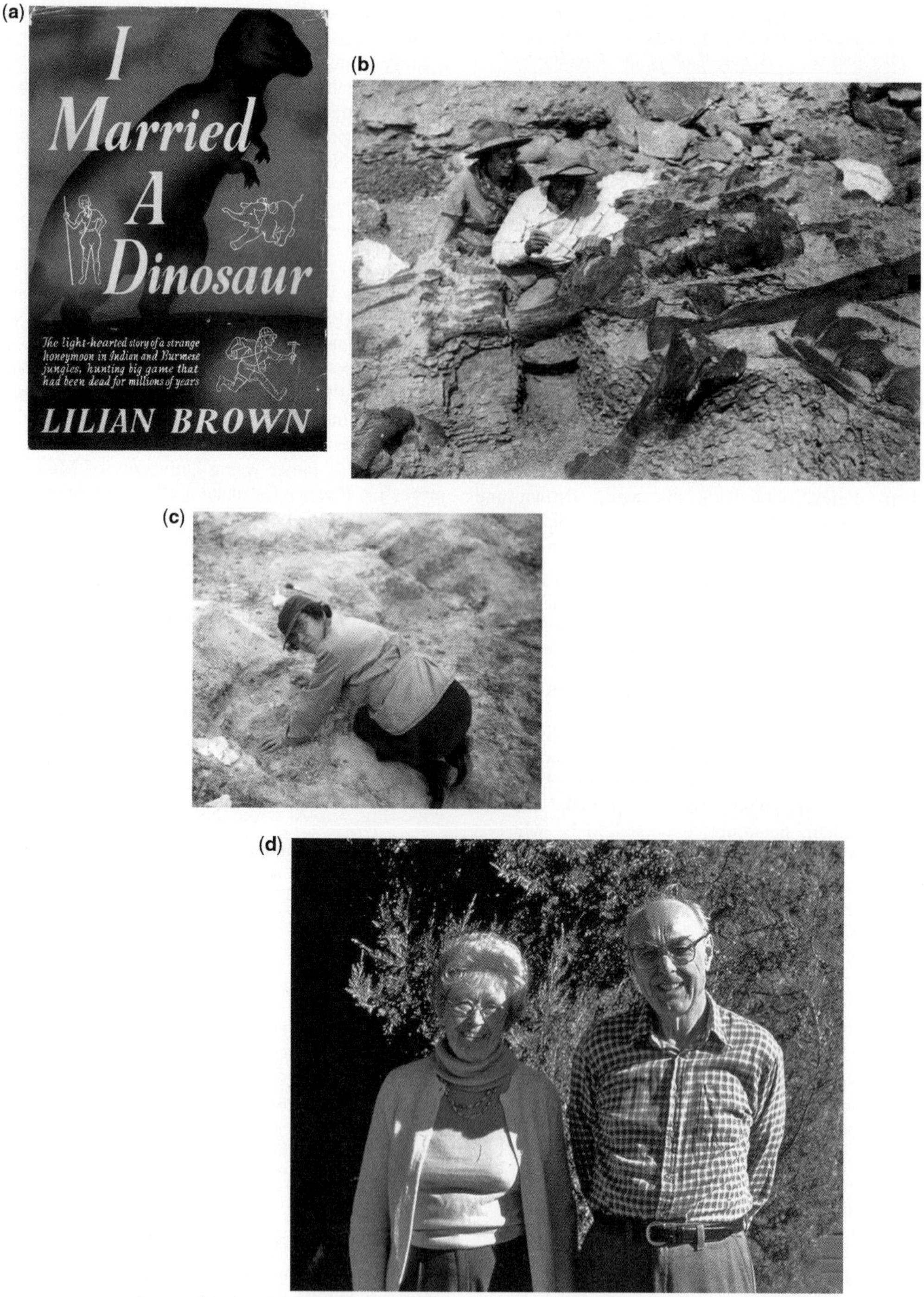

Fig. 5. American couples: (**a**) Lilian Brown's *I Married a Dinosaur Book* cover (Geo Harrap & Co, London); (**b**) rather 'staged' 'staged' photographs of 'BB' & Lilian Brown in the Utah dinosaur quarry (modified from Bird 1985); (**c**) Ruth Romer working at Ishgulasto in Argentina, image from Jim Jensen, http://dinosaurjim.com/html/nelda_wright.html; (**d**) Margaret and Ned Colbert at their home outside Flagstaff, April 1987 (photograph courtesy of and © Dr Randall F. Miller).

Margaret got to see much of the world travelling and assisting Ned (e.g. Colbert 1980) (Fig. 5d).

She continued to work illustrating his books and even helped designed the Society of Vertebrate Paleontology (SVP) logo (Elliot 2000). Margaret then really blossomed again as an artist after her children were grown, aged 60, when she created important museum murals (e.g. at the New Mexico Museum of Natural History and at the Petrified Forest National Park Visitor Center), as well as sculptures, paintings, and black and white drawings; see, for example, Colbert (1980, 1982, 1983), which are illustrated copiously by her. Allmon (2006) reckoned Margaret's colour reconstructed scenes were more pleasing than her simple black and white vignettes (e.g. see Colbert 1996).

Ann Brimacombe Elliot (2000) has provided an account of Margaret's life, and her grandson Matthew has given a brief memorial (Colbert 2007). Michael Crichton (of *Jurassic Park* fame) was inspired by her work and regarded her as 'one of a new generation of illustrators . . . whose reconstructions incorporate the new perception of how dinosaurs behaved' (in Elliot 2000).

Irene Longman

Irene Maud Longman (née Bayley) (1877–1963) was born in the Huon Valley, at Franklin, Tasmania, the daughter of a pastor. As a student Irene lived with the family of the famous geologist T. W. Edgeworth David as a boarder, coming under the influence both of wife Cara (Caroline) David, a staunch educationalist, and the man himself, who fostered her interest in the geological history of Australia (Fallon 2002). She met and fell in love with Heber A. Longman (1880–1954) on the railway platform in Toowoomba in 1902 and they married in 1904; sadly, they had no children, Irene having seven miscarriages in their first 12 years. She helped her husband on his newspaper in Toowoomba and, when he became Assistant Director in 1911 and later Director of the Queensland Museum in Brisbane, she helped him prepare the finds of *Kronosaurus queenslandicus* and other reptiles in the 1920s–1930s (Turner 1986, 2005*a* with photograph; Rich & Vickers-Rich 2003; Turner & Mather 2005). Irene Longman became the first women in the Queensland parliament (1928–1929) (Gregory 2005; Turner 2009*c*) on the platform that women should be paid for all the work they do (still unrealized, of course)!

Others

Others of whom we know little include dinosaur palaeontologist Baron Franz Nopcsa's (1877–1933) younger sister, Ilona Nopcsa von Felsoe-Szilvas (1883–1952), who found the first dinosaur bones in Hungary (Romania) on their estate (Weishampel & Reif 1984) and Miss Häberlein (*c.* 1840s?–unknown), the daughter of Bavarian medic/fossil dealer Dr Carl Häberlein, who apparently benefited from the then-exorbitant sale of the first complete *Archaeopteryx* to the BMNH in 1861, which provided her dowry! (Rupke 1994; Shipman 1998).

Achievers – vertebrate palaeontologists

Mignon Talbot

Professor Mignon Talbot (1869–1950) (Fig. 6a) was the first woman to find, serendipitously, and describe a dinosaur (Talbot 1911). The verdict is still out on its relationships; perhaps a coelurosaur, cf. *Coelophysis*, a ceratosaur or cf. tetanuran theropods (Weishampel & Young 2001). In her time it was thought to be Triassic in age and linked with *Eubrontes* tracks.

Born in Iowa City in 1869, she was educated in geology at Ohio State University, gaining her PhD in geology in 1904 from Yale. She notched up many other firsts in her career, most notably she became Professor of Geology and Geography at Mt Holyoak College from 1904 to 1935 (Alumnae Association 1937); she died after an active life in 1950 (Haff 1952, Sarjeant 1978–1987, Suppl. I; Aldrich 1982).

'Her' incomplete dinosaur, *Podokesaurus holyokensis* is based on delicate bones from a gravel pit (now known to be Jurassic) from eastern USA. Talbot recounted later in life:

> On one of the sandstone pieces was a streak of white that looked like a pick mark. I was pretty sure it was only a pick mark, but I went down to see. And I saw vertebrae, and I saw ribs, and I saw bones – and I said, 'Oh, Ellen, come quick, come quick, I've found a real live fossil!' By that I meant that the fossil was the bones of the real creature, not just tracks. Many tracks had been discovered in the Connecticut valley, but few actual skeletons of dinosaurs. So I said I had found a real live fossil, and she said, 'Have you lost your mind?'.
>
> –(Talbot words quoted from www.mtholyoke.edu/~dalbino/books/lester/dinosaur.html)

Talbot originally interpreted her specimen as a herbivore at a meeting of the Paleontological Society in December 1910. Subsequently mentored in her investigation by Richard Swan Lull (1867–1957), then a professor at Yale University, she identified it as theropod. His colleague young Friedrich von Huene (1875–1969) from Tübingen was visiting America at that time (Turner 2009*a*) and viewed her specimen (and met her?) and created a new family based on the genus, related to coelurosaurs:

> Professor Lull said I must give a paper. I said, 'I can't – Don't know a thing about dinosaurs.' Professor Lull

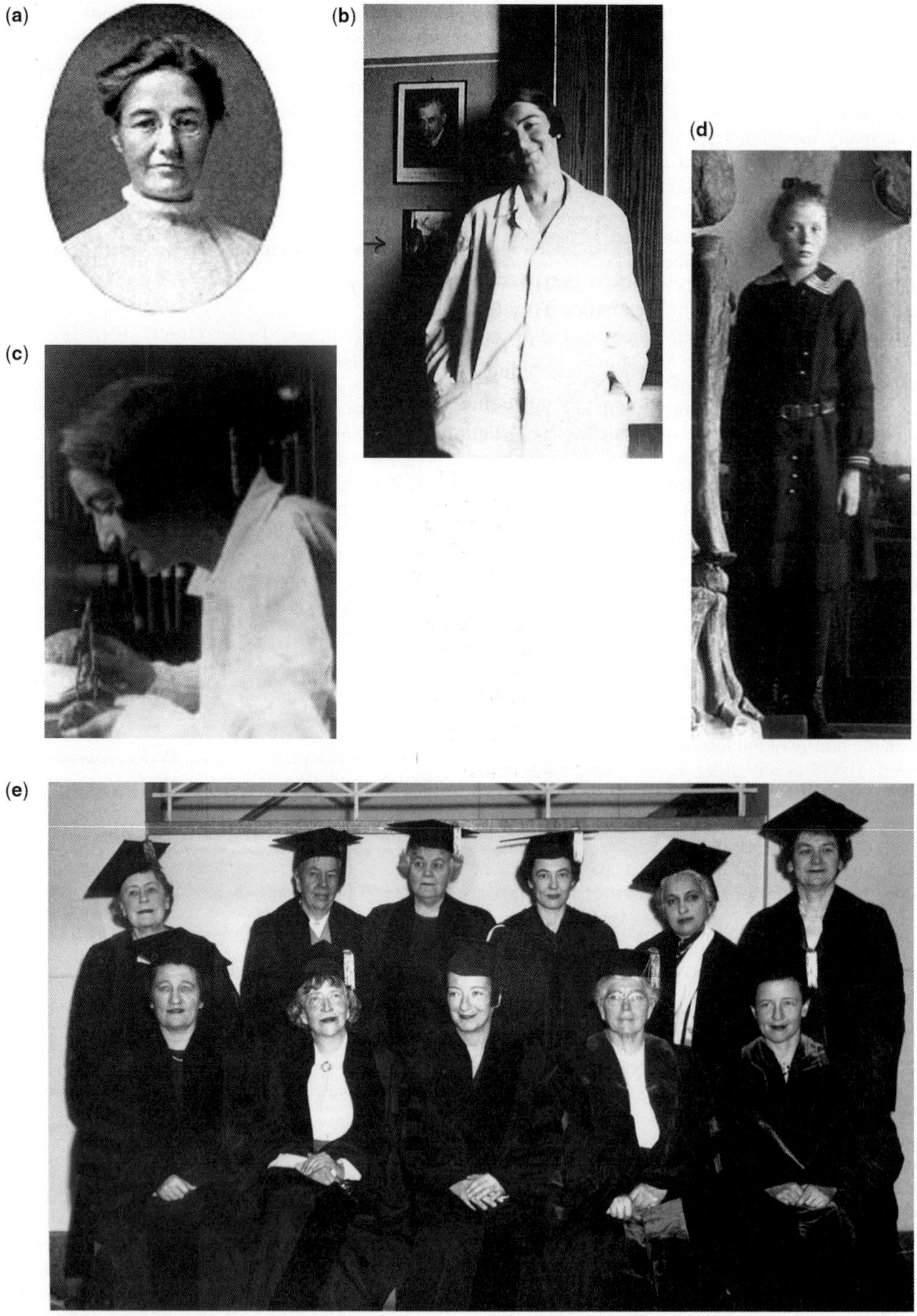

Fig. 6. First researchers. (**a**) Young Professor Mignon Talbot; (**b**) young Tilly Edinger in front of a photograph of her mentor Louis Dollo (modified from Kohring & Kreft 2003); (**c**) Tilly Edinger with endocast and calipers some time in the mid-1920s (photograph courtesy of the Museum of Comparative Zoology, Harvard University, Cambridge, Massachusetts, from Buchholtz & Seyfarth 2001); (**d**) young Erika von Hoyningen-Huene, aged about 14 in her father's

said, 'Well, study them up then. You've got to describe it.' And that is why I read and later published the short scientific description to which Professor Lull subsequently made additions. Professor Lull suggested later that this dinosaur was insectivorous or a wading form which fed upon amphibians or some smaller reptiles. Most of the geologists who saw the fossil do not think that it was a young one as there are no certain indications of cartilage in places where cartilage turns to bone with age. I didn't want to keep the fossil in South Hadley. I wanted it to be either at Washington or at Yale for permanent exhibition. I thought it should be with its kind.

–(Talbot words quoted from www.mtholyoke.edu/~dalbino/books/lester/dinosaur.html)

Miss Talbot urged that the little dinosaur, *Podokesaurus holyokensis* (swift-footed saurian), should be sent to Washington or New Haven; but it seemed to a higher authority that Mount Holyoke should keep it on exhibition as a local specimen in Williston Hall, the old science building.

No more bones have yet been found and the original was lost when her college museum was burnt in 1916 (Ogilvie & Harvey 2000; Weishampel & Young 2001). Professor Lull's half-scale model effigy is in their Clapp Laboratory, as well as pictures and a full-scale reproduction of the cast.

Johanna Gabrielle Ottelie 'Tilly' Edinger

Tilly Edinger (1897–1967) (Fig. 6b, c, e) was born in Frankfurt, Germany, the third and youngest daughter of an eminent physician and pioneer neurologist Ludwig Edinger (1855–1918) (Fig. 6b) and Anna Goldschmidt (1863–1929), a descendant of the Warburg banking family, which on her mother's side had been in Frankfurt am Main since the Middle Ages. Anna was an active charity and social worker, which eventually led to her being commemorated with a bronze statue in City Park. Thus, Tilly was born into a well-positioned upper-middle-class Jewish family with education as a priority. She had hearing problems and was educated at home by a governess, with French and English languages as a high priority. At the age of 12 Tilly entered the only secondary school for girls in Frankfurt at that time, where she stayed from 1910 to 1916.

Her family encouraged Tilly to follow her inclination as far as education was concerned. Initially, she decided to study geology; after reading Abel (1912) on palaeobiology she had wanted to become a palaeontologist but in 1919 moved into zoology, partly because geology was thought 'unsuitable for a woman at that time' and also she thought it would be easier to get employment as a biologist. She undertook science courses at the universities of Heidelberg, Münich and Frankfurt, finally submitting a doctoral thesis in palaeontology in 1921 at the latter. Her PhD research under Fritz Drevermann (1875–1932) of the Senckenberg Museum in Frankfurt (SMF) was on the Triassic marine reptile *Nothosaurus*, which she even contributed as a theme for some contemporary German postcards (see Kohring & Kreft 2003, p. 472, figs 18 & 19).

The field of vertebrate palaeontology was Tilly's abiding passion all her life, specifically the evolution of the central nervous system. Her wealthy background allowed her to pursue her passion when she moved as an unpaid research assistant to SMF, as a curator of the vertebrate collection. She went on to study various reptiles, such as *Mixosaurus*, being mentored especially by 'her dear Professor', Friedrich von Huene at Tübingen (Kohring & Kreft 2003; Turner 2009*a*, *b*: Geologenarchiv, Freiburg Universität (GAF), von Huene letters), and examining the brain casts of nothosaur, plesiosaur and dicynodont reptiles, dinosaurs and *Archaeopteryx*. She was one of the few pre-World War II women in German science (Kölbl-Ebert 2001; Mohr & Vogt 2003), where despite gaining habilitation giving the right to professorship, teaching and research since the early part of the century, women were not yet a natural part of the system. She followed her father in his interest, and almost single-handedly founded modern palaeoneurology in the 1920s when she was working at SMF (Fig. 6c). This specialist subdiscipline deals with fossil endo-(internal) casts; Tilly examined multiple members of a single taxon from different geological horizons to show differences and used comparative anatomy to compare with modern brains. Initially, she worked on the theoretical framework of brain evolution but her seminal paper was an extensive 250-page review on fossil brains in 1929, which she dedicated to her father. She called it 'mein große Gehirnarbeit' ['my great brain treatise'] (Buchholtz & Seyfarth 1999).

Fig. 6. (*Continued*) museum in the Institut für Geowissenschaften, Eberhard Karls Universität, Tübingen (IFGT) (Photograph courtesy of IFGT); (**e**) Tilly Edinger at a degree ceremony at Wellesey College. The Edinger group photograph is courtesy of the Wellesley College Archives. Photograph by I. MacLaurin. President Clapp and honorary degree recipients on 17 March 1950, inauguration of Margaret Clapp. Front row (left to right): Caroline Taylor White, Esther Forbes, Tilly Edinger, Connie Myers Guion, Dorothy Fosdick. Back row (left to right): Anne O'Hare McCormick, Mabel Newcomer, Ruth Baker Pratt, President Margaret Clapp, Vijaya Lakshmi Pandit, Mildred McAfee Horton. (Belle Sherwin received her degree in absentia).

After the Nazis came to power in April 1933, despite her Jewish descent, Tilly managed to keep a low profile with the help of the new SMF Director, Rudolf Richter, until the Reichskristalnacht (10 November) in 1938, when she was plunged into a time of dread. She realized that there was no future for her as a scientist in her own country and city. When the axe fell on her job, her work place and her life, she like others, had to find champions, like Friedrich von Huene, who, because of his sympathetic pietist Christianity and strong anti-Nazi stance (Turner 2009*a*), continued to talk to her and write letters on her behalf. He helped her gain a passport to leave Germany in early 1939, with Tilly moving first to England where she obtained a visa from the Notgemeinschaft (Society for the Preservation of Science and Learning and Emergency Association of German Scientists in Exile); she supported herself as a translator of medical texts, and then moved to America, arriving in New York aboard the SS *Britannic* on 11 May 1940. More letters sent in the USA could find her no academic home and so Al Romer at MCZ created a position for her and made the way open for her to survive and work at Harvard, becoming one of the few successful fugitives (Edinger letters in Kohring & Kreft 2003).

Her life and letters show poignantly the difficulties of pursuing science not just as a Jew in the 1930s, when the anti-Jewish terrorism of the Third Reich forced her to leave Germany, but as a woman with a disability (Kölbl-Ebert 2001; Kohring & Kreft 2003); in some (S. Turner pers. obs.), she corresponds with von Huene about her difficulties, and those of his daughter Erika (Fig. 6d; q.v. below), and about how she tried to stay 'invisible' after 1933. She tells him how because of her partial deafness she won't come to meetings because that would mean having to sit up front (too exposed a position for her in the Third Reich); and then about Romer (her 'angel') who enabled her continued work in the USA (Buchholtz & Seyfarth 2001). Letters of reference to enable Tilly's emigration show the esteem in which she was held:

> She is a research scientist of the first rank and is favourably known as such all over the world. She is everywhere recognised as the leading specialist on the study of the brain and nervous system of extinct animals and on the evolution of the gross structure of the brain. She is so pre-eminent in this field that she may really be said to have created a new branch of science, that of paleo-neurology a study of outstanding value and importance.
>
> (Simpson G. G. 1938, held in the Wellesley archive, cited in Buchholtz & Seyfarth 1999).

In London she worked on a survey of relative pituitary body size in living and fossil vertebrates, which was an extension of work initiated by Nopcsa (1917) and published in 1942. Her work, while citing recent experiments on mammals to support her hypothesis that 'an increase in body size within and between species is accompanied by an increase in the size of the anterior lobe of the pituitary gland relative to the brain as a whole and a resulting relative increase in the secretion of growth hormones' (cited in Buchholtz & Seyfarth 1999), also contained material on this trend in reptiles and birds. She cited the gigantism in dinosaurs as a good example. Although her later work was on the Equidae within the last 40 Ma, it had implications for saurians and has been widely used and quoted in papers by Nopcsa (1926) and Jerison (1968). Her contribution to Marsh's (1880) interpretation of the brain casts of the toothed birds as reptilian instead of avian is well documented (Buchholtz & Seyfarth 1999, 2001), and she challenged the accepted view of changes in brain size during vertebrate evolution, particularly mammals.

Edinger spent her whole time in the United States at MCZ, but despite Romer's misgivings about her deafness (e.g. Kohring & Kreft 2003), she did teach comparative vertebrate anatomy at Wellesley College for three semesters from 1943 to 1945. Her research reputation brought her many prestigious awards and positions, including honorary doctorates from Wellesley College (1950, Fig. 6e), Giessen (1957) and Frankfurt (1964). She was a founding member of the SVP and elected their first female president in 1963. She was also a key contributor with Romer, Nelda Wright (q.v. below) and Richard van Frank to the *Bibliography of Fossil Vertebrates* (Romer *et al.* 1962). She received fellowships from the Guggenheim Foundation in New York in 1943 and the American Association of University Women in 1950. She was one of 288 displaced scholars listed by Duggan & Drury (1948) who received funding from the Emergency Committee In Aid of Displaced Foreign Scholars. Tilly was one of only two palaeontologists who received support, the other being Otto Henry Haas who went on to work at the American Museum of Natural History, New York. After World War II, despite the treatment she had received and the betrayal felt in 1938, Tilly was important in reaching out to and rehabilitating German geoscientists in the late 1940s–early 1950s. Tilly was a remarkable woman whose story is still not well known despite the major biography by Kohring & Kreft (2003) and others, but much is in German and so sadly still inaccessible to the majority. Hopefully this will change with some judicious translation (Schultze 2007).

Tilly Edinger died too soon on 27 May 1967 from fatal head injuries when she was hit by a truck just in front of the MCZ; her lifelong impaired hearing was held responsible (Buchholtz & Seyfarth 2001; Kohring & Kreft 2003). She was 69 years old, no longer teaching but still researching; her unfinished work of the last decade of her life, a comprehensive annotated bibliography summarizing palaeoneurology from 1804 to 1966, was completed by her colleagues and published posthumously in 1973. This work remains a key text today. Tilly contributed to that interdisciplinary area of palaeontology and zoology, which has had such a profound effect on saurian research. Her contribution is not to be underestimated.

Erika von Hoyningen-Huene

Erika Martha (1905–1969) was the eldest daughter of Friedrich von Huene and 'Dora' Lawton. Born in Tübingen, Germany, she was one of only two female vertebrate palaeontologists in the pre-World War II history of German science, working during the 1930s–1940s, and her work has mostly been forgotten probably because she is overshadowed by her father. Erika studied under her father, probably getting interested as a young girl by helping her father in the Institute and Museum of Geology and Palaeontology (now IFG) (Fig. 6e). She completed her doctorate under the supervision of Prof. Dr Edwin Hennig, and with help from Otto H. Schindewolf in the fateful early 1933 when Hitler came to power (Turner 2009*a*). Her topic was Upper Triassic Rhaetic bonebed vertebrates including dinosaur and other reptiles. As taught by von Huene senior, who always stressed their importance, she did her own drawings. Erika was given material and visited museums in Europe, England and America. She wrote only seven papers, one describing a new rhynchocephalian *Pachystropheus rhaeticus* from Somerset; by contrast, she described a mosasaur, a rare find from Timor Island.

A friend of George Gaylord Simpson from the time they met when he visited Tübingen in the 1920s, she tried to contribute; Simpson (1935) noted particularly her pioneering work on Triassic early mammals. As with Edinger, but rather because she was a woman and a pietist, the Nazi regime affected her life and work post-April 1933 when women in general were discriminated against (e.g. Kölbl-Ebert 2001) and work was difficult to find (Edinger, q.v.: letters to F. von Huene). This changed when World War II began because, as a woman, she was not drafted and during 1940–1944, with an invite from Schindewolf, Erika moved to Berlin and carried out some work for him in the geological survey (Reichsamt für Bodenforschung then in the building next to the Humboldt Museum, HMB), although perhaps only informally or on contract and not a paid job (we are seeking documents to confirm this part of her life). By the time the war ended and men returned to their jobs, Erika had come back home to help care for her parents. She went to work for a protestant order, apparently grappling again with the religious constraints her upbringing had placed upon her. For a time she tried to continue her science and, as von Huene senior was Acting Director of IFG for 2 years after the war, she may have had hopes of a place but in the end she gave up (last paper published was Huene 1949).

Erika von Huene's last years were devoted to managing nursing homes in Tübingen and Berlin-Frohnau. She died in Berlin, a week after her father's death but as graves are not permanent in Germany we have been unable to locate her; her personal papers were also lost there (von Huene family pers. comm. 2009).

Pamela Robinson

Pamela Lamplugh Robinson (1919–1994) was born in Manchester. After early private schooling she attended Manchester Girls' High School, then university education began at the University of Hamburg in 1938, where she studied the premedical curriculum until, interrupted by the threat of war, she returned to Britain and spent 2 years at the British Woollen Industries Research Association in Leeds. Whilst there, she attended evening lectures given by Dr Dorothy Helen Rayner (1912–2002), vertebrate palaeontologist and Stratigraphy and Palaeontology lecturer at the university (Varker 2004), which fired her enthusiasm for the subject. Following war service from 1942 to 1945 at the Royal Ordnance Factory in Yorkshire, she spent a year and a half as librarian at the GSL. In 1947, aged 28, Robinson finally enrolled for an undergraduate degree course in geology at University College London (UCL), graduating with first class honours in 1951 and being awarded a UCL Research Scholarship the same year to begin postgraduate research in the Zoology Department.

Robinson remained at UCL, first as Assistant Lecturer in Zoology (1952–1955) and then Lecturer (1955–1966), during which time she gained a PhD degree (1957) on the Triassic gliding lizard *Kuehneosaurus* from Somerset, which remains unpublished. Instead, she published a major review of Mesozoic geology and fauna from vertebrate bearing fissure sediments in the Mendip Hills and Gloucestershire, UK (Robinson 1957). That year Robinson made the first of many visits to India at the invitation of Professor M. Mahalanobis (1893–1972), Head of the Indian Statistical Institute (ISI), Calcutta, where she energetically set up and established the Geological Studies Unit; she initiated research programmes in vertebrate palaeontology and Gondwana stratigraphy in collaboration with her Indian colleagues and supervised several research students, becoming a pioneer in Gondwana studies. Her benchmark review 'The Indian Gondwana Formations' (Robinson 1967), stands as an essential reference. She was promoted to Reader in Palaeozoology in 1966 and was Alexander Agassiz Visiting Professor at Harvard University in the fall semester of 1972. She received the GSL Wollaston Fund in 1973, largely in recognition of her work in promoting and establishing vertebrate palaeontology in India. Her research changed course in the 1970s with her growing interest in palaeoenvironmental studies and palaeoclimatic modelling. She took early retirement in 1982 devoting herself to Indian philosophy and gardening.

As an excellent, if demanding, teacher with an immense breadth and depth of knowledge of biology and geology, Robinson's work contributed greatly to Mesozoic palaeontology especially her influence in the Indian subcontinent. She never married and had no children. Her students included L. B. Halstead (a.k.a Tarlo: 1933–1991) known for his work on pliosaurs in the late 1950s–early 1960s (Sarjeant 1993); he (pers. comm. to S. Turner in the 1960s), as others, found her patient, helpful, charming and thoroughly entertaining, but also she could be intimidating, imperious and quite terrifying; her archive and Triassic reptile fissure fossils are deposited at the NHM in London (Milner & Hughes 1995; B. Hughes unpublished MS notes; R. J. G. Savage unpublished MS biographical notes: A. Milner pers. comm. 2009).

Minna Lang

Dr Minna Lang (1891–1959) of Meiningen in Thuringia, Germany (Thenius 1960) was one of the very few co-authors of F. von Huene and the only woman (Turner 2009*a*, *b*), writing two papers with him in the 1950s on the work of Hugo Rühle von Lilienstern (1882–1946) and Thuringian reptiles (Lang & Huene 1952, 1956). She also published a paper in 1936 on the private palaeontological museum set up by von Lilienstern in his home in Bedheim, eastern Germany (Mohr *et al.* 2008); the town coat of arms portrays a *Plateosaurus*-like dinosaur. She was then a high-school teacher in southern Thuringia. Minna had studied physics at Frankfurt University and in 1916 gained her doctorate on abosorption of Roentgen rays in gases. Her sister (perhaps a medical doctor) in Suebia, an historic name given to the area of the Württenberg Region of Germany, wrote a biography of her according to Mohr *et al.* (2008*b*). Huene and Lang had a long and voluminous correspondence from 1947 to 1958, mainly on religious matters but also on historical topics and dinosaurs (GAF von Huene letters). She worked in the Kunstsammlung, Theatre-Museum and later lived in Pforzheim.

Cherrie Bramwell

Cherrie Diane Bramwell (1944–? unknown) was born in east London; her father ran a chemist's shop and she was an only child. She obtained a part-time degree through Birkbeck College and then became Bev Halstead's second PhD student at Reading University during the 'swinging sixties' (hence the hot pants attire featured in a UK women's magazine carrying her first fruit bat 'Balls', when researching the pterosaurs) (Sarjeant 1995). When she began her research Halstead sent her to study H. G. Seeley's Cambridge Greensand collection of pterodactyl bones (e.g. Seeley 1901) and such was her fervour that she reckoned that the ghost of Henry Grover Seeley (1839–1909: see, for example, Cleevely 1983) was looking over her shoulder at the Sedgwick Museum as she worked! (pers. comm. to S. Turner *c.* 1969).

Bramwell teamed up with aeronautical engineer George R. Whitfield in the Applied Physics department at Reading University to research flight mechanics of *Pteranodon* in 1969; their work is a classic on the flight dynamics of this amazing vertebrate (Bramwell & Whitfield 1970). After deciding that she would use a fruit bat's wings as the most appropriate extant structure for pterodactyl wings, she used her pet as a founder of a colony of the bats in the Physics Department of Reading University, going on to do useful research on blood supply (with application in medicine), and creating, with designer Steven Winkworth, a life-sized pterosaur model that flew over the cliffs in Dorset, UK, featured in the BBC TV programme 'Pterodactylus *Lives*' in 1984. Notable for her media presence through to the 1980s; popularizing science on children's television and announcing to Robyn Williams' ABC Radio *Australian Science Show* that constipation, not asteroids, might have killed off the dinosaurs. Bramwell fell out of a tree when filming and broke her back. Rumours that she later died have not been confirmed and she may be one of Dean Falk's (2000) immortals. She did have at least one son.

Elizabeth L. Nicholls

American 'Betsy' L. Nicholls (1946–2004) was born in Oakland, California in the post-World War II 'baby boomer' year. Her father, a university professor at University of California (UC) Berkeley, initiated her interest in palaeontology when he took her to visit his colleague Sam P. Welles

(1909–1997) in her ninth year (R. L. Carroll in Korth & Massare 2006). Betsy looked at the fossils around his room and is reputed to have said 'I want to be a palaeontologist' (D. Brinkman pers. comm. June 2009). She went on to work on saurians, mostly marine reptiles. When Betsy was 10, the Nicholls family left the USA and moved to Melbourne, Australia, where she experienced a very different culture. She returned in the late 1960s to do her undergraduate studies in the Department of Palaeontology at UC Berkeley under the direction of Welles.

In 1969 Betsy moved to Alberta, Canada with her husband Jim, a fellow geologist, who had accepted a position with the Geology Department, at the University of Calgary. Here she completed an MSc on Campanian turtles in 1972 whilst raising two daughters (one of which later found *Prosaurolophus maximus*: Currie & Koppelhus 2005). She began her career in Canada by discovering, collecting and studying the oldest known plesiosaur from North America, remains of which were found in mountains SW of Calgary. During this time she became increasingly involved with dinosaur extraction at Dinosaur Park (Fig. 7). She raised funds herself, collecting and preparing a Liassic plesiosaur from near Crowsnest Pass in SW Alberta, an ornithomimid dinosaur from Dinosaur Park, and a hadrosaur-prosaurolophid skull and skeleton, now on display in the University of Calgary and at the Royal Tyrrell Museum (RTM), Drumheller, Alberta, respectively. In 1989 Betsy completed her doctoral thesis on marine reptiles from Morden, Manitoba, under the supervision of Anthony Russell of the University of Calgary's Biology Department. The following year she started work as RTM's marine reptile specialist, then Curator of Marine Reptiles in 1991, continuing to focus on Triassic marine reptiles from NE British Columbia (BC). Throughout her 14 years at RTM she lived in Calgary and made the daily trek to Drumheller, a journey of 170 km.

Nicholls became one of Alberta and Canada's most celebrated and accomplished vertebrate palaeontologists. She gained international recognition for discovering and describing new species of marine reptiles from the Wapiti Lake region, BC, a project that established western Canada as an important world locale for Triassic reptiles; for example, she named the ichthyosaur genera *Metashastasaurus* (with Manabe) and *Parvinatator* (with Brinkman). In 1997 Jack M. Callaway and Nicholls edited an important book on *Ancient Marine Reptiles* (proceedings of a 1994 SVP symposium) that summarizes end-of-twentieth-century knowledge on many groups and posed the questions for the coming millennium (Carroll in Korth & Massare 2006). Other career highlights include collecting and researching the world's largest known ichthyosaur found in the Pink Mountain region of NE British Columbia. In 2000, Nicholls received the Rolex Award for Enterprise (featured in Nicholls 2001) for her pivotal role in recovering the remains of this long reptile and new primitive marine reptiles from the Wapiti Lake area, as well as North America's oldest known plesiosaur from north of Crowsnest Pass (Eberth 2004).

Fig. 7. Elisabeth 'Betsy' Nicholls in the field in British Columbia, Canada (photograph courtesy of Don Brinkman).

'I was overwhelmed. It was the largest ichthyosaur I had ever seen', Betsy said of her first encounter with the fossil that she later named *Shonisaurus sikanniensis*. Over 21 m long, this ichthyosaur with its slender, elongated snout, is the largest prehistoric marine reptile found to date. The specimen was discovered in 1991 in an isolated area of BC, embedded in a bank of the Sikanni Chief River, in densely wooded, uneven terrain infested with mosquitoes and visited by bears. Frequently submerged by the river, the fossil was under serious threat of erosion, but its inaccessible location had prevented palaeontologists from reaching it except for a few weeks in the summer. Nicholls overcame the challenges of this logistical nightmare. It took 6 years to raise funds and three gruelling excursions between 1999 and 2001 to extract the huge fossil, the skull alone of which weighs 1.5 tonnes. Betsy joined forces with Makoto Manabe of the National Science Museum in Tokyo (NSMT), to work on this extraordinary specimen, which she had already revealed had no teeth showing that this huge marine reptile resorted to suction feeding, like beaked whales, swallowing small invertebrates in the water.

'It was all worth it', said Betsy on receiving her Rolex Award, thanks to which she was able to finance 4 years of painstaking laboratory work to remove the giant ichthyosaur from its limestone matrix. Her research paper was accepted for publication just before she died from cancer in her 57th year; Betsy's article, coauthored with Manabe in 2004, established *Shonisaurus sikanniensis* as a new species and opened new avenues of research on ichthyosaur evolution. The legacy of Betsy Nicholls was toasted on 2 November 2004, at a memorial ceremony held for her at RTM and at NSMT.

In paying tribute to her work Manabe stated:

> Elizabeth had this energetic, determined attitude. She really was a field scientist, always ready to go to the remotest places to push science forward. Now, colleagues and students must keep up with her passion.

A special issue of the Rochester Institute of Vertebrate Paleontology and Drumheller Museum (Korth & Massare 2006, with pictures of Betsy) is a fitting tribute to her inspiring life, and is also notable for its many women authors. A book edited by Phil Currie and Eva Koppelhus (2005) is also dedicated to her memory.

Irene Vanderloh

Irene Vanderloh (1917–2009) was an amateur palaeonologist, born on July 23 in Steveville, Alberta, Canada, now a ghost town, near Dinosaur Provincial Park. She collected small theropod dinosaur bones in or near the park and her finds led to important discoveries, including two maniraptorans, the type of *Saurornitholestes langstoni* and a *Troodon formusus*, both partial skeletons (Spalding 1999). She died on 23 August 2009 at Brooks, Alberta (Darren Tanke pers. comm. Sept 2009).

Mary Wade

Mary Julia (which she hated) Wade (1928–2005) (Fig. 8a, c) was born in Adelaide, South Australia and was home taught until a late age. Inspired by the legendary Douglas Mawson (1882–1958) and later Martin Glaessner (1906–1989) at the University of Adelaide, she attained her PhD (on Tertiary foraminifera) in 1959. As she could only rise to the rank of temporary Lecturer in Adelaide and because her research was being constrained, she decided to leave.

Thus, Mary did not blossom as a vertebrate palaeontologist until the early 1970s when she made the move to the Queensland Museum, invited by Director Alan Bartholomai (Wade pers. comm. to S. Turner 2004; Rozefelds & Turner 1998), and began a collaboration with R. A. 'Tony' Thulborn, who had moved from Britain to take up a lectureship at the University of Queensland in early 1974. In the early 1970s they also collected new material of the rare Jurassic dinosaur *Rhoetosaurus*. The main result of their co-operation was work on the thousands of footprints in the 'Great Dinosaur Stampede' of Lark Quarry, Winton (e.g. Thulborn & Wade 1984, 1989; Wade 1989; Turner 1997, 1998, 2007), now a highly prized State Park fossil site and inspiration for the scene in the '*Jurassic Park*' movie.

Mary made a major study of the Australian Cretaceous ichthyosaur *Platypterygius australis*, and was working with Thulborn on a plesiosaur when she died, too young (Cook 2005; Turner 2005*b*). She continued her association with outback Queensland after her retirement, consulting for the Hughenden and Richmond museums, and seeking reptile bones in drought-ridden paddocks, her last foray with Thulborn and the senior author to look for the Cretaceous dicynodont near the Flinders River in 2003. Mary was a complex mixture of naive country girl with extreme Christian Science beliefs who, nevertheless, would strike to the heart of any scientific matter; her earlier work on the Precambrian Ediacara fauna being another of her legacies.

Joan Wiffen

Joan Wiffen (1922–2009), 'the Dragon Lady of New Zealand' (Fig. 8b), was a self-trained amateur palaeontologist who pioneered dinosaur hunting and brought to light most of her country's Mesozoic reptilian record. She was brought up in Hawkes Bay, the King Country area of North Island, New Zealand, and it is widely recorded that her father, a Mr Pob, did not believe in education for girls and so it was not until after war work in World War II that she was able to improve her education while working as a clerk for 6 years, eventually becoming a teacher. She married M. A. 'Pont' Wiffen in 1953 and lived with her husband and their two girls in the village of Haumoana near Hastings.

It had been previously thought that no dinosaurs had lived on this long-isolated island until Joan and her husband in their 50s, when most people contemplate retirement, took up 'saurian' prospecting. Pont had registered for evening classes in geology

Fig. 8. Gondwanans: (**a**) Mary Wade of the Queensland Museum; (**b**) Joan Wiffen, the 'Dragon lady' of New Zealand at Mangahouanga, North Island (photograph courtesy of Ewan Fordyce); (**c**) Mary Wade with assistant Cathy Mobbs excavating a Lower Cretaceous plesiosaur in Queensland (photographs a and b courtesy of Queensland Museum).

and Joan first attended when he was ill. She had been intrigued with fossils as a child but now became a dedicated amateur. Bone histology and skeletochronology are rarely used to gain insights into ontogeny of extinct taxa: exceptions are a well-preserved growth series of plesiosaurs that Joan found. Her discoveries from Mangahouanga Stream in Hawke's Bay, beginning in 1974, irrevocably changed ideas of New Zealand's palaeontological history (Wiffen 1991). Wiffen discovered fragmentary fossils of late Cretaceous period dinosaurs, including an ankylosaur (probably a nodosaur), a carnosaur and a sauropod, the first major finds from New Zealand. With Pont and team they also found mosasaurs (*Mosasaurus flemingi*, *Prognathodon overtoni*, *Rikisaurus tehoensis*, etc.), a plesiosaurid, *Tuarangisaurus* Wiffen and Moisley (1986), a pterosaur, a large marine protostegid turtle and many other finds (see Farlow & Brett-Surman 1997, p. 50), often working in conjunction with Ralph Molnar, then of Queensland Museum (see Molnar 2009). In 1995 Joan was awarded a CBE ('Commander of the British Empire') or for her vertebrate work.

Halszka Osmólska

Halszka Osmólska (1930–2008) was born in Poznan, Poland; she was a young girl when the fateful Nazi invasion began World War II. Osmólska entered Poznan University in the Faculty of Mathematics and Natural Science in 1949, in the time of severity shortly after the end of World War II; in 1952 she went to the Geology Faculty of Warsaw University. Then, despite an interest in dinosaurs, on the advice of professors she completed her Master's (1955), then PhD (1962) and Habilitation (1971) on Devonian and Carboniferous trilobites, there being few fossil vertebrates in Poland. Nevertheless, she went on to become the most well known of Polish dinosaur researchers describing several new mostly Late Cretaceous taxa and also primitive crocodilians. As an undergraduate student in 1953, Osmólska joined the team organized by Professor Roman Kozlowski (1889–1977) at the resurrected Laboratory of Palaeozoology (now the Institute of Palaeobiology Polish Academy of Sciences), first as a research assistant, then more permanent in 1965, first as a professor assistant, then docent and, beginning in 1983, as a full Professor in Palaeontology. She rose to become Director in 1983–1989. In the rather complicated political period of 1974–1989 the only organization to which she belonged was 'Solidarity'.

Following Chapman Andrews' AMNH successes, Soviet scientists were eager to return to Mongolia; and the expeditions of 1948–1949 included at least one woman, 'M.' Lookijnova (photograph in Farlow & Brett-Surman 1997, fig. 4.3); her dress and the flowers in her grasp appear typical of a Russian maiden. Although this earlier expedition was carried out by Russians, the situation in Polish science changed only after Stalin's death (in March 1953), as political terror decreased and scientists were gradually allowed to go abroad. Co-operation began in the early 1960s with the new Academy of Sciences in the Mongolian People's Republic and the Polish Academy of Sciences; Osmólska took part under the leadership of Zofia Kielan-Jaworowska in the Polish–Mongolian dinosaur expeditions to the Gobi desert, in 1963–1971 (Kielan-Jaworowska 1969; Lavas in Farlow & Brett-Surman eds 1997, fig. 4.6), which discovered astonishing new specimens of dinosaurs, mammals and other animals (Wojciech 2008).

Osmólska was an enthusiastic member of eight of these large-scale palaeontological expeditions to the Gobi desert, and of a number of smaller field trips, mostly in tandem with her colleague and compatriot Teresa Maryanska (now retired). They also went to Ulan Bator to work in the Museum of the Geological Institute of the Mongolian Academy of Sciences, where Osmólska also began to work with Mongolian R. Barsbold and students. She started with a description of an enigmatic ornithomimosaurian *Deinocheirus mirificus*. The material of isolated huge forelimbs was a real challenge that introduced her to the large theropod domain, which was followed by an anatomical account of the ornithomimid *Gallimimus bullatus*. Osmólska also worked on small and medium-sized representatives of the maniraptorid Dromaeosauridae (*Hulsanpes*), Troodontidae (*Borogovia, Tochisurus*) and Oviraptorosauria (*Oviraptor*), studies of importance to understand the avian origin of the maniraptoran stem. She co-operated in studying different ornithischians, such as Protoceratopsidae (Maryanska & Osmólska 1975), Pachycephalosauria (erected as a new ornithischian suborder by Maryanska & Osmólska 1974) and Hadrosauria. She was also interested in the functional meaning of characters in biomechanical (Maryanska & Osmólska 1983) and physiological terms (Osmólska 1979, 1985, 1986). Seminal discussion on phylogeny within the theropods (Barsbold *et al.* 2000) and ornithischians (Maryanska & Osmólska 1984, 1985) round out her scientific output.

On the basis of her international acclaim, she was invited to co-edit the scholarly modern compendium *The Dinosauria* (Weishampel *et al.* 1990, 2004). For her scientific activity she gained several prestige awards, and was decorated, among others, with the Polish Cross of Merit. Her compatriot, Borsuk-Bialynicka (pers. comm. 2009), remembers her as 'a helpful and unselfish advisor . . . a charming person, of brilliant intellect, very modest, cooperative and full of (a) sense of humor'.

The role of women as illustrators

One of the most important roles that women played in the history of 'saurian' research was that of illustrator. Many women undertook this role, such as early Americans Harriet Huntsman, Graciana

Lewis and Cecilia Beaux (Aldrich 1982), and many more in the twentieth century including Jamaican Pam Gaskell, who worked for R. J. Carroll on his vertebrate palaeontology book and died in 1978 of Gleesal melanoma. Only a few can be highlighted herein. As noted above, several wives of the earliest saurian palaeontologists including Mrs Buckland, Mantell and Hitchcock were skilled artists and illustrators who helped their husbands illustrate their works.

From the mid-nineteenth century some women were professional illustrators receiving commissions for scientific papers or books and lectures both professional or popular; proof can be found in their letters. One of the most important employers was (and is) the BMNH in London (now the NHM) and here we give one case study.

The Woodward sisters – Gertrude Mary Woodward

The following excerpt is from a letter to Dr William Dickson Lang (1878–1966), newly Keeper of Geology, BMNH, dated 7 November 1928 from Miss Gertrude M. Woodward (1854–1939), the second of five daughters of Henry Bolingbroke Woodward FRS, FGS (1832–1921; a former Keeper) and Ellen Sophia Page (1837–1913):

> Dear Dr. Lang,
>
> Many thanks for your letter of this morning re diagram of comparative thickness of strata. I could make a copy of it for £2.10.00.
>
> (NHM, Woodward A. B., Archive)

This shows that she was quite well paid for her services as £1.00 in 1930 would be worth £33.40 today! Other museums also asked for commissions; the following letter is from Liverpool:

> Dear Miss Woodward, I have received £9.10.0 from Professor Wanner, and now have pleasure in sending it on to you. I have not yet had proofs of the plates. I hope they will do justice to your careful work. I am greatly obliged to you for the trouble you took. With kind regards.
>
> (Jason J. Simpson, Director of the Museums, Liverpool)

Gertrude was an excellent colour-wash illustrator; few of her works are referred to in the records even though she is known to have illustrated works by Sir Edwin Ray Lankester KCB FRS (1847–1929) (Lankester 1921) and the infamous Piltdown fossils for Arthur Smith Woodward (1864–1944). She also became a lifelong friend of Beatrix Potter who was a keen palaeontologist and a frequent visitor to the BMNH. As noted earlier, Beatrix was Sophia Hutton's granddaughter and cousin to Harriet Hunter, who also knew the Woodwards (Lear 2007).

Sometimes illustrators were also asked to provide models, as in the case of the more prominent of the two sisters.

Alice Bolingbroke Woodward

Alice Woodward (1862–1951) was one of the most prolific and well-known illustrators of the late nineteenth and early twentieth centuries (Cinamon 1989). Her scientific work, however, is overshadowed by her children's book illustrations, and thus it is fitting that her work and role as an illustrator is evaluated here.

Alice was born in Chelsea, London. As noted above, her father was then BMNH Keeper of Geology and he later became president of the Geological Society of London from 1894 to 1896. Indeed, he proposed the introduction of women into the Society in 1895, for them to be allowed to listen papers read at evening meetings or in special cases to use the library, considering that the time was ripe for an examination of the place of women within the GSL (Herries-Davies 2007; Burek 2009*b*). *It did not happen.* In 1864 he founded the *Geological Magazine* (Herries-Davies 2007), flagship of the more gender-democratic Geological Association (Burek & Higgs 2007*b*) of which, interestingly, his wife Ellen later indexed the first 40 volumes (Lightman 2004).

Alice was the middle of seven children, five girls, two boys. All were educated at home by governess and all were encouraged to draw as part of their education. Many of the drawing lessons were held in the British Museum in the Roman and Greek galleries. As a result all of the girls became artists, the two noted here undertaking palaeontological drawings; the two boys became scientists, one becoming government geologist to Western Australia. Henry 'Harry' Page Woodward (1858–1917) studied geology at the University of London and emigrated to Australia, and in 1888 became the Government Geologist for Western Australia. His *Mining Handbook to the Colony of Western Australia* (1894) was considered essential reading and his map of the area beautifully executed (Crawford 1990). By the time Alice was a teenager she was an accomplished drawer and started illustrating many of her father's lectures, also producing scientific illustrations for her father's colleagues (Fig. 9a, b). Mounted on large sheets of paper, such drawings were designed to be viewed in a lecture hall at a considerable distance. They played an important role in spreading the scientific message to students, interested amateurs and lay folk. As she was already being paid for her work, she can be considered a professional illustrator. These earnings formed the start of savings to allow her to finance her studies at the then South Kensington School, later to become the

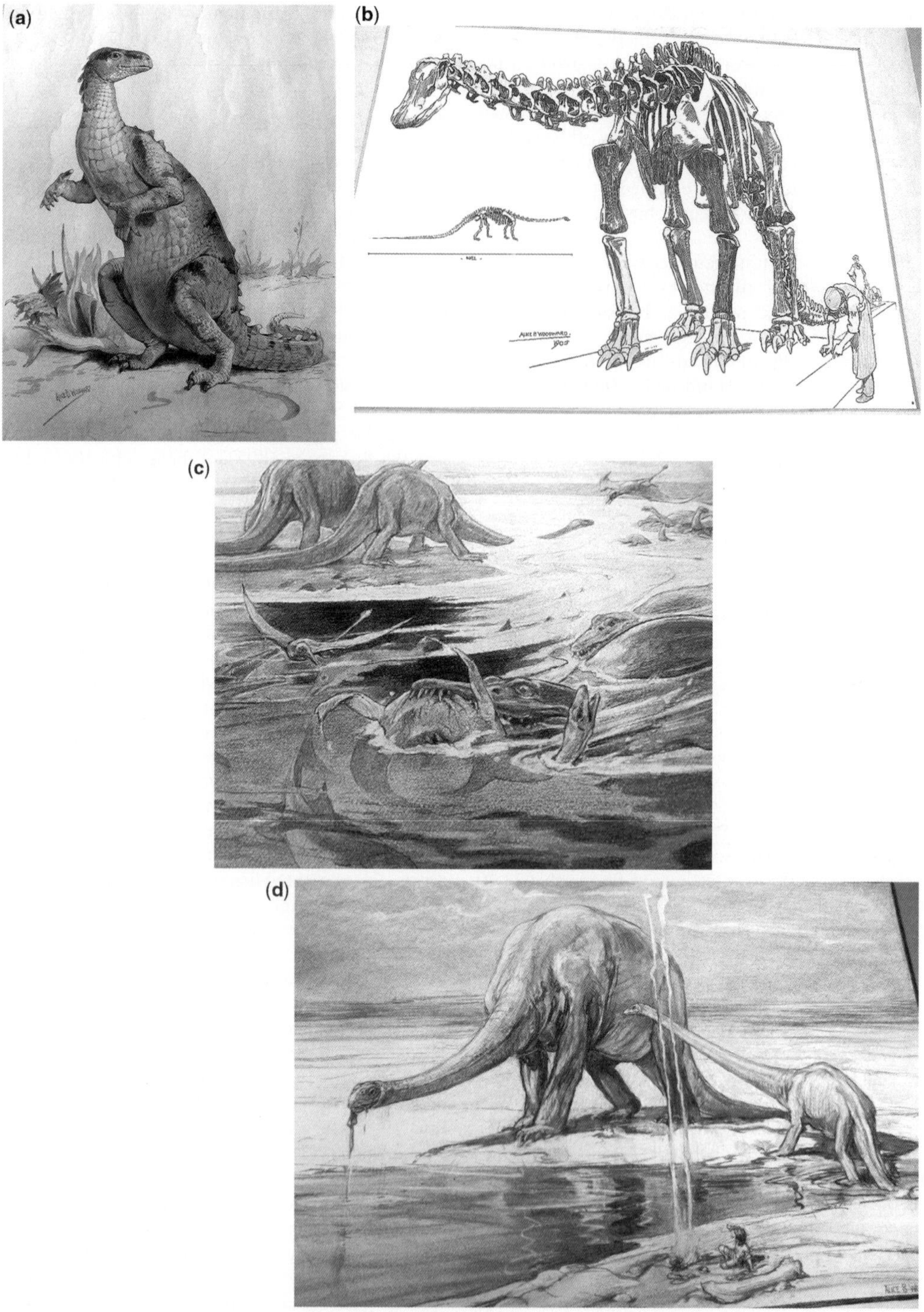

Fig. 9. Alice B. Woodward's dinosaur illustrations: (**a**) drawing of reconstructed *Iguanodon*; (**b**) 1905 drawing of remounted *Diplodocus* skeleton; (**c**) *c.* 1910 reconstruction of dinosaurs and saurians in the former Thames Valley (in NHM drawing collection, unpublished); and (**d**) '*Gigantosaurus*' with small child lighting a fire, presumably for scale (photographed by C. V. Burek with permission from originals at NHM, © Alice B. Woodward Estate).

Royal College of Art. In the 1880s she moved on to the Westminster Art School and then to the Académie Julian in Paris. In London Alice took lessons from noted American artist Joseph Pennell (1857–1926) and British artist Maurice Greiffenhagen (1862–1931). The association with the former led to her receiving commissions to illustrate children's books from J. M. Dent & Sons and Macmillan & Co., London.

After this her career took off, her work appeared in more popular publications including the *Illustrated London News* (Fig. 9d) and the last two volumes of *Bon-Mots of the Nineteenth Century*, taking over from Aubrey Beardsley, as well as *Black Beauty* and *Alice's Adventures in Wonderland*. By 1896 she was also illustrating for Blackie and Son Ltd in Glasgow. By 1907 her main publisher was George Bell & Sons with *The Peter Pan Picture Book*, her most famous work that has been in continuous production since 1907, a remarkable 100 years. Alice also exhibited drawings and paintings at the 91 Art Club in Chelsea, which catered for women artists. In all, her work appears in over 80 publications.

Less well known are her scientific drawings, 22 of which are held in the NHM archives. The dinosaurs, some illustrated here for the first time are *Diplodocus* (Fig. 9b), '*Gigantosaurus*' (Fig. 9d), *Iguanodon* (Fig. 9a), and others discovered from the Thames Valley and England (Fig. 9c). Other animals include *Triceratops* and mammals from overseas; the former was used for a BMNH postcard made using the Giclee printing process, which delivers a fine stream of ink in pure colour and exceptional detail. She based her illustrations on actual fossils, as is seen in the *Illustrated London News* (Woodward 1925), where it is noted that the 'restored figure of the *Iguanodon* was based upon fossils found in the Isle of Wight by Hulke J. W., F.R.S'. (Spokes 1927). Here the skin is shown covered by large scales (Fig. 9a), now disputed. On the back of the sketch of this early restoration of *Iguanodon* and which she sketched in 1895 at the age of 33, and which may also have been used in the *Illustrated London News*, is written:

> Animal is shown in the attitude in which it usually walked. The fore limbs are much shorter than the hind limbs, which are very powerful, having three toes to each foot and the same number of joints as in a bird's foot. The ponderous tail no doubt gave support to the animal when in an erect position and was also used in swimming.

On the back of her '*Gigantosaurus*' drawing of 1925 she describes her philosophy when interpreting the fossils she was given to illustrate:

> The fossil hunter who discovers gigantic fragments of creatures of the past must sometimes try to visualise the huge monsters to whom they belong. Could the *Gigantosaurus* whose humerus is double the size of that of *Diplodocus carnegii*, rise before him, it would be indeed a terrifying spectacle.

Woodward herself divided her illustrations into two, her scientific drawings, which she signed with her name, and other book illustrations decorated with a butterfly motif. Although not now necessarily the most accurate, her scientific work was known for its accuracy and precision. However, sometimes her commissioners wanted even greater precision. The following extract is from a letter dated 16 December 1924 written from her home address in Clay Hill, Bushey. It concerns her drawing for Dr F. Bather (also BMNH) of *Pteranodon* which she calls '*Piranodon*':

> Dear Dr. Bather,
>
> I have darkened and cleared his right hind foot and brightened his eye (without pulling a window in). I send it you prayerfully that it may pass this time.
>
> Yours very sincerely,
>
> Alice B. Woodward

The reply shows that it had passed the test

> Dear Miss Woodward
>
> Thank you for Pteranodon [his underlining]. I have approved it and send it on to the office. Sorry he has given you so much trouble.

Her drawings were also very life-like and put into landscapes (e.g. Fig. 9a, c, d), some (e.g. Fig. 9b) featured in the BMNH postcard series until at least the 1960s. This use of figures within the landscape is interesting albeit as a motif to understand size (e.g. Fig. 9c, d). Alice completed another 50 illustrations for Henry Robert Knipe (1854–1918), for his (1905) *Nebula to Man* and (1912) *Evolution in the Past*, some used and acknowledged by the Reverend H. N. Hutchinson (1856–1927) in the preface to a new (1910) edition of his popular book on extinct 'monsters'. The Bushey Museum's exhibition (mentioned earlier: Anon. 2008) has further relevance as it includes a set of Alice's intricate and beautifully illustrated dinosaur postcards, a significant communication tool when they first appeared during the early twentieth century.

The esteem in which Alice was held can be illustrated in various ways. One example occurred in early 1925, when in January she was visited by a Mr Greenwood from a landscape gardening firm, Messrs Pulman, with a view to a commission. In a letter to her in March, Dr Bather (BMNH) establishes that this firm has been engaged by Lord Leverhulme (1851–1925), the wealthy and philanthropic soap baron, (i.e. 'new money', which was then not to be treated with respect??) to:

> make some life-size figures of extinct animals, mammoth, Brontosaurus, and the like – for a park in Liverpool.

> I do not quite understand why he came to me. At any rate I gather that they want someone to make small scale models. I said that we could not undertake this with our staff, as it would be a very long piece of work requiring great care and research . . .
>
> I was so unfortunate as to annoy my visitor.

He goes on to say:

> However the reason I write to you is that it might be worth your while to call on Messrs Pulman and to see whether your skill and knowledge would be of any service to them. I have no idea whether you can undertake such work but if you can't I know no one else in this country.

Alice replies a day later, on 3 March, saying that she will write to them that day but that 'I am working for the *Illustrated London News* just at present but that will be done shortly'.

The second episode occurred when Alice died in 1951. Her sister Katherine wrote to the museum offering them the originals of her drawings as she was clearing out the studio. She originally approached Dr Helen Muir-Wood (1896–1968, Deputy Keeper of Palaeontology). On 3 October 1951 the then Keeper of Geology, W. N. Edwards, wrote to her:

> I am so sorry to hear of the death of your sister Alice. Dr Muir Wood has passed on to me your suggestion that the Natural History Museum might like to have some of Miss Alice's drawings and most certainly we should be very glad of any you can spare. She must have done a very great many drawings of fossils and of reconstructions of past life and she was for long a familiar figure in this department.

Katherine Woodward responds immediately on 4 October:

> I will shortly pack and send some of the original prehistoric drawing, which appeared in the Illustrated London News . . . I know she would have been glad for the Museum to have some of her work.

Her postcard is addressed to Dr Muir Wood, BMNH, Cromwell Rd, S. W. The writing is very spidery, showing her age.

Further letters follow until on 20 November, Katherine finalizes logistics of the gift:

> I am having a taxi on Thursday and bringing up A.B.'s drawings up to the Museum – sorry I've been so long. Remembrances, from K.E.W.

and 2 days later:

> Dear Mr. Edwards,
>
> Here at length are the drawings of Prehistoric creatures by my late sister Alice – I could not get up to bring them sooner.

Five of those drawing were of dinosaurs and thanks to the foresight of her sister, they have been preserved for all time in the NHM Library (two of which are reproduced here as Fig. 9b, c).

Alice also occasionally did work for others internationally, such as a new insectivorous armoured dinosaur from Canada, *Albertosaurus* of Nopcsa, 1923, with the restoration made under his direction.

These exchanges illustrate the high esteem in which she was held both by members of the NHM and the scientific and business world. Alice Bolingbroke Woodward is, perhaps, one of the foremost forgotten illustrators of the extinct saurians in a man's world. Her work reflected the reconstruction style of the day but sometimes she produced scenes that leap from the page and brighten the day for any palaeontologist, some of which have not been surpassed for recreating an environmental 'feel'. She showed visually the Mesozoic settings for dinosaurs and reconstructed them according to how she thought they would fit with the fossil remains. Without a doubt, her associations with her father and his colleagues would have helped her but her skill and deductions must not be underestimated.

No portrait of Alice or Gertrude seems to exist. Both Woodward sisters were held in great esteem by their peers and they were in great demand for their accurate drawing and watercolours. Theirs was, and remains, an important contribution to the history of saurian research.

Further work remains to be carried out on the overall contribution of the Woodward family to the advance of geology in general. They are truly a dynasty that deserves to be explored in greater detail.

Cecilia Beaux

E. Cecilia Beaux (1855–1942), born in Philadelphia, Pennsylvania, was one of America's finest portrait painters throughout the latter part of the nineteenth through to the early twentieth century. She was just a 20-year old artist (Fig. 10a, b) when employed by Edward Drinker Cope (1840–1897) to illustrate for his Hayden expedition volume on American western Cretaceous reptiles (Aldrich 1982, figs 8 & 9). She studied under William Sartain in Philadelphia and then at the Academié Julien and Academié Lazar in Paris, possibly slightly earlier than, but perhaps contemporary with, Alice Woodward in France. She died in Green Alley, Pennsylvania, no doubt carrying memories of the massive accolade from William Merritt Chase (1849–1916) that she was '. . . not only the greatest living woman painter, but the greatest who has ever lived' (http://www.linesandcolors.com, accessed 2009). She is the obvious retort to

Fig. 10. Cecilia Beaux (American, 1855–1942). Self-Portrait No. 3, 1894. Oil on canvas. 25 × 20 inches (63.5 × 50.8 cm). © National Academy Museum, New York.

the fact that Cope had a 'low opinion of women's intelligence' (Gould 1981, 155).

Harriet Huntsman

Harriet 'Hattie' Huntsman (unknown) was the accomplished American artist who helped Samuel Wendall Williston (1851–1918) illustrate his work on *The Paleontology for Kansas* for the Kansas Geological Survey (Aldrich 1982, fig. 7). Williston was himself an accomplished artist but the dinosaur bone illustrations of Huntsman add greatly to this work.

Hattie also worked for her brother-in-law Erasmus Haworth (1855–1932) who was the State Geologist for Kansas. The search for more data on her life and career continues, although family records of the Haworth Association (www.haworthassociation.org/family) reveal that Erasmus Haworth married her sister Ida E. Huntsman from Oskaloosa, Iowa in 1889.

Lois Darling

Lois Darling née MacIntyre? (1917–1989) was an American illustrator who worked for Ned Colbert on the *Ghost Ranch Dinosaurs* (Colbert 1996) and his (1989) *Coelophysis* monograph. Interestingly, Natascha Heintz of Norway, daughter of emigré Russian Anatol, is the only woman vertebrate palaeontologist listed in his *Men and Dinosaurs* (Colbert 1968).

Nelda Wright

Nelda Wright (1901–1992), an American research assistant was junior author to R. S. Lull, who from 1922 to 1936 was Director and then to 1956 Curator Emeritus of the New Haven Peabody Museum, on the magnum opus *Hadrosaurian dinosaurs of North America* (Lull & Wright 1942). Although written in the late 1930s, it still remains a major reference; hadrosaurid systematics were a mess until 1942, when Lull and Wright proposed the genus *Anatosaurus*. She had been illustrating other people's work at Yale (e.g. Blount 1935), and did work for Lull's earlier (1931) book on fossils; perhaps he tried to encourage her to conduct research. They travelled to many institutions, presumably she drawing specimens if not doing all the photography; (Ken Carpenter pers. comm. 2009: 'I am not sure of her role in the monograph besides the text figures'). Nate Murphy, formerly of the Judith River Institute, has claimed to be either her grandson or her nephew and that she was married to Clifford Price but others claim that she never married.

Post-World War II Nelda had transferred to the MCZ at Harvard University and was working with and for Al Romer, organizing, drawing and editing, and was involved in the *Bibliography of VP of North America* and even in the field on at least one occasion (Fig. 11a, b). She appears, like Tilly Edinger, at early meetings of the Society of Vertebrate Paleontology, became a member and, unlike Tilly, was made an honorary member. After Romer's death in November 1973, Nelda Wright finished the task of preparing his last manuscript and maps on 'The Stratigraphy of the Permian Wichita Redbeds of Texas' for publication.

Karen Alf

American Karen Alf (1954–2000) got started doing preparation at the Black Hills Institute in Hill City, South Dakota, then went to Denver in 1998, where she joined the Denver Museum of Natural History (DMNH) as a volunteer, before Ken Carpenter hired her on a temporary basis to help build the palaeontology exhibit. She continued later as a member of staff running a fossil preparation class with patience and clarity of instruction. Alf collaborated with Carpenter on the global distribution of eggs, nests, etc. (Carpenter & Alf 1994); she is also the woman operating the jackhammer at the Garden Park site, Colorado in the second colour

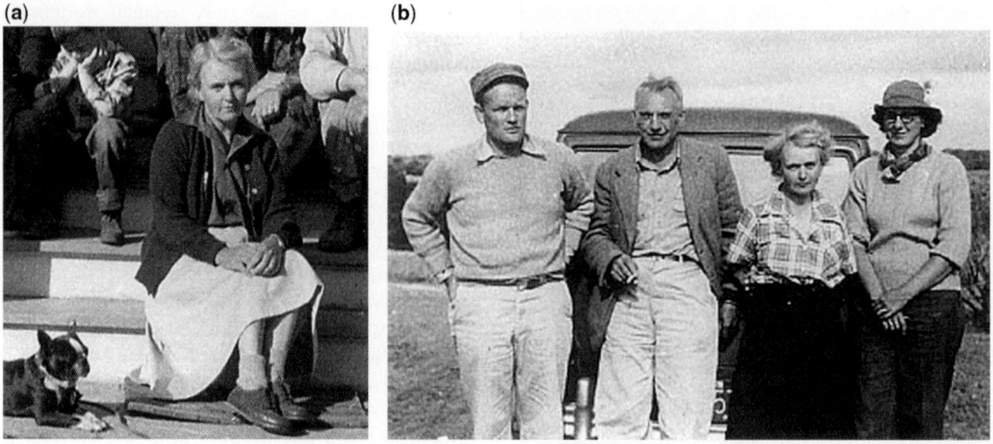

Fig. 11. (**a**) Nelda Wright and pet dog. (**b**) Nelda Wright and group (original used courtesy of Don Baird). Nelda Wright and dog with permission of Jim Jensen: http://dinosaurjim.com/html/nelda_wright.html.

plate in Carpenter's (1999) *Eggs, Nests, and Baby Dinosaurs*. Alf wanted to try her hand at research, hence her work in Cañon City with the discovery of a *Preprismatoolithus* egg clutch in the Morrison Formation. Under Carpenter's tutelage, she studied how eggshell gets distributed by erosion, finding it to be quite durable. She worked on the DMNH 'Prehistoric Journey' fossil exhibit and was a meticulous preparator as evidenced by the quality of the juvenile *Coelophysis* mount, along with another *Coelophysis* skeleton and that of *Sphenocoelus unitensis*. Karen went on to run her own fossil preparation business, 'Of Primitive Origins', with varying success until her premature death.

The important role that women have played as artists in palaeontology, including dinosaur and saurian studies, has been clearly demonstrated. They had the skills and verve to draw the actual specimens, as did the earlier women mentioned, for family and colleagues; as Margaret Colbert did for Ed and, more recently, as Jenny Middleton did for her husband Beverly Halstead. These women have recreated the animals anew to depict the fossil creatures not only for scientists to discuss but for the joy of many.

Other roles

Many women, such as research assistants, editors and typists, however, remain anonymous (see e.g. Turner 2007); Lull (in his and Nelda Wright's (q.v.) hadrosaur monograph) acknowledged his daughter (?) Dorothy; Colbert (1996) did acknowledge his editor, Diana Lubick and Anne Cole, the hard-working assistant who typed his illegible manuscripts. Others worked as writers, popularizing ideas about 'saurians'. In the nineteenth–early twentieth century these include the examples below and several others, such as Maria Hack who wrote about the ancient Earth and Isabella Duncan author of *Pre-Adamite Man* (Rudwick 1992).

Arabella Buckley

Arabella Burton Buckley (Mrs Fisher) (1840–1929), English secretary to Charles Lyell, wrote popular books, some self-illustrated. Some discussion of her life is included in Burek (2007). Her works included *The Fairyland of Science* (1879); *Through Magic Glasses and Other Lectures: A Sequel to 'The Fairy-Land of Science'* (1880); *Winners in Life's Race, or, The Great Backboned Family* and *A Short History of Natural Science and of the Progress of Discovery from the Time of the Greeks* were both published in 1882 by E. Stanford of London. She also published through Appleton in New York including *Life and her Children* (1881) on invertebrates but moved to Cassell and Macmillan of London for books published between 1903 and 1909; including the series *Eyes and No Eyes*. The 1903 *Winner's in Life's Race* or the *Great Back-boned Family*, with a preface written in 1882, dealt with reptiles and saurians but strangely no dinosaurs per se; the artists for this one include 'Miss Suft'. A number of her books were reprinted in the early 1990s and several are currently available as facsimile reprints (Elibron Series).

Some books appear to have been written some time after lectures given to children and friends; a preface written in 1878 but published years later states that at first she hesitated as 'written words can never produce the same effect as *viva voce* delivery' – was she the David Attenborough of her day? The children became adults and kept up the demand for her books, even after her death. She made no claim to originality but hoped to spread the message and knowledge of science to young people, in which she was most successful. Nevertheless, she did correspond with Charles Darwin, and Barber (1980) noted the Darwinian agenda of her books. In one letter Darwin wrote '... you have treated evolution with much dexterity and truthfulness' (www.darwinproject.ac.uk).

Ina von Grumbkow

Viktorine Helene Natalie, known as 'Ina', von Grumbkow (1872–1942), (Fig. 12a, b) was born in Övelgönne near Hamburg; she was a remarkable woman, as befits an early female student at the Prussian University in the early 1900s. She is first noted as the fiancée of Walter von Knebel, the leader of an ill-fated expedition to the Askja volcano in Iceland in 1907. von Knebel and his artist companion Max Rudolff disappeared, presumed drowned, whilst working in a canvas boat. Ina refused to accept his disappearance without trace and, stimulated by rumour, led her own expedition to Askja in 1909, subsequently writing a best-seller about her experience (Grumbkov 1909), which is still in print (Mohr *et al.* 2008*a*). Her group, which included the (much younger) geologist Hans Reck (1886–1937), whom she later married, found nothing; Reck had descended by rope to the edge of the boiling sulphurous water of what became Lake Knebel to search. They built a cairn in memory of the lost men near the Vitl Crater.

Fig. 12. (**a**) Victorine Helene Natalie 'Ina' von Grumbkow (photograph by S. Turner from an exhibition at the Humboldt Museum, Berlin). (**b**) Ina's oil painting of the Tendaguru dinosaur excavation in 1912 in what was German East Africa (photograph by S. Turner from the Humboldt Museum exhibition).

Reck became famous for his work in geomorphology, volcanology and Pleistocene mammals, and, although he had a congenital heart problem, was invited to assist Walter Janensch (1878–1969) of the Humboldt Museum, Berlin for the German East African Tendaguru dinosaur dig (in present-day Tanzania) in East Africa in 1912 (Maier 2003). Her husband recognized Ina's great organizational skills and so Ina also went along to play a major role in the field of what was one of the largest dinosaur bone digs ever, with respect to manpower and logistics, before the modern age. Ina managed the bush camp, dealing with the health and welfare of the expedition workforce. An accomplished artist, she gives us a vivid illustration of the site (Fig. 12b); she went again to Africa after World War I (Reck 1924, 1925). The marriage broke up after World War I and Reck later died of a heart attack in Africa. Ina returned to live in Berlin where she died in early World War II (Mohr *et al.* 2008*a*).

Benefactors and facilitators

Here are noted other women behind the scenes; some rich (but not famous), others less so. Surprisingly, women took key roles as organizers and providers early on in the saurian world, such as the wealthy anonymous woman who supported the *Kronosaurus* expedition from the MCZ at Harvard University into Australia in 1932 (Turner & Wade 1986). These days we rarely question when a woman becomes a director or a leader of expeditions (for example, see Vickers-Rich later). In the late nineteenth and early twentieth century few sought or reached such positions. Mainly these possibilities came about in the 'New' or communist worlds. One example epitomizes the new emancipated woman of the twentieth century.

Miss Annie Alexander (1867–1950)

American Annie Montague Alexander (her mother's maiden name) (Fig. 13c–e) was Hawaiian born. Her grandparents were early missionaries and her wealthy father allowed her to be educated and to indulge her taste for adventure (Stein 2001). She gained a liberal education at Lasell College and then entered the University of California. After choosing to study natural history and attending John C. Merriam's lectures on palaeontology in 1901 she became fascinated by extinct mammals and reptiles. Alexander offered to underwrite the costs of his summer collecting expedition if she could take part in the fieldwork. Merriam became her mentor. She went on not only to collect numerous specimens but, after the death of her father in 1904, she decided to give back by creating one of the finest natural history museums. Probably having already determined that she was not one for the traditional path of wife and mother, at 37 Alexander could follow her father's example and espouse her love of natural history.

Thus began the long rewarding association of Miss Alexander with the Department and Museum of Paleontology at Berkeley (UCMP, see www.ucmp.berkeley.edu/archives/alexanderpapers with photograph accessed 3 March 2009; Anon. 1980); Stein (2001) shows her watching 'with fascination' as a saurian she had discovered was excavated. She paid field expenses and was at Fossil Lake, Oregon in 1901, Shasta County, California in 1902 and 1903, and the West Humboldt Range, Nevada in 1905, helping excavate Merriam's (1905) find of some of the largest (Triassic) ichthyosaur skeletons in the world and the most complete in North America. Alexander enjoyed and endured the hard work and hardships of fieldwork (Fig. 13b), searching for and packing ichthyosaur fossils, and she also did much of the cooking! In 1905 she wrote:

> My dear friend Miss Wemple stood by me through thick and thin. Together we sat in the dust and sun, marking and wrapping bones. No sooner were these loaded in the wagon for Davison to haul to Mill City than new piles took their places. Night after night we stood before a hot fire to stir rice, or beans, or corn, or soup, contriving the best dinners we could out of our dwindling supply of provisions. We sometimes wondered if the men thought the fire wood dropped out of the sky or whether a fairy godmother brought it to our door, for they never asked any questions . . . .
>
> (Alexander 1905, UCMP www.ucmp.berkeley.edu/archives/alexanderpapers, accessed June 2009)

In 1906 she began to make regular contributions to support departmental research. After Merrian left in 1920, to her displeasure, and the Paleontology Faculty was merged with the Department of Geological Sciences, Alexander arranged for the UCMP to be an independent unit, establishing an endowment in 1934. Beyond this, she made many gifts for special purposes – supporting faculty on sabbatical leave, student research visits to museums, extra funds for field expenses. Through her support of Merriam and his successors, Matthew, Camp and Stirton, at UCMP, she made possible virtually all the subsequent contributions that have come out of that institution (D. Brinkmann pers. comm.; Zullo 1969, Sarjeant 1978–1987, Suppl. II; Vickers-Rich & Archbold 1991; see discussion of her by Hilton 2003). She is noted for her skilful handling of administrators, with offers of financial support for particular programmes carefully thought out, and always stipulating special conditions that the university had to meet as its part of the bargain. Knowledgeable in money

Fig. 13. Miss Annie Alexander: (**a**) young in 1901; (**b**) Alexander in her field gear on expedition in Nevada, 1905 (modified from University of California Museum of Palaeontology, Berkeley photograph); (**c**) Miss Alexander, the philanthropist, dinosaur lover and collector (reproduced from University of California Museum of Palaeontology, Berkeley see www.ucmp.berkeley.edu/archives/alexanderpapers accessed 3 March 2009).

matters since childhood (Stein 2001), she is said to have chided the treasurer for not getting enough return on university investments; her own were doing much better! In 1930 she approached big business and banks seeking funds for the construction of a university museum but the Depression was underway and so she put pressure on the university to at least provide a fireproof building for the fossil collections. Alexander appreciated the value of scientific research and had an excellent grasp of the discipline; she also understood the necessity for proper documentation and preservation of fossils, etc. if they were to be of scientific value. An excellent judge of people, she played an important role in the selection of key personnel; her pleas had led to the appointment of W. D. Matthew as Professor of Paleontology and UCMP Director in 1928, and she supported him and his protegé G. G. Simpson. Alexander shared her life with Louise Kellogg for 42 years in a devoted 'Boston marriage' (This term became commonplace after the publication of Henry James's book *The Bostonians* (1886) in which he detailed a marriage-like relationship between two 'New Women'.) Still going strong, Miss Alexander celebrated her 80th birthday during an expedition to Baja California. Conversely, she did not desire publicity nor did she enjoy having taxa named after her. Nevertheless, see taxa later.

American woman power

Phoebe Catherine Finley Pack (1907/08?–unknown), together with her husband Arthur

(Newton) Pack (1893–1975), were the celebrated owners and gracious hosts of the Ghost Ranch where Colbert (1996, with photograph) worked in the 1940s; he dedicated his book to them. She and Arthur, together with one William 'Bill' Carr, a former employee of the American Museum of Natural History, founded the Ghost Ranch Museum which opened in 1959. Carr later became the first Director of the Arizona Sonora Desert Museum, again supported by nearly half a million dollars of aid from the Packs. Phoebe is listed in the University of Arizona's Womens' Plaza of Honour and was awarded the Founders' Award of the Tucson Metropolitan Chamber of Commerce in 1994.

Ruth Hall (unknown), American philanthropist, featured in Elliot (2000), helped set up the Ghost Ranch Dinosaurs Museum with her husband Jim, the first resident Director of the Ranch, also helping Colbert (1996, with photograph); he eulogizes her educational efforts in his book and notes her status as 'ardent student and protector' of the Triassic vertebrates of dinosaur quarry. She has her own wing, the Ruth Hall Paleontology Museum, named in her honour and represents the innumerable unnamed volunteers who have helped excavate on dino digs.

Billie R. Unterman (1906–1973), American palaeontologist who showed that 'smaller cities offered unusual opportunities' (Rossiter 1982, p. 302), with husband 'G. E.' (see Colbert 1984) built and later directed a natural history museum in Vernal, Utah, which became known as 'Dinosaurland'. She helped to erect the famous cast of a *Diplodocus carnegiei* on the lawn. They laid out an instructive scenic dinosaur drive through the surrounding country on Utah Highway 40 (White 1973).

These three represent all those wonderful landowners from traditional to modern who have facilitated the study of dinosaurs, etc., on their land, providing such as bulldozers, food, lodging and water, etc., plus 'woman'-power!

The fictional world

Almost as soon as they were scientifically determined, dinosaurs began to appear in literature, some written by women (q.v. Buckley) (Haste 1993; Torrens 1993; Sarjeant 1994; Allmon 2006). The women portrayed in books and later in films (e.g. *Godzilla*), except perhaps for Raquel Welsh in *One Million Years BC* (e.g. Torrens 1993), are generally 'screamers' and not accurate portrayals of science. The woman in *Jurassic Park*, Dr Ellie Sattler (actor Laura Dern), however, was an interesting portrayal, a palaeobotanist who wasn't phased by *Triceratops* poo! Truth is actually stranger than fiction and one woman, Karen Chin (e.g. Chin 1995), is the world's leading expert on dinosaur scatology. Haste (1993) also pointed out all the DNA-recreated dinosaurs in the fictional park were females, 'good mothers', intelligent and caring, and supposedly therefore without aggression (contrary to the end result).

Media messages on dinosaurs can be interpreted as either a good or a misleading communication tool. Mythologies have been created, such as The Loch Ness Monster, 'Nessie', being a plesiosaur, and a female one at that (what would Anning have thought about that?!). Politicians and the general public grasp on to certain themes and apparent 'hard' scientific 'fact', such as the asteroid impact debate, sometimes to detrimental effect, as discussed by sociologist Elizabeth Clemens (1986). Interestingly, women geoscientists are retesting the evidence for the Alvarez Impact Hypothesis for dinosaur demise at the Cretaceous–Tertiary (K–T) boundary; Gerta Keller at Princeton University is attempting to check the Chicxulub meterorite story (Nield 2007). Dr Angela Milner at NHM (pers. comm. to S. Turner 2009) has recently presented evidence on the 'Timing and causes of vertebrate extinctions across the Cretaceous–Tertiary boundary' at international meetings and is a strong opponent of dinosaur myths and misconceptions, with lectures to the Royal Society and the Royal Society of Edinburgh.

The story of Sue – a female affair!

'Sue' (*c*. 70 Ma), American, a famous named specimen of *Tyrannosaurus rex* (see Gore 1993), which on detailed examination was found to be robust at death if not totally healthy. Rega & Brochu (2002) concluded that Sue had healed osteomyelitis from infection of the left fibula and right humerus, plus healed fractures of right and left ribs from earlier trauma, possible exuberant vertebral osteophyte formation; erosive lesions; jaw lesions – fungal or neoplastic (see Gore 1993).

The specimen was found and named after Sue Hendrickson from Montana who is a marine archaeologist, adventurer and explorer who joined several expeditions (e.g. Larson & Donnan 2004). In South Dakota in 1990 she found the eponymous and remarkable *Tyrannosaurus rex* skeleton 'Sue', the largest and most complete found to date (Gore 1993). This specimen became the object of a benchmark litigation case involving landowners (including Sioux Indians), collectors and museums, and which was finally acquired by the Field Museum in Chicago; both Sue and 'Sue' have spawned many books and interest in dinosaurs. And, notably, four of the 45 *T. rex*'s known have been discovered by women (D. Spalding pers. comm.).

Dinosaurs and other saurians named after women

Sadly, and much to Mary Anning's chagrin, none of the early reptiles she found were named after her. This is now being redressed; in Paris, Peggy Vincent has described with Philippe Taquet the second-ever plesiosaur discovered by Anning, from the MNHN collections (Vincent & Taquet 2010), and has redescribed a pliosaur from Lyme Regis and proposed a new specific name to honour Anning.

The Cretaceous plesiosaur *Hydrotherosaurus alexandriae* plus *Shastasaurus alexandrae* and *Thalattosaurus alexandrae*, Triassic ichthyosaurs, were named by Merriam to commemorate Miss Alexander, but there is nothing for her dinosaur-finding compatriot Talbot. Ruth Romer has a primitive pelycosaur from New Mexico, *Ruthiromia elcobriensis* named after her by Eberth & Brinkman in 1983, and in 1965 Chase named *Neldasaurus wrighti*, a Permian temnospondyl amphibian from Texas, for Nelda Wright.

In recent times Borsuk-Bialynicka named a euparkeriid *Osmolskina* in honour of her friend and colleague Halszka Osmólska; also named for her is the Mongolian oviraptorid *Citipati osmolskae* Clark *et al.* 2001, the Chinese dromaeosaurid *Velociraptor osmolskae* and the archosauriform reptile *Osmolskina czatkowicensis*. Pat Vickers-Rich and her husband Tom honoured their daughter Leaellyn Rich (see Fig. 14), the collector of the Cretaceous *Leaellynosaurus* from Victoria; Leaellyn, then a keen 10-year old collector herself, often accompanied her parents on digs in Australia (Gore 1993; Connolly 1997).

Betsy Nicholls probably has the highest number of 'honour taxa', including a primitive chelonioid *Nichollsemys baieri* Brinkman *et al.* 2006 from the Bearpaw Formation of southern Alberta; early Cretaceous plesiosaur *Wapuskanectes betsynichollsae* Druckenmiller & Russell 2003 from NW Alberta; and another from the same Ft McMurray area, *Nichollssaura borealis* Druckenmiller & Russell 2008 [for *Nichollsia* preoccupied]. Another named after her is a tiny squirrel-sized carnivorous dinosaur from Alberta called *Hesperonychus elizabethae*, the smallest of its type ever discovered in North America (Longrich & Currie 2009). Betsy first discovered the small claws and pelvis in 1982. University of California researcher Nicholas Longrich says 'Until we found this animal, basically we had no evidence for any small carnivores being present in North America'. Betsy has had the largest and smallest named after her. An honour indeed!

Fig. 14. One modern saurian women, Professor Patricia Vickers-Rich (1944–), Australian/American geologist, palaeontologist and author of Monash University Science Centre and Geosciences Department, Australia was the inspiration for a 'Palaeontologist Barbie'.

A further, slightly older small reptile, the early Triassic *Kalisuchus* from Australia, was named by Tony Thulborn in 1979 for the goddess (but actually for his finest hunting *female* feline), but in general we are hard pressed to find many saurian taxa honouring the work of women through the ages.

Conclusions

What we learnt in producing this paper is that first thoughts about women in the 'saurian' world usually only come up with the ubiquitous Anning and one or two others, thus supporting the conclusions more widely drawn by Burek & Higgs (2007*a*). Many are 'hidden away' or forgotten.

In general, there is a dearth of women scientists reflected in histories, textbooks and media (e.g. Benton 1990; Naish & Martill 2007, 2008). Nevertheless, with prompting, colleagues around the world have helped us define the contribution of women from different backgrounds from the 1700s onward (Table 1); many have contributed as artists and writers, and many books on saurians, especially those for children, are written by women. There are now a growing number of female vertebrate palaeontologists at the forefront; they are not listed here and their work will judged in good time (a first database of women 'saurian' workers has begun during the research for this

Table 1. *Women geological pioneers in many countries, notably those mentioned in the text and 'saurian' pioneers that lived, worked and died mainly within the nineteenth century**

Name	Dates	Specialty	Country	Achieved
Martine de Bertereau, Baronne de Beausoleil et d'Auffenbach	1600–1630	G	France	Mines and mining
Miss Sarah Congreve	1737–1836	P	England	Collected reptiles
Miss Mary Congreve	1745–1823	P	England	Collected reptiles
Etheldred Benett	1776–1845	P	England	Collected reptiles, book
Mrs M. H. Smith	1784–1866	P	England	Collected reptiles
Lady Hester Stanhope	1776–1839	P	Lebanon	Collected reptiles
Mary Philpot	1777–1838	P	England	Collected reptiles
Elizabeth Philpot	1780–1857	P	England	Collected reptiles
Mary Somerville (née Fairfax)	1780–1872	G	Scotland Ireland	Book
Margaret Philpot	1786–1845	P	England	Collected reptiles
Mrs Maria Graham	1785–1842	G	England	Chilean earthquake
Mary Ann Mantell	1795–1869	VP	England	Specimen, drawings, book illustration
Mary Buckland (née Morland)	1797–1857	VP	England	Field, drawings of reptiles
Lady Eliza Maria Gordon Cumming of Altyre	*c.* 1798–1842	P	Scotland	Specimens, especially fossil fish
Mary Anning	1799–1847	VP	England	Collected reptiles, research
Clémentine Cuvier	1805–1827	P	France	
Anne Maria Pinney	*c.* 1810–unknown	P	England	Collected fossils
Barbara Yelverton Marchioness Hastings	1810–1858	P	England	Collected reptiles
Orra White Hitchcock	1796–1863	VP	USA	Drawing first dinosaur tracks
Elizabeth Cary Agassiz	1822–1907		USA	Research assistant education
Mrs Margaret Hobson (née Adamson)	1837–?	VP	England	Drawings early Australian fossils
Mrs Harriet Sophia Holland	1835–1908	Collector	England	Collected fossils
Arabella Buckley	1840–1929	G	England	Books
Mary Christen Thompson (née Sydney)	1847–1923	G	Swiss?/Ireland	Quaternary research
Cecilia Beaux	1855–1942	VP	USA	Drawings
Agnes Crane	1852–1911	VP	England	Research fossil fish
Annie Greenly (née Barnard)	1852–1927	G	England	Line Method mapping GSL Greenly Fund
Fanny R. M. Hitchcock	18xx–unknown	VP	USA?	Research fossil fish
Anne Montague Alexander	1867–1950	VP	USA	Collected reptiles, museum foundation
Mignon Talbot	1869–1950	VP	USA	First dinosaur specimen
Alice Bolingbroke Woodward	1862–1951	VP	England	Drawings, book illustration
Ina von Grumbkow	1872–1942	VP	Germany	Site management, drawings
Harriett Mary Hutton	1873–1937	P	English	Collected reptiles
Irene Longman	1877–1963	VP	Australia	Research assistant
'Tilly' Edinger	1897–1967	VP	Germany	Research

Sources: Lambrecht *et al.* 1938; Sarjeant 1978–1987; Cleevely 1983; Burek & Higgs 2007*b*.
Abbreviations: G, general geology; P, palaeontology; VP, vertebrate palaeontology/Mesozoic reptiles.
*Not an exhaustive list.

chapter Turner, www.paleodeadfish.com). More specifically, there are still only a relative handful of women who entered the research world, either as professionals or known amateurs, and those mostly in the last 30 years and still mainly concentrated in the northern hemisphere (Table 2). At least in the early twenty-first century women are more likely to gain degrees, jobs, research grants, be

Table 2. *'Saurian' women through time and place before the late twentieth century when women's work was still restricted mostly to the northern hemisphere*

Year	England	Europe	North America	Soviet/Russia	Australasia
1970–1979	Bramwell Collins	Mendrez			Wade Wiffen
1960–1969	Bramwell Robinson	Heintz	Edinger	Osmolska	Wiffen
1950–1959			Mason Edinger		
1940–1949			Edinger	Lookijnova	
1930–1939		Edinger von Huene	Wright		
1920–1929	Pearson	Edinger			
1910–1919			Talbot		
1900–1909	Woodward				
1850–1899	Hutton Smith				
1800–1849	Anning Congreve Hastings Philpots Holland Woodhouse				

Note: This table shows past women researchers on 'saurians' but includes some early collectors as they were pioneers and did contribute to taxonomic understanding.

involved in the field, in leading expeditions, running conferences and publishing at the highest level.

We have to admit, though, that many women in this history and most amateurs are unsung heroes; we don't know all their names. A prime example is Gary Larsen's giant lady with fine red shoes (1985, featured on the 1989 edition cover) who caused the extinction of the dinosaurs(!).

Note: If they are not an integral part of the text, references by the women discussed here regarding the taxa named by or for them are supplied separately in SUP 18419 or can be found in the *Bibliography of Fossil Vertebrates* (e.g. Romer *et al.* 1962).

For unstinting help we acknowledge many living women vertebrate palaeontologists and D. Brinkman (Calgary), M. Maisch (Tübingen, Stuttgart) and N. Bardet (Paris), who made useful critical readings of the manuscript. Others who gave additional help and support are: M. Aldrich, J. Athersuch, M. Borsuk-Bialynicka, A. Brook, E. A. Buchholtz, C. Burrow, K. Carpenter, A. Cheese *The Helpful Mouse* bookseller, K. Chin, A. Cook, J. Cooper, L. Dingus, D. Eberth, the Mary Evans Picture Library, M. Ginter, T. Goodhue, I. Graham, H. Hölder, the von Huene family, J. Jensen, C. Jung, C. Klug, D. Merriam, D. Martill, R. F. Miller, A. Milner, B. Mohr, R. Oudans, the late W.-E. Reif, K. Riddington, A. Seilacher, D. Spalding, J. Stacey, M. Taylor, P. Taquet, R. A. Thulborn, D. Weishampel, and librarians and archivists at the NHM (for access to the Woodward archives) and the Institut für Geowissenschaften, Eberhard Karls Universität, Tübingen.

References

ABEL, O. 1912. *Palaeobiologie*. E. Schweizerbart'sche Verlagsbuchhandlung, Naegele & Dr. Sprosser, Stuttgart.

ALDRICH, M. L. 1982. Women in paleontology in the United States 1840–1960. *History of Geology*, **1**, 14–22.

ALDRICH, M. L. & LEVITON, A. E. 2001. Orra White Hitchcock (1796–1863), geological illustrator: another belle of Amherst. *Geological Society of America Annual Meeting, November 5–8, Program & Abstracts, 2001*, 103-0, 157–158 + pl. 19.

ALLEN, D. E. 1976. *The Naturalist in Britain – A Social History*. 1978 Pelican edition, Harmondsworth.

ALLMON, W. D. 2006. The pre-modern history of the post-modern dinosaur: phases and causes in post-Darwinian dinosaur art. *Earth Sciences History*, **25**, 5–36.

ALUMNAE ASSOCIATION 1937. *One Hundred Year Biographical Directory of Mount Holyoke College 1837–1937*. Bulletin Series, **30**, No. 5, Alumnae Association of Mount Holyoke College, South Hadley, MA.

ANON. 1938. Harriett Mary Hutton. *Quarterly Journal and Proceedings of the Geological Society, London*, **94**, cxxxiv–cxxv.

ANON. 1975. *The British Medical Journal*, **1**, 507–508.

ANON. 1980. Annie Alexander – the intrepid collector. *Pacific Gas & Electric Progress*, **57**, 7. (July).

ANON. 2008. http://en.wikipedia.org/wiki/Alice_B._Woodward.

ANON. 2009. Obituary I. Vanderloh: *Brooks Bulletin online* – http://www.brooksbulletin.com/obituaries.

ARNOLD, C. 2007. *Giant Sea Reptiles of the Dinosaur Age*. Clarion Books, New York.

BARBER, L. 1980. *The Heyday of Natural History*. Jonathon Cape, London.

BARSBOLD, R., CURRIE, P. J., MYHRVOLD, N. P., OSMÓLSKA, H., TSOGTBAATAR, K. & WATABE, M. 2000. A pygostyle from a non-avian theropod. *Nature*, **403**, 155.

BENTON, M. J. 1990. *The Reign of the Reptiles. The Stories of Some of the Most Fascinating Creatures Ever to Inhabit the Earth*. Crescent Books, New York.

BIRD, R. T. 1985. *Bones for Barnum Brown. Adventures of a Dinosaur Hunter*. V. T. Schreiber & Texas Christian University Press, Austin, TX.

BLOUNT, I. W. H. 1935. The anatomy of normal and reduplicated limbs in Amphibia, with special reference to musculature and vascularization. *Journal of Experimental Zoology*, **69**, 407–457.

BRAMWELL, C. D. & WHITFIELD, G. R. 1970. Flying speed of the largest aerial vertebrate. *Nature*, **225**, 660–661.

BROWN, F. R. 1987. *Let's Call Him Barnum*. self-published.

BROWN, L. 1951. *I Married a Dinosaur*. George G. Harrap, London.

BROWN, L. 1958. *Bring 'Em Back Petrified*. The Adventurer's Club, London.

BUCHHOLTZ, E. A. & SEYFARTH, E.-A. 1999. The gospel of the fossil brain: Tilly Edinger and the science of paleoneurology. *Brain Research Bulletin*, **48**, 351–361.

BUCHHOLTZ, E. A. & SEYFARTH, E.-A. 2001. The study of 'fossil brains': Tilly Edinger (1897–1967) and the beginnings of paleoneurology. *BioScience*, **51**, 674–682.

BUCKLAND, W. 1824. Notice on the *Megalosaurus* or great Fossil Lizard of Stonesfield. *Transactions of the Geological Society, London*, Series 2, **1**, 1–12.

BUCKLEY, A. B. 1879. *The Fairyland of Science*. E. Stanford, London. 2nd edn published by Macmillan, London (1909).

BUCKLEY, A. B. 1880. *Through Magic Glasses and Other Lectures: A Sequel to 'The Fairy-Land of Science'*. E. Stanford, London.

BUCKLEY, A. B. 1881. *Life and her Children: Glimpses of Animal Life from the Amoeba to the Insects*. Appelton, New York.

BUCKLEY, A. B. 1882. *Winners in Life's Race, or, The Great Backboned Family*. E. Stanford, London.

BUCKLEY, A. B. 1882. *A Short History of Natural Science and of the Progress of Discovery From the Time of the Greeks*. E. Stanford, London.

BUCKLEY, A. B. 1903. *Eyes and No Eyes*. Cassell, London.

BUREK, C. V. 2001*a*. Where are the women in geology? *Geology Today*, **17**, 110–114.

BUREK, C. V. 2001*b*. *The first lady geologist, or collector par excellance?* http://chesterrep.openrepository.com/cdr/bitstream/10034/12138/1/burek-firstladygeologist.pdf, accessed July 2009.

BUREK, C. V. 2003. Mary Anning (1799–1847). *In*: LERNER, K. L. & LERNER, B. W. (eds) *World of Earth Science*. Gale Cengage, 2003. eNotes.com. 2006. 18 May 2009. http://www.enotes.com/earth-science/anning-mary.

BUREK, C. V. 2004. Benett, Etheldred Anna Maria (1776–1845). *In*: LIGHTMAN, B. (ed.) *Dictionary of Nineteenth Century British Scientists*, Volume 1 A–C. Thoemmes Continuum Press, Bristol, 179–181.

BUREK, C. V. 2007. The role of women in geological higher education – Bedford College London and Newnhan College Cambridge, UK. *In*: BUREK, C. V. & HIGGS, B. (eds) *The Role of Women in the History of Geology*. Geological Society, London, Special Publications, **281**, 9–38.

BUREK, C. V. 2009*a*. The role women have played in developing the science of geology 1797–1918–19 in Britain. *Open University Geological Society Journal*, **29**, Symposium edition 2008, 18–25.

BUREK, C. V. 2009*b*. The first female Fellows and the status of women in the Geological Society of London. *In*: LEWIS, C. L. E. & KNILL, S. J. (eds) *The Making of the Geological Society*. Geological Society, London, Special Publications, **317**, 373–407.

BUREK, C. V. & HIGGS, B. 2007*a*. The role of women in the history and development of geology: an introduction. *In*: BUREK, C. V. & HIGGS, B. (eds) *The Role of Women in the History of Geology*. Geological Society, London, Special Publications, **281**, 1–8.

BUREK, C. V. & HIGGS, B. 2007*b*. *The Role of Women in the History of Geology*. Geological Society, London, Special Publications, **281**, 1–342.

CADBURY, D. 2000. *The Dinosaur Hunters. A True Story of Scientific Rivalry and the Discovery of the Prehistoric World*. Fourth Estate, London.

CALLAWAY, J. M. & NICHOLLS, E. L. (eds) 1997. *Ancient Marine Reptiles*. Academic Press, London.

CARPENTER, K. 1999. *Eggs, Nests, and Baby Dinosaurs: A Look at Dinosaur Reproduction (Life of the Past)*. Indiana University Press, Bloomington, IN.

CARPENTER, K. C. & ALF, K. 1994. Global distribution of dinosaur eggs, nests, and baby skeletons. *In*: CARPENTER, K., HIRSCH, K. F. & HORNER, J. R. (eds) *Dinosaur Eggs and Babies*. Cambridge University Press, New York, 15–30.

CHEVALIER, T. 2009. *Remarkable Creatures*. Harper Collins, London.

CHIN, K. 1995. Lesson from the Leavings. *Natural History*, **104**, 67.

CINAMON, G. 1989. Alice B. Woodward. *The Private Library*, Fourth series, **2**, 148–177 [not seen, off web].

CLEEVELY, R. J. 1983. *World Palaeontological Collections. British Museum (Natural History)*. Mansell Publishing Ltd for Trustees. BMNH, London.

CLEEVELY, R. J. 1998. *The First Female Palaeontologist. The Linnean*, **14**, 25–26.

CLEMENS, E. S. 1986. Of asteroids and dinosaurs; the role of the press in the shaping of scientific debates. *Social Studies of Science*, **16**, 421–456 [not seen, quoted in Haste 1993].

COLBERT, E. H. 1951. *The Dinosaur Book*. 2nd edn. McGraw-Hill/American Museum of Natural History, New Hampshire.

COLBERT, E. H. 1980. *A Fossil Hunters Notebook. My Life with Dinosaurs and Other Friends*. E. P. Dutton, New York.
COLBERT, E. H. 1982. *Dinosaurs, Mammoths and Cavemen. The Art of Charles R. Knight*. E. P. Dutton, New York.
COLBERT, E. H. 1983. *Dinosaurs: An Illustrated History*. Hammond, Maplewood, NJ.
COLBERT, E. H. 1984. *The Great Dinosaur Hunters and Their Discoveries*. Dover, New York.
COLBERT, E. H. 1989. The Triassic dinosaur *Coelophysis*. *Museum of Northern Arizona Bulletin*, **57**, 1–160.
COLBERT, E. H. 1992. *William Diller Matthew, Palaeontologist. The Splendid Drama Observed*. Columbia University Press, New York.
COLBERT, E. H. 1996. *The Little Dinosaurs of Ghost Ranch*. Columbia University Press, New York.
COLBERT, M. 2007. *Margaret Matthew Colbert: A Life of Art and Science*. www.vertpaleo.org/society/margaretmatthewcolbert.cfm, accessed 2009.
CONEYBEARE, W. D. & PHILLIPS, W. 1822. *1st Outlines of the Geology of England and Wales with an Introductory Compendium of the General Principles of that Science and Comparative Views of the Structure of Foreign Countries*. Wm. Phillips, London.
CONNOLLY, P. 1997. (Upfront) Digging the Dinos. *Who Weekly* (magazine), 23 January, no. 278, 32–34.
COOK, A. 2005. Dr Mary Wade. *The Australian Geologist TAG*, **137**, 45.
CREESE, M. R. S. & CREESE, T. M. 1994. British women who contributed to research in the geological sciences in the nineteenth century. *British Journal for the History of Science*, **27**, 23–54.
CRICHTON, M. 1991. *Jurassic Park*. Century, London.
CUMBERLAND, G. 1829. Some account of the order in which the fossil Saurians were discovered. *Quarterly Journal of Science, Literature and Art*, **27**, 345–349. Quoted in *Gentleman's Magazine*, **XCIX**.
CURLE, R. 1963 (undated binding). Mary Anning 1799–1847. *Dorset Worthies*, **4**, 1–3.
CURRIE, P. & KOPPELHUS, E. 2005. *Dinosaur Provincial Park – A Spectacular Ancient Ecosystem Revealed*. Indiana University press, Bloomington, IN.
CURWEN, E. C. 1940. *The Journal of Gideon Mantell. Surgeon and Geologist Covering the Years 1818–1852*. Oxford University Press, Oxford.
DEAN, D. R. 1999. *Gideon Mantell and the Discovery of Dinosaurs*. Cambridge University Press, Cambridge.
DINGUS, L. & NORELL, A. M. 2007. The Bone Collector. *Discover*, March 27, www.discovermagazine.com, accessed December 2009.
DUGGAN, S. & DRURY, B. 1948. *The Rescue of Science and Learning – The Story of the Emergency Committee in Aid of Displaced Foreign Scholars*. Macmillian, New York.
EBERTH, D. 2004. Betsy Nicholls Memorial. www.vrtpaleo list, Friday 22 October, accessed 2009.
EDMONDS, J. M. 1978. The fossil collection of the Misses Philpot of Lyme Regis. *Proceedings of the Dorset Natural History & Archaeological Society*, **98** (for 1976), 43–48.
EDMONDS, W. 1979. *The Iguanodon Mystery*. Kestrel Books Penguin.
ELLIOT, A. B. 2000. *Charming the Stones*. Kent State University Press, Kent, OH.
FALK, D. 2000. Careers in science offer women an unusual bonus: immortality. *Nature*, **407**, 833.
FALLON, P. 2002. *So Hard the Conquering. A Life of Irene Longman*. MPh thesis, Faculty of Humanities, Griffith University.
FARLOW, J. O. & BRETT-SURMAN, M. K. (eds) 1997. *The Complete Dinosaur*. Indiana University Press, Bloomington, IN.
FORDE, H. A. 1925. *The Heroine of Lyme Regis. The Story of Mary Anning, the Celebrated Geologist of Lyme*. Wells Gardner and Darton and Co. Ltd, London.
FOWLES, J. 1991. *A Short History of Lyme Regis*. Dovecote Press, Philpot Museum, Lyme Regis.
GARDINER, B. G. 2000. Beatrix Potter's fossils and her interest in Geology. *The Linnean*, **16**, 31–47.
GOODHUE, T. W. 2002. *Curious Bones – Mary Anning and the Birth of Paleontology*. Great Scientists. Morgan Reynolds, Greensboro, NC.
GOODHUE, T. W. 2004. *Fossil Hunter – The Life and Times of Mary Anning (1799–1847)*. Academica Press, Bethesda.
GORDON, E. O. 1894. *The Life and Correspondence of William Buckland, D.D., F.R.S.* John Murray, London.
GORE, R. 1993. Dinosaurs. *National Geographic*, **183**, 2–53.
GOULD, S. J. 1981. *The Mismeasure of Man*. W. W. Norton, New York.
GREGORY, H. 2005. *Great Queensland Women*. Office for Women, Queensland Government, Brisbane.
HAFF, J. C. 1952. Memorial to Mignon Talbot. *Proceedings Volume of the Geological Society of America, Annual Report for 1951*. 157–158.
HALSTEAD, L. B. & HALSTEAD, J. 1983. *Terrible Claw. The Story of a Carnivorous Dinosaur*. William Collins, London.
HASTE, H. 1993. Dinosaurs as metaphor. *In*: SARJEANT, W. A. S. (ed.) *Beverly Halstead; His Life and Publications. Halstead Memorial Volume. Modern Geology*, **18**, 349–370.
HILTON, R. 2003. *Dinosaurs and Other Mesozoic Reptiles of California*. University of California Press, Berkeley, CA.
HOARE, R. C. 1831. *The History of Modern Wiltshire, 1822–44*, 6 vols. Hughes, Harding, Maver and Lepard, London.
HOWE, S. R., SHARPE, T. & TORRENS, H. 1981. *Ichthyosaurs: A History of Fossil 'Sea-Dragons'*. National Museum of Wales, Cardiff.
HUENE, E. VON 1949. Studie ueber die Umwandlung des Landfusses in den Schwimmfuss bei Sauropterygiern und Placodontiern, gezeight an der Vorderextremitaet. *Neues Jahrbuch für Mineralogie, Geologie und Paläontologie*, **90**, 96–162.
HUTCHINSON, H. N. 1910. *Extinct Monsters and Creatures of Other Days*. Chapman & Hall, London.
JAMES, H. 1886. *The Bostonians*. Macmillan & Co, London.
JERISON, H. J. 1968. Brain evolution and *Archaeopteryx*. *Nature*, **219**, 1381–1382.
KIELEN-JAWOROWSKA, Z. 1969. *Hunting for Dinosaurs*. MIT Press, Cambridge, MA.
KNIPE, H. R. 1905. *Nebula to Man*. Dent, London.

KNIPE, H. R. 1912. *Evolution in the Past*. Herbert, London.

KÖLBL-EBERT, M. 1997. Mary Buckland née Morland 1791–1857. *Earth Science History*, **16**, 33–38.

KÖLBL-EBERT, M. 2001. On the origin of women geologists by means of social selection: German and British comparison. *Episodes*, **24**, 182–193.

KOHRING, R. & KREFT, G. (eds) 2003. *Tilly Edinger Leben und Werk einer juedische Wissensachaftlerin*. E. Schweizerbart'sche Verlagsbuchhandlung (Naegele u. Obermiller), Senckenberg Buch, **76**, 1–637.

KORTH, W. W. & MASSARE, J. A. (eds) 2006. Special Issue. *In Memory of Elizabeth 'Betsy' Nicholls. Paludicola*, **5**, 1–266.

LAMBRECHT, K., QUENSTEDT, W. & QUENSTEDT, A. 1938. *Palaeontologii: Catalogus Bio-Bibliographicus*. Fossilium Catalogus. s'Gravenshage, Junk.

LAMING, S. & LAMING, D. 2007. Etheldred Benett (1776–1845): the first woman geologist? *In*: BUREK, C. V. & HIGGS, B. (eds) *The Role of Women in the History of Geology*. Geological Society, London, Special Publications, **281**, 247–249.

LANG, M. 1936. Die Lebewelt der Keuper-Zeit im Paläontologischen Museum in Bedheim. *Natur und Volk*, **66**, 582–586.

LANG, M. & HUENE, F. VON 1952. *Die Saurier Thüringens, nach Erhebungen ihres centralen Betreuers Dr. med. u. Dr. rer. nat. h.c. Hugo Rühle von Lilienstern*. Gustav Fischer, Jena, 1–42.

LANG, M. & HUENE, F. VON 1956. Hugo Rühle von Lilienstern (1882–1946). *Paläontologische Zeitschrift*, **30**, 215–217.

LANG, W. D. 1936. Mary Anning, 'Fossilist'. *Proceedings of the Geological Association*, **47**, 65–67.

LANG, W. D. 1954. Mary Anning and Anna Maria Pinney. *Proceedings of the Dorset Natural History and Archaeological Society*, **76** (1956 for 1954), 146–152.

LANKESTER, R. 1921. A Remarkable Flint Implement from Selsey Bill. *Proceedings of the Royal Society of London*, Series B, **92**, 645.

LARSON, G. 1985. *Valley of the Far Side*. [1989 12th printing.] Andrews and McMeel, Kansas City, KS.

LARSON, P. L. & DONNAN, K. 2004. *Rex Appeal. The Amazing Story of Sue, the Dinosaur that Changed Science, the Law, and my Life*. Invisible Cities Press, Montpelier, VT.

LAVAS, J. R. 1993. *Dragons From the Dunes. The Search for Dinosaurs in the Gobi Desert*. Author self-published, Auckland, New Zealand.

LEAR, L. 2007. *Discoveries and Delights in the Details of a Life*. Beatrix Potter Society. www.bpotter.com/Documents, accessed 2009.

LIGHTMAN, B. (ed.) 2004. *Dictionary of 19th Century Scientists*. Thoemmes Continuum, London.

LONGRICH, N. R. & CURRIE, P. J. 2009. A microraptorine (Dinosauria–Dromaeosauridae) from the Late Cretaceous of North America. *Proceedings of the National Academy of Sciences*, 10.1073/pnas.0811664106, online preprint 16 March 2009.

LULL, R. S. 1931. *Fossils that they tell us of Plants and Animals of the Past*. Yale University Press, New Haven, CT.

MAIER, G. 2003. *African Dinosaurs Unearthed*. Indiana University Press, Bloomington, IN.

MANTELL, G. 1822. *Fossils of the South Downs or Illustrations of the Geology of Sussex*. Lupton Relfe, London.

MANTELL, G. 1832. Notice on the geology of the environs of Tunbridge Wells. *In*: BRITTON, J. (ed.) *Descriptive Sketches of Tunbridge Wells and the Calverley Estate*. W. J. Britton, London.

MARCHÉ, T. 1991. *Orra White Hitchcock: A Virtuous Woman*. National Art Education Association, Reston, VA.

MARSH, O. C. 1880. *Odontornithes: A Monograph on the Extinct Toothed Birds of North America*. US Geological Exploration 40th Parallel (King), **7**. Synopsis of American Cretaceous Birds, appendix, 191–199.

MARYANSKA, T. & OSMÓLSKA, H. 1974. Pachycephalosauria, a new suborder of ornithischian dinosaurs. *Palaeontologica Polonica*, **30**, 45–102.

MARYANSKA, T. & OSMÓLSKA, H. 1975. Protoceratopsidae (Dinosauria) of Asia. *Acta Palaeontologica Polonica*, **33**, 133–181.

MARYANSKA, T. & OSMÓLSKA, H. 1983. Some implications of hadrosaurian postcranial anatomy. *Neues Jahrbuch für Geologie und Palaontologie Monatshefte*, **28**, 205–207.

MARYANSKA, T. & OSMÓLSKA, H. 1985. On ornithischian phylogeny. *Acta Palaeontologica Polonica*, **30**, 137–150.

MAYER, W. 2009. Geological observations by the Reverend Charles P. N. Wilton (1795–1859) in New South Wales and his views on the relationship between religion and science. *In*: KÖLBL-EBERT, M. (ed.) *Geology and Religion: A History of Harmony and Hostility*. Geological Society, London, Special Publications, **310**, 197–209.

MERRIAM, J. C. 1905. A primitive ichthyosaurian limb from the middle Triassic of Nevada. University of California, Berkeley.

MILNER, A. & HUGHES, B. 1995. Pamela Lamplugh Robinson, 1919–1994. *Society of Vertebrate Paleontology News Bulletin*, **164**, 54–55.

MOHR, B. A. R. & VOGT, A. 2003. Berliner Geowissenschaftlerinnen an der Friedrich-Wilhelms-Universität von 1906 bis 1945, eine Fallstudie. *Mitteilungen des Museums für Naturkunde Berlin, Geowissenschaften*, **6**, 53–69.

MOHR, B., ENNING, A., GEISSLER, Y. & KLINGSPOR, N. 2008*a*. Ina Reck – Forschungsreisende zwischen Island und Afrika. *Museum für Naturkunde* (Humboldt Museum), **22**, 52–53.

MOHR, B. A. R., KUSTATSCHER, E., HILLER, C. & BÖHME, G. 2008*b*. Hugo Rühle von Lilienstern and his palaeobotanical collection: an East-West German Story. *Earth Sciences History*, **27**, 278–296.

MOLNAR, R. 2009. Obituary – Joan Wiffen. *Geological Society of New Zealand Newsletter*, **150**, 38–41.

NAISH, D. 2009. *The Great Dinosaur Discoveries*. A. & C. Black, London.

NAISH, D. & MARTILL, D. M. 2007. Dinosaurs of Great Britain and the role of the Geological Society of London in their discovery: basal Dinosauria and Saurischia. *Journal of the Geological Society, London*, **164**, 493–510.

NAISH, D. & MARTILL, D. M. 2008. Dinosaurs of Great Britain and the role of the Geological Society of

London in their discovery: Ornithischia. *Journal of the Geological Society, London*, **165**, 613–623.

NASH, S. E. 1990. The collections and life history of Etheldred Benett (1776–1845). *Wiltshire Archaeological and Natural History Magazine*, **83**, 163–169.

NICHOLLS, E. 2001. Excavation Impossible (excavation of marine reptile from river in British Columbia, Canada). *Geographical*, **73**, October 1.

NICHOLLS, E. L. & MANABE, M. 2001. A new ichthyosaur from the Triassic Pardonet Formation of British Columbia: Bridging the Triassic–Jurassic gap. *Journal of Earth Sciences*, **38**, 983–1002.

NICHOLLS, E. L. & MANABE, M. 2004. Giant ichthyosaurs of the Late Triassic – a new species of *Shonisaurus* from the Pardonet Formation (Norian: Late Triassic). *Journal of Vertebrate Paleontology*, **24**, 838–849.

NIELD, T. 2007. Impact factor. GeoNews no. 6. *Geoscientist*, **9**, 17 September.

NOPCSA, F. VON 1917. Uber Dinosaurier. 2. Die Riesenformen unter den Dinosauriem, *Centralblatt für Mineralogie, Geologie und Paläontologie*, **1917**, 332–351.

NOPCSA, F. VON 1926. Heredity and evolution. *Proceedings of the Zoological Society of London*, **1926**, 633–665.

OGILVIE, M. B. & HARVEY, J. D. 2000. *The Biographical Dictionary of Women in Science: Pioneering Lives from Ancient Times to the Mid-20th Century*. Routledge, New York.

OSMÓLSKA, H. 1979. Nasal salt gland in dinosaurs. *Acta Palaeontologica Polonica*, **24**, 205–215.

OSMÓLSKA, H. 1985. Antorbital fenestra of archosaurs and its suggested function. *Fortschritte der Zoologie*, **30**, 159–162.

OSMÓLSKA, H. 1986. Structure of nasal and oral cavities in the protoceratopsid dinosaurs (Ceratopsia, Ornithischia). *Acta Palaeontologica Polonica*, **31**, 145–157.

PIERCE, P. 2006. *Jurassic Mary: Mary Anning and the Primeval Monsters*. Sutton Publishing, Stroud.

REGA, E. A. & BROCHU, C. A. 2002. Palaeopathology in a mature specimen of *Tyrannosaurus rex*. *In*: BROCK, G. A. & TALENT, J. A. (eds) *IPC 2002 Sydney Australia*. Geological Society of Australia, Abstracts, **68**, 134.

RICH, T. H. & VICKERS-RICH, P. 2003. *A Century of Australian Dinosaur Collecting*. Queen Victoria Museum & Monash Science Centre, Monash, Australia.

ROBERTS, G. 1834. *The History and Antiquities of the Borough of Lyme Regis and Charmouth*. Samuel Bagster, London.

ROBINSON, P. L. 1957. The Mesozoic fissures of the British Channel area and their vertebrate faunas. *Zoological Journal of the Linnean Society of London*, **43**, 260–282.

ROBINSON, P. L. 1967. The Indian Gondwana formations – a review. *In*: *Gondwana Stratigraphy. IUGS Symposium, Buenos Aires, 1967. Reviews*. Unesco, Paris, 201–268.

ROLFE, W. D. I., MILNER, A. C. & HAY, F. G. 1988. The price of fossils. *In*: CROWTHER, P. R. & WIMBLEDON, W. A. (eds) *The Use and Conservation of Palaeontological Sites*. Special Papers in Palaeontology, **40**, 139–171.

ROMER, A. S., WRIGHT, N. E., EDINGER, T. & VAN FRANK, R. 1962. *Bibliography of Fossil Vertebrates Exclusive of North America, 1509–1927*. Geological Society of America, Memoirs, **87**, 1–772.

ROSSITER, M. 1982. *Women Scientists in America: Struggles and Strategies to 1940*. John Hopkins University Press, Baltimore, MD.

ROZEFELDS, A. & TURNER, S. 1998. Dr Mary Wade – Collector and facilitator. Queensland Field Work 1971–1992. Poster, 14th Australian Geological Convention, Townsville, July 1998. *Geological Society of Australia, Abstracts*, **49**, 384.

RUDWICK, M. J. S. 1992. *Scenes from Deep Time. Early Pictorial Representations of the Prehistoric World*. University of Chicago Press, Chicago, IL.

RUPKE, N. A. 1983. *The Great Chain of History: William Buckland and the English School of Geology (1814–1849)*. Clarendon Press, Oxford.

RUPKE, N. A. 1994. *Richard Owen. Victorian Naturalist*. Yale University Press, New Haven, CT.

SARJEANT, W. A. S. 1978–1987. *Geologists and the History of Geology*, 3 vols and supplements. Robt E. Krieger, Malabar, FL.

SARJEANT, W. A. S. 1993. Lambert Beverly Halstead (1933–1991): his life, his discoveries and his controversies. *In*: SARJEANT, W. A. S. (ed.) *Beverly Halstead; His Life and Publications. Halstead Memorial Volume. Modern Geology*, **18**, 5–59.

SARJEANT, W. A. S. 1994. Geology in Fiction. *In*: BRANAGAN, D. F. & MCNALLY, G. H. (eds) *Useful and Curious Geological Enquiries Beyond the World. Pacific-Asia Historical Themes. 19th International INHIGEO Symposium, Sydney, 4–8 July 1994*. INHIGEO: University of Sydney Conference Publications, Springwood, NSW, 318–337.

SARJEANT, W. A. S. (ed.) 1995. *Vertebrate Fossils and the Evolution of Scientific Concepts. Writings in Tribute to Beverly Halstead, by Some of his Friends*. Gordon & Breach/OPA, Amsterdam.

SCHMIDT, D. & LANG, M. 1996. 'In Memoriam Hugo Rühle von Lilienstern 1882–1946' (mit Beiträgen von R. Werneburg, Rühle von Lilienstern). Hüringischer Geologischer Verein, Freundeskreis Bedheim; Gemeinde der Steinsburgfreunde, Hennebergisch-Fränkischer Geschichtsverein (Herausgeber).

SCHULTZE, H.-P. 2007. Book Review. *Tilly Edinger Leben und Werk einer juedische Wissensachaftlerin*. E. Schweizerbart'sche Verlagsbuchhandlung (Naegele u. Obermiller), Senckenberg Buch nr 76, 639 pp [*Tilly Edinger, Life and Work of a Jewish Scientist*] Eur 39.80 (about $48). *Journal of Vertebrate Paleontology*, **27**, 772–773.

SEELEY, H. G. 1901. *Dragons of the Air. An Account of Extract Flying Reptiles*. Meltner, London.

SHIPMAN, P. 1998. *Taking Wing. Archaeopteryx and the Evolution of Bird Flight*. Simon & Schuster, New York.

SIMPSON, G. G. 1935. The first mammals. *The Quarterly Review of Biology*, **10**, 154–180.

SPALDING, D. 1999. *Into the Dinosaurs' Graveyard. Canadian Digs and Discoveries*. Doubleday, Toronto.

SPAMER, E. E., BOGAN, A. E. & TORRENS, H. 1989. Recovery of the Etheldred Benett collection of fossils mostly from Jurassic–Cretaceous strata of Wiltshire England, Analysis of the taxonomic nomenclature of Benett (1831), and notes and figures of type specimens contained in the collection. *Proceedings of the Academy of Natural Sciences of Philadelphia*, **141**, 115–180.

SPOKES, S. 1927. *Gideon Algernon Mantell.* John Bale & Sons & Danielson, London.

SPOKES, S. 1929. Gideon Mantell's spine. *The British Medican Journal*, **1929**, 1178, 21 December.

STEIN, B. R. 2001. *On Her Own Terms, Annie Montague Alexander and the Rise of Science in the American West.* University of California Press, Berkeley, CA.

STEMMLER, R. 2006. The power to educate and inspire. *Alcheringa*, Special Publication, **1**, 307–312.

STRADER, W. H. & RINKER, C. A. 1989. A child centered approach to dinosaurs. *Early Child Development and Care*, **43**, 65–76.

TALBOT, M. 1911. *Podekosaurus holyokensis*, a new dinosaur from the Triassic of the Connecticut Valley. *American Journal of Science*, **31**, 469–479.

TAQUET, P. 2003. Quand les Reptiles marins anglais traversaient la Manche. Mary Anning et Georges Cuvier, deux acteurs de la découverte et de l'étude des Ichthyosaures et des Plésiosaures. *Annales de Paléontologie*, **89**, 37–64.

TAYLOR, M. A. & TORRENS, H. S. 1995. Fossils by the sea. *Natural History*, **104**, 66–71.

THACKRAY, J. C. (ed.) 1999. *To See the Fellows Fight: Eyewitness Accounts of Meetings of the Geological Society of London and its Club, 1822–1868.* British Society for the History of Science, Monographs, **12**.

THARP, L. H. 1959. *Adventurous Alliance: The Story of the Agassiz Family of Boston.* Brown, Little & Co., Boston, MA.

THENIUS, E. 1960. Käthe Lange: So Lange es Tag ist. Leben und Wirken von Dr. phil. Minna Lang (1891–1959). In *Mitteilungen der Geologischen Gesellschaft in Wien*, **53**, 311.

THULBORN, R. A. 1979. A proterosuchian thecodont from the Rewan Formation of Queensland. *Memoirs of the Queensland Museum*, **19**, 14–27.

THULBORN, R. A. & WADE, M. 1984. Winton dinosaur footprints. *Memoirs of the Queensland Museum*, **21**, 413–517.

TICKNELL, C. 1996. *Mary Anning of Lyme Regis.* Foreword John Fowles. Lyme Regis Philpot Museum, Lyme Regis, Dorset.

TORRENS, H. 1978. Harriett Mary Hutton. *Newsletter of the Geological Curators' Group*, **2**, 128–129.

TORRENS, H. S. 1985. Women in Geology, 2 – Etheldred Benett. *Open Earth*, **21**, 12–13.

TORRENS, H. 1993. The dinosaurs and 'Dinomania' over 150 years. *In*: SARJEANT, W. A. S. (ed.) *Beverly Halstead; His Life and Publications. Halstead Memorial Volume. Modern Geology*, **18**, 257–286.

TORRENS, H. 1995. Mary Anning (1799–1847) of Lyme, 'the greatest fossilist the world ever knew'. *British Journal for the History of Science*, **28**, 257–284.

TORRENS, H. 2008. A saw for a jaw. *Geoscientist*, no 12, 18–21, 18 December.

TORRENS, H. S., BENAMY, E., DAESCHLER, E. B., SPAMER, E. E. & BOGAN, A. E. 2000. Etheldred Benett of Wiltshire, England, the first lady geologist – Her fossil collection in the Academy of Natural Sciences of Philadelphia, and the rediscovery of 'lost' specimens of Jurassic Trigoniidae (Mollusca: Bivalvia) with their soft anatomy preserved. *Proceedings of the Academy of Natural Sciences of Philadelphia*, **150**, 59–123.

TRENCHARD, D. 1999. *Women of Dorset.* Dorset Books, Tiverton Devon.

TURNER, S. 1986. A short history of vertebrate palaeontology in Queensland. *History of Earth Sciences Journal*, **5**, 50–65.

TURNER, S. 1997. Mary Wade. *In*: MACKAY, J. (comp.). *Brilliant Careers. Women Collectors and Illustrators in Queensland.* Queensland Museum, Brisbane, 75–77, 80.

TURNER, S. 1998. Women in paleontology in Australia. *In*: GOOD, G. A. (ed.) *Sciences of the Earth. An Encyclopedia of Events, People, and Phenomena.* Garland Press, New York, 848–852.

TURNER, S. 2005*a*. Heber Albert Longman (1880–1954), Queensland Museum scientist: a new bibliography. *Memoirs of the Queensland Museum*, **51**, 237–257.

TURNER, S. 2005*b*. Obituary Dr Mary Wade (3 Feb 1928–14 Sept 2005). *The Queensland Geologist*, **105**, 4.

TURNER, S. 2007. Invincible but mostly invisible: Australian women's contribution to geology and palaeontology. *In*: BUREK, C. V. & HIGGS, B. (eds) *The Role of Women in the History of Geology.* Geological Society, London, Special Publications, **281**, 165–201.

TURNER, S. 2009*a*. Reverent and exemplary: 'dinosaur man' Friedrich von Huene (1875–1969). *In*: KÖLBL-EBERT, M. (ed.) *Geology and Religion: A History of Harmony and Hostility.* Geological Society, London, Special Publications, **310**, 223–243.

TURNER, S. 2009*b*. Huene Bibliography: an annotated list of the von Huene reprints in boxes in von Huene Library, room 216, upper floor, Institut für Geowissenschaften, Sigwartstrasse 10, Universität Tübingen, 34pp updated, based on original plus Reif & Lux versions. *In*: KÖLBL-EBERT, M. (ed.) *Geology and Religion: A History of Harmony and Hostility.* Geological Society, London, Special Publications, **310**, appendix on GSL website [NB. now at Museum Löwentor, Stuttgart].

TURNER, S. 2009*c*. Not so quiet persuasion: the canon of women in the geological sciences. Review of Cynthia V. Burek, & Barbara Higgs, eds, *The Role of Women in the History of Geology.* London: The Geological Society, Special Publication 281, 2007. Pp. viii+342. £85 HB. *Metascience*, **18**, 405–404.

TURNER, S. & MATHER, P. 2005. Founders of the Museum and the women who shared their vision. *WISENET Journal*, **68**, (April), 18.

TURNER, S. & WADE, M. 1986. The records in the rocks. Geology. *In*: MATHER, P. (ed.) *A Time for a Museum. The History of the Queensland Museum 1862–1986.* Queensland Museum, Brisbane, 126–149.

VARKER, W. J. 2004. Obituary. Dorothy Helen Rayner 1912–2002. *Proceedings of the Yorkshire Geological Society*, **55**, 160.

VICKERS-RICH, P. & ARCHBOLD, N. 1991. Squatters, priests and professors: a brief history of Vertebrate Palaeontology in *Terra Australis*. *In*: VICKERS-RICH, P., MONAGHAN, J. M., BAIRD, R. F. & RICH, T. H. (eds) *Vertebrate Palaeontology of Australasia.* Pioneer Design Studios in co-operation with Monash

University Publications Committee, Clayton, Victoria, 1–43.

VINCENT, P. & TAQUET, P. 2010. Un spécimen de plésiosaure du Lias de Lyme Regis: le deuxième plésiosaure découvert par Mary Anning. *Geodiversitas*, **32**, 5–18.

WADE, M. 1989. The stance of dinosaurs and the Cossack dancer syndrome. *In*: GILLETTE, D. D. & LOCKLEY, M. G. (eds) *Dinosaur Tracks and Traces*. Cambridge University Press, Cambridge, 73–82.

WEISHAMPEL, D. B. & REIF, W.-E. 1984. The work of Franz Baron Nopcsa (1877–1933): dinosaurs, evolution and theoretical tectonics. *Jahrbuch der geologischen Bundes-Anstalt Wien*, **127**, 187–203.

WEISHAMPEL, D. B. & WHITE, N. M. (eds) 2003. *The Dinosaur Papers*. Smithsonian Institution, Washington, DC.

WEISHAMPEL, D. B. & YOUNG, L. 2001. *Dinosaurs of the East Coast*. John Hopkins University Press, Baltimore, MD.

WEISHAMPEL, D. B., DODSON, P. & OSMÓLSKA, H. (eds) 2004. *The Dinosauria*, 2nd edn. University of California Press, Berkeley, CA.

WIFFEN, J. 1991. *Valley of the Dragons: The Story of New Zealand's Dinosaur Woman*. Random Century, Glenfied, New Zealand.

WIFFEN, J. & MOISLEY, W. L. 1986. Late Cretaceous reptiles (Families Elasmosauridae and Pliosauridae) from the Mangahouanga Stream, North Island, New Zealand. *New Zealand Journal of Geology and Geophysics*, **29**, 205–252.

WHITE, A. 1973. Obituary Billie Unterman. *Society of Vertebrate Paleontology News Bulletin*, **99**, 65–66.

WOJCIECH, M. 2008. Memorial for Prof. Halszka Osmólska 1930–2008. www.palaeo.pan.pl/documents/Osmolska_GW_2008_04_03 accessed December 2008.

WOODWARD, A. B. 1895. *Illustrated London News*, **107**, 18 May (2933).

WOODWARD, A. B. 1910. 'Big Game in Merry England: the quarry of the pre-historic Britain', subtitled 'In the Thames Valley tens of thousands of years ago: a sabre-toothed tiger and the bison it killed: a cave lion: and hyeanas'. *The Illustrated London News*, 5 November, 708.

WOODWARD, A. B. 1925. Larger than any known land animal: a fossil hunter's vision of 1927, Gideon the enormous Gigantosaurus, subtitled 'As it probably appeared in life in Tanganyika: the huge dinosaur, Gigantosaurus, visualised by a fossil hunter dreaming by his desert fire, beside an unearthed humerus twice as long as that of the 80 ft Diplodocus in the Natural History Museum'. *Illustrated London News*, 17 January, 98–99.

WOODWARD, H. 1911. On a new species of *Eryon* from the Upper Lias, Dumbleton Hill. *Geological Magazine*, **5**, 307–311.

ZULLO, J. L. 1969. Annie Montague Alexander: her work in paleontology. *Journal of the West*, **8**, 183–199.

Wilhelm (Guillermo) Schulz and the earliest discoveries of dinosaurs and marine reptiles in Spain

XABIER PEREDA SUBERBIOLA[1]*, JOSÉ-IGNACIO RUIZ-OMEÑACA[2,3], NATHALIE BARDET[4], LAURA PIÑUELA[2] & JOSÉ-CARLOS GARCÍA-RAMOS[2,5]

[1]*Universidad del País Vasco/EHU, Facultad de Ciencia y Tecnología, Dpto. Estratigrafía y Paleontología, Apdo. 644, 48080 Bilbao, Spain*

[2]*Museo del Jurásico de Asturias (MUJA), 33328 Colunga, Spain*

[3]*Grupo Aragosaurus-IUCA, Paleontología, Facultad de Ciencias, Universidad de Zaragoza, Pedro Cerbuna 12, 50009 Zaragoza, Spain*

[4]*UMR 7207 du CNRS, Département Histoire de la Terre, Muséum National d'Histoire Naturelle, 8 rue Buffon, 75005 Paris, France*

[5]*Departamento de Geología, Universidad de Oviedo, c/Jesús Arias de Velasco s/n, 33005 Oviedo, Spain*

**Corresponding author (e-mail: xabier.pereda@ehu.es)*

Abstract: Wilhelm Schulz (1805–1877), known in Spain as Guillermo Schulz, was one of the most outstanding representatives of the geology and mining industry in Spain during the nineteenth century. Schulz is, likewise, the author detailing the first discoveries of dinosaurs and marine reptiles in Spain. In 1858 Schulz described a supposed dinosaur tooth from the Jurassic of Ruedes (Asturias) as belonging to a shark. Schulz's description, mainly the occurrence of crenulated edges, suggests that the tooth was that of a large theropod. It probably comes from the altered grey marls of the Upper Jurassic (Kimmeridgian) Lastres Formation. Although the exact year of the discovery before 1858 is not known, the Ruedes tooth (currently lost) is presumably the earliest known discovery of a dinosaur body fossil in the Iberian Peninsula. Moreover, Schulz mentioned in 1858 the discovery of plesiosaur remains from the Liassic near Villaviciosa (Asturias). The material probably comes from the Pliensbachian marls and limestone rhythmites (Jamesoni zone) of the Rodiles Formation. As no figure was provided and the specimen is currently lost, we have no definitive certainty about its affinities. However, it represents the earliest marine reptile fossil found in Spain.

The German mining engineer Wilhelm Philip Daniel Schulz (1805–1877), known in Spain as Guillermo Schulz (Fig. 1), was one of the most outstanding representatives of the geology and mining industry of Spain during the nineteenth century (see Rábano & Truyols 2005 and references therein). Schulz was born in 1805 in a mining establishment near Kassel in the Prussian region of Habichtswald, where his father worked as Mining Inspector (Obergeschworener). He studied mining industry at the University of Göttingen and had Professor Johann Haussman as teacher. Having arrived in Spain in 1826, Schulz undertook significant studies on geology and the mining industry, mainly in the NW part of the Iberian Peninsula (Galicia and Asturias). In 1830 he was appointed Commissioner of Mines (Comisario de Minas) in the service of the Spanish Government. Schulz was promoted and worked as the Inspector of District (Inspector de Distrito) in Galicia and Asturias from 1833 to 1841. In these regions he carried out a huge amount of field research. As a result of this work, Schulz found important mineral deposits and discovered the first Palaeozoic fossils in Galicia. He stimulated the development of cartographical studies, and was the author of the first geological map (or, at least, one of the first ones: see Boixereu Vila 2008) produced in Spain: *Petrographical Map of the Kingdom of Galicia* (*Mapa petrográfico del Reyno de Galicia*) at a scale of 1:400 000 (Schulz 1835). Between 1853 and 1857 Schulz was the Director of the Special School of Mining Engineers (Escuela Especial de Ingenieros de Minas) in Madrid, and the President of the Commission of the Geological Map of Spain (Comisión del Mapa Geológico de España), which was the precursor organism of the current Geological and Mining Institute of Spain (Instituto Geológico y Minero de España). From 1853 Schulz was also the President of the Council of Mining (Junta Facultativa de

From: MOODY, R. T. J., BUFFETAUT, E., NAISH, D. & MARTILL, D. M. (eds) *Dinosaurs and Other Extinct Saurians: A Historical Perspective*. Geological Society, London, Special Publications, **343**, 155–160.
DOI: 10.1144/SP343.8 0305-8719/10/$15.00

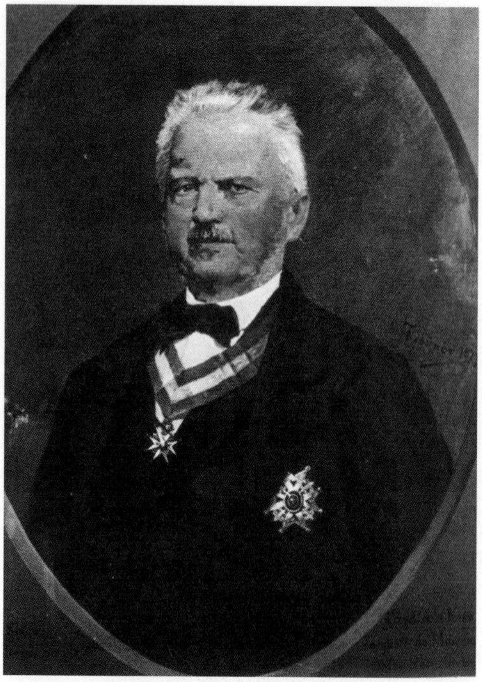

Fig. 1. Wilhelm (Guillermo) Schulz (1805–1877) with the Order of Charles III. Oil painting (original in colour) in the Portrait Gallery of the formerly Consejo Superior de Minería y Metalurgia, now in the Ministerio de Industria, Turismo y Comercio of Madrid. Reproduced courtesy of the Instituto Geológico y Minero de España (IGME). A copy of this painting is kept at the Instituto Geológico y Minero de España, Madrid.

Minería) and took part in the project of writing new Spanish laws on mining. One of his most noteworthy scientific works was the *Descripción geológica de la Provincia de Oviedo*, published in 1858 (the geological map was published one year before, in 1857). Schulz retired in 1861 and died in Aranjuez, near Madrid, in 1877 (for more detail on the life and work of Schulz see Marcos Vallaure 1988; Puche & Ayala-Carcedo 2001; Rábano & Truyols 2005).

This paper deals with a less well-known aspect of the research carried out by Schulz: his contribution to the study of vertebrate fossils, as he was the author of the first discoveries of dinosaurs and marine reptiles in Spain.

The earliest discovery of a dinosaur body fossil in Spain

In his work *Descripción geológica de la Provincia de Oviedo* (Fig. 2), Schulz (1858, p. 109) described,

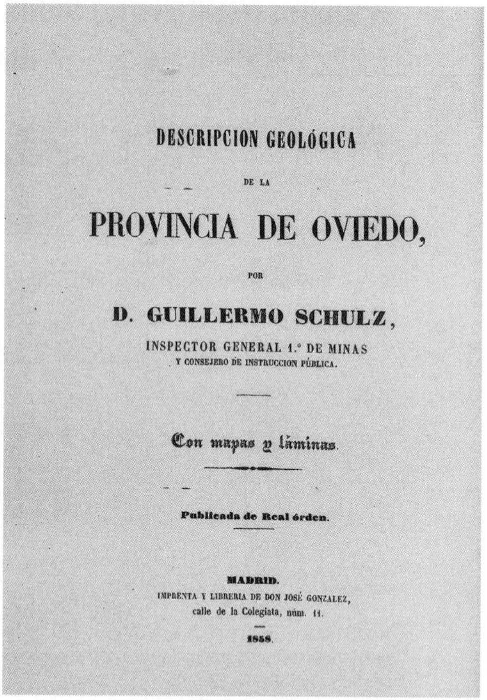

DESCRIPCION GEOLÓGICA

DE LA

PROVINCIA DE OVIEDO,

POR

D. GUILLERMO SCHULZ,

INSPECTOR GENERAL 1.° DE MINAS

Y CONSEJERO DE INSTRUCCION PÚBLICA.

Con mapas y láminas.

Publicada de Real órden.

MADRID.

IMPRENTA Y LIBRERIA DE DON JOSÉ GONZALEZ,

calle de la Colegiata, núm. 11.

1858.

Fig. 2. Title page of Schulz (1858), the work containing the first mention of the discovery of both dinosaur and marine reptile fossils in the Spanish palaeontological literature.

without illustration, a tooth from the Jurassic of Ruedes (Asturias) as belonging to a squalid shark. The translation into English of the original Spanish quotation (see Appendix 1) is as follows:

> To finish here our indications about the Liassic fossils of Asturias, we should mention an admirable tooth of *Squalus* (primitive shark) found by Mr. José de Elduayen in the light-coloured Liassic marls near Ruedes approximately two miles [Spanish miles; *c.* 11 km] south of Gijón; this tooth, which lacks the base and the tip, was (when complete) at least four inches [*c.* 10 cm] long; it is dark brown, very brilliant externally and both cutting edges show a very thin saw; the convex edge is a little blunter and does not reach the base since it stops at approximately 4 cm of it.

According to Schulz, the tooth, dark brown in colour, was found in the light-coloured marls of the Liassic. However, more probably, it comes from the weathered grey marls of the Upper Jurassic Lastres Formation, which is of Kimmeridgian age (García-Ramos *et al.* 2004) (see Fig. 3). Schulz (1858) thought that the fossiliferous marls and sandstones of the Asturias coast between

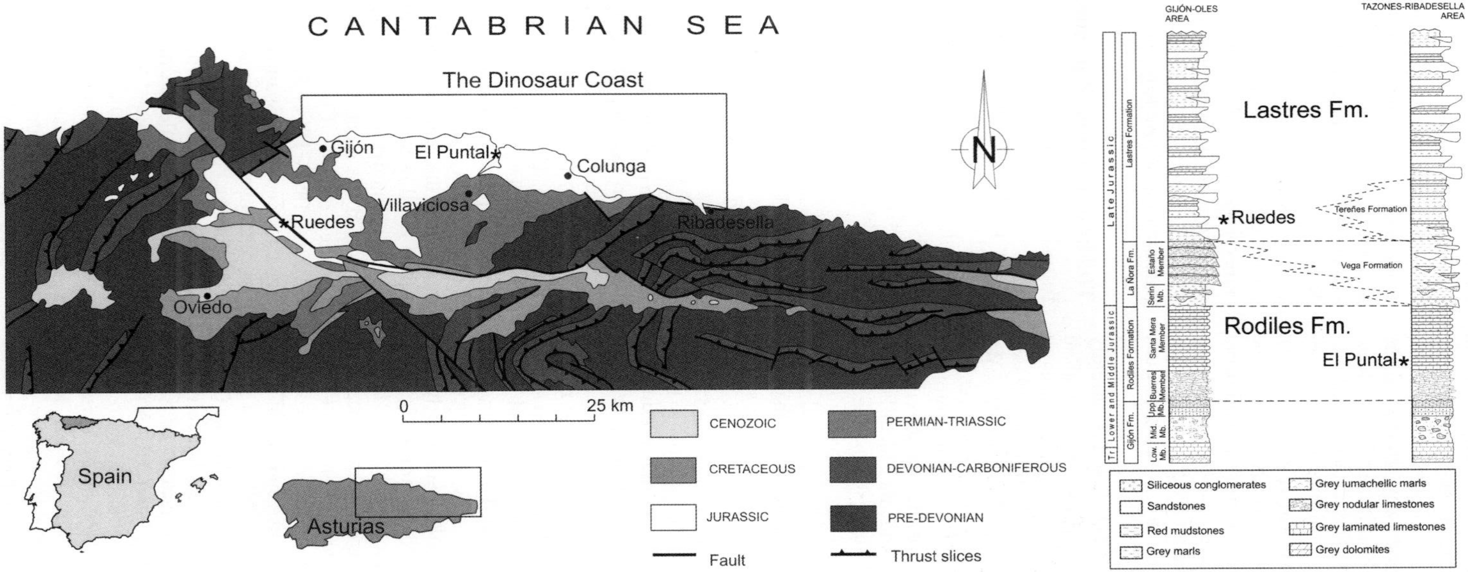

Fig. 3. Geological map of the 'Dinosaur Coast' in Asturias, showing the location of the vertebrate sites mentioned by Schulz (1858); and a stratigraphical log of the Jurassic of Asturias and the formations that have yielded historical vertebrate remains. Modified from García-Ramos *et al.* (2004).

Gijón and Ribadesella corresponded to the Lower Liassic, but these facies are in fact from the Malm (Suárez Vega 1974; García-Ramos & Gutiérrez Claverol 1995).

In 1873 the Ruedes tooth was referred to the theropod *Megalosaurus* by the geologist Justo Egozcue (see Appendix 2). This author stated precisely that the tooth was kept in the collections of the School of Mines of Madrid (Egozcue 1873), but, although we suspect he was able to examine the specimen, we cannot confirm this. Following Egozcue, subsequent Spanish authors, such as Calderón (1877) and Mallada (1902), referred this tooth to *Megalosaurus* or to a 'megalosaur', respectively.

The whereabouts of the Ruedes tooth is currently unknown. The specimen has not been found in the collections of the Museo Histórico-Minero D. Felipe de Borbón y Grecia (formerly Museo de la Escuela de Minas) in Madrid, where the fossils collected by the Marquis of Elduayen are housed (Calvo Pérez 2002; Pereda Suberbiola & Ruiz-Omeñaca 2005). However, the description made by Schulz (1858) and the identification made by Egozcue (1873) suggest that the tooth belonged to a theropod. First, the curved form of the crown and the presence of crenulated edges are typical of, although not exclusive to, theropod dinosaurs (Currie 1997). Second, the large size of the tooth (crown height *c.* 10 cm) is in agreement with its interpretation as that of a large-sized theropod. Although the exact year of the discovery before 1858 is not known, the Ruedes tooth is presumably the earliest known discovery of a dinosaur body fossil in the Iberian Peninsula.

This tooth, with the basal portion of the mesial edge unserrated (in agreement with the description of Schulz 1858), could pertain to a carnosaur theropod (Ruiz-Omeñaca *et al.* 2009). Theropod remains are rather scarce in the Jurassic rocks of Asturias but a small collection of isolated fossils (all housed in the Museo del Jurásico de Austurias, Colunga, Spain (MUJA)) has been recovered from 1996 to date in several Upper Jurassic coastal localities. This material includes 12 teeth from the Lastres and Vega formations, both Kimmeridgian in age on the basis of charophytes and ammonoids (Schudack 1987; Olóriz *et al.* 1988). Some of the teeth have been provisionally assigned to the Carnosauria and Maniraptora clades as indeterminate genus and species (Ruiz-Omeñaca *et al.* 2009). The largest teeth (MUJA 1217 and MUJA 1226), up to 31 mm in fore–aft basal length, are referred to as Theropoda indet., and probably pertain to individuals that reached 8–9 m in body length. The presence of megalosaurids (*sensu* Holtz *et al.* 2004) in the Asturias record cannot yet be confirmed.

The Asturias tooth was not the first dinosaur identified in Spain as, prior to Egozcue, the naturalist Juan Vilanova (1872, 1873) specifically mentioned the discovery of dinosaur body fossils from the Lower Cretaceous of Utrillas (Teruel) and Morella (Castellón). The Vilanova collection, currently kept in the Museo Nacional de Ciencias Naturales in Madrid, contains the earliest discovered dinosaur body fossils from Spain that are still preserved in an institutional collection (Pereda Suberbiola & Ruiz-Omeñaca 2005). The first original figure of Spanish dinosaur remains published in the literature was provided 50 years later by the palaeontologist José Royo Gómez (1926).

The first mention of plesiosaur fossils found in Spain

In the published work on the geology of Asturias, Schulz (1858, p. 108) also mentioned the discovery of plesiosaur remains from the Lower Jurassic near Villaviciosa (Asturias). The translation into English of the original Spanish quotation (see Appendix 3) is as follows:

> Between El Puntal and Tazones of Villaviciosa we have found in the dark marls part of a skeleton and the paddles of a plesiosaur, whose largest vertebrae reach 6 cm of diameter; it is known that this extinct genus of aquatic reptiles had a long neck, a small head and four legs of approximately the same size that finish in paddles.

The skeleton probably comes from the lower Pliensbachian marls and limestone rhythmites (Jamesoni Zone) of the Rodiles Formation to the north of El Puntal (J.-C. García-Ramos personal observation) (see Fig. 3). Unfortunately, no figure was provided by Schulz and we have no definitive certainty about the plesiosaurian affinities of this specimen. Currently lost, the specimen found in El Puntal represents the earliest discovery of a marine reptile fossil in Spain (Bardet *et al.* 2008*b*).

Plesiosaur remains were described as early as the end of the nineteenth century from the Lower Jurassic of the Coimbra region in Portugal (Sauvage 1897–1898). Specimens from the Jurassic and Cretaceous of Spain had not been described and illustrated until more recently (see Bardet *et al.* 2008*b*). For example, an incomplete plesiosaur skeleton was discovered in the lower Pliesbachian rocks of the Rodiles Formation (Jamesoni Zone, Santa Mera Member: see Suárez Vega 1974; Valenzuela *et al.* 1986) in the Santa Mera cliffs, near Villaviciosa (Asturias). The material (MUJA 0518), which consists of an incomplete postcranial skeleton from a presumably juvenile individual, has been referred to Plesiosauroidea indet. (Bardet *et al.* 2008*a*). It is the most complete plesiosaur specimen found to date in Spain (Bardet *et al.* 2008*a*). This material may correspond to vertebrate remains (referred to as ichthyosaur) from the same locality and horizon previously mentioned by Suárez Vega (1974).

Finally, isolated marine reptile remains from the Lower Jurassic (Hettangian–Sinemurian; Gijón Formation) and Upper Jurassic (Kimmeridgian; Tereñes Formation) of Asturias have also been found in the last few years (Ruiz-Omeñaca *et al.* 2006, 2010).

Summary and conclusions

The mining engineer, of German origin, Wilhelm 'Guillermo' Schulz was the author detailing the first discoveries of dinosaurs and marine reptiles in Spain. These funds were described in a book on the geology of Asturias published in 1858. Although the specimens are currently lost, they provide evidence of the discoveries made before 1858 of a possible large theropod tooth (misinterpreted by Schulz as that of a shark, but later referred to *Megalosaurus* by Justo Egozcue in 1873) in the Upper Jurassic (Kimmeridgian) rocks near Gijon, and of a presumed plesiosaur skeleton in the Liassic (Pliensbachian) marls of the Asturian coast near Villaviciosa. Schulz was an outstanding personality and played a pioneering role in the history of Spanish geology. Although dinosaur and plesiosaur remains were found in Spain during the nineteenth century, their study was not highlighted and the first significant discoveries and interpretations were not made until some time afterwards.

We would like to express our thanks to B. Calvo, I. Rábano, T. de Torres and J. Truyols for their assistance, and especially to the Instituto Geológico y Minero de España (IGME) for permission to reproduce Figure 1. We also thank the two anonymous referees for their critical reviews of the manuscript. Financial support was provided by the Regional Ministry for Culture and Tourism of the Principality of Asturias (Protocolo CN-04-226), the Spanish Ministry for Education and Science (projects CGL2007-62469/BTE and CGL2007-64061/BTE) and the Basque Government (research group GIC07/14-361). This work is a contribution to the 'Convenio específico de colaboración/Convention de Collaboration' between the UPV/EHU (Bilbao), the CNRS (France) and the MNHN (Paris, France).

Appendix 1

Extract from Schulz (1858, p. 109, second paragraph) where a dinosaur tooth from the Jurassic of Ruedes (Asturias) is described as belonging to a squalid shark. The original spelling has been retained. See the text for a translation into English.

> Al terminar aquí por ahora nuestras indicaciones sobre los fósiles del Lías de Asturias, debemos hacer mencion de un admirable diente de *Squalus* (primitivo tiburon) hallado por el Sr. D. José de Elduayen en las margas rubias del Lías en términos de Ruedes á dos leguas cortas Sud de Gijon, este diente, cuya base y punta faltan, tendría (cuando completo) por lo menos cuatro pulgadas de largo, es de color pardo obscuro, por fuera muy reluciente y está adornado en ambos filos de finísima serreta; pero la del filo de curva convexa es algo mas obtusa y no llega hasta la base, pues termina primorosamente á unos cuatro centímetros de ella.

Appendix 2

Extract from Egozcue (1873) where the Asturias tooth is referred to the theropod dinosaur *Megalosaurus*. The original spelling has been retained:

> El señor Egozcue dice, que con motivo de haber leido con sumo interés en el acta de la sesión del 5 de Febrero último que el Sr. Juan Vilanova posee unos huesos largos de *Iguanodon*, hallados en la zona de los lignitos cretáceos de Utrillas, le habia ocurrido presentar á la Sociedad, como lo hace, un diente de *Megalosaurus*, que en las colecciones de la Escuela de Minas venia figurando como correspondiendo á un animal de una clase muy distinta, y que, procedente tambien de una localidad española, creia se examinaria con gusto, en atencion á la suma rareza de ejemplares de restos fósiles de reptiles citados hasta ahora en nuestro suelo, y á ser esta la primera vez que públicamente se menciona en él la pasada existencia del género á que indudablemente corresponde. Agrega que ese diente tiene un doble interés si se considera la antigüedad del yacimiento en que se recogió. No es en efecto, añade, el ejemplar á la vista de los señores socios, sino el que, atribuido á un *Squalus* en la pág. 109 de la interesantísima DESCRIPCION GEOLOGICA DE ASTURIAS por el Sr. Schulz, se halló por el Sr. D. José de Elduayen en las margas rubias del grupo liásico, en término de Ruedes, á dos leguas cortas al Sur de Gijón; y como por los demas fósiles que el autor del susodicho trabajo menciona recogidos en las mismas margas hay que deducir que cuando menos corresponden al tramo medio del grupo liásico (ó sea al verdadero liásico de d'Orbigny), resulta que esa es tambien por lo menos la edad geológica del *Megalosaurus* á que perteneció el repetido diente; circunstancia que en la época en que se halló (ántes del año 1858) no hubiera dejado de llamar la atención, pero que ya hoy no es tan sorprendente, toda vez que M. J. Martin cita ese género (Bulletin de la Soc. géol. de France, t. XXII, p. 385), á un nivel todavía algo más bajo: al de la *Aricula* [*sic*] *Contorta.*

Appendix 3

Extract from Schulz (1858, p. 108, second paragraph) where the discovery of a plesiosaur skeleton from the Lower Jurassic near Villaviciosa (Asturias) is mentioned.

The original spelling has been retained. See the text for a translation in English:

> Entre el Puntal y Tazones de Villaviciosa hemos hallado en las margas negras parte del esqueleto y aletas de un *Plesiosauro*, cuyas vértebras mayores llegan á seis centímetros de diámetro, siendo sabido que este género extinguido de reptiles acuáticos tenia el cuello muy largo, cabeza chica y cuatro brazos ó remos casi iguales que terminaban en aletas . . .

References

BARDET, N., FERNÁNDEZ, M., GARCÍA-RAMOS, J. C., PEREDA SUBERBIOLA, X., PIÑUELA, L., RUIZ-OMEÑACA, J. I. & VINCENT, P. 2008*a*. A juvenile plesiosaur from the Pliensbachian (Lower Jurassic) of Asturias, Spain. *Journal of Vertebrate Paleontology*, **28**, 258–263.

BARDET, N., PEREDA-SUBERBIOLA, X. & RUIZ-OMEÑACA, J. I. 2008*b*. Mesozoic marine reptiles from the Iberian Peninsula. *Geo-Temas*, **10**, 1245–1248.

BOIXEREU VILA, E. 2008. ¿Es el mapa de Extremadura y Norte de Andalucía de Frédéric Le Play (1834) el primer mapa geológico de España? *Geo-Temas*, **10**, 43–46.

CALDERÓN, S. 1877. Enumeración de los vertebrados fósiles de España. *Anales de la Sociedad Española de Historia Natural*, **5**, 413–443.

CALVO PÉREZ, B. 2002. *El Museo Histórico-Minero Don Felipe de Borbón y Grecia*. Universidad Politécnica de Madrid, Escuela Técnica Superior de Ingenieros de Minas, Madrid.

CURRIE, P. J. 1997. Theropods. *In*: FARLOW, J. O. & BRETT-SURMAN, M. K. (eds) *The Complete Dinosaur*. Indiana University Press, Bloomington, IN, 216–233.

EGOZCUE, J. 1873. Noticia sobre la existencia en España de restos fósiles de *Megalosaurus* y de *Hyena spelaea* y *brunnea* (Session of June, 4). *Anales de la Sociedad Española de Historia Natural, Actas*, **2**, 29–30.

GARCÍA-RAMOS, J. C. & GUTIÉRREZ CLAVEROL, M. 1995. La cobertera mesozoico-terciaria. *In*: ARAMBURU, C. & BASTIDA, F. (eds) *Geología de Asturias*. Trea, Gijón, 81–94.

GARCÍA-RAMOS, J. C., PIÑUELA, L. & LIRES, J. 2004. *Guía del Jurásico de Asturias. Rutas por los yacimientos de huellas de dinosaurios*, Zinco Comunicación, Gijón.

HOLTZ, T. R., MOLNAR, R. E. & CURRIE, P. J. 2004. Basal Tetanurae. *In*: WEISHAMPEL, D. B., DODSON, P. & OSMOLSKA, H. (eds) *The Dinosauria*, 2nd edn. University of California Press, Berkeley, CA, 71–110.

MALLADA, L. 1902. Explicación del Mapa Geológico de España. Tomo IV: Sistemas Permiano, Triásico, Liásico y Jurásico. *Memorias de la Comisión del Mapa Geológico de España*, **22**, 1–514.

MARCOS VALLAURE, A. 1988. Prólogo. Guillermo Schulz: su obra científica y su perfil humano. *In*: *Guillermo Schulz. Descripción geológica de la provincia de Oviedo.* Facsímil de la edición de 1858 con un prólogo de Alberto Marcos Vallaure. Biblioteca asturiana, **3**. Alvízoras Libros, Oviedo, 7–24.

OLÓRIZ, F., VALENZUELA, M., GARCÍA-RAMOS, J. C. & SUÁREZ DE CENTI, C. 1988. The first record of the genus *Eurasenia* (Ammonitina) from the Upper Jurassic of Asturias (northern Spain). *Géobios*, **21**, 741–748.

PEREDA SUBERBIOLA, X. & RUIZ-OMEÑACA, J. I. 2005. Los primeros descubrimientos de dinosaurios en España. *Revista Española de Paleontología*, número extraordinario, **10**, 15–28.

PUCHE, O. & AYALA-CARCEDO, F. J. 2001. Guillermo P. D. Schulz y Schweizer (1800–1877): su vida y obra en el bicentenario de su nacimiento. *Boletín Geológico y Minero*, **112**, 105–122.

RÁBANO, I. & TRUYOLS, J. (eds) 2005. Miscelánea Guillermo Schulz (1805–1877). *Cuadernos del Museo Geominero*, **5**, 1–256. Instituto Geológico y Minero de España, Madrid.

ROYO GÓMEZ, J. 1926. Los descubrimientos de reptiles gigantescos en Levante. *Boletín de la Sociedad Castellonense de Cultura*, **7**, 147–162.

RUIZ-OMEÑACA, J. I., GARCÍA-RAMOS, J. C., PIÑUELA, L., BARDET, N., BERMÚDEZ-ROCHAS, D. D., CANUDO, J. I. & PEREDA SUBERBIOLA, X. 2006. Restos directos de vertebrados del Jurásico de Asturias. *In*: FERNÁNDEZ-MARTÍNEZ, E. (ed.) *XXII Jornadas de la Sociedad Española de Paleontología y simposios de los proyectos PICG 493, 503, 499, y 467*. Libro de resúmenes, Universidad de León, 171–173.

RUIZ-OMEÑACA, J. I., PIÑUELA, L., GARCÍA-RAMOS, J. C. & CANUDO, J. I. 2009. Dientes de dinosaurios carnívoros (Saurischia: Theropoda) del Jurásico Superior de Asturias. *In*: HUERTA HURTADO, P. & TORCIDA FERNANDEZ-BALDOR, F. (eds) *Actas de las IV Journados Internacionales sobre Paleontologia de Dinosaurios y su Entorno*. Colectivo Arqueológico y Paleontológico de Salas, Salas de los Infantes, Burgos, Spain, 273–291.

RUIZ-OMEÑACA, J. I., BARDET, N., PIÑUELA, L., GARCIA-RAMOS, J. C. & PEREDA-SUBERBIOLA, X. 2010. El fosil de plesiosaurio (Sauropterygia) más antiguo de la Península lbérica: una vértebra del Hettangiense – Sinemuriense de Asturias. *Geogaceta*, **46**, 79–82.

SAUVAGE, H. E. 1897–1898. *Les Vertébrés fossiles du Portugal. Contributions à l'étude des poissons et des reptiles du Jurassique et du Crétacé*. Direction des Travaux Geologiques du Portugal Mémoires et Communications du Service géologique du Portugal, Lisbon, 1–46.

SCHUDACK, M. 1987. Charophytenflora und fazielle Entwicklung der Grenzschichten mariner Jura/Wealden in den Nordwestlichen Iberischen Ketten (mit Vergleichen zu Asturien und Kantabrien). *Palaeontographica, Abteilung B: Palaeophytologie*, **204**, 1–80.

SCHULZ, G. 1835. *Descripción geognóstica del Reino de Galicia, acompañada de un mapa petrográfico de este país*. Imprenta de Herederos de Collado, Madrid.

SCHULZ, G. 1858. *Descripción geológica de la Provincia de Oviedo*. Imprenta de D. José González, Madrid.

SUÁREZ VEGA, L. C. 1974. Estratigrafía del Jurásico de Asturias. *Cuadernos de Geología Ibérica*, **3**, 1–369.

VALENZUELA, M., GARCÍA-RAMOS, J. C. & SUÁREZ DE CENTI, C. 1986. The Jurassic sedimentation in Asturias (N Spain). *Trabajos de Geología*, **16**, 121–132.

VILANOVA, J. 1872. *Compendio de Geología*. Imprenta de Alejandro Gómez Fuentenebro, Madrid.

VILANOVA, J. 1873. Restos de *Iguanodon* en Utrilla. (Session of 5 February.) *Anales de la Sociedad Española de Historia Natural, Actas*, **2**, 8.

The history of dinosaur collecting in central India, 1828–1947

MATTHEW T. CARRANO[1]*, JEFFREY A. WILSON[2] & PAUL M. BARRETT[3]

[1]*Department of Paleobiology, Smithsonian Institution, P.O. Box 37012, MRC 121, Washington, DC 20013-7012, USA*

[2]*Museum of Paleontology and Department of Geological Sciences, University of Michigan, 1109 Geddes Road, Ann Arbor, MI 48109-1079, USA*

[3]*Department of Palaeontology, The Natural History Museum, Cromwell Road, London SW7 5BD, UK*

**Corresponding author (e-mail: carranom@si.edu)*

Abstract: The history of dinosaur collecting in central India (former Central Provinces and Central India Agency) began in 1828 when W. H. Sleeman discovered isolated sauropod caudal vertebrae in the Lameta Formation near Jabalpur. Subsequently, the area became a focal point for fossil collection, leading to a series of further discoveries that continues today.

The earliest discoveries were made by numerous collectors for whom palaeontology was a secondary pursuit, and who were employed in the armed forces (W. H. Sleeman and W. T. Nicolls), medicine (G. G. Spilsbury) or as geologists (T. Oldham, H. B. Medlicott, T. W. H. Hughes and C. A. Matley). Most of their finds were concentrated around Jabalpur or farther south near Pisdura and often consisted of isolated, surface-collected bones.

Charles Matley undertook the two most extensive collecting efforts, in 1917–1919 and 1932–1933 (Percy Sladen Trust Expedition). As a result he discovered significant deposits of dinosaurs on Bara Simla and Chhota Simla, revisited Pisdura, and mapped the Lameta Formation. Many new dinosaur taxa resulted from Matley's studies, which still represent most of the known Lameta Formation dinosaur fauna. Current scientific understanding places these fossils among the Sauropoda (as titanosaurians) and Theropoda (as abelisaurids and noasaurids). Early reports of armoured ornithischians were erroneous; these materials also pertain to sauropods and theropods.

Supplementary material: A list of the archival documents in the Natural History Museum, London that were used for this study is available at http://www.geolsoc.org.uk/SUP18418.

Dinosaur fossils have been collected from the latest Cretaceous deposits of central India since the early nineteenth century, beginning with a series of British soldiers, geologists and amateur naturalists. This work extended through to Indian independence, whence it continues to the present day with ongoing exploration and excavation led by members of the Indian palaeontological community. Despite this long history, which begins almost contemporaneously with early studies of dinosaur fossils in Europe, the early efforts associated with Indian palaeontology have been poorly documented. As a result, important information about the identities, geological settings and exact geographical locations of the fossils have been overlooked, leading to confusion and debate in the more recent scientific literature.

Here we review the early history of collecting in central India, a region consisting of the former Central Provinces (1861–1950) and Central India Agency (1854–1956), and now corresponding to the states of Madhya Pradesh and Chhattisgarh with portions of neighbouring Maharashtra (Fig. 1). We focus on this time and place in order to strengthen the historical and scientific foundation for ongoing palaeontological research throughout the Indian subcontinent. Much of the information we present below has been collected from available historical literature, but we also include evidence from previously unpublished archival sources. The latter include letters, bills of lading and project reports associated with the fieldwork of Charles A. Matley, which are now housed at the Natural History Museum, London. These documents provide important new data concerning collecting efforts, localities and the fossils recovered.

Institutional Abbreviations: AMNH, American Museum of Natural History, New York, USA; GSI, Geological Survey of India, Kolkata, India; IM, Indian Museum, Kolkata, India; NHM, The Natural History Museum, London, UK.

From: Moody, R. T. J., Buffetaut, E., Naish, D. & Martill, D. M. (eds) *Dinosaurs and Other Extinct Saurians: A Historical Perspective*. Geological Society, London, Special Publications, **343**, 161–173.
DOI: 10.1144/SP343.9 0305-8719/10/$15.00

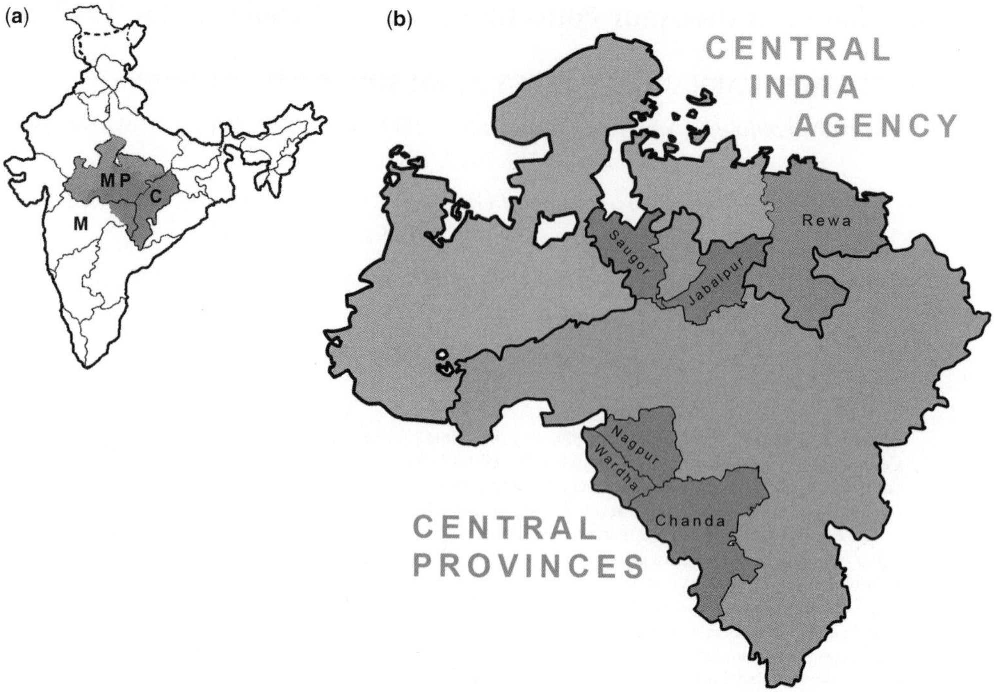

Fig. 1. Map of India showing location of areas discussed in the text. (**a**) Map of present-day India showing state boundaries; coloured areas represent the pre-independence area of the Central Provinces and Central India Agency. (**b**) 1909 boundaries of the Central Provinces and Central India Agency, showing districts and states (darker tones) where palaeontological work took place. Abbreviations: C, Chhattisgarh; M, Maharashtra; MP, Madhya Pradesh. Colours: blue, Central Provinces; green, Central India Agency.

Initial discoveries: 1828–1872

The first discoveries of dinosaur bones from the Indian subcontinent were made by W. H. Sleeman in the valley of the Narmada (= Nerbudda, Nerbadá) River in the early 1800s (Sleeman 1844). Sleeman, a captain (and eventually a lieutenant colonel) in the Bengal Army, was perhaps best known for his pursuit and suppression of the thaggi (= thuggee), a cult that practiced robbery and murder against travellers. (For these efforts, Sleeman is remembered today in the name of the village of Sleemanabad.) He also documented a long-term interest in natural history in his memoirs (Sleeman 1844). Among these, his initial discoveries were made just 0.9 km NE of his home in Jabalpur (= Jubbulpore) and concerned a 'petrified forest' in the stratum just below the basalt that caps the Jabalpur ridges (now recognized as one of the Deccan Traps) (Prinsep 1832). This discovery most probably occurred in 1828 (Sleeman 1844), although an 1830 date has also been suggested (Prinsep 1832; Medlicott 1860). Sleeman also found fossil bones with these silicified tree trunks, two of which he sent to Dr G. G. Spilsbury, a civil surgeon in Jabalpur, who returned to the site and procured one additional specimen some time prior to 1832 (Prinsep 1832; Spilsbury 1837; Matley 1921*a*). Sleeman also visited the Saugor area in 1830 and discovered a similar deposit of petrified tree trunks below the Deccan Traps, but did not report any additional bones (Sleeman 1844).

Spilsbury sent all three specimens to James Prinsep in Kolkata in 1832 (Matley 1921*a*). Prinsep, a local antiquarian and the first to translate the Brahmi script into English, was unable to identify them owing to their poor preservation, although he observed that 'the osseous structure of the first two is very apparent' (Prinsep 1832, p. 456; see also Prinsep 1833). These two bones were then passed to Dr Thomas Oldham, the first Director of the Geological Survey of India, who brought the bones from Jabalpur in 1862, and then to Mr Hugh Falconer. Falconer described and illustrated the bones, which he recognized to be reptilian caudal vertebrae, but this work was not published until after his death (Falconer 1868). Richard Lydekker (1877) studied the caudal vertebrae and a femur (collected by Medlicott from an overlying horizon some years later; see later) and made them the type series of the sauropod dinosaur *Titanosaurus indicus*. The locations of these specimens are now unknown, although Lydekker (1888) noted that they were originally deposited in the Indian Museum, Kolkata. A plaster cast of one caudal vertebra was presented to the British Museum (Natural History) by Falconer in 1867 and survives in the Natural History Museum, London as NHM 40867 (Fig. 2a; Table 1). As the original specimens cannot be located, this cast should be regarded as a plastotype for this species.

The Saugor area was visited again in the 1850s by W. T. Nicolls, a captain in the Madras Army (Matley in Huene & Matley 1933), who reported finding two fossiliferous localities near the village of Narayanpur (= Narrainpore). One site produced mostly fossil wood but also a fragment of bone. At the second locality Nicholls described 'fragments of large bones strewed on the surface of the black regur soil', at least one of which preserved the concave face of a vertebral centrum (Carter 1854, p. 322). Medlicott (1860, p. 199) identified these

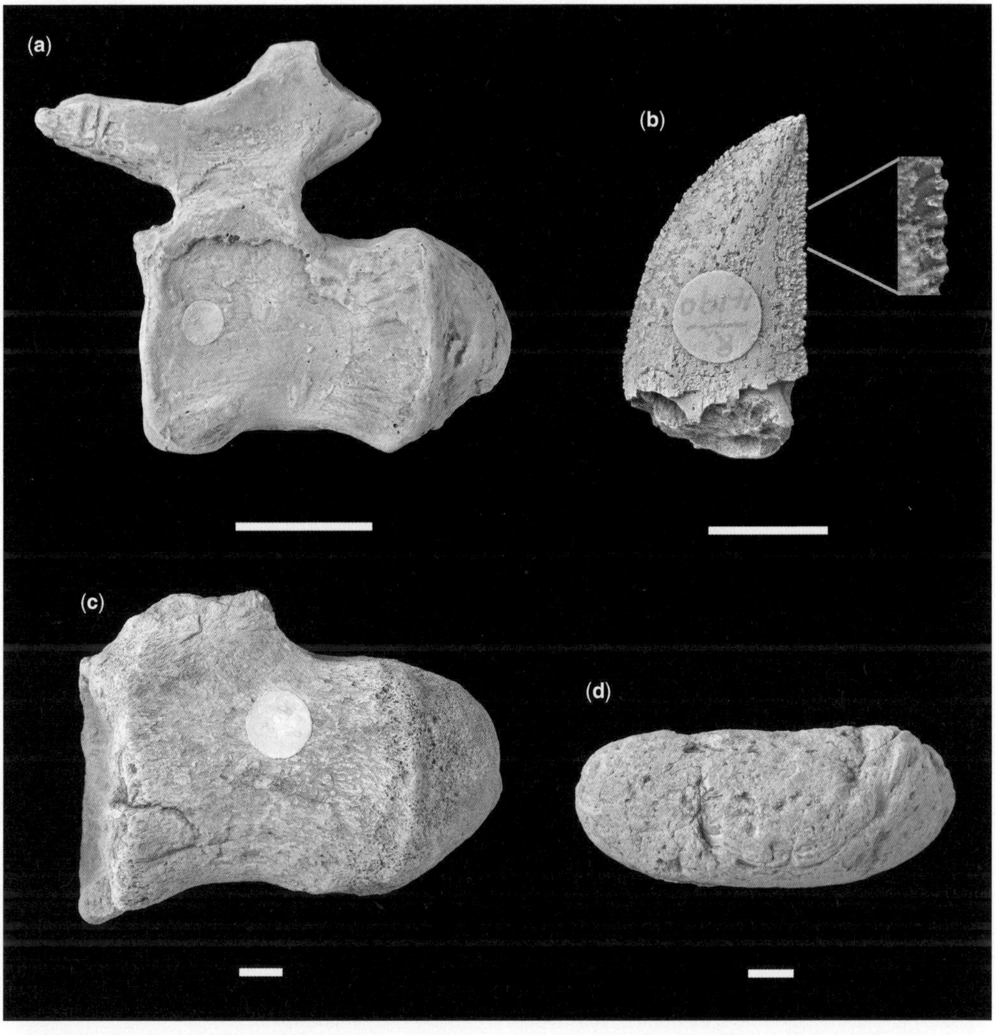

Fig. 2. Representative fossil specimens collected from the Late Cretaceous beds of central India, 1848–1933. (**a**) Plaster cast of syntypic caudal vertebra of *Titanosaurus indicus* (plastotype, NHM 40867). (**b**) Holotype tooth of *Massospondylus rawesi* (NHM R 4190), showing enlargement of serrated posterior carina. (**c**) Titanosaur caudal vertebra (NHM R902). (**d**) Coprolite from Pisdura (NHM uncatalogued, 'specimen 66'). Scale bars: (a) 5 cm; and (b)–(d) 1 cm.

Table 1. *Chronology of dinosaur expeditions in central India by year and district, 1828–1947, with specimens known to have been collected*

Collector(s)	Year(s)	Locality	Specimen(s)	Current status
Sleeman, Spilsbury	1828–1832	Jabalpur	Two sauropod caudal vertebrae	Types, *Titanosaurus indicus* (GSI/IM, lost; cast, NHM 40867)
Nicolls	1850s	Saugor	Vertebral centrum	Bombay Branch, Asiatic Society (lost)
Rawes	pre-1859	Takli	Theropod tooth	Type, *Massospondylus rawesi* (NHM R4190)
Blanford	pre-1859	Pisdura	Two sauropod vertebrae	Type, *Titanosaurus blanfordi* (GSI), *cf. Laplatasaurus madagascariensis* (GSI)
			Coprolites, turtle carapace	Lost
Hislop	pre-1859	Pisdura	Dinosaur femur, vertebrae; molluscs; coprolites	Lost
			Two turtle carapaces	*Hydraspis leithi* (unknown; cast, NHM R1728)
Medlicott	1871–1872	Jabalpur	Sauropod femur	*cf. Antarctosaurus* sp. (GSI K22/754)
		Karhayia	Large vertebrate remains	Unknown
Hughes	1870s	Pisdura	Dinosaur bones, coprolites, shells	Unknown
Matley	1917	Jabalpur	Numerous sauropod and theropod specimens	*Titanosaurus indicus*; types, *Lametasaurus indicus* (GSI), *Antarctosaurus septentrionalis*, *Coeluroides largus*, *Compsosuchus solus*, *Dryptosauroides grandis*, *Indosaurus matleyi*, *Indosuchus raptorius*, *Jubbulpuria tenuis*, *Laevisuchus indicus*, *Ornithomimoides* (?) *barasimlensis*, *Ornithomimoides mobilis* (all GSI; see Huene & Matley 1933 for specimen numbers)
	1919	Jabalpur	Second theropod	Unknown; possibly refers to one of the taxa above
		Lameta Ghat	Sauropod	Unknown
	1920	Pisdura	Coprolites, turtle, mollusc, sauropod caudals	*Titanosaurus blanfordi* (unknown)
		Panchgaon	Sauropod caudal vertebra	*Titanosaurus blanfordi* (unknown)
Brown	1922	Bara Simla	Theropod skull, titanosaur osteoderm	*cf. Indosuchus* (AMNH 1753, 1955, 1960), titanosaur (AMNH 1959)
Das-Gupta	1924	Bara Simla	Theropod tooth	Type, *Orthogoniosaurus matleyi* (unknown)
Matley	1932	Jabalpur	Sauropod, theropod, plants	Unknown
		Pisdura	Sauropod caudal vertebrae; coprolites	NHM R5920–R5921; R12377–R12378 (also many unregistered bones and coprolites)
	1933	Rewa State	Dinosaurs	Unknown
		Chhota Simla	Associated titanosaur postcrania	NHM R5903, R5931–R5933, R5935, 16481
		Amakhoh	Dinosaur limb bones	Unknown

bones as mammalian, and mentioned the similarities between the beds at Narayanpur and those at Jabalpur:

> a similar bed is found ... covered by a trap ... colossal vertebrate bones, are embedded in the calcareous bed. These bones are much too broken for identification. They are supposed to have belonged to large Pachyderms, or possibly to cetacea.

The vertebra was favourably compared to the sauropod vertebrae later discovered at Pisdura (Hislop 1861, p. 190). These materials were collected and brought to the Bombay Branch of the Asiatic Society, but could not be found when requested by Charles Matley in 1925 (Matley in Huene & Matley 1933, p. 6) and are now presumed lost.

Three additional collections were made in the years prior to 1859 but, unfortunately, their specific dates are not recorded. Among the earliest of these was the discovery by Mr Rawes of a single dinosaurian tooth in the Nagpur area, Maharashtra. Although it was originally reported to have come from the intertrappean Takli Beds (Hislop 1861, 1864), which were at the time considered to be Eocene in age, Lydekker (1879, 1890) suggested that the tooth actually came from the underlying infratrappean Lameta Beds. Lydekker (1879, 1890) recognized the theropod affinities of the tooth, but considered it to be most similar to 'anchisaurid' teeth of *Thecodontosaurus* and *Massospondylus* (then thought to be theropods). This specimen was named *Massospondylus rawesi* by Lydekker (1890). Although the tooth can now be identified as a theropod (and resembles those of abelisaurids), it bears no diagnostic features that allow its referral to an existing or novel theropod genus (Fig. 2b).

Second came the first reported discoveries at Pisdura (= Phisdura, Phizdura, Pijdura), about 320 km from Jabalpur, in Chanda (now Chandrapur) District. Here, W. T. Blanford collected two sauropod dinosaur vertebrae that were later described by Lydekker as the type of *Titanosaurus blanfordi* (Lydekker 1879), although the smaller of the two was later referred to as *cf. Laplatasaurus madagascariensis* by Huene (1929, p. 39). Lydekker (1877, p. 41) also mentioned 'a considerable series of caudal vertebrae', along with coprolites and a turtle carapace, but none of these materials were ever described in detail, and their current whereabouts are not known. This was the first mention of coprolites from Pisdura.

Third, and subsequent to Blanford's visit, the Reverend Stephen Hislop also collected at Pisdura (Hislop 1860). Importantly, he noted a very similar arrangement of the beds to what had been observed at Jabalpur: 'On the west side of Phizdura, which is only 3 miles E.S.E. Of Mángali, there is a hill of trap ... It also overlies a fossiliferous deposit' (Hislop 1860, p. 163). Hislop was also the first to observe that most of the fossils were found as surface materials in a nearby field. His collection included vertebrae and a femur from a large dinosaur, in association with a tooth, a fish vertebra, a turtle plastron, and typical Lameta Formation molluscs and coprolites ('some of them huge enough': Hislop 1864, p. 282). Hislop originally considered the large bones to be mammalian ('Pachyderms': Hislop 1860, p. 163). They were too heavy to ship, but he made drawings in order to permit them to be studied by Falconer, who identified them as reptilian (Hislop 1861, 1864). Unfortunately, many of Hislop's notes were only published posthumously (Hislop 1864). Although most of the specimens were not seen by Lydekker during his time in India just a few years later (he noted, 'I do not at all know what has become of the specimens collected by Mr Hislop': Lydekker 1879, p. 24), he eventually described the turtle carapace and referred it to *Hydraspis leithi* (Lydekker 1890).

Between 1871 and 1872 H. B. Medlicott conducted a study of the 'infratrappean' rocks of the Jabalpur District, and documented the presence of vertebrate bones at both Jabalpur and 65 km to the WSW at Karhayia (= Kareia) (Medlicott 1872). At Jabalpur he collected an approximately 1.3 m-long sauropod femur (GSI K22/754), originally made part of the type series of *Titanosaurus indicus* (Lydekker 1877) but later removed to *cf. Antarctosaurus* sp. (Huene & Matley 1933, p. 29). Below Kareia, in the bed of the Sher River, Medlicott noted the presence of 'large vertebrate remains, though scarcely perfect enough for identification' that had 'weathered from beneath the trap' (Medlicott 1872, p. 119). Huene & Matley (1933) noted that these fossils probably came from the Greensand Zone.

At about the same time geologist T. W. H. Hughes followed upon Hislop's report and visited the Pisdura site, which he noted occurred in a field at the southern end of Pisdura Hill. The fossils were found as surface float, as they continue to be today, 'having been turned up by the ploughing of the land' (Hughes 1877). Hughes noted the presence of shells, coprolites and bones, specifically mentioning among the latter both limbs and vertebrae.

Subsequent to these reports and the works of Richard Lydekker, no further collecting in the Central Provinces appears to have been reported for nearly 45 years.

Expeditions of Charles A. Matley: 1917–1933

First expeditions, 1917–1924

A second, renewed phase of collecting began with Charles Matley, a British geologist and field

Fig. 3. Charles A. Matley. Photograph courtesy of NHM Archives.

officer based at the Geological Survey of India (Fig. 3). His first discoveries came in October 1917 during a visit to Jabalpur. There, on the western slope of Bara Simla, he found numerous remains of sauropod and theropod dinosaurs (Table 1) (Matley 1921*a*, *b*). Further excavation revealed that these remains came from two specimens in two different layers: a sauropod tentatively identified as *Titanosaurus indicus* in 'a red and green marly clay about 4 feet above the lower limestone'; and a smaller theropod from a slightly lower 'soft greenish sandstone at the base of the lower limestone' (Matley 1918, pp. clxxxvi–clxxxvii). Matley termed these two beds the Ossiferous Conglomerate and the Carnosaur Bed, respectively (Matley 1921*a*; Huene & Matley 1933); the latter would eventually produce abundant remains of large and small theropods, as well as sauropods (Fig. 4) (Huene & Matley 1933).

In February 1919 Matley travelled NE of Jabalpur to prospect the surrounding Lameta Formation outcrops. This 2-week trip took him as far as the Mahanadi River, about 65 km away (Fig. 5). For transport, he relied primarily on camels (Matley unpublished Second Percy Sladen Trust Expedition (PSTE) Report). He also revisited the Bara Simla site in early 1919, where he found a second theropod specimen in the upper (sauropod-bearing) layer. The material consisted of 'two teeth, three ribs, and a vertebra' (Matley 1919, pp. cxcviii–cxcix).

Some of the preparation of these materials was accomplished in the field, primarily thanks to the work of Durgansankar Bhattacharji from the Indian Geological Survey (Matley in Huene & Matley 1933, p. 1). Bhattacharji worked extensively with Matley through many field seasons and provided important field expertise for his work, in addition to discovering several important dinosaur specimens at Bara Simla and Chhota Simla (Matley 1921*a*, pp. 155–156). Bhattacharji also kept extensive notes on the disposition and locations of the bones at these sites, but unfortunately his notebook has not been located (Matley letter to Bather dated 31 March 1921).

Matley realized that a more detailed appreciation of the geology of the Jabalpur area was needed and visited the type section of the Lameta beds at Lameta Ghat in October 1919 for this purpose. There he surface-collected dinosaur bones (mostly sauropod) at many sites, but also noted several *in situ* at Amakhoh, Kothi, and south of Sagona (Fig. 5) (Matley 1921*a*).

Matley made 'a hurried visit' to Pisdura in 1920, where he found fossils similar to those previously noted in a ploughed field east of the village (Matley 1921*a*, p. 161). These included large coprolites, part of a turtle and numerous molluscs, as well as a series of six caudal vertebrae that he assigned to *Titanosaurus blanfordi* (Table 1; Fig. 2c, d). With them he associated a tibia, a metacarpal and possible scapula. On the east side of an outlier hill, south of the village of Panchgaon, he reported the presence of another caudal vertebra of *T. blanfordi* (Matley 1921*a*, p. 161). Matley also visited nearby Dongargaon, but did not report finding any fossils and questioned whether the beds might be younger than the type Lameta strata (Matley letter to Bather dated 31 March 1921).

Most of the Bara Simla sauropod bones remained in India, but the majority of other specimens (including many theropod materials) were sent to London in two shipments, the cost of which was borne by the Government of India (Matley letter to Bather dated 20 May 1925). The first was sent in 1922 (exact date unknown, but it must have preceded Matley's 1923 writing of the description of *Lametasaurus*, as it is mentioned therein), and probably included the type of *Indosuchus* and those portions of the type materials of *Laevisuchus*, *Jubbulpuria*, *Dryptosauroides* and *Ornithomimoides mobilis* bearing 'K20' Geological Survey of India (GSI) catalogue numbers. The second shipment was made in April 1925; a list of

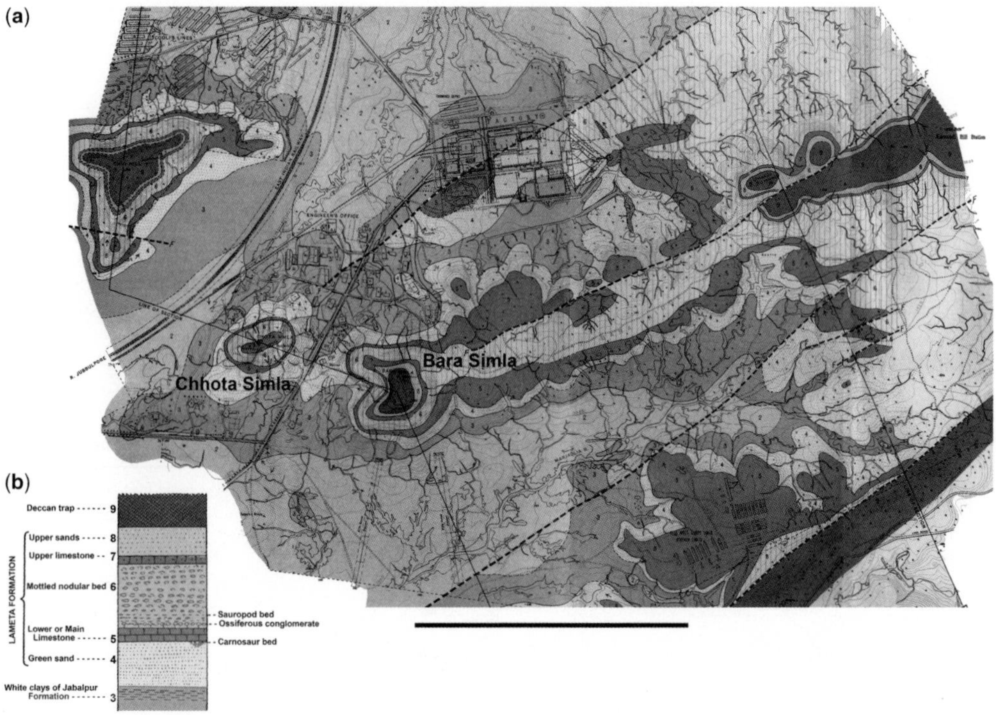

Fig. 4. (**a**) Geological map of the Jabalpur region, showing Lameta Formation outcrops at Chui Hill, Chhota Simla, and Bara Simla; scale bar, 1 km (modified from Matley 1921*a*). (**b**) Geological profile of the Lameta Formation at Jabalpur (modified from Huene & Matley 1933 by the addition of colours corresponding to strata in the main map).

these specimens includes both 'K20' and 'K22' GSI catalogue numbers, but no additional type specimens. These materials were received at the British Museum (Natural History) by A. S. Woodward, Keeper of the Geological Department. It is not known whether the remaining types from Bara Simla (those with 'K27' numbers) remained permanently in India or were sent to England for study as part of later shipments (see the subsection on 'Percy Sladen Trust expedition, 1932–1933' later).

In 1922 Barnum Brown visited India on an extensive tour, during which he married his wife Lilian (Brown 1950). He visited Matley's Bara Simla site, and while there collected several theropod specimens and a large osteoderm for the American Museum of Natural History (AMNH) (Table 1) (Huene & Matley 1933; Chatterjee 1978; Novas *et al.* 2004). This latter element was initially identified as the tail club of an armoured dinosaur (Huene & Matley 1933; Coombs 1978), but it has recently been reinterpreted as a titanosaur osteoderm (Chatterjee & Rudra 1996; D'Emic *et al.* 2009). Although it has not been explicitly mentioned before, a letter from Matley to W. D. Lang (16 December 1932) makes it clear that Brown was working at the same site, and in the same bed, as the one that produced the original Bara Simla theropod materials: '[t]he deposits at Jubbulpore seem to be worked out (Barnum Brown exploited my Carnosaur Bed since I was last there)'. This information casts doubt on the supposed associations between the elements collected by Brown (Chatterjee 1978) and indicates that they have the same likelihood of being associated as any of the other Carnosaur Bed specimens.

The first dinosaur to be described from Bara Simla was *Lametasaurus indicus*, first thought to be a theropod (Matley 1918, 1921*a*, pp. 154–155) and then a species of the stegosaur *Omosaurus* (Fig. 6) (Matley letter to Andrews dated 26 August 1922), but eventually given its own genus name (Matley 1924). Matley completed the paper while working as a geologist in Jamaica and asked C. W. Andrews of the British Museum (Natural History) to submit it on his behalf. After some delay it was issued in 1924 in the volume for 1923 of the *Records of the Geological Survey of India* (Matley letter to Woodward dated 23 February 1924). Although Matley now considered *Lametasaurus* to be a stegosaur, having associated it with the numerous small osteoderms also found at the site, it was later re-identified as a theropod by

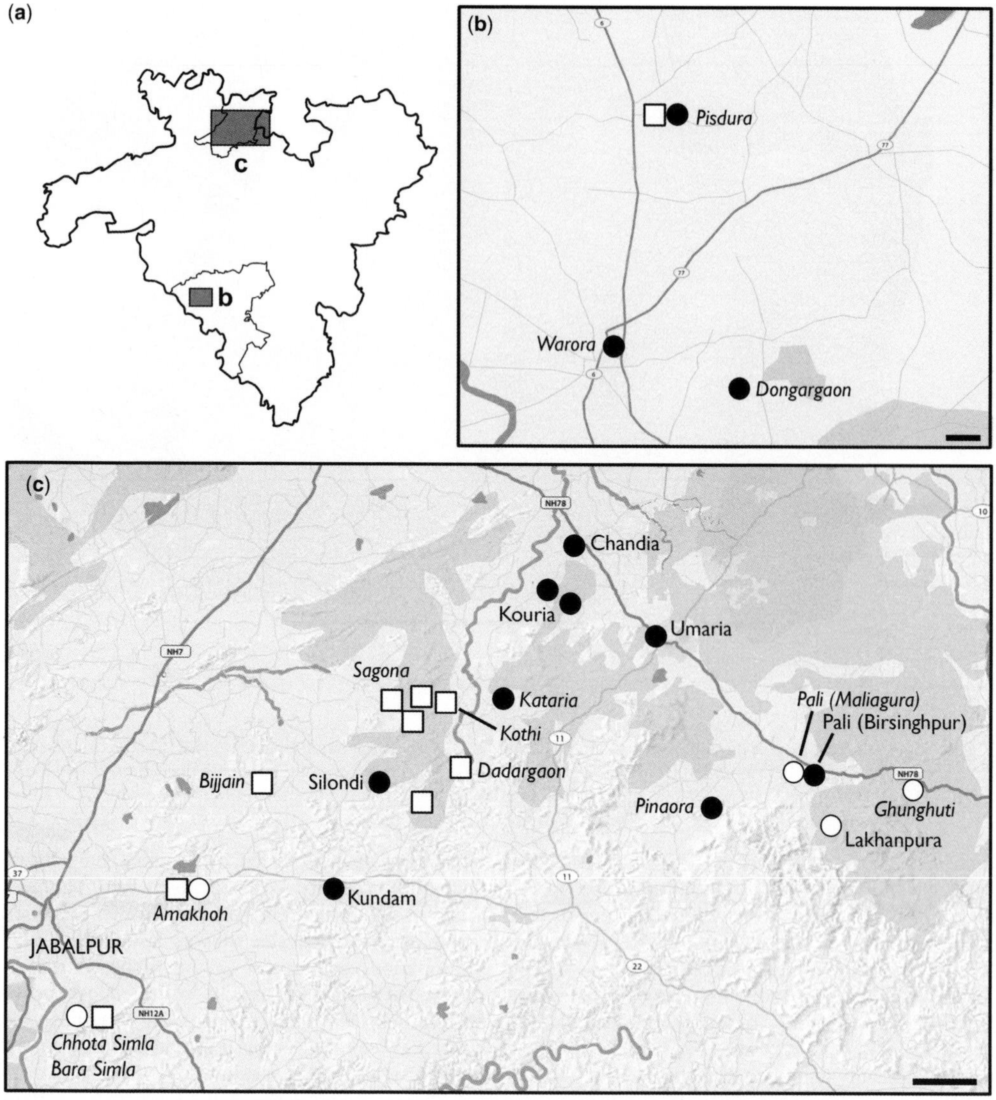

Fig. 5. Travels of C. A. Matley in central India, 1917–1933. (**a**) Outline map of the Central Provinces, with boxes showing location and size of inset maps of the Chandrapur (b) and Jabaplur (c) regions. (**b**) Chanda district (Chandrapur); scale bar, 2 km. (**c**) Jabalpur region (Jabalpur and western Rewa districts); scale bar, 10 km. Symbols: squares, 1917–1919; circles, PSTE, 1932–1933; open symbols, dinosaur-producing sites; closed symbols, non-dinosaurian fossils only. Base maps for (b) and (c) © 2008 Yahoo, Inc.

D. K. Chakravarti of the Geological Museum at Banares (Benares) Hindu University (Chakravarti 1934, 1935). The whereabouts of the type series of *Lametasaurus*, which includes a sacrum, ilia, tibia and osteoderms, are no longer known.

Bara Simla was next visited by H. C. Das-Gupta, who led a group of students from Presidency College (Kolkata) to the site in 1924. The 'small collection' made by Das-Gupta included a single theropod tooth, which he made the type of *Orthogoniosaurus matleyi* (Das-Gupta 1930) and placed in the family Anchisauridae (Thecodontosauridae); at that time this family was considered to represent a group of small carnivorous dinosaurs. Huene & Matley (1933, p. 59) did not consider the tooth 'sufficiently diagnostic' to serve as the basis of a new genus, although the tooth does resemble those of abelisaurid theropods.

Finally, Matley made a 2-day trip to Narayanpur in March 1925 to the site originally discovered by

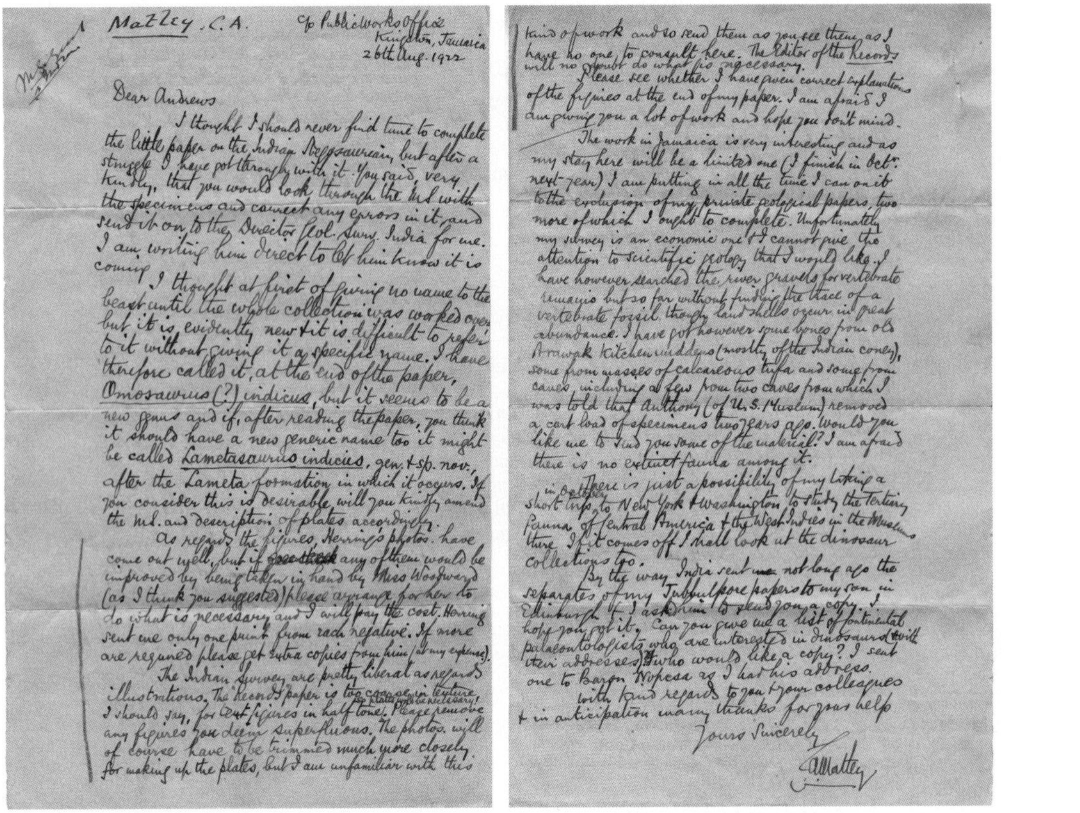

Matley, C.A.
C/o Public Works Office
Kingston, Jamaica
26th Aug. 1922

Dear Andrews

I thought I should never find time to complete the little paper on the Indian Stegosaurian, but after a struggle I have got through with it. You said, very kindly, that you would look through the MS with the specimens and correct any errors in it, and send it on to the Director Geol. Surv. India for me. I am writing him direct to let him know it is coming.

I thought at first of giving no name to the beast until the whole collection was worked over but it is evidently new & it is difficult to refer to it without giving it a specific name. I have therefore called it, at the end of the paper, Omosaurus (?) indicus, but it seems to be a new genus and if, after reading the paper, you think it should have a new generic name too it might be called Lametasaurus indicus, gen. & sp. nov., after the Lameta formation in which it occurs. If you consider this is desirable will you kindly amend the MS. and description of plates accordingly.

As regards the figures, Herring's photos. have come out well, but if any of them would be improved by being taken in hand by Miss Woodward (as I think you suggested) please arrange for her to do what is necessary and I will pay the cost. Herring sent me only one print from each negative. If more are required please get extra copies from him (at my expense).

The Indian Survey are pretty liberal as regards illustrations. The Records paper is too coarse in texture, I should say, for text figures in half tone. Please remove any figures you deem superfluous. The photos. will of course have to be trimmed much more closely for making up the plates, but I am unfamiliar with this kind of work and so send them as you see them, as I have no one to consult here. The Editor of the Records will no doubt do what is necessary.

Please see whether I have given correct explanations of the figures at the end of my paper. I am afraid I am giving you a lot of work and hope you don't mind.

The work in Jamaica is very interesting and as my stay here will be a limited one (I finish in Oct. next year) I am putting in all the time I can on it to the exclusion of my private geological papers, two more of which I ought to complete. Unfortunately my survey is an economic one & I cannot give the attention to scientific geology that I would like. I have however searched the river gravels for vertebrate remains but so far without finding the trace of a vertebrate fossil though land shells occur in great abundance. I have got however some bones from old Arawak kitchen middens (mostly of the Indian coney), some from masses of calcareous tufa and some from caves, including a few from two caves from which I was told that Anthony (of U.S. Museum) removed a cart load of specimens two years ago. Would you like me to send you some of the material? I am afraid there is no extinct fauna among it.

There is just a possibility of my taking a short trip, in October, to New York & Washington to study the Tertiary fauna of Central America & the West Indies in the Museums there. If it comes off I shall look at the dinosaur collections too.

By the way India sent me not long ago the separates of my Jubbulpore papers to my son in Edinburgh & I asked him to send you a copy. I hope you got it. Can you give me a list of continental palaeontologists who are interested in dinosaurs (with their addresses) who would like a copy? I sent one to Baron Nopcsa as I had his address.

With kind regards to you & your colleagues & in anticipation many thanks for your help

Yours sincerely

CAMatley

Fig. 6. Letter from C. A. Matley to C. W. Andrews dated 26 August 1922. Courtesy of NHM Archives.

Nicolls but was unsuccessful in locating any new materials (Matley in Huene & Matley 1933, p. 6).

Matley published a comprehensive study of the dinosaurs from central India in collaboration with F. von Huene (Huene & Matley 1933) in which they documented the prior history of dinosaur collecting in the region and described several new taxa. Among these were nine theropods and one sauropod in addition to the previously described *Lametasaurus* and new specimens of *Titanosaurus indicus*. These materials have been studied numerous times in the succeeding decades (e.g. Walker 1964; Chatterjee 1978), and, although many are now considered *nomina dubia*, nearly all the specimens appear to represent abelisaurid and noasaurid theropods and titanosaurian sauropods (Wilson & Upchurch 2003; Novas *et al.* 2004; Carrano & Sampson 2008).

Percy Sladen Trust expedition, 1932–1933

With his promising initial results, Matley applied for funds from the Percy Sladen Trust on 22 April 1932 (Matley letter to Swinton dated 30 April 1932), which he was awarded in November 1932 (Trustees' minutes, October–November 1932). In addition to £200 from the Trust, he also received £48 15s from the Gloyne Fund, £50 from the British Museum (Natural History) Purchase Fund, and he utilized logistical support from the Geological Survey of India in the form of field assistant A. M. N. Ghosh, as well as *c.* £100 from his personal funds (Matley letters to Swinton dated 30 April 1932; Lang 15 October 1932; NHM Director enclosed with letter to Lang dated 15 January 1935). These resources enabled him to make several trips to Jabalpur, Pisdura and the surrounding areas over a period of 5 months, from 18 November 1932 to 17 April 1933 under the Percy Sladen Trust Expedition (PSTE) (Fig. 5; Table 2).

The PSTE began with a week of work at the sites Matley had already discovered at Bara Simla and Chhota Simla. These sites produced numerous sauropod and theropod materials as well as fossil plants.

The next 2 weeks were spent in Chanda district, at Pisdura and Warora. The visit to Pisdura (December 1932) revealed that fossil materials

Table 2. *Chronology, locations and specimens associated with C. A. Matley's explorations under the Percy Sladen Trust Expedition, 1932–1933*

Dates	District/ state	Location(s)	Material(s)
28 November–8 December 1932	Jabalpur	Bara Simla, Chhota Simla	Titanosaur and theropod (at least seven specimens), plants
9–21 December 1932	Chandrapur	Pisdura	Coprolites, turtle, titanosaur, theropod, molluscs
		Warora	Dinosaur limb, fish scales, gastropods, cyprinids
22–24 December 1932	Jabalpur	Jabalpur (return via Chanda)	None listed
3 January–6 February 1933	Rewa	Obra, Munda, Bhundi, Pali (Birsinghpur)	None
		Kouria (near Jogin; Machrar Nadi, at Bansa)	Plants
		Chandia (nulla near Jhala; Barwar, 3.25 km SSE)	Plants
		Pali (south of Maliagura)	Probable rib fragments
		Ghunghuti (on Kachodhar road)	Two large bones, limb fragment
		Lakhanpura (SE)	Bone fragment
		Changera	*Limnaea, Paludina, Bullinus*
		Pinaora	*Limnaea, Paludina, Bullinus*
		Umaria (railway cutting near Narsaha nulla)	Spiriferidae, *Productus*
6–8 February 1933; 14 February–17 April 1933	Jabalpur	Chhota Simla	Titanosaur, theropod, scutes (160 specimens total)
		Bara Simla	Plants, including cycads
9–13 February 1933	Jabalpur	Amakhoh	Limb bones, lamellibranchs
Weekend trip, 1933	Narsinghpur	Karhayia	Plants

Note: Dates and locations primarily from Matley's unpublished Second PSTE Report; see Figure 5 for the map.

could be found at several localities, not just the original site discovered by Hislop. According to Matley:

> [t]his distribution suggested that the fossils were derived from below. Two of the richest localities were selected for excavation and trial holes were also made at other favourable spots, but in no case did the undisturbed Lameta clay produce a single fossil. As two of the localities lay at the foot of a slope capped by an outlier of Deccan Trap two trenches were dug up the slope as far as the Trap, but in neither case did they reveal a bone or mollusc in situ.
>
> (Matley unpublished Interim PSTE Report, 1 January 1933)

Matley believed that 'four species and probably three genera of Titanosaurs' were present at Pisdura (Matley unpublished Interim PSTE Report), including *T. blanfordi*, *cf. T. indicus*, ?*Antarctosaurus* sp. and *cf. Laplatasaurus madagascariensis*. At Warora, he discovered a dinosaur limb bone, numerous gastropods and cyprids, and fish scales (Matley unpublished Interim PSTE Report).

Matley returned to Jabalpur and explored the surrounding area of the district in early January 1933, but reported finding no fossils. He then embarked on an extensive tour of Rewa State, where he discovered fossil plants and several deposits containing molluscs. He found fragmentary dinosaur bones at Pali, Ghunghuti and Lakhanpura, but none were well enough preserved to be identified.

Returning to Jabalpur district on 14 February 1933, Matley soon discovered a new dinosaur bone bed on the SE face of the nearby Chhota Simla hill. The site included an associated titanosaur skeleton, as well as other sauropod and theropod materials (Matley letter to Lang dated 9 March 1933). This discovery necessitated a re-evaluation of the field schedule, such that Matley eventually decided to extend his trip by several weeks, from 24 March to 21 April (Matley letters to Lang dated 23 February and 9 March 1933).

This extension permitted a brief trip to Amakhoh and a weekend visit to Karhayia. At Amakhoh, Matley discovered six or seven incomplete limb bones, which, although poorly preserved, were apparently more abundant than anywhere in the vicinity aside from Jabalpur. Nothing was found at Karhayia aside from plant fossils (Matley unpublished Second PSTE Report).

Matley was unable to utilize camels for travel during most of the PSTE. However, he noted that most of the Jabalpur villages could now be reached by 'bullock carts' and used these as a means of transport, in addition to motor vehicles where it was possible to so do (Matley unpublished Second PSTE Report). He did obtain camels once in Rewa State, but as these were all females and most were pregnant they proved unsatisfactory and were 'discharged' before reaching Patpara.

The materials collected under the PSTE were sent to London in two shipments for preparation and study. The first consisted of 11 packages, primarily Pisdura specimens, held under the care of the Director of the Geological Survey of India in Kolkata. These were shipped through the Calcutta branch of Mackinnon Mackenzie on the British India cargo vessel S.S. *Lahore* on 9 May 1933 and were received at the British Museum (Natural History) in June (Swinton letter to Matley dated 28 June 1933). The second shipment consisted of 25 packages of Jabalpur material left in the care of the Superintendent of the Gun Carriage Factory (Jabalpur). These were sent by mail to Mackinnon Mackenzie in Mumbai, repacked into 18 boxes, shipped via sea and received at the British Museum (Natural History) in July (Swinton letter to Matley dated 20 July 1933).

Matley also returned to England, on the S.S. *Mashobra* from Kolkata via Madras and Marseilles (Matley letters to Lang dated 9 March and 25 April 1933), and took up residence at Barmouth, North Wales, before removing to Leamington Spa. His Indian materials were eventually prepared in London. Some were exhibited at a 'Conversazione' held at the Geological Society of London on 3 July 1935, including the Chhota Simla titanosaur limb and several Pisdura coprolites (Matley letters to Lang dated 17 May, 10 June and 10 August 1935). Matley also delivered a lecture on his experiences hunting dinosaur bones in India to the Geological Association on 3 January 1936 (Matley letter to Swinton dated 16 December 1935).

It was Matley's intention to work on the Pisdura coprolites himself. He intended for some materials to remain permanently in London, and 'as regards the remainder the Geological Survey of India should have the first choice' (Matley letter to Lang dated 19 June 1933). In addition, Matley requested that casts be made of the materials for distribution to various Indian museums, including a full set of casts for the Indian Museum in Kolkata, and a smaller collection of casts representing particularly important finds for the Nagpur Museum (Matley letter to Lang dated 8 January 1935). These appear to have been done as requested, based on mention of their shipments (Swinton letter to Matley dated 3 June 1936).

Nearly all of the Indian materials sent to the British Museum (Natural History) appear to have been returned in a single shipment, which left the museum on 30 June 1936 (NHM Archives, file DF 110/4, Boxes Despatched Book No. 4). In a letter to Matley (23 May 1936), Swinton informed him that the museum had packed 'practically all your material', including 'type specimens etc. (vertebrates)'. As no type specimens were erected from the PSTE finds, this statement can only refer to the type materials from Matley's 1917–1919 expeditions. Although not specified, we infer that this must have included *Lametasaurus* and some (or all) of the other theropod types from Bara Simla, which Matley refers to as having been shipped to London (Matley 1924). This shipment also included casts of specimens for the Indian Museum (Swinton letter to Matley dated 3 June 1936).

This left only a few specimens in the permanent care of the Natural History Museum, London. Among them is the associated titanosaur hind limb from Chhota Simla, which was described as *Titanosaurus indicus* by Swinton (1947). These materials are now under restudy by the present authors, and details of their discovery and history will be presented elsewhere.

Summary and conclusions

Although the early discoveries of dinosaurs from India have often been mentioned in palaeontological literature, there has been some confusion and lack of clarity regarding the ordering of events, the specific materials collected and their localities, and the present disposition of specimens. Our recent archival research helps to enlighten these aspects of several important chapters in Indian palaeontology.

It is now clear that several different collectors were active in the latter half of the nineteenth century, but that many of the materials they collected are now lost. In addition, the Bara Simla and Chhota Simla sites, near Jabalpur, have held a central role in Indian dinosaur palaeontology since its beginnings. Although Richard Lydekker is often noted for his extensive work with Indian fossils, most of the materials he studied were found by a variety of collectors.

In the early twentieth century Charles Matley was instrumental in amassing the largest and most scientifically important collection of dinosaurs from India prior to 1947. His contributions, some only recently recognized, include an associated titanosaur skeleton, the first dinosaur bone bed from the subcontinent and the earliest-discovered noasaurid remains. His expeditions also marked an important example of long-term collaboration between British and Indian scientists.

With the onset of Indian independence from Great Britain, dinosaur palaeontology in India became a predominately national affair. The subsequent decades have seen the field grow in size and scope, but the initial discovery localities of Jabalpur and Pisdura remain important. Today new collections and discoveries are made regularly, and the Indian dinosaur record holds a significant place in the study of dinosaur evolution, extinction and biogeography.

We are grateful to several people at the Natural History Museum, London, for their assistance during the research for this paper, including Mrs P. Parry and Mr J. Hatton (NHM Archives) for access to archival materials, and Mr P. Crabb (NHM Image Resources) for specimen photography. The present manuscript was improved thanks to the helpful comments of Dr S. Chatterjee and Dr G. V. R. Prasad. This project was funded in part by a grant from the Special Funds of the NHM (awarded to P. M. Barrett). Additional thanks are given to the staff of the Smithsonian Libraries (Natural Museum of Natural History) for their help in acquiring copies of several obscure references.

References

BROWN, L. M. 1950. *I Married a Dinosaur*. Dodd, Mead, New York.

CARRANO, M. T. & SAMPSON, S. D. 2008. The phylogeny of Ceratosauria (Dinosauria: Theropoda). *Journal of Systematic Palaeontology*, **6**, 183–236.

CARTER, H. J. 1854. Summary of the geology of India, between the Ganges, the Indus, and Cape Comorin. *Journal of the Bombay Asiatic Society*, **5**, 179–335.

CHAKRAVARTI, D. K. 1934. On the systematic position of *Lametasaurus indicus*. *In*: *Proceedings of the 21st Indian Science Congress*. Indian Science Association, Calcutta (Kolkata), 352.

CHAKRAVARTI, D. K. 1935. Is *Lametasaurus indicus* an armored dinosaur? *The American Journal of Science*, Series 5, **30**, 138–141.

CHATTERJEE, S. 1978. *Indosuchus* and *Indosaurus*, Cretaceous carnosaurs from India. *Journal of Paleontology*, **52**, 570–580.

CHATTERJEE, S. & RUDRA, D. K. 1996. KT events in India: impact, rifting, volcanism and dinosaur extinction. *Memoirs of the Queensland Museum*, **39**, 489–532.

COOMBS, W. P. JR 1978. The families of the ornithischian dinosaur Order Ankylosauria. *Palaeontology*, **21**, 143–170.

DAS-GUPTA, H. C. 1930. On a new theropod dinosaur (*Orthogoniosaurus matleyi*, n. gen. et n. sp.) from the Lameta beds of Jubbulpore. *Journal of the Asiatic Society of Bengal, New Series*, **16**, 367–369.

D'EMIC, M. D., WILSON, J. A. & CHATTERJEE, S. 2009. The titanosaur (Dinosauria: Sauropoda) osteoderm record: review and first definitive specimen from the Upper Cretaceous of India. *Journal of Vertebrate Paleontology*, **29**, 165–177.

FALCONER, H. 1868. Memorandum of two remarkable vertebrae sent by Dr. Oldham from Jubbulpore–Spilsbury's bed. *In*: MURCHISON, C. (ed.) *Palaeontological Memoirs and Notes of the Late Hugh Falconer. Volume I. Fauna Antiqua Sivalensis*. Robert Hardwicke, London, 418–419 (written in 1862 and published posthumously).

HISLOP, S. 1860. On the Tertiary deposits, associated with trap-rock, in the East Indies. *Quarterly Journal of the Geological Society, London*, **16**, 154–166.

HISLOP, S. 1861. Remarks on the geology of Nágpur. *Journal of the Bombay Branch of the Royal Asiatic Society*, **6**, 194–206.

HISLOP, S. 1864. Extracts from letters relating to the further discovery of fossil teeth and bones of reptiles in Central India. *Proceedings of the Geological Society*, **20**, 280–282.

HUENE, F. VON 1929. Los saurisquios y ornitisquios del Cretáceo Argentino. *Anales del Museo de La Plata*, Serie 2, **3**, 1–194.

HUENE, F. VON & MATLEY, C. A. 1933. The Cretaceous Saurischia and Ornithischia of the Central Provinces of India. *Memoirs of the Geological Survey of India: Palaeontologia Indica*, **21**, 1–72.

HUGHES, T. W. H. 1877. The Wardha Valley coal-field. *Memoirs of the Geological Survey of India*, **13**, 1–154.

LYDEKKER, R. 1877. Notices of new and other Vertebrata from Indian Tertiary and Secondary rocks. *Records of the Geological Survey of India*, **10**, 30–43.

LYDEKKER, R. 1879. Indian Pretertiary Vertebrata. 3. Fossil Reptilia and Batrachia. *Memoirs of the Geological Survey of India: Palaeontologia Indica*, Series 4, **1**, 1–35.

LYDEKKER, R. 1888. *Catalogue of Fossil Reptilia and Amphibia in the British Museum (Natural History). Volume 1 (containing Ornithosauria, Crocodilia, Dinosauria, Squamata, Rhynchocephalia, and Proterosauria)*. Trustees of the British Museum (Natural History), London.

LYDEKKER, R. 1890. Note on certain vertebrate remains from the Nagpur district. *Records of the Geological Survey of India*, **23**, 21–24.

MATLEY, C. A. 1918. Note on some dinosaurian remains recently discovered in the Lameta beds at Jubbulpore. *Journal of the Asiatic Society of Bengal, New Series*, **14**, clxxxvi–clxxxvii.

MATLEY, C. A. 1919. On the remains of carnivorous dinosaurs from the Lameta beds at Jubbulpore. *Journal of the Asiatic Society of Bengal, New Series*, **15**, cxcviii–cxcix.

MATLEY, C. A. 1921*a*. On the stratigraphy, fossils and geological relationships of the Lameta Beds of Jubbulpore. *Records of the Geological Survey of India*, **53**, 142–164.

MATLEY, C. A. 1921*b*. The rocks near Lameta Ghat (Jubbulpore district). *Records of the Geological Survey of India*, **53**, 165–169.

MATLEY, C. A. 1924. Note on an armoured dinosaur from the Lameta Beds of Jubbulpore. *Records of the*

Geological Survey of India, **55**, 105–109. [Publication date 1924, issue date 1923.]

MEDLICOTT, H. B. 1860. On the geological structure of the central portion of the Nerbudda District. *Memoirs of the Geological Survey of India*, **2**, 96–278.

MEDLICOTT, H. B. 1872. Note on the Lameta or infra-trappean formation of Central India. *Records of the Geological Survey of India*, **5**, 115–120.

NOVAS, F. E., AGNOLÍN, F. L. & BANDYOPADHYAY, S. 2004. Cretaceous theropods from India: a review of specimens described by Huene and Matley (1933). *Revista del Museo Argentino de Ciencias Naturales, Nuevo Series*, **6**, 67–103.

PRINSEP, J. 1832. Note on the Jabalpúr fossil bones. *Journal of the Asiatic Society of Bengal*, **1**, 456–458.

PRINSEP, J. 1833. Note on the fossil bones discovered near Jabálpur. *Journal of the Asiatic Society of Bengal*, **2**, 583–588. [Includes communication from G. G. Spilsbury.]

SLEEMAN, W. H. 1844. *Rambles and Recollections of an Indian Official. Volume I.* J. Hatchard, London.

SPILSBURY, G. G. 1837. Notice of new sites of fossil deposits in the Nerbudda Valley. *Journal of the Asiatic Society of Bengal*, **6**, 487–489.

SWINTON, W. E. 1947. New discoveries of *Titanosaurus indicus* Lyd. *Annals and Magazine of Natural History*, Series 11, **14**, 112–123.

WALKER, A. D. 1964. Triassic reptiles from the Elgin area: *Ornithosuchus* and the origin of carnosaurs. *Philosophical Transactions of the Royal Society of London, Series B, Biological Sciences*, **248**, 53–134.

WILSON, J. A. & UPCHURCH, P. 2003. A revision of *Titanosaurus* Lydekker (Dinosauria – Sauropoda), the first dinosaur genus with a 'Gondwanan' distribution. *Journal of Systematic Palaeontology*, **1**, 125–160.

Spinosaurs before Stromer: early finds of spinosaurid dinosaurs and their interpretations

ERIC BUFFETAUT

Centre National de la Recherche Scientifique, UMR 8538, Laboratoire de Géologie de l'Ecole Normale Supérieure, 24 rue Lhomond, 75231 Paris Cedex 05, France (e-mail: eric.buffetaut@sfr.fr)

Abstract: When Stromer described *Spinosaurus aegyptiacus* and erected the family Spinosauridae in 1915 he mentioned that teeth from the Cretaceous of the Djoua region of eastern Sahara, considered by Haug as belonging to a fish, probably belonged to *Spinosaurus*. The teeth from Djoua had been collected by the French Foureau–Lamy Mission, which had crossed the Sahara from 1898 to 1900. Earlier finds of spinosaurid specimens include the jaw fragments from the Early Cretaceous of Portugal referred by Sauvage to a new species of *Suchosaurus*, *S. girardi*. The genus *Suchosaurus* had been erected by Owen in 1841, with *S. cultridens* as type species, on the basis of ribbed and compressed teeth from the Wealden of England that he considered as belonging to a crocodilian. The *Suchosaurus* material from Portugal actually belongs to *Baryonyx*, as do most of the teeth from the Wealden of England referred to *Suchosaurus*. The teeth described by Owen had been obtained from a quarry in Tilgate Forest (Sussex) by Mantell, who described and illustrated some of them in several of his publications, notably *Illustrations of the Geology of Sussex* in 1827. Several of these specimens can be identified in the collections of the Natural History Museum, London. Mantell's earliest published illustrations of these teeth are predated by Cuvier's illustration of a tooth from Tilgate Forest sent to him by Mantell, published in 1824. It thus appears that baryonychine teeth were among the first dinosaur remains to be described and illustrated (as crocodilian teeth) at the time of the discovery of *Megalosaurus* and *Iguanodon*, and well before the term 'dinosaur' was coined. It was not until the description of *Baryonyx walkeri* in 1986 that the real affinities of *Suchosaurus* could be elucidated. Because of their peculiar morphology, spinosaurid teeth from various parts of the world were frequently mistaken for those of other reptiles.

Between 1910 and 1914 fieldwork in Egypt under the direction of the Bavarian palaeontologist Ernst Stromer von Reichenbach (1870–1952) resulted in the collection of a considerable number of Mesozoic and Cenozoic vertebrate fossils (see Nothdurft & Smith 2002 for a recent account of Stromer's researches). The results of Stromer's work in Egypt were published by the Bavarian Academy of Sciences in a series of monographs, the first of which appeared in 1914 (see Stromer 1936 for a list). In 1915 Stromer described one of the most remarkable discoveries, an incomplete skeleton of an unusual theropod dinosaur, found by his collector Richard Markgraf in the Cenomanian strata of the Baharija oasis, in the western desert of Egypt. He erected the new taxon *Spinosaurus aegyptiacus* for this specimen, which he placed in a new theropod family, the Spinosauridae (Stromer 1915). Stromer subsequently referred to the Spinosauridae additional theropod material from Baharija, which he called '*Spinosaurus B*' (Stromer 1934), and he discussed *Spinosaurus* again in a general review of the Baharija depression and its fossils (Stromer 1936). Although Stromer's original descriptions were detailed and careful, the real significance of the Spinosauridae as a highly unusual family of theropods was not immediately appreciated, and the destruction of the specimens in a British air raid on Munich in 1944 added to the uncertainty concerning this group of dinosaurs. It was only after the discovery in the Wealden of England of another unusual theropod, described as *Baryonyx walkeri* by Charig & Milner (1986), that a better image of the Spinosauridae began to emerge when it was realized that *Spinosaurus* and *Baryonyx* were closely related dinosaurs (Paul 1988; Buffetaut 1989, 1992), showing a number of unusual specializations, especially in the structure of their jaws and teeth, which to some extent are reminiscent of those of fish-eating crocodilians (Charig & Milner 1997).

In the light of our current knowledge of that group of dinosaurs, re-examination of various fossils reveals that a number of spinosaurid specimens, mostly isolated teeth, had been found and reported, from different localities, before Stromer's original description of *Spinosaurus aegyptiacus*, but had not been interpreted as belonging to dinosaurs, largely because of their fragmentary nature. They are reviewed in the present paper, and their

From: Moody, R. T. J., Buffetaut, E., Naish, D. & Martill, D. M. (eds) *Dinosaurs and Other Extinct Saurians: A Historical Perspective*. Geological Society, London, Special Publications, **343**, 175–188.
DOI: 10.1144/SP343.10 0305-8719/10/$15.00

interpretations are discussed. As will be shown later, it appears that spinosaur remains were among the first dinosaur specimens to be scientifically described and figured, by such eminent palaeontologists as Gideon Mantell, Georges Cuvier and Richard Owen, although their real significance went unrecognized at the time because they were mistaken for crocodilian teeth.

The first *Spinosaurus* teeth from the Sahara: the Foureau-Lamy mission (1898–1900)

In the paper in which he described *Spinosaurus aegyptiacus*, Stromer (1915) mentioned an earlier description of material, probably belonging to a spinosaurid, consisting of two isolated teeth from the eastern part of the Sahara (Fig. 1c). They had been found during the Foureau–Lamy Mission, one of the most remarkable colonial endeavours of late-nineteenth century France (Foureau 1902; Abadie & Abadie 1989; Buffetaut 2005). This expedition, led by an army officer, François Lamy (1858–1900), and a civilian, the explorer Fernand Foureau (1850–1914; Fig. 1a), started from the French colony of Algeria in October 1898 and crossed the Sahara from north to south, to reach Lake Chad in 1900. Its aim was supposed to be peaceful and scientific, but the explorers were accompanied by a large contingent of several hundred colonial troopers led by French officers and non-commissioned officers, equipped with an impressive assortment of weapons, including field guns. One of the undisclosed aims of the mission was to subdue the Tuareg tribes of the southern Sahara, who in 1881 had murdered a group of French soldiers led by Colonel Flatters, and thus to strengthen French rule in that part of Africa. Furthermore, by pushing further south to Lake Chad, the Foureau–Lamy Mission was to establish a continuous territorial link between the French possessions in North Africa and those of the Congo region in Central Africa, thus thwarting

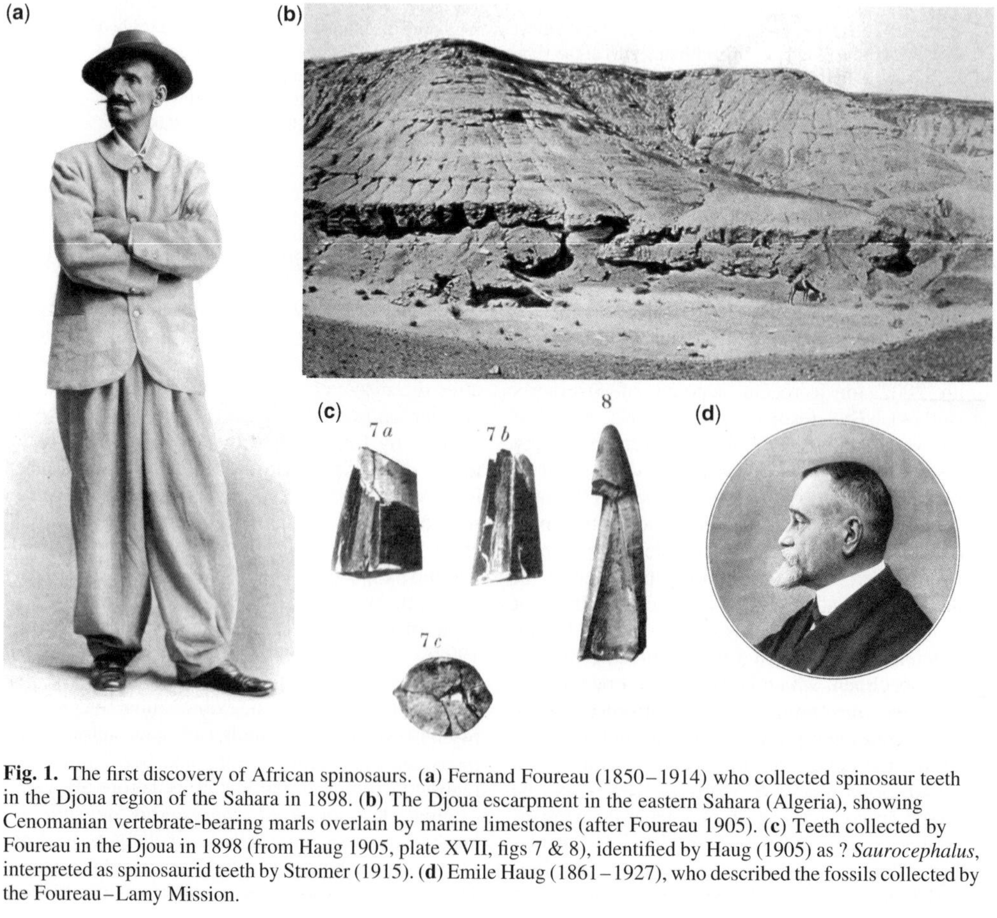

Fig. 1. The first discovery of African spinosaurs. (**a**) Fernand Foureau (1850–1914) who collected spinosaur teeth in the Djoua region of the Sahara in 1898. (**b**) The Djoua escarpment in the eastern Sahara (Algeria), showing Cenomanian vertebrate-bearing marls overlain by marine limestones (after Foureau 1905). (**c**) Teeth collected by Foureau in the Djoua in 1898 (from Haug 1905, plate XVII, figs 7 & 8), identified by Haug (1905) as ? *Saurocephalus*, interpreted as spinosaurid teeth by Stromer (1915). (**d**) Emile Haug (1861–1927), who described the fossils collected by the Foureau–Lamy Mission.

British efforts to link Nigeria with the Anglo-Egyptian Sudan (only a couple of months before the start of the Foureau–Lamy Mission, in September 1898, France and Britain had been on the brink of war following the incident at Fashoda, on the Upper Nile, where Kitchener's Anglo-Egyptian troops had stopped the eastward progression of a French military expedition led by Major Marchand).

After enduring considerable hardships during their crossing of the Sahara and the regions just south of the desert, where the natives, to the astonishment of the French explorers, were not exactly friendly, the Foureau–Lamy Mission finally reached the banks of Lake Chad in January 1900, only to engage in fighting against the troops of the local ruler and slave-holder, Rabah, who eventually was defeated and killed at Kousseri on 22 April 1900, during a battle in the course of which Lamy was fatally wounded. Meanwhile, Fernand Foureau had left the rest of the party and reached the French possessions on the Congo, from which he sailed to France with what was left of the specimens that had been collected by the expedition, reaching Marseilles on 2 September 1900.

These collections formed the basis of a massive two-volume report on the scientific results of the Foureau–Lamy Mission, published in 1905, which included papers, many of them written by Foureau himself, on the geography, meteorology, geology, palaeontology, botany, zoology and ethnography of the regions that had been visited. In the section on geology, Foureau (1905) described the geological succession in the Djoua escarpment of the SE Sahara (now part of Algeria), where he had collected fossils in November 1898. There, Cenomanian marine limestones overlie gypsiferous red clays and sandstones containing vertebrate remains (Fig. 1b). A similar succession is frequently encountered on the outskirts of the Sahara, notably in southern Morocco and western Algeria. The fossils collected by Foureau in the Djoua had originally been entrusted for description to Ernest Munier-Chalmas (1843–1903), but he died before he could complete their study, and they were finally described in the palaeontology section of the report by Emile Haug (1861–1927: Fig. 1c), a geologist and invertebrate palaeontologist who succeeded Munier-Chalmas at the Geology Department of the Sorbonne. On the basis of relatively scanty material, Haug (1905) identified various fish (including a lungfish), chelonians and dinosaurs (on the basis of a single caudal vertebra and large bone fragments). This was the first report of dinosaur bones from the Sahara (Buffetaut 2005). The teeth later interpreted by Stromer (1915) as possibly belonging to *Spinosaurus* were referred by Haug to ? *Saurocephalus*, an ichthyodectid fish. Unfortunately, it has not been possible to re-examine the original specimens. A search for the fossils collected by Foureau in the palaeontology collection of University Paris 6, where they should be kept, yielded only a single fish vertebra, and the present whereabouts of the *Spinosaurus*-like teeth are unknown. Nevertheless, on the basis of the illustrations published by Haug, there is every reason to believe that Stromer was right in supposing that they possibly belonged to *Spinosaurus aegyptiacus*. His assessment was based on their shape and size, although he admitted that the systematic significance of isolated dinosaur teeth should not be overestimated. Comparison of the teeth from the Djoua escarpment with *Spinosaurus* teeth from the Albian of Tunisia and the Cenomanian of Morocco, and with figures of the type specimen of *Spinosaurus aegyptiacus* from the Cenomanian of Egypt, reveals strong similarities in the conical shape of the crown, smooth enamel and presence of well-defined carinae. Foureau's finds from the Djoua can thus be considered as the first discovery of spinosaurid remains in Africa.

Spinosaurus teeth are found in abundance in Albian–Cenomanian red beds in various regions on the outskirts of the Sahara, notably in Tunisia (Bouaziz *et al.* 1988), SW Algeria and southern Morocco (Amiot *et al.* 2004). The specimens from the Djoua escarpment were found in a similar geological setting. The vertebrate-bearing beds of that part of SE Algeria have attracted relatively little attention. Lapparent (1960) noted that the Djoua valley is relatively rich in vertebrate remains, including dinosaurs, but did not record *Spinosaurus* specimens from that area (see below for a possible explanation).

An early spinosaurid find from Portugal: Sauvage, *Suchosaurus* and *Baryonyx*

While Stromer could recognize the spinosaurid affinities of the teeth from the Djoua escarpment on the basis of their resemblance with the type of *Spinosaurus aegyptiacus*, identifying isolated teeth or fragmentary jaw remains of less derived taxa of spinosaurid theropods remained extremely difficult until the discovery and description of the holotype of *Baryonyx walkeri*, from the Wealden of Surrey, in the 1980s and 1990s (Charig & Milner 1986, 1990, 1997). *Baryonyx* teeth differ from those of *Spinosaurus* in several respects, being more compressed labiolingually, with serrated carinae, and a ribbed and wrinkled enamel (Buffetaut 2007). Although they are more reminiscent of 'normal' theropod teeth than *Spinosaurus* teeth in their compression and serrations, the fairly strong ornamentation of their enamel is reminiscent of crocodilian teeth, which, in the nineteenth century, led to systematic misinterpretations, *Baryonyx* teeth being routinely ascribed to crocodiles (see below).

A case in point is that of jaw fragments containing broken teeth from the Early Cretaceous (Barremian) of Boca do Chapim, near Cape Espichel on the Portuguese coast south of Lisbon (Fig. 2). The specimens were collected by the Swiss geologist Paul Choffat (1849–1919; Fig. 2a), who worked for many years in Portugal (Fleury 1920), and studied by the French palaeontologist Henri-Emile Sauvage (1842–1917; Fig. 2b). Sauvage was the leading French expert on Mesozoic fish and reptiles in the late nineteenth century, at a time when most French vertebrate palaeontologists were more interested in fossil mammals (Buffetaut *et al.* 1993). In addition to short preliminary papers (Sauvage 1896, 1898), he published a memoir on the Mesozoic fish and reptiles of Portugal (Sauvage 1897–1898), in which he described the above-mentioned jaw fragments as a new species of the genus *Suchosaurus* Owen, *S. girardi*. Sauvage did not doubt that *Suchosaurus* was a crocodilian, and listed it in the section concerning the family Goniopholididae, but he noted that the position of the genus was uncertain. Although no diagnosis was given for the new species *Suchosaurus girardi*, the jaw fragments were described as indicating a species close to *S. cultridens* from the Wealden of the Isle of Wight (the type specimen of *Suchosaurus cultridens* in fact came from Sussex: see below).

The *Suchosaurus* material from Boca do Chapim (Fig. 2c) was redescribed by Buffetaut (2007) as belonging to *Baryonyx* sp., this being the first mention from Portugal of that taxon, originally described from England and otherwise known from various localities in Spain (see reviews in Ruiz-Omeñaca *et al.* 2005; Buffetaut 2007), and possibly in Niger (*Cristatusaurus* and *Suchomimus* probably being junior synonyms of *Baryonyx*: Milner 2003). Sauvage had been the first to describe *Suchosaurus* – and thus (unwittingly) *Baryonyx* – remains from outside England. The reinterpretation of this Portuguese material prompted a re-examination of the original *Suchosaurus* material from the Wealden of England, the results of which are presented below.

Richard Owen and *Suchosaurus*

Teeth now identifiable as belonging to a *Baryonyx*-like theropod were first given a Linnean name by Richard Owen (1804–1892; Fig. 3a), in Part ii of his *Odontography* (Owen 1840–1845), which was published in 1841 (according to Woodward & Sherborn 1890). There (Owen 1840–1845, p. 287) he used the name *Crocodilus cultridens* for teeth from the Wealden of Tilgate Forest, near Cuckfield (Sussex), that had been provided by Gideon Mantell. *Suchosaurus* was used as a subgenus of *Crocodilus* on p. 290 and in the caption of plate

Fig. 2. *Suchosaurus* from Portugal. (**a**) Paul Choffat (1849–1919), the Swiss geologist who collected Barremian fossil vertebrates at Boca do Chapim. (**b**) Henri-Emile Sauvage (1842–1917), the French palaeontologist who described the fossils from Boca do Chapim in 1897–1898. (**c**) Two jaw fragments containing teeth, described by Sauvage (1897–1898) as *Suchosaurus girardi*, reinterpreted by Buffetaut (2007) as *Baryonyx* sp. (from Sauvage 1897–1898, plate IV, figs 4 and 5).

62A, in which figure 10 shows a tooth from Tilgate Forest (kept in the collection of the Natural History Museum, London, under collective number BMNH 36536; Fig. 3b). Owen mainly compared the teeth of *Crocodilus (Suchosaurus) cultridens* with those of the 'Argenton crocodile', described by Cuvier from beds now known to be Eocene in age in central France. The Argenton specimens are now referred to *Pristichampsus*, a ziphodont eusuchian crocodile (Gervais 1853). Owen (1841, p. 287 in Owen 1840–1845) noted that in *Crocodilus cultridens*, 'the crown of the teeth is thicker than in the Argenton species, and the anterior and posterior edges are unbroken [i.e., not serrated]; a few longitudinal ridges traverse the crown of the tooth in this species, which makes the transition to the ordinary crocodilian teeth'.

In his *Report on British Fossil Reptiles*, in which he erected the 'distinct tribe or sub-order' Dinosauria, Owen (1842) discussed *Suchosaurus* at greater length, again as a sub-genus of *Crocodilus*. He again drew attention to similarities with the 'Argenton crocodile', but also mentioned resemblance with 'the teeth of the Megalosaur'. Comparing *Suchosaurus* teeth with that of the gavial, he noted a basic difference that can, indeed, be used to distinguish spinosaur teeth from those of most crocodilians (Owen 1842, p. 68): 'The crown is laterally compressed, subincurved, with two opposite trenchant edges, one forming the concave, the other the convex outline of the tooth. In the Gavial, the direction of the flattening of the crown and the situation of the trenchant edges are the reverse, the compression being from before backwards, and the edges being lateral'. Owen noted that the teeth in question had been referred by Meyer (1832, p. 115) to the genus *Teleosaurus* (on the basis of figures published by Cuvier 1824 and Mantell 1827 – see below), but commented that 'no portions of the skeleton of a Teleosaur have hitherto been found in the Wealden' (Owen 1842, p. 68).

In his *Report* Owen also suggested that large biconcave vertebrae with a compressed, wedge-shaped, body – collected by Mantell from Wealden strata – very probably belonged to *Suchosaurus*, but no special reason was given for associating the vertebrae with the teeth. In later discussions of *Suchosaurus* (Owen 1878, 1884*a*, *b*) he, again, mentioned these vertebrae, and provided illustrations of two specimens. Lydekker (1888) considered that the vertebra figured by Owen (1878), BMNH 2138, in fact belonged to an iguanodontid, while another vertebra (BMNH 2123), originally figured by Mantell (1827, plate IX, fig. 11) and discussed by Owen (1842), could be referred to *Hylaeosaurus*. However that may be, in view of the lack of similarity with the opisthocoelous dorsal centra of spinosaurids, it is unlikely that the above-mentioned vertebrae belong to the same taxon as the *Suchosaurus* teeth.

Owen (1878) discussed *Suchosaurus* again in a paper on Wealden and Purbeck crocodilians, in which he reproduced the engraving of the tooth from Tilgate Forest, together with the above-mentioned vertebra. Although he still tentatively associated the vertebrae with the teeth, he admitted that 'hitherto these teeth have not been found so associated with any part of the skeleton of the same species as to yield unequivocally further characters of the present extinct Crocodilian' (Owen 1878, p. 14). His description of *Suchosaurus* teeth differed little from that published in 1842. However, he noted that *Suchosaurus cultridens* 'indicates a nearer affinity or transition to the Dinosaurian order than does any of the mesozoic *Crocodilia*, known by their cranial as well as by their dental, vertebral, and dermal characters' (Owen 1878, p. 14).

In his *History of British Fossil Reptiles*, a massive review comprising two volumes of text and two volumes of plates that largely consists of reprints of his earlier publications, Owen (1884*a*, pp. 433–435) reproduced his 1878 description almost *verbatim*, but deleted the final sentence about the 'nearer affinity or transition to the Dinosaurian order'. The illustration he provided (Owen 1884*b*, plate 5) differs from that published in 1878 in that it concentrates on specimens referred to *Suchosaurus* (instead of including *Goniopholis* material). In addition to the already illustrated large amphicoelous centrum, it also shows a smaller dorsal vertebra with a partly preserved neural arch. The tooth crown from Tilgate Forest is figured again in side and back views, together with similar views of a *Megalosaurus* tooth crown, presumably for comparison (Fig. 3c). Whether Owen intended to emphasize the similarities or the differences between *Suchosaurus* and *Megalosaurus* teeth is uncertain. The caption of the plate indicates *Suchosaurus laevidens*, instead of *cultridens*, for the tooth crown. This is probably a *lapsus calami*, as Owen did not mention this specific name elsewhere. Lydekker (1888) and Woodward & Sherborn (1890) considered *Suchosaurus laevidens* as a junior synonym of *S. cultridens*.

Despite his remarks about possible affinities with the Dinosauria, Owen consistently placed *Suchosaurus* among the crocodilians in his various publications on this taxon. This interpretation was generally followed by subsequent authors who mentioned this enigmatic form. One of the first to do so was Pictet (1853), who placed *Suchosaurus* (misspelled as *Succhosaurus*) among his 'crocodiliens douteux' ('doubtful crocodilians') and reproduced Owen's illustration of the tooth from Tilgate

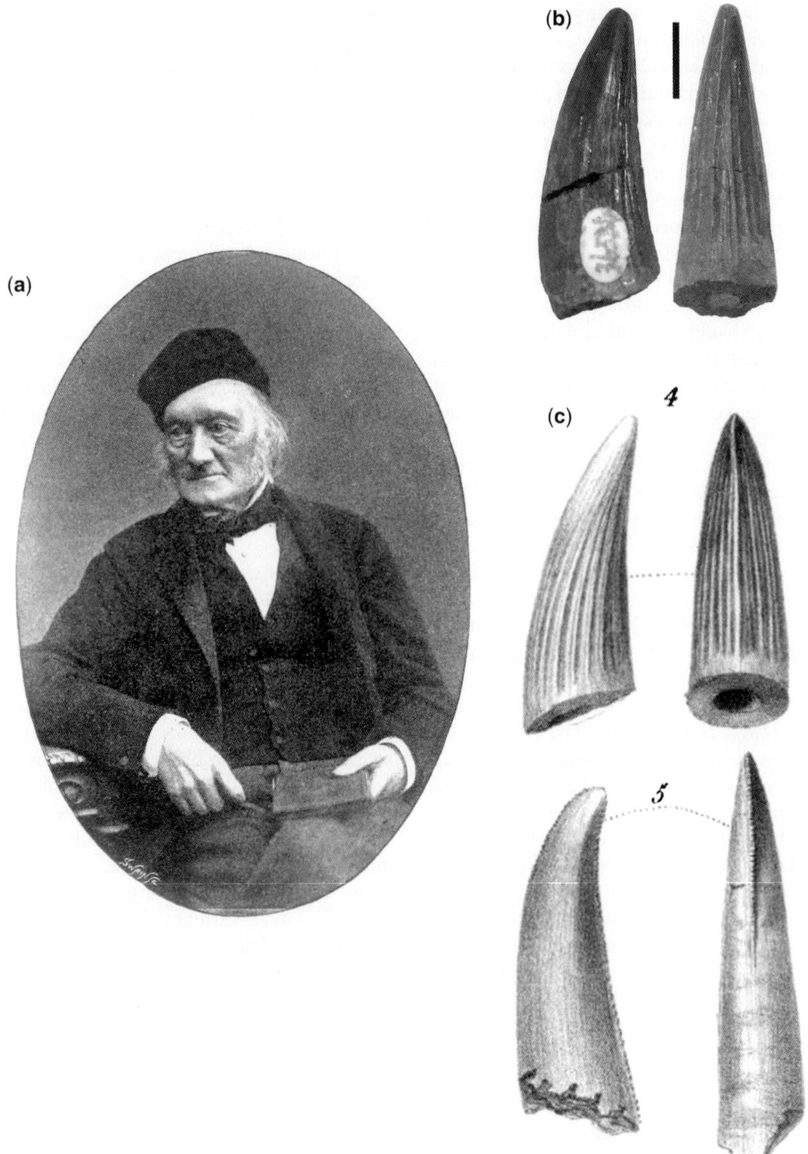

Fig. 3. Richard Owen and *Suchosaurus cultridens* from the Wealden of England. (**a**) Richard Owen (1804–1892), who erected the taxon *Suchosaurus cultridens* in 1841. (**b**) The type of *Suchosaurus cultridens*, under collective number BMNH 36536 (Natural History Museum, London), in lingual (?) and posterior views (scale bar, 10 mm). (**c**) The same tooth (above, 4) figured by Owen (1884*b*, plate 5), with a *Megalosaurus* tooth (below, 5) for comparison. This engraving of the type of *Suchosaurus cultridens* appeared in Owen's publications of 1840–1845, 1878 and 1884*b*.

Forest. Laurillard (1867) placed *Suchosaurus* among the crocodilians from the Secondary formations, with vertebrae with weakly concave or sometimes even flat articular faces. He rightly noted that Mantell had referred teeth from the Wealden to a kind of gavial but wrongly considered him as the author of the name *Crocodilus cultridens*. Owen was correctly identified as the author of the generic name *Suchosaurus*. The description of the teeth followed Owen. Dollo (1883) considered *Suchosaurus* as a crocodilian and noted in what respects it differed from *Goniopholis* and

Bernissartia, but did not elaborate on its systematic position. Woodward (1885) placed *Suchosaurus* among the 'Goniopholidae' and commented that it was very imperfectly known. Following Owen, he emphasized the peculiar position of the carinae on the tooth crown. In a general review of the history of fossil crocodiles, Woodward (1887) discussed *Suchosaurus* again, providing an illustration (fig. 15) of a tooth which is clearly that figured by Owen but differs from Owen's figures in several details and was probably redrawn from the original. He remarked (Woodward 1887, p. 325) that 'at present it is too imperfectly understood to be relegated to any definite family position'. Similarly, Lydekker (1888) considered *Suchosaurus* as a crocodilian of the 'amphicoelian series' of uncertain position at the family level. Nicholson & Lydekker (1889) considered that it 'not improbably' belonged to the Goniopholididae, although its precise affinities were not yet determined. Zittel (1887–1890) listed it as a genus *incertae sedis* among the Macrorhynchidae [= Pholidosauridae]. Van den Broeck (1900) also considered *Suchosaurus* as a longirostrine form belonging to the Macrorhynchidae. Probably following Zittel's opinion, Romer (1956) placed it among the Pholidosauridae, as did Konzhukova (1964), Kuhn (1968) and Steel (1973).

One of the few authors who did not consider *Suchosaurus* as a crocodilian was Plieninger, who in 1846 placed it (misspelled as '*Succhosaurus*') in a group he called the 'Akidodonten', characterized by laterally compressed teeth with cutting edges (Plieninger 1846*a*). *Suchosaurus* was included in the akidodonts with teeth inserted in sockets (which distinguished them from akidodonts with ankylosed teeth), together with various other forms now considered as phytosaurs, rauisuchians or dinosaurs, including *Thecodontosaurus* and *Megalosaurus*. In a complement to his earlier paper, Plieninger (1846*b*) discussed his Akidodonten in more detail and placed '*Succhosaurus*' among the 'Thecodonten', themselves a subdivision of the Dactylopoden, one of the two main subgroups of the Akidodonten, the other subgroup being the Pachypoden (a taxon originally erected by Hermann von Meyer (1845) for various taxa now placed among the Dinosauria and including, according to Plieninger, *Megalosaurus* and *Hylaeosaurus*). The concept of akidodonts never gained widespread acceptance, and Plieninger's interpretation of *Suchosaurus* as something other than a crocodile was soon forgotten. One of the few authors to have partly followed Plieninger, albeit only temporarily, was Bronn, who, in his *Index Palaeontologicus* (1849, p. 693) placed *Suchosaurus* among the 'Saurii incertae sedis' and the '? Dactylopodes', together with various other taxa Plieninger had referred to the Akidodonten. However, soon thereafter Bronn (1851–1852) returned to Owen's original interpretation and classified *Suchosaurus* among the amphicoelous crocodiles.

Another researcher who doubted the crocodilian nature of *Suchosaurus* was Hulke, who in 1879 briefly mentioned it in a paper on the ornithopod *Vectisaurus*. In it he compared the vertebrae of *Vectisaurus* with those referred by Owen to *Suchosaurus*. In a footnote (Hulke 1879, p. 423), he noted 'From evidence in my possession I rather incline to regard *Suchosaurus* as not improbably a Dinosaur'. He did not mention what this evidence was nor whether it was based on the teeth or on the vertebrae at that time referred to *Suchosaurus*.

Although an inspection of the Natural History Museum collection in London shows that isolated teeth collected from the Wealden of Sussex and the Isle of Wight were routinely labelled as *Suchosaurus*, that taxon was seldom mentioned in print after the end of the nineteenth century, presumably because it was based on insufficient material and therefore rather enigmatic (for an exception see Allen (1949), who listed *Suchosaurus* among vertebrates found in Wealden bone beds). Interestingly, one of the few reports of *Suchosaurus* finds in the twentieth century is from Spain, where Royo y Gómez (1927) mentioned the presence of that genus in the Wealden of Morella, in Castellón Province. No description of this material seems to have been published, although Bataller (1960) mentioned it again, noting that *Suchosaurus* was a longirostrine crocodilian. Baryonychine teeth from the Aptian of that area were reported by Canudo *et al.* (2004), and it thus seems likely that the *Suchosaurus* material mentioned by Royo y Gómez did belong to spinosaurids. It will be difficult to confirm this, however, as most of the fossil material mentioned by Royo y Gómez appears to have been lost during the Spanish Civil War (Sanz *et al.* 1982).

After the description of *Baryonyx walkeri* by Charig & Milner (1986, 1990) had revealed the peculiar characters of its teeth, isolated teeth from the Wealden of England showing these characters were identified as *Baryonyx* (Martill & Hutt 1996) rather than as *Suchosaurus*. Milner (2003) was the first to note that teeth in the Natural History Museum collections previously identified as *Suchosaurus* in fact belong to *Baryonyx* (see also Buffetaut 2007; Fowler 2007). The similarities between *Suchosaurus cultridens* teeth (including the type specimen, under collective number BMNH 36536; Fig. 3b) and *Baryonyx* teeth have been discussed by Buffetaut (2007). They include a similar labiolingual compression, carinae in the same position, more or less extensive ribbing of the crown and a fine wrinkling of the enamel. The fine serrations on the carinae that are visible on the teeth of the holotype of *Baryonyx walkeri* are not always clearly visible on *Suchosaurus* teeth (this lack of serrations was noted by Owen, see earlier), but this seems to be the result of wear. There seems to be no doubt that the teeth referred by Owen to *Suchosaurus cultridens* belong to a spinosaurid theropod, very probably *Baryonyx*, not to a crocodilian. However, as noted by Buffetaut (2007), it does not seem advisable to use the taxon name *Suchosaurus cultridens* instead of *Baryonyx walkeri* because it cannot really be demonstrated that the isolated tooth described and illustrated by Owen and the partial skeleton on the basis of which *Baryonyx walkeri* was erected by Charig & Milner (1986) belong to the same species. There is a fairly large amount of variation, notably in enamel ornamentation, among the 'baryonychine' teeth from the Wealden of England, and it cannot be excluded that more than one species is present (Buffetaut 2007; Naish & Martill 2007).

The original discoverer: Gideon Mantell and the gavial from Tilgate Forest

As noted above, Owen's *Suchosaurus cultridens* was based on teeth found by Gideon Mantell (1790–1852; Fig. 4a) at the famous quarry in Tilgate Forest (Fig. 4b), near Cuckfield, Sussex, that also yielded the original material of *Iguanodon*. Mantell first described teeth from Tilgate Forest referable to crocodilians in his *Fossils of the South Downs* (1822). He distinguished three distinct types on the basis of crown morphology. Attribution to crocodiles or monitors was suggested by William Clift, the curator of the Hunterian Museum of the Royal College of Surgeons, who at that time was Mantell's mentor in comparative anatomy. Mantell's variety b corresponded to 'a slender, delicate tooth, rather compressed, curvature gradual, apex slightly acuminated' (Mantell 1822, p. 50). Compression of the crown suggests that this may have been a *Baryonyx* tooth, but in the absence of an illustration no firm conclusion can be drawn.

Mantell described the fossils from Tilgate Forest in much greater detail, and figured many of them for the first time in his *Illustrations of the Geology of Sussex* (1827). Having by then become familiar with the work of Cuvier (see below), he distinguished two main types of crocodile teeth (Mantell 1827, p. 65). One consisted of teeth with an obtuse crown (they are now referred to *Goniopholis*). The others were more slender and curved, resembling the crocodile from Caen described by Cuvier (now called *Teleosaurus*) or the 'crocodile of the Ganges' or gavial. The teeth later described by Owen as *Suchosaurus cultridens* were part of that second group. Owen (1842) indicated that the

Fig. 4. Gideon Mantell and the original discovery of *Suchosaurus*/*Baryonyx* at Tilgate Forest. (**a**) Gideon Mantell (1790–1852), who collected spinosaurid teeth from quarries in Tilgate Forest, near Cuckfield, Sussex, around 1820. (**b**) Tilgate Forest quarry, as illustrated by Mantell (1833). (**c**) A *Baryonyx* tooth from Tilgate Forest (scale bar, 10 mm), Natural History Museum, London, collective number BMNH 36536, illustrated (**d**) as plate V, figure 6 of Mantell's *Illustrations of the Geology of Sussex* (1827).

teeth figured by Mantell (1827) on his plate V under numbers 5, 6 and 8 belonged to *Suchosaurus cultridens*. Although Mantell's figures are not of the highest quality, it has proved possible to locate at least some of these teeth in the collections of the Natural History Museum. In particular, one of the teeth (Fig. 4c) under collective number 36536 is certainly the specimen figured by Mantell (1827) on plate V, figure 6 (Fig. 4d). Not only are the shape and dimensions the same, but the specimen shows a break at the level of the upper third of the crown that is clearly shown on Mantell's figure. The 30 mm-long tooth is compressed labiolingually, bears an anterior convex carina and a posterior concave carina, and both the labial and lingual faces show ridges (seven on both sides). The enamel is covered with a fine wrinkling of the type seen in *Baryonyx* and '*Suchosaurus*' teeth (Charig & Milner 1997; Buffetaut 2007). Although the carinae are fairly worn, faint serrations can be seen at the base of the posterior carina. There is no doubt that this tooth (as well as several others in the Mantell collection at the Natural History Museum) belongs to a *Baryonyx*-like spinosaurid theropod. This also applies, as mentioned earlier, to the tooth figured by Owen (1841 (of 1841–1845), 1878 and 1884*b*) as *Suchosaurus cultridens*, which can be considered as the type of that species, and is also part of the Mantell collection at the Natural History Museum under collective number 36536 (Fig. 3b, c).

In his 'Tabular arrangement of the organic remains of the county of Sussex' (1829a – also published separately as *A Scientific Catalogue of the Organic Remains of Sussex*, Mantell 1829*b*) and reprinted as an appendix to *The Geology of the South–East of England* (Mantell 1833), Mantell listed crocodilians among the fossil vertebrates from the 'Tilgate Beds', with reference to the illustrations of his 1827 book. Together with various other crocodilian remains (mainly teeth), figures 5, 6 and 8 of 'plate 7' (by which Mantell certainly meant his plate V, since plate VII shows only turtle remains) are listed as belonging to *Leptorhynchus*, with a footnote indicating that this is 'the fossil species of Caen' (Mantell 1829*a*, *b*, p. 214, 1833, p. 394). The name *Leptorhynchus* had, in fact, first been used by Clift (1829) for portions of elongate crocodilian lower jaws collected on the banks of the Irrawaddy, in Burma, by John Crawfurd's embassy to the Burmese court in Ava in 1826–1827 (for more details on Crawfurd's collecting activity see Buffetaut 1987). Clift (1829, p. 375) had rightly concluded that this crocodile, now known to be from Pleistocene deposits, was 'allied to, if not identical with, the great gavial'. Why Mantell chose to use this name for the 'species of Caen' is unclear, but the teleosaurids from the Bathonian of Caen were at that time commonly referred to as 'gavials', including by such leading authorities as Cuvier and Geoffroy Saint-Hilaire (Buffetaut 2008). Moreover, as mentioned above, Clift had helped Mantell with the identification of several of his vertebrate fossils, including *Iguanodon* remains (Buffetaut 1999), and the use of a name he had coined may reflect his influence. Be that as it may, that designation confirms that Mantell considered the teeth later described as *Suchosaurus* as belonging to a long-snouted, gavial-like crocodilian. Interestingly, even after these teeth had been redescribed and named by Owen, some authors still depicted *Suchosaurus* as a long-snouted, gavial-like crocodilian. Ansted (1844, pp. 437–438) thus noted that 'judging from the structure of the teeth (which somewhat resemble those of the Megalosaurus), the *Suchosaurus* was probably a long-snouted crocodile, not unlike the Gavial or piscivorous crocodile of the Ganges'. Similarly, Gray & Adams (1863, p. 225) mentioned that 'the *Suchosaurus* was a long-snouted crocodile resembling the gavial of the Ganges. The crowns of its teeth were slender, compressed, and acute'.

In later works, Mantell (1833, 1839) added little on the crocodile remains from Tilgate Forest, and they were less fully illustrated than in his 1827 book. His main interests now were *Iguanodon* and other giant 'saurians', and the crocodiles took second place. In his *Wonders of Geology* (1839, p. 386), he apparently got confused about the identification of the teeth from Tilgate Forest, remarking that 'they appear to referable to two kinds – the one belonging to that division of crocodiles, with a long slender muzzle, named *gavial*; the other to a species of crocodile, properly so-called, and resembling a fossil species found at Caen'. After he sold his fossil collection to the British Museum and it was transferred there in 1838, access to the crocodile teeth he had collected became much more difficult, as he noted with some bitterness in *Petrifactions and their Teachings* (Mantell 1851, p. 172): 'There were a considerable number of teeth of crocodilian reptiles from the Wealden in my collection, but I do not know in what part of the Museum they are placed'. After Owen erected the taxon *Suchosaurus* in 1841, Mantell used that name in some of his books. In *The Medals of Creation* (Mantell 1844, pp. 720–721), in particular, he noted that:

> In the strata of Tilgate Forest, associated with innumerable remains of reptiles of various kinds, teeth of the Crocodilian type, belonging to two genera, are not uncommon. The first kind (*Suchosaurus cultridens* of Prof. Owen) is a tooth about an inch in length, of a slender acuminated form, compressed laterally, and gently recurved, with a sharp edge in front and behind; resembling, in its general figure, the tooth of

a Megalosaurus, with the serrations on the edges worn off (Pl.VI, fig. 7). The sides of the crown are marked with a few longitudinal grooves. Some biconcave vertebrae found in the same quarries, and characterised by the compressed wedge-shaped form of the centre (*Foss.Til.For.* pl. ix, fig. 11), are supposed by Professor Owen to belong to the same reptile as the teeth above described; but it is hazardous to pronounce on the identity of these detached teeth and bones, without more corroborative proof than has hitherto been obtained.

Mantell's caution concerning Owen's attribution of the biconcave vertebrae to *Suchosaurus* was clearly justified. His remark about the serrations on the edges of the teeth being worn off is worth noting, too, as wear very probably explains the more or less complete lack of serrations on many *Suchosaurus*/*Baryonyx* teeth from the Wealden.

In retrospect, Gideon Mantell should thus be considered as the first palaeontologist to have (unwittingly) discovered spinosaurid teeth – in the Wealden of Tilgate Forest, probably around 1820. In the entry in his journal for 26 September 1820, for instance (Curwen 1940), Mantell noted that he had obtained a crocodile tooth from a quarry at Cuckfield (see Dean 1999 for further details about Mantell's researches at Tilgate Forest). However, he was not the first to figure such fossils.

Georges Cuvier: the first illustration of a spinosaur tooth

The story of how Georges Cuvier (1769–1832; Fig. 5a) contributed to Mantell's work on the *Iguanodon* remains from Sussex has often been told (Buffetaut 1999; Dean 1999). What has often been overlooked is that among the fossils brought to Paris by Charles Lyell in June 1823, to be examined by Cuvier, were not only *Iguanodon* specimens, but also remains of other vertebrates collected by Mantell in the Wealden of Tilgate Forest, including crocodile and turtle material. In the second edition of his *Recherches sur les ossemens fossiles* (Cuvier 1824, pp. 161–163), Cuvier included a whole section entitled 'Des os de crocodiles des sables ferrugineux du dessous de la craie, trouvés dans le Comté de Sussex, par M. Mantell' ['On the crocodile bones from the iron-sand below the Chalk, found in the county of Sussex, by Mr Mantell']. In it he referred to Mantell's mention of the Tilgate Forest fossils, including crocodiles, in his *Fossils of the South Downs* (Mantell 1822), and added that Mantell had sent him some teeth and vertebrae that he had identified as, indeed, belonging to crocodiles. Mantell's identification was thus confirmed by the leading authority of the time on fossil vertebrates. Cuvier noted that the biconcave vertebrae (probably from goniopholidids) resembled those of the crocodiles from Caen & Honfleur (now referred to thalattosuchians: Buffetaut 2008). Concerning the teeth, he simply noted that most of them were more obtuse than in the common crocodiles, and thus resembled some large, obtuse teeth from the Swiss Jura that had been sent to him by Mr Hugi from Solothurn (retrospectively, it appears that the teeth from the

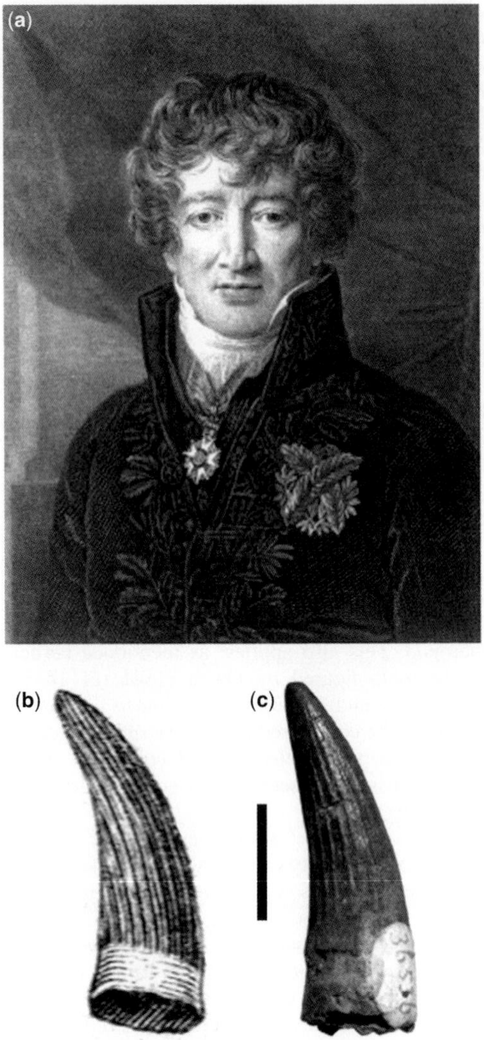

Fig. 5. Georges Cuvier and the first illustration of a spinosaurid tooth. (**a**) Georges Cuvier (1769–1832), who figured a spinosaurid tooth sent to him by Mantell in the second edition of his *Recherches sur les ossemens fossiles* (1824). (**b**) Spinosaurid tooth from Tilgate Forest figured by Cuvier (1824, plate X, fig. 30). (**c**) The original specimen (scale bar, 10 mm), Natural History Museum, London, collective number BMNH 36536 – also illustrated by Mantell (1827), see Figure 4.

Jura belonged to the teleosaurid *Machimosaurus* (see Krebs 1967), whereas the obtuse teeth from Tilgate Forest belonged to goniopholidids). Cuvier did not comment on the other, slender teeth sent to him by Mantell. However, he illustrated four of the teeth from Tilgate Forest on his plate X, as figures 25, 26, 27 and 30. Figures 25, 26 and 27 show teeth with a blunt apex that in all likelihood belong to goniopholidids. The 30 mm-long tooth shown in figure 30, however, is more slender, more recurved, with a pointed apex (Fig. 5b). Although the drawing lacks details, except for the ribbing of the enamel and the boundary between the crown and root, because of remarkable correspondence in size and shape there is every reason to believe that it depicts the tooth figured by Mantell (1827) on plate V, figure 6 (Fig. 4d). This tooth, as mentioned above, is kept in the collection of the Natural History Museum under collective number 36536, and belongs to a *Baryonyx*-like spinosaurid theropod (Fig. 5c). The first illustration of a spinosaurid fossil was thus published in 1824 by Cuvier, who, as was his wont, had no qualms about publishing or illustrating the discoveries of his correspondents before they had done so themselves (see Buffetaut 2000 about Cuvier's publication of *Iguanodon* teeth). Mantell obviously had no ill feelings about that and was proud to note in his *Illustrations of the Geology of Sussex* (1827, p. 64) that 'M. Cuvier, in his immortal work, confirms our conjectures'. The last, posthumous, edition of Cuvier's *Recherches sur les ossemens fossiles* (Cuvier 1836) simply reproduces the second edition and does not mention Mantell's intervening publications.

Other misinterpretations of spinosaurid teeth

Because of their morphological convergence with those of crocodilians and other fish-eating reptiles, isolated spinosaurid teeth have frequently been misinterpreted. The longest-lasting case is that of the '*Suchosaurus*' teeth from the Wealden of England, which were mistaken for crocodile teeth for nearly two centuries, as discussed earlier. In Africa, it seems that in many cases spinosaurid teeth were misidentified as those of non-dinosaurian reptiles by various collectors. For instance, in his review of the dinosaurs of the Sahara, Lapparent (1960, p. 49) noted that *Spinosaurus aegyptiacus* was lacking from the central Sahara. However, spinosaurid teeth are abundant at several of the sites he explored, notably in the Albian of Tunisia (Bouaziz *et al.* 1988; Buffetaut & Ouaja 2002) and it seems very unlikely that he did not find any; the most likely explanation is that he mistook them for crocodilian teeth (which are mentioned in his lists of fossils). Similarly, Lavocat (1954) did not mention *Spinosaurus* among the vertebrates he collected from the Cenomanian Kem Kem beds of southern Morocco, although spinosaurid teeth are very abundant there (Amiot *et al.* 2004). A clear example of misidentification of spinosaurid material from North Africa is provided by the paper by Schlüter & Schwarzhans (1978) on an Early Cretaceous bone bed in southern Tunisia, in which teeth that clearly belong to *Spinosaurus* were referred to *Plesiosaurus* sp. Similar misidentifications also occurred in Asia. Kobayashi *et al.* (1964) identified as ichthyosaurian a tooth from the Early Cretaceous of Thailand that apparently belongs to the spinosaurid *Siamosaurus suteethorni* (Buffetaut *et al.* 2008). It has recently been shown (Buffetaut *et al.* 2008) that teeth from the Early Cretaceous of Guangxi, South China, referred by Hou *et al.* (1975) to a pliosaur (*Sinopliosaurus fusuiensis*), in fact belong to a *Siamosaurus*-like spinosaurid.

Conclusions

Although Stromer's original description of *Spinosaurus aegyptiacus* was published in 1915, it is only since the 1980s that a more complete and detailed picture of spinosaurid anatomy, evolution and biogeography has begun to emerge. It is all the more unexpected to realize that spinosaurid teeth were, in fact, among the first dinosaur fossils to be found, described and illustrated, albeit unwittingly, more or less at the same time as *Megalosaurus* and *Iguanodon*, in the first decades of the nineteenth century. It appears that *Baryonyx*-like teeth were collected by Gideon Mantell in Sussex around 1820. Georges Cuvier was the first to publish an illustration of such a tooth in 1824, followed by Mantell in 1827. These teeth, however, were generally considered as belonging to crocodilians, and when Richard Owen erected the taxon *Suchosaurus cultridens* to designate them he placed it among the crocodiles. Although Owen realized that they were peculiar in many respects and hinted at possible affinities with dinosaurs, he persistently classified *Suchosaurus* as a crocodilian, an interpretation that was accepted by most subsequent authors, including Henri-Emile Sauvage when he described material from Portugal that closely resembled the specimens from the English Wealden.

When Stromer described *Spinosaurus aegyptiacus* in 1915 he emphasized the peculiar character of the teeth of this unusual theropod, and this led him to regard the teeth from the Djoua, collected by Foureau and described by Haug, as belonging to *Spinosaurus*. However, the smooth, almost uncompressed, teeth of *Spinosaurus aegyptiacus* were sufficiently different from the ribbed, labiolingually compressed teeth of *Suchosaurus cultridens* to prevent recognition of the fairly close relationships between these two forms. It was not until Charig & Milner (1986, 1990, 1997) described *Baryonyx walkeri* on the basis of a partial skeleton that its close affinities with *Spinosaurus* were recognized (Paul 1988; Buffetaut 1989, 1992). Only then did the morphological diversity of spinosaurid teeth become apparent. This in turn led to a reappraisal of *Suchosaurus* teeth as those of a *Baryonyx*-like spinosaurid (Milner 2003; Buffetaut 2007; Fowler 2007).

Besides its historical interest, the story of the various spinosaurid elements that have been misinterpreted as belonging to other groups of reptiles (or fish) since the days of Mantell, Cuvier and Owen is also an incitement to look for such fossils in old collections. Spinosaurid teeth misidentified as those of crocodiles or other reptiles may await rediscovery in unexpected places.

Dr I. Rouget helped me in my (unfortunately unsuccessful) search for Foureau's material from the Djoua in the palaeontological collection of University Paris 6. Professor M. Ramalho kindly made the *Suchosaurus* material from Portugal at my disposal at the Museu Geológico in Lisbon. Special thanks to Dr A. Milner for her constant support of my research on spinosaurid material in the collections of the Natural History Museum (London) and for her review of this paper. Dr J. I. Ruiz-Omeñaca is thanked for his useful comments. Dr A.-M. Lezine (CNRS) kindly scanned the photograph of Fernand Foureau for me.

References

ABADIE, J. C. & ABADIE, F. 1989. *Sahara-Tchad (1898–1900). Carnets de route de Prosper Haller, médecin de la Mission Foureau-Lamy*. L'Harmattan, Paris.

ALLEN, P. 1949. Notes on Wealden bone-beds. *Proceedings of the Geologists' Association*, **60**, 275–283.

AMIOT, R., BUFFETAUT, E., TONG, H., BOUDAD, L. & KABIRI, L. 2004. Isolated theropod teeth from the Cenomanian of Morocco and their palaeobiogeographical significance. *Revue de Paléobiologie*, Volume Spécial, **9**, 143–149.

ANSTED, D. T. 1844. *Geology, Introductory, Descriptive and Practical*. John Van Voorst, London.

BATALLER, J. R. 1960. Los vertebrados del Crétácico español. *Notas y Comunicaciones del Instituto Geologico y Minero de España*, **60**, 141–164.

BOUAZIZ, S., BUFFETAUT, E., GHANMI, M., JAEGER, J. J., MARTIN, M., MAZIN, J. M. & TONG, H. 1988. Nouvelles découvertes de vertébrés fossiles dans l'Albien du Sud tunisien. *Bulletin de la Société géologique de France*, **4**, 335–339.

BRONN, H. G. 1849. *Index Palaeontologicus, 2. Abtheilung*. Schweizerbart, Stuttgart.

BRONN, H. G. 1851–1852. *Lethaea Geognostica. 3. Auflage*, Volume 2. Schweizerbart, Stuttgart.

BUFFETAUT, E. 1987. *A Short History of Vertebrate Palaeontology*. Croom Helm, London.

BUFFETAUT, E. 1989. New remains of the enigmatic dinosaur *Spinosaurus* from the Cretaceous of Morocco and the affinities between *Spinosaurus* and *Baryonyx*. *Neues Jahrbuch für Geologie und Paläontologie, Monatshefte*, **1989**, 79–87.

BUFFETAUT, E. 1992. Remarks on the Cretaceous theropod dinosaurs *Spinosaurus* and *Baryonyx*. *Neues Jahrbuch für Geologie und Paläontologie, Monatshefte*, **1992**, 88–96.

BUFFETAUT, E. 1999. Mantell, Cuvier, Buckland and the identification of *Iguanodon*: a contribution based on unpublished annotations by Mantell. *Oryctos*, **2**, 101–109.

BUFFETAUT, E. 2000. Mantell, Cuvier, Buckland and the identification of *Iguanodon*: a correction. *Oryctos*, **3**, 95–97.

BUFFETAUT, E. 2005. Les premiers dinosaures sahariens. *Pour la Science*, **331**, 8–11.

BUFFETAUT, E. 2007. The spinosaurid dinosaur *Baryonyx* (Saurischia, Theropoda) in the Early Cretaceous of Portugal. *Geological Magazine*, **144**, 1021–1025.

BUFFETAUT, E. 2008. A l'aube de la paléontologie des vertébrés: Cuvier, Geoffroy Saint-Hilaire et les «gavials» de Honfleur, du Havre et de Caen. *Bulletin de la Société géologique de Normandie*, **95**, 153–162.

BUFFETAUT, E. & OUAJA, M. 2002. A new specimen of *Spinosaurus* (Dinosauria, Theropoda) from the Lower Cretaceous of Tunisia, with remarks on the evolutionary history of the Spinosauridae. *Bulletin de la Société géologique de France*, **173**, 415–421.

BUFFETAUT, E., CUNY, G. & LE LOEUFF, J. 1993. The discovery of French dinosaurs. *Modern Geology*, **18**, 161–182.

BUFFETAUT, E., SUTEETHORN, V., TONG, H. & AMIOT, R. 2008. An Early Cretaceous spinosaurid theropod from southern China. *Geological Magazine*, **145**, 745–748.

CANUDO, J. I., GASULLA, J. M., ORTEGA, F. & RUIZ-OMEÑACA, J. I. 2004. Presencia de Baryonychinae (Theropoda) en el Aptiense inferior (Cretácico Inferior) de Laurasia: Cantera Mas de la Parreta, Formacion Arcillas de Morella (Morella, Castellón). *III Jornadas Internacionales sobre Paleontología de Dinosaurios y su Entorno*, abstract. Colectivo Arqueologico–Paleontologico, *Salas de Los Infantes* (Abstract).

CHARIG, A. J. & MILNER, A. C. 1986. *Baryonyx*, a remarkable new theropod dinosaur. *Nature*, **324**, 359–361.

CHARIG, A. J. & MILNER, A. C. 1990. The systematic position of *Baryonyx walkeri*, in the light of Gauthier's reclassification of the Theropoda. *In*: CARPENTER, K. & CURRIE, P. J. (eds) *Dinosaur Systematics: Approaches and Perspectives*. Cambridge University Press, Cambridge, 127–140.

CHARIG, A. J. & MILNER, A. C. 1997. *Baryonyx walkeri*, a fish eating dinosaur from the Wealden of Surrey. *Bulletin of the Natural History Museum, Geology Series*, **53**, 11–70.

CLIFT, W. 1829. On the fossil remains of two new species of *Mastodon*, of other vertebrate animals found on the left bank of the Irawadi. *Transactions of the Geological Society, London*, **2**, 369–375.

CURWEN, E. C. 1940. *The Journal of Gideon Mantell*. Oxford University Press, Oxford.

CUVIER, G. 1824. *Recherches sur les ossemens fossiles, deuxième édition*, Volume 5, 2e partie. Dufour & d'Ocagne, Paris.
CUVIER, G. 1836. *Recherches sur les ossemens fossiles, quatrième édition*, Volume 9. Edmond d'Ocagne, Paris.
DEAN, D. R. 1999. *Gideon Mantell and the Discovery of Dinosaurs*. Cambridge University Press, Cambridge.
DOLLO, L. 1883. Première note sur les crocodiliens de Bernissart. *Bulletin du Musée royal d'Histoire naturelle de Belgique*, **2**, 309–340.
FLEURY, E. 1920. Une phase brillante de la géologie portugaise. Paul Choffat. 14 Mars 1849–6 Juin 1919. *Mémoires de la Société Portugaise des Sciences Naturelle, Série Géologique*, **9**, 1–54.
FOUREAU, F. 1902. *D'Alger au Congo par le Tchad*. Masson, Paris.
FOUREAU, F. 1905. Géologie. Description géologique de l'itinéraire. *In*: FOUREAU, F. (ed.) *Documents scientifiques de la Mission saharienne*, Volume 2. Masson, Paris, 555–696.
FOWLER, D. 2007. Recently rediscovered baryonychine teeth (Dinosauria: Theropoda): new morphologic data, range extension and similarity to ceratosaurs. *Journal of Vertebrate Paleontology*, **27**, Suppl. 3, 76A.
GERVAIS, P. 1853. Observations relatives aux reptiles fossiles de France. *Comptes Rendus de l'Académie des Sciences de Paris*, **36**, 374–377.
GRAY, A. & ADAMS, C. B. 1863. *Elements of Geology*. Harper & Brothers, New York.
HAUG, E. 1905. Paléontologie. *In*: FOUREAU, F. (ed.) *Documents scientifiques de la Mission saharienne*, Volume 2. Masson, Paris, 751–832.
HOU, L., YEH, H. & ZHAO, X. 1975. Fossil reptiles from Fusui, Kwangshi. *Vertebrata Palasiatica*, **13**, 23–33.
HULKE, J. W. 1879. *Vectisaurus*, a new Wealden dinosaur. *Quarterly Journal of the Geological Society, London*, **35**, 421–424.
KOBAYASHI, T., TAKAI, F. & HAYAMI, I. 1964. On some Mesozoic fossils from the Khorat Series of East Thailand and a note on the Khorat Series. *Japanese Journal of Geology and Geography*, **34**, 181–192.
KONZHUKOVA, E. D. 1964. Crocodilia. *In*: ORLOV, YU. A. (ed.) *Osnovyi Paleontologii*, Volume 12. Nauka, Moscow, 506–523 (in Russian).
KREBS, B. 1967. Der Jura-Krokodilier *Machimosaurus* H. v. Meyer. *Paläontologische Zeitschrift*, **41**, 46–59.
KUHN, O. 1968. *Die vorzeitlichen Krododile*. Oeben, Krailing bei München.
LAPPARENT, A. F. DE 1960. Les dinosauriens du «Continental Intercalaire» du Sahara central. *Mémoires de la Société géologique de France*, **88A**, 1–57.
LAURILLARD, C. 1867. Crocodiliens fossiles. *In*: ORBIGNY, C. D' (ed.) *Dictionnaire universel d'Histoire naturelle*, Volume 4, Houssiaux, Paris, 476–481.
LAVOCAT, R. 1954. Sur les Dinosauriens du Continental Intercalaire des Kem-Kem de la Daoura. *Comptes Rendus du 19e Congrès Géologique International (Alger, 1952)*, **15**, 65–68.
LYDEKKER, R. 1888. *Catalogue of the Fossil Reptilia and Amphibia in the British Museum (Natural History). Part I*. British Museum (Natural History), London.
MANTELL, G. A. 1822. *The Fossils of the South Downs or Illustrations of the Geology of Sussex*. Lupton Relfe, London.
MANTELL, G. A. 1827. *Illustrations of the Geology of Sussex*. Lupton Relfe, London.
MANTELL, G. A. 1829*a*. A tabular arrangement of the organic remains of the county of Sussex. *Transactions of the Geological Society of London*, Series 2, **3**, 201–216.
MANTELL, G. A. 1829*b*. *A Scientific Catalogue of the Organic Remains of Sussex*. Richard Taylor, London.
MANTELL, G. A. 1833. *The Geology of the South-East of England*. Longman, Rees, Orme, Brown, Green & Longman, London.
MANTELL, G. A. 1839. *The Wonders of Geology*, 3rd edn. Relfe & Fletcher, London.
MANTELL, G. A. 1844. *The Medals of Creation*. Bohn, London.
MANTELL, G. A. 1851. *Petrifactions and their Teachings*. Bohn, London.
MARTILL, D. M. & HUTT, S. 1996. Possible baryonychid dinosaur teeth from the Wessex Formation (Lower Cretaceous, Barremian) of the Isle of Wight, England. *Proceedings of the Geologists' Association*, **107**, 81–84.
MEYER, H. VON 1832. *Palaeologica zur Geschichte der Erde und ihrer Geschöpfe*. Siegmund Schmerber, Frankfurt am Main.
MEYER, H. VON 1845. System der fossilen Saurier. *Neues Jahrbuch für Mineralogie, Geognosie, Geologie und Petrefakten-Kunde*, **1845**, 278–285.
MILNER, A. C. 2003. Fish-eating theropods: a short review of the systematics, biology and palaeobiogeography of spinosaurs. *In*: HUERTA HURTADO, P. & TORCIDA FERNÁNDEZ-BALDOR, F. (eds) *Actas de las II Jornadas Internacionales sobre Paleontologı́a de Dinosaurios y su Entorno (2001), Colectivo Arqueológico–Paleontológico, Salas de Los Infantes*, 129–138.
NAISH, D. & MARTILL, D. M. 2007. Dinosaurs of Great Britain and the role of the Geological Society of London in their discovery: basal Dinosauria and Saurischia. *Journal of the Geological Society, London*, **164**, 493–510.
NICHOLSON, H. A. & LYDEKKER, R. 1889. *A manual of palaeontology for the use of students with a general introduction on the principles of palaeontology*, Volume II. William Blackwood, Edinburgh.
NOTHDURFT, W. & SMITH, J. 2002. *The Lost Dinosaurs of Egypt*. Random House, New York.
OWEN, R. 1840–1845. *Odontography*. Hippolyte Baillière, London.
OWEN, R. 1842. Report on British fossil reptiles. Part II. *Reports of the meetings of the British Association for the Advancement of Science*, **11**, 61–204.
OWEN, R. 1878. Monograph on the fossil Reptilia of the Wealden and Purbeck Formations. Supplement n○VIII. Crocodilia (*Goniopholis, Petrosuchus and Suchosaurus*). *Palaeontographical Society Monographs*, **1878**, 1–15.
OWEN, R. 1884*a*. *A History of British Fossil Reptiles*, Volume I. Cassell, London.
OWEN, R. 1884*b*. *A History of British Fossil Reptiles*, Volume II. Cassell, London.
PAUL, G. 1988. *Predatory Dinosaurs of the World: A Complete Illustrated Guide*. Simon and Schuster, New York.
PICTET, F. J. 1853. *Traité de paléontologie ou histoire naturelle des animaux fossiles considérés dans leurs*

rapports zoologiques et géologiques. Tome premier. Baillière, Paris.

PLIENINGER, T. 1846*a*. Über ein neues Sauriergenus und die Einreihung der Saurier mitflachen, schneidenden Zähnen in eine Familie. *Jahreshefte des Vereins für vaterländische Naturkunde in Württemberg*, **2**, 148–154.

PLIENINGER, T. 1846*b*. Nachträgliche Bemerkungen zu dem Vortrage (S. 148 dieses Heftes) über ein neues Sauriergenus und die Einreihung der Saurier mit flachen, schneidenden Zähnen in eine Familie. *Jahreshefte des Vereins für vaterländische Naturkunde in Württemberg*, **2**, 247–254.

ROMER, A. S. 1956. *Osteology of the Reptiles*. University of Chicago Press, Chicago, IL.

ROYO Y GÓMEZ, J. 1927. Sur le faciès wealdien d'Espagne. *Comptes Rendus de la Société géologique de France*, **10**, 125–128.

RUIZ-OMEÑACA, J. I., CANUDO, J. I., CRUZADO-CABALLERO, INFANTE, P. & MORENO-AZANZA, M. 2005. Baryonychine teeth (Theropoda : Spinosauridae) from the Lower Cretaceous of La Cantalera (Josa, NE Spain). *Kaupia*, **14**, 59–63.

SANZ, J. L., CASANOVAS, M. L. & SANTAFÉ, J. V. 1982. Paleontología. *In*: *Geología y Paleontología (Dinosaurios) de las Capas rojas de Morella (Castellón, España), Diputación Provincial de Castellón y Diputación de Barcelona, Castellón and Barcelona*, 69–169.

SAUVAGE, H. E. 1896. Les crocodiliens et les dinosauriens des terrains mésozoïques duPortugal. *Bulletin de la Société géologique de France*, **24**, 46–48.

SAUVAGE, H. E. 1897–1898. *Vertébrés fossiles du Portugal. Contribution à l'étude des poissons et des reptiles du Jurassique et du Crétacique*. Direction des Travaux Géologiques du Portugal, Lisbon.

SAUVAGE, H. E. 1898. Les reptiles et les poissons des terrains mésozoïques du Portugal. *Bulletin de la Société géologique de France*, **26**, 442–446.

SCHLÜTER, T. & SCHWARZHANS, W. 1978. Eine Bonebed-Lagerstätte aus dem Wealden Süd-Tunesiens (Umgebung Ksar Krerachfa). *Berliner geowissenchaftliche Abhandlungen, A*, **8**, 53–65.

STEEL, R. 1973. Crocodylia. *Handbuch der Paläoherpetologie*, **16**, 1–116.

STROMER, E. 1915. Ergebnisse der Forschungsreisen Prof. E. Stromers in den Wüsten Ägyptens. II. Wirbeltierreste der Baharîje-Stufe (unterstes Cenoman). 3. Das Original des Theropoden *Spinosaurus aegyptiacus*. *Abhandlungen der Königlich Bayerischen Akademie der Wissenschaften, Mathematisch-physikalische Klasse*, **28**, 1–32.

STROMER, E. 1934. Ergebnisse der Forschungsreisen Prof. E. Stromers in den Wüsten Ägyptens. II. Wirbeltierreste der Baharîje-Stufe (unterstes Cenoman). 13. Dinosauria. *Abhandlungen der Bayerischen Akademie der Wissenschaften, Mathematisch-naturwissenschaftliche Klasse, Neue Folge*, **22**, 1–79.

STROMER, E. 1936. Ergebnisse der Forschungsreisen Prof. E. Stromers in den Wüsten Ägyptens. VII. Baharîje-Kessel und -Stufe mit deren Fauna und Flora. Eine ergänzende Zusammenfassung. *Abhandlungen der Bayerischen Akademie der Wissenschaften, Mathematisch-naturwissenschaftliche Klasse, Neue Folge*, **33**, 1–102.

VAN DEN BROECK, E. 1900. Les dépôts à *Iguanodon* de Bernissart et leur transfert dans l'étage purbeckien ou aquilonien du Jurassique supérieur. Exposé comprenant une revue de la faune des vertébrés du Purbeckien et du Wealdien dans le Sud-Est de l'Angleterre. *Bulletin de la Société belge de Géologie, de Paléontologie et d'Hydrologie*, **14**, 39–112.

WOODWARD, A. S. 1885. On the literature and nomenclature of British fossil Crocodilia. *Geological Magazine*, **2**, 496–510.

WOODWARD, A. S. 1887. The history of fossil crocodiles. *Proceedings of the Geologists' Association*, **9**, 288–344.

WOODWARD, A. S. & SHERBORN, C. D. 1890. *A Catalogue of British Fossil Vertebrata*. Dulau, London.

ZITTEL, K. A. 1887–1890. *Handbuch der Palaeontologie. I. Abtheilung. Palaeozoologie. III Band. Vertebrata (Pisces, Amphibia, Reptilia, Aves)*. Oldenbourg, München.

Yorkshire dinosaurs: a history in two parts

MARTIN A. WHYTE[1]*, MIKE ROMANO[1] & WILL WATTS[2]

[1]*Department of Geography, University of Sheffield, Dainton Building, Brookhill, Sheffield, Sheffield S10 2TN, UK*

[2]*Scarborough Museums Trust, Woodend Creative Workspace, The Crescent, Scarborough YO11 2PW, UK*

**Corresponding author (e-mail: m.a.whyte@sheffield.ac.uk)*

Abstract: Evidence of dinosaurs in Yorkshire is largely confined to the Middle Jurassic Ravenscar Group (Aalenian–Bathonian) and consists of both skeletal material and trace fossils. The oldest record is of unfigured limb elements, recorded by Williamson in 1837 and ascribed by Owen to *Cetiosaurus*, but they have not been more recently described. There are no other published records of dinosaur bone from the Ravenscar Group until 2003, when Romano and Whyte recorded recent discoveries including a sauropod caudal vertebra, ribs, disarticulated pectoral and limb elements. Non-dinosaurian skeletal material includes crocodile, turtle and fish.

In contrast, dinosaur tracks are extremely abundant in the Ravenscar Group. Although some may have been observed around 1895, the first definite identification of dinosaur tracks was by Brodrick in 1907. A modern resurgence in interest began about 1970 when Sarjeant first formally named a track from Yorkshire. Subsequent publications have amply documented the abundance and diversity of dinosaur tracks within the Ravenscar Group. In 1995 the first new ichnotaxon from Yorkshire, *Deltapodus brodricki*, was described; this was followed by the recognition of sauropod tracks and swimming tracks. There are scattered records of dinosaur bone from other marine units in the Jurassic and Lower Cretaceous. The Yorkshire records are of great international significance, especially in the Middle Jurassic where there is a dearth of material from other areas.

The evidence of dinosaurs in Yorkshire is confined to the Cleveland Basin (Fig. 1) and particularly to the coastal stretch that has become known as the 'Dinosaur Coast'. From the late Triassic to the late Cretaceous, an interval of over 150 Ma embracing almost the whole of the stratigraphic range of the dinosaurs, the Cleveland Basin accumulated a thick (more than 1800 m) and almost entirely marine sequence of mudrocks, sandstones, limestones and ironstones (Rawson & Wright 1995, 2000; Osborne & Bowden 2001; Romano & Whyte 2003; Whyte & Romano 2007, 2008) (Fig. 2). The only exception to this is during the Middle Jurassic (Aalenian–Bathonian) when regional uplift (Underhill & Partington 1993) led to the accumulation of the Ravenscar Group, a 240 m-thick paralic sequence of fluvial sandstones and mudrocks with occasional thin marine intercalations (Romano & Whyte 2003; Whyte & Romano 2007, 2008) (Fig. 3). The rocks of this brief, at most 11 Ma, interlude are the principal repository of dinosaur evidence within the basin. The term 'Dinosaur Coast' might in this light seem to be something of a misnomer, and a disservice to the abundant other interests of the succession including marine reptiles, ammonites and belemnites. Indeed, prior to the work of the Sheffield Dinosaur Track Research Group, it was these latter groups for which the coast was best known. However, the structure of the Cleveland Anticline, which formed following basin inversion in the early Cenozoic, combined with present-day erosion levels are such that the rocks of the Ravenscar Group do have a considerably greater representation than might be expected from either their relative thickness (12%) or their relative temporal span (7%). Coastal profiles, such as that in the Rotunda Museum in Scarborough (now the William Smith Museum of Geology), indicate that between Flamborough Head and Redcar, a distance of approximately 32 km, there are significant outcrops of the Ravenscar Group along more than 45% of the coastal region. The group is particularly well exposed on the coast both north and south of Scarborough, and can also be well seen to the east of Whitby. The Ravenscar Group also makes up about 32% of the inland outcrop within the area of the basin (Fig. 1), although rock exposure is sparse.

From a historical perspective, research on Yorkshire's dinosaurs and on other contemporary

From: Moody, R. T. J., Buffetaut, E., Naish, D. & Martill, D. M. (eds) *Dinosaurs and Other Extinct Saurians: A Historical Perspective*. Geological Society, London, Special Publications, **343**, 189–207.
DOI: 10.1144/SP343.11 0305-8719/10/$15.00

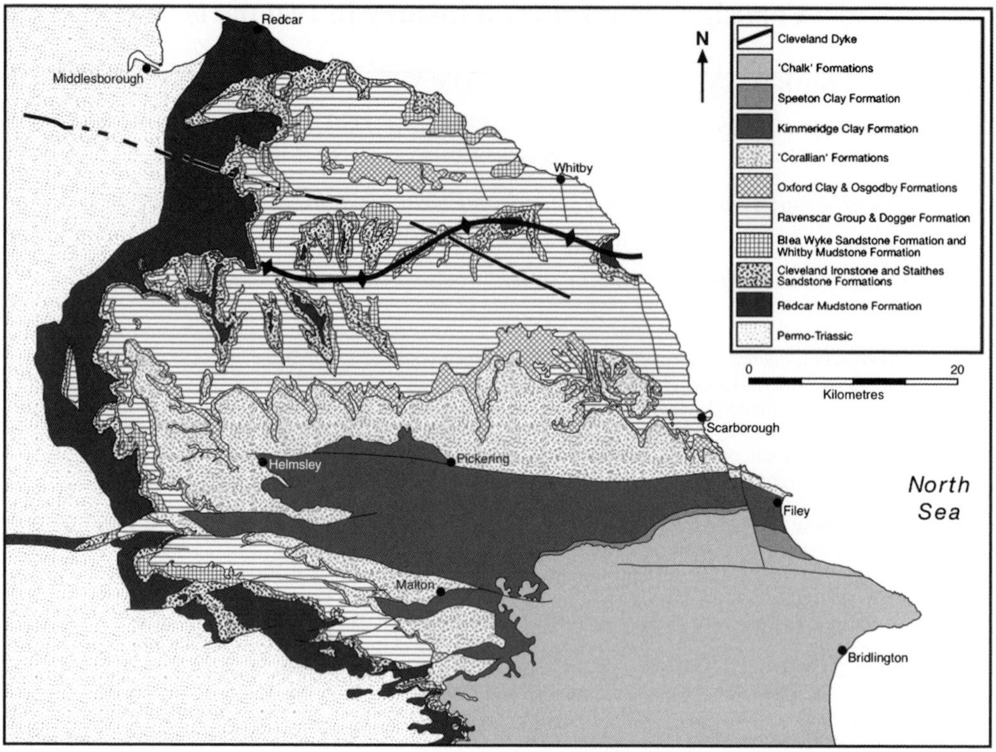

Fig. 1. Simplified geological map of North Yorkshire showing principal localities mentioned in the text. The axial trace of the Cleveland Anticline is represented by a thick black continuous line.

terrestrial vertebrates can be considered as falling into two parts in several ways:

- distinction can be made between evidence from within the largely non-marine Ravenscar Group and the rarer fragmentary finds from older and younger marine formations;
- within the Ravenscar Group there is both skeletal evidence and trace fossil evidence;
- the history of research on both body fossil and ichnological evidence can be divided into an early phase with initial discoveries and reports, and a later phase of modern study within the last three decades. The two phases are temporally separated by intervals when little or no new evidence was recorded and when palaeontological studies of the fossil vertebrates essentially went into abeyance.

Yorkshire was not alone in suffering a palaeontological interregnum, and Benton & Spencer (1995) have commented on a general decline in British vertebrate palaeontological activity within the early–mid parts of the twentieth century. In Cleveland, the gap was partly filled by keen local amateurs including C. Ivens, D. Watson, P. A. Dixon, A. Staniforth, D. Wright and the latter's son, J. K. Wright, who went on to be a professional geologist, but their discoveries were not well recorded or publicized at the time.

Skeletal material from the Ravenscar Group

Williamson's bones

The first record of dinosaurs from the Ravenscar Group was paradoxically from one of its marine intercalations, the Scarborough Formation (Williamson 1837) (Fig. 3). The skeletal material came from White Nab (Fig. 4a) to the south of Scarborough (Williamson 1837) and possibly from the sea quarry worked to provide stone for Scarborough Harbour. The source horizon, which contains ammonites (Williamson 1837), is probably the same as that identified by Wright (Wright 1860; Hudleston 1874) as containing 'saurian (*Ichthyosaurus* and *Plesiosaurus*) remains'. Williamson (1837, pp. 232–233) described the find as:

> In this seam a mass of extraordinary bones was found, at White Nab, near Scarborough. Two of the bones

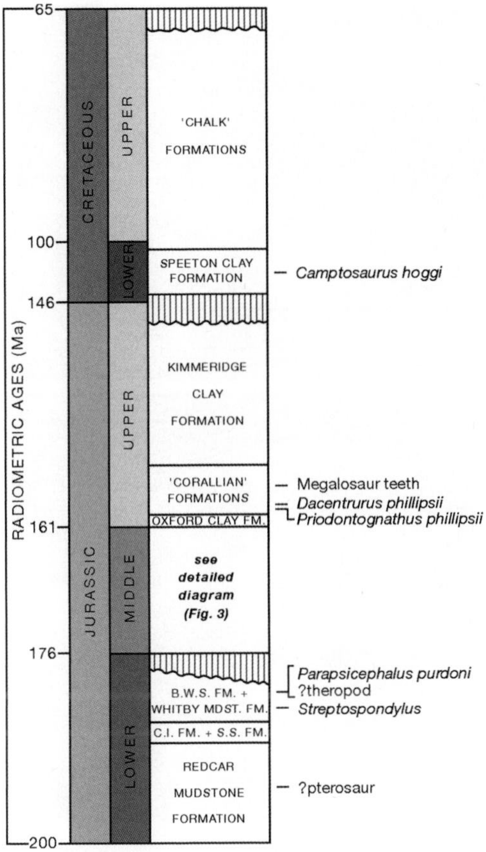

Fig. 2. Summary stratigraphy of the Cleveland Basin showing positions of skeletal finds. Lithostratigraphical units are shown in correct relative thickness. C.I., Cleveland Ironstone; S.S., Staithes Sandstone; B.W.S., Blea Wyke Sandstone.

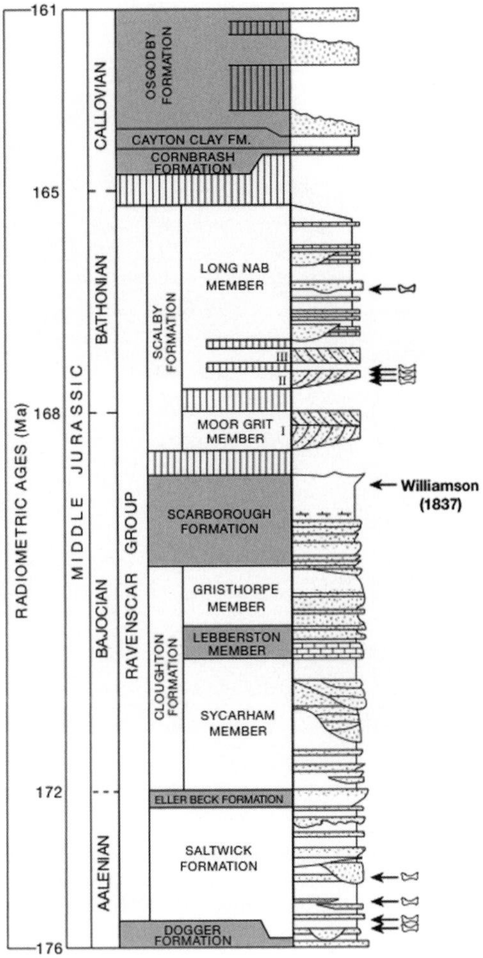

Fig. 3. Detailed stratigraphy of the Middle Jurassic of the Cleveland Basin showing positions of skeletal finds. Shaded lithostratigraphical units are marine. I, II and III are sedimentary prisms of Eschard *et al.* (1991). Vertical lines indicate principal hiatuses.

agree in form with those represented in fig. 4 and 5, of Mr. Mantell's 'Illustrations of Tilgate Forest,' and supposed by him to be the metatarsal bones of the Iguanodon. The longitudinal circumference of the Scarborough specimens is $11\frac{1}{2}$ inches, and the transverse $10\frac{1}{2}$ inches. The same mass contains also three bones, which resemble the humerus of an unknown Saurian, given in Pl. 14, fig. 3 and 6, of the same work. Their length is 14 inches; the circumference about the middle of the shaft, $8\frac{1}{2}$ inches; and around the condyle, 16 inches. There are two other bones which are supposed to be tibias. They are ten inches long; and their circumference at the superior extremity is $15\frac{1}{2}$ inches. The circumference at the vertebral extremity of the fragment of a rib is $5\frac{1}{2}$ inches, and about the middle of the bone 6 inches.

The same mass encloses also a singular bone, something resembling in form the humerus of an Ichthyosaurus: the length of the supposed, cubital, articulating extremity is $8\frac{1}{2}$ inches, and the diameter 7; while the diameter of the cylindrical part, at four inches from the above extremity is $3\frac{1}{2}$ inches. The entire length of the bone when perfect is uncertain, but it appears to have been of gigantic size.

The only portion of a vertebra is a fragment $4\frac{1}{2}$ inches long by $2\frac{1}{2}$ inches in diameter. It is very possible that these remains may belong to the Megalosaurus; and if this should prove to be the case, we shall have in the superior beds of the great oolite of Yorkshire, some of the interesting fossils of the Stonesfield slate.

This record predated Owen's (1842) coining of the term Dinosauria and, as pointed out by Torrens (1997), before that point there were no dinosaurs as such. However, it is clear that Williamson

Fig. 4. White Nab and skeletal material on display in the William Smith (Rotunda) Museum, Scarborough. (**a**) View of White Nab from the Holbeck landslide, south of Scarborough. (**b**) Sauropod metatarsal (SGN FP OB 08), locality unknown. (**c**) Chelonian carapace (SGN FP OB 16), Scalby Formation, north of White Nab, near Scarborough. (**d**) Fish (*Heterolepidotus* sp.) (SGN FP OB 17), Scalby Formation, north of White Nab, near Scarborough.

(1837) was familiar with the literature describing both *Iguanodon* and *Megalosaurus*. Although Williamson was then only 21, his medical training and extensive knowledge of natural history (Williamson 1896) gave him a good background in vertebrate anatomy from which to make such comparisons. This, together with his local connections, meant that he was in fact uniquely placed to deal with such discoveries. He came from a well known Scarborough family, different members of which specialized in fossil collecting and in lapidiary work for the Georgian tourist market (Williamson 1896). At this time his father, a cousin of the collector William Bean and himself an important early collector, was curator of the Scarborough (Rotunda) Museum (Williamson 1884, 1896) and in the bone paper Williamson (1837) also described plesiosaur remains found by his father in the Scarborough Formation. Williamson had also been influenced by William Smith, who for a while resided in the Williamson household (Williamson 1884, 1896), and the main purport of Williamson's (1837) paper was to establish details of the stratigraphy and faunal succession within the Cleveland Basin. This paper was a composite of two separate papers read to the Geological Society in 1834 (Williamson 1834) and 1836 (Williamson 1836) and even late in life Williamson still complained that the editors had not dealt with the material very expeditiously (Williamson 1896).

Williamson's (1837) specimen makes Yorkshire only the fifth area in England and the sixth area in Europe or the world from which material, later recognized as dinosaurian, had been recorded in print. But this has been subsequently omitted in most histories of early 'dinosaur' research (e.g. Colbert 1961, 1983; Halstead & Halstead 1981; Weishampel *et al.* 1990; Benton 1996; Sarjeant 1997*a*; Dean 1999; Cadbury 2001; McGowan 2001; Delair & Sarjeant 2002) and Williamson's (1837) paper has not been included in either a published dinosaur bibliography (Chure & McIntosh

1989) or in the recent review of the role of the Geological Society of London in early dinosaur discoveries (Naish & Martill 2007, 2008). There are several reasons for this:

- Williamson (1837) did not complicate things for later workers by naming his material other than to list it as 'Megalosaurus?'
- The material was assigned by Owen (1841, 1842) to his genus *Cetiosaurus*, which he thought was a huge swimming crocodile and which he did not include within his Dinosauria.
- Owen (1841, 1842) never fully described or figured the material and made only passing references to it without ever acknowledging Williamson or his paper. Thus, although Delair & Sarjeant (1975), in their account of early dinosaur discoveries, noted that Owen (1841, 1842) had used material from Scarborough, they considered it to be of 'unknown history'. Similarly, Sarjeant (1997*b*) recorded only that Owen (1842) had used material from Yorkshire.
- Although the dinosaurian affinites of *Cetiosaurus* had been recognized by Mantell in 1850 (Cadbury 2001), they were not widely accepted until the 1870s (McIntosh *et al.* 1997; Upchurch *et al.* 2004), by which time the White Nab material had been completely eclipsed by other sauropod finds (e.g. Phillips 1871).
- The material has not been more recently re-studied; owing in part to problems in tracing it.

In his first work on *Cetiosaurus*, which included reference to the material from White Nab, Owen (1841) did not name any species. However, in the published report of the famous Plymouth meeting he named four species (Owen 1842). These were: *C. brevis* and *C. brachyurus*, both based on Wealden material; *C. medius* for Middle Jurassic (Bathonian) material from Oxfordshire (Chipping Norton and Endslow), Buckinghamshire and Northamptonshire; and *C. longus* for material from the Portland Stone (Tithonian) of Garsington, Oxfordshire (Owen 1842). The White Nab vertebra and metatarsals were referred to the latter species, *C. longus* (Owen 1842). Another account of the Plymouth meeting, however, used only *C. hypoolithicus* for the Chipping Norton (Oxfordshire) material and *C. epioolithicus* for the material from White Nab (listed as White Hale) (Anon. 1842). This French report (Anon. 1842) appears to be a summary of Owen's actual address and has even been credited to him (Chure & McIntosh 1989), so these species names may have been early manuscript names. In later works Owen (1875, 1884) based a fuller description of *C. longus* almost entirely on Great Oolite (Bathonian) material from Kirtlington in Oxfordshire, and mentioned only that he had material of the same species from Yorkshire. *C. longus* was transferred to the genus *Cetiosauriscus* by McIntosh (1990) but all Owen's *Cetiosaurus* species, with the possible exception of *C. brevis*, are now considered to be *nomina nuda* (Upchurch & Martin 2003; Naish & Martill 2008). Williamson's bones are best regarded as Sauropoda indet. but this assemblage has been recorded as both *Cetiosaurus medius* (= *C. hypoolithicus*) and *Cetiosauriscus longus* by Weishampel (1990), who also located it in West Yorkshire. Although replaced in North Yorkshire by Weishampel *et al.* (2004), it is listed as 'Sauropoda indet. (including *Cetiosaurus hypoolithicus*, *C. longus* and *C. medius*)'.

The White Nab material is consistently listed as being within the collections of the Scarborough Museum (Owen 1841, 1842; Phillips 1875; Fox-Strangways 1892). Its acquisition may, perhaps, be recorded by a single line entry in the museum reports that reads 'Rev Thomas Irvin – Fine specimen of Fossil Bone, found near Carnelian Bay' (Carnelian or Cornelian Bay lies on the south side of White Nab) (Scarborough Philosophical Society 1837). However, Williamson's material cannot now be confidently identified. In the mid-1990s members of the Sheffield Dinosaur Track Research Group did come across some bone, including an isolated sauropod metatarsal (Fig. 4b), within the Scarborough Museum collections, but these were not numbered and had no associated information as to their provenance. At that time, because they had not been catalogued, we were prevented from borrowing the specimens, and despite our interest and despite the lack of context the largest metatarsal was subsequently and somewhat misleadingly figured by Bowden (in Osborne & Bowden 2001) as 'found at Scarborough'.

Later skeletal records from the Ravenscar Group

Subsequent to Williamson's (1837) record and prior to the time when the Sheffield Dinosaur Track Research Group began the modern phase of ichnological study (see below) there were no published records of dinosaur skeletal material from the Ravenscar Group. Indeed, the only vertebrate skeletal finds recorded during this approximately 150 year interval were several fish (identified as *Heterolepidotus* sp.) and a tortoise carapace found in ironstone nodules in a channel deposit near the base of the Scalby Formation (Unit II of Eschard *et al.* 1991) on the north side of White Nab. This material (Fig. 4b, c), now in the Scarborough Museum collections, was found by members of the local group of amateurs in the 1950s and, although its occurrence was noted by Rawson & Wright (1992, 2000), it has never been fully described. As the widespread abundance of dinosaur footprints became increasingly obvious so the apparent absence of skeletal evidence became an escalating problem. This has been partly resolved by a number of finds of skeletal material (Romano & Whyte 2003) (Fig. 3). These finds come from two groups of horizons within the Saltwick and Scalby formations (Fig. 3).

The specimens from the Saltwick Formation have been recorded in loose blocks at several localities, and range from small scraps of bone to ribs and large limb bones (Fig. 5a). Most appear to come from ferruginous channel deposits, which also contain mud clasts and plant fragments, but a single well-preserved sauropod caudal vertebra came from a palaeosol horizon.

Within the Scalby Formation (Fig. 3), skeletal material has been found in a lag deposit at the base of a complex channel sequence at the base of Unit II and also from a location in the upper part of this unit (Fig. 5b). The skeletal material from the former is largely indeterminate but includes ribs and a vertebra. As the channel cuts down into the Scarborough Formation it is possible that some of this bone may be reworked from this formation. An isolated fragment of crocodile scute has also been found in a younger sediment lens at the same locality. Searches at other locations at the base of Unit II have, however, failed to produce skeletal material.

The youngest horizon in the Scalby Formation to yield skeletal evidence is a channel deposit within the Long Nab Member (Fig. 3) from which parts of long bone elements have been recovered. This particular deposit, which is ferruginous and contains abundant coalified plant remains and rip-up mudstone clasts, is similar in facies to some of the bone-bearing deposits of the Saltwick Formation, but other occurrences of this facies have been searched without success.

Although work on these recent discoveries is still at an early stage, it is clear that all the principal groups identified as track makers, viz dinosaurs, crocodiles, turtles and fish (Romano & Whyte 2003; Whyte & Romano 2007), are also present in the skeletal record. One skeletal element that is curiously lacking and whose apparent absence is difficult to explain is dinosaur, or indeed reptilian, teeth. The scarcity of bone relative to the abundance of prints is, however, also still remarkable, and this may be partly due to rapid solution by the acidic groundwaters and seasonally high water tables that are evidenced by the sphaerosiderite-rich, gley palaeosols (Romano & Whyte 2003). The rapid recycling of phosphorous, a limiting element for life (Filippelli 2002), by scavengers and soil organisms may be another factor. Such rapid recycling is evident in some modern situations, such as the plains of northern Tanzania (Fig. 6a), even though these are generally drier and less acidic environments than those envisaged for the Ravenscar Group. In these modern situations the bones that survive longest are larger more resistant elements (Fig. 6b). Where preservation has occurred in the Ravenscar Group it also appears to be selective, and is linked either to transport and rapid burial within channel deposits or to incorporation within palaeosols. Even in these situations the skeletal material was apparently widely dispersed in a series of local 'hot spots'. Thus, future bone finds may be expected at intermittent intervals and locations as coastal erosion proceeds. In this context the significance of the absence of records from the Cloughton Formation and, perhaps, also the upper parts of both the Saltwick and Scalby formations (Fig. 3) is not clear. It is possible that it may be simply a chance effect, but it could also signify some particular edaphic effect mitigating against bone preservation at these horizons. Hesselbo *et al.* (2003) have commented on the absence of charcoal from the Cloughton Formation

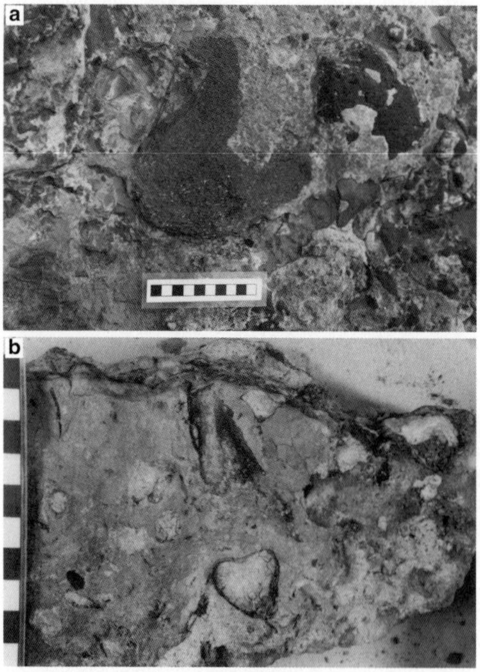

Fig. 5. Dinosaur skeletal material from the Ravenscar Group. (**a**) Large bone fragment (centre) and plant debris in basal lag deposit, Saltwick Formation. (**b**) Bone fragment (top centre) and ironstone nodules in channel deposit, Scalby Formation. Scale bar is 10 cm.

Fig. 6. Modern skeletal remains, Tanzania, Africa. (**a**) Dismembered skeleton of an African water buffalo (*Syncerus caffer*), which had been recently killed, Ngorogoro National Park. (**b**) Naturally occuring group of bleached bones (?*Loxodonta africana*), Tarangire National Park.

as evidence of a wetter and less seasonal climate. The greater degree of marine influence in the Cloughton Formation (Hancock & Fisher 1981) and upper Saltwick Formation (Butler *et al.* 2005) might also be a factor. Similarly, the upper parts of the Scalby Formation may have been affected by leaching during the lacuna prior to the transgression of the Cornbrash Formation (Fig. 3) or by marine pore waters subsequent to the transgression.

Vertebrates in the 'marine formations'

The Whitby Mudrock Formation (Toarcian) of the Cleveland Basin is justly famous for its assemblage of marine reptiles, including ichthyosaurs, plesiosaurs and crocodiles, which have been known since the mid-eighteenth century (Benton & Taylor 1984; Benton & Spencer 1995; Osborne 1998). Marine reptile remains are also well known from parts of the Redcar Mudstone (Hettangian–Sinemurian), Cleveland Ironstone Formation (Pliensbachian), Cornbrash Formation (Callovian), Osgodby Formation (Callovian), Corallian (Oxfordian), Kimmeridge Clay Formation (Kimmeridgian), Speeton Clay Formation (Lower Cretaceous) and Chalk (Upper Cretaceous) (Phillips 1875; Fox-Strangways 1892; Benton & Spencer 1995). Among a number of important recent finds is the Speeton plesiosaur on display in the William Smith Museum of Geology. By comparison the record of terrestrial vertebrates from these and other marine formations is not surprisingly meagre (Fig. 2). However, it is, nevertheless, both historically and scientifically significant.

Owen (1841, 1842; Anon. 1842) attributed to *Streptospondylus* a vertebra recorded from the 'jet rock' (now Mulgrave Shale Member, Whitby Mudrock Formation) of Whitby (Fig. 2). The specimen was then in the collections of 'Mr Ripley, surgeon of Whitby' (Owen 1842). He is most probably Richard Ripley, a noted fossil collector and at one time a joint secretary of the Whitby Literary and Philosophical Society (Cleevely 1983; Osborne 1998). Curiously, Fox-Strangways (1892), who also has a misprinted date (1871) for Owen's (1842) work, lists the material as a 'phalangeal bone'. Later figured by Owen (1884), this is effectively the joint second record of a dinosaur from Yorkshire, although again this genus was at first considered to be a huge marine crocodile and not immediately included within the Dinosauria (Owen 1841, 1842). Initially, a compound of several animals, the type of the genus *Streptospondylus* Meyer 1832 is now considered to be a theropod (Holtz *et al.* 2004; Sadleir *et al.* 2008). Another possible theropod bone, a femur, has been recorded from the Alum Shale Member of the Whitby Mudstone Formation (Huene 1926; Benton & Taylor 1984; Benton & Spencer 1995) (Fig. 2). Both specimens should be in the collections of the Whitby Museum but cannot at present be located. Pending their 're-location', re-examination and description, it is best, as recommended by Naish & Martill (2007), to regard both specimens as Tetanurae indet. They are, however, of potential significance in view of the scarcity of Upper Lias theropods (Benton & Taylor 1984; Benton & Spencer 1995; Weishampel *et al.* 2004).

The Alum Shale Member is also the source, in Loftus Quarry, 18 km NW of Whitby, of a partial pterosaur skull (British Geological Survey GSM 3166), the type specimen of *Parapsicephalus purdoni* (Newton 1888; Benton & Taylor 1984; Benton & Spencer 1995) (Fig. 2). This is the earliest rhamphorhynchid pterosaur (Benton 1993; Benton & Spencer 1995). Pterosaur remains have also recently been found in this member at other locations (pers. obs.; Manning pers. comm.). An elongate nodule developed round an elongate hollow bone, which might be part of a pterosaur manual phalangial bone, has been found by us in the Redcar Mudstone Formation (Sinemurian) at the eponymous location. While pterosaur remains might have found their way into the shales by several pathways, the dinosaur elements would most probably have been washed into the depositional basin as parts of bloated and decaying cadavers (cf. Schäfer 1972; Jana & Das 2002).

The earliest records of dinosaurs from the Upper Jurassic 'marine formations' are teeth attributed to *Megalosaurus bucklandi* from the Coralline Oolite Formation (Oxfordian) of the Malton area (Phillips 1875; Hudleston 1878; Fox-Strangways 1892) (Figs 2 & 7b). It is probably these teeth that Owen (1841) suggested might belong to *Cetiosaurus* but, by the next year, he was referring to them as *Megalosaurus* (Owen 1842). These are the joint second record of dinosaurs from Yorkshire and the first to actually be placed within the Dinosauria. Young & Bird had earlier included descriptions of vertebrate teeth from the oolitic limestones of the Malton area in the second edition of their work (Young & Bird 1828). However, neither of the two tooth types described (Young & Bird 1828) appears to be megalosaurid.

The bone of a 'very large saurian' recorded by Hudleston (1878) from the Malton Oolite Member (Oxfordian) at Slingsby, 9.5 km WNW of Malton, became the type of ?*Dacentrurus phillipsi* (Seeley 1893; Galton 1983; Benton & Spencer 1995). Although Galton (1983) considered the taxon to be a *nomen dubium*, this juvenile stegosaur femur (Fig. 7a) is still the only evidence for Oxfordian Stegosauridae so far recorded from anywhere in the world (Galton & Upchurch 2004). Unidentified bone fragments have also been recorded from approximately the same horizon in the nearby Malton Bypass Section (Wright 1978; Galton 1983). Another thyreophorian from Yorkshire may be the nodosaurian ankylosaur, *Priodontognathus phillipsii* (Seeley 1869, 1875; Lydekker 1893; Galton 1980; Benton & Spencer 1995). There is, however, some doubt about the source of this specimen, which might not even be from Yorkshire (Galton 1980). Galton (1980), in part influenced by the specimen's salty taste, did, however, favour an origin from coastal exposures of the Lower Calcareous Grit Formation of Yorkshire. Naish & Martill (2008) considered the taxon's relegation to *nomen dubium* by Vickaryous *et al.* (2004) as 'probably unjust'.

Most recently, Norman & Barrett (2002) described and attributed to the iguanodontid *Camptosaurus hoggi* the stratigraphically youngest known dinosaur material from the Cleveland Basin. This specimen had been found in the D Beds (layer D7D) of the Speeton Clay Formation (Early Cretaceous, late Berriasian) by E. V. and C. W. Wright in 1960. The associated elements, a femur, tibia, astragalus and partial fibula (Natural History Museum London BMNH R8676), of a right leg are consistent with the taphonomic model of derivation through gradual disintegration of a floating carcass.

The vertebrate ichnology of the Ravenscar Group

The start of the story

The first record of vertebrate tracks from the Cleveland Basin of Yorkshire is in a paper by Hargreaves (1913), who recorded that Mr Rowntree had found a footprint from Cayton Bay, *c.* 6 km south of Scarborough (Fig. 1), about 18 years earlier 'which Mr Lamplugh pronounced to be probably crocodilian'. Since this specimen has not been traced, it has not proved possible to confirm its crocodilian origin, although it is more likely that it was made by a dinosaur. Consequently, the statement by Osborne & Bowden (2001) that the first dinosaur footprints were discovered on the Yorkshire coast in 1895 at Saltwick may in part be correct concerning the date and maker, but not the locality. Compared with the first authenticated discovery of vertebrate (dinosaur) tracks elsewhere in the world, this was quite a late discovery, since the earliest record of fossilized footprints was in 1802 in the USA; although, in fact, these were not described for another 40 years (Thulborn 1990). However, it was not until the early part of the next century that the first vertebrate tracks were described from the Cleveland Basin. In a series of papers in the first decade of the twentieth century, Harold Brodrick, a barrister by profession, but also a keen amateur geologist and speleologist, recorded tracks from the Saltwick Formation (or lower part of the 'Inferior Oolite' as it was then known) in Saltwick Bay (Fig. 8) just to the east of Whitby (Brodrick 1907, 1908, 1909*a*, *b*). It is perhaps appropriate that Brodrick's first (1907) paper should be entitled 'A find!!!', and published in the *Whitby Philosophical Society*, but also rather ironic that Brodrick was of Lancastrian origin. This unusual title for a scientific paper did not escape Sheppard (1908), who rather disparagingly commented that 'it savours of a Patent Medicine advertisement'. All the finds described by Brodrick were of tridactyl forms, and in his most comprehensive paper (1909*b*) he attempted to classify the tracks into six distinct types. The large slab (Fig. 8) described in this paper is mounted on the wall in Whitby Museum

Fig. 7. Dinosaur material in the Yorkshire Museum, York. (**a**) Femur of juvenile stegosaur (holotype of *Omosaurus phillipsi* of Seeley (1893), YORYM 498), Coralline Oolite Formation, Slingsby, Yorkshire. (**b**) Megalosaurid tooth (YORYM 1986/2F), Coralline Oolite Formation, near Malton, Yorkshire. Scale bar is 10 cm.

(Osborne & Bowden 2001, left-hand side of the photograph on their p. 19). Although Brodrick generally refrained from suggesting what animals were responsible for making the tracks, he did liken some of them to those of *Iguanodon* from the 'Wealden beds' (Brodrick 1907, 1908). Sarjeant (1987, p. 5) regarded Brodrick's work as 'the true starting-point of British Jurassic palaeoichnology'. However, in reality, this did not initiate a rush to print; in fact, rather the reverse.

The beginning of the decline

At around the same time that Brodrick was publishing his findings, only a few other new discoveries were appearing in print (Kendall 1908; Sheppard 1908) and these were mainly concerned with identifying the source horizon of Brodrick's material. Even in the following decade, reports of prints were particularly sparse (Fox-Strangways & Barrow 1915; Hargreaves 1913, 1914); although progress was made in recognizing what was to become known as the 'Burniston footprint bed' (Hargreaves 1914; Romano & Whyte 2003) in Burniston Bay, approximately 3 km north of Scarborough (Fig. 9), the source of a number of the earlier (and later) finds.

Coinciding with the onset of World War I, publications on vertebrate footprints ceased for a while (Fig. 10) and, apart from two isolated reports (Kendall & Wroot 1924; Black *et al.* 1934) in the decade after the war, did not begin to recover again until well after the cessation of World War II. As mentioned by Romano & Whyte (2003) this dearth of papers between 1920 and 1970 on Yorkshire tracks (four papers were published) was recognized in a seminal paper by Sarjeant (1974) on the study of vertebrate footprints in the British Isles. This meagre publication rate was also reflected the other side of the Pennines, where

Fig. 8. View of Saltwick Bay, east of Whitby, with inset of slab drawn and described by Brodrick (1909*b*).

Fig. 9. View of section at Crook Ness, Burniston Bay, north of Scarborough, showing the position of the 'Burniston footprint bed' (arrowed) as identified by Hargreaves (1914).

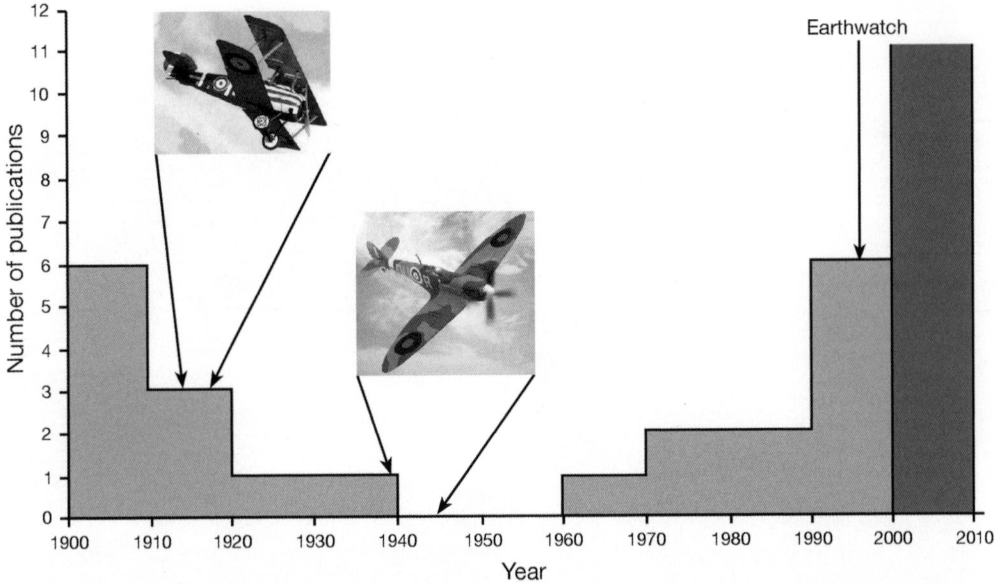

Fig. 10. Histogram showing numbers of papers published on dinosaur tracks from the Cleveland Basin per decade from 1900 to present. The duration of the world wars is indicated, together with the initiation of Earthwatch projects (see the text for details). The different ornament used in the last decade column highlights that it is not yet complete.

around 18 papers were published on the Triassic Cheshire (Lancashire) prints during the same period. However, when these two areas are compared in total papers published up to and including 1970, seven times as many publications (nearly 100 as against 13) appeared on the Cheshire Triassic prints than for Yorkshire; although, significantly, Henry C. Beasley, 'by far the most important figure in the history of British vertebrate ichnology' (Sarjeant 1974, p. 295), contributed to about one-fifth of these for the Cheshire area. Interestingly, Williamson (1867) published on a Cheshire footprint but, as he died in 1895, may never have known that there were footprints in the Cleveland Basin.

The renaissance

In the mid-1950s there was a renewed interest, especially among amateurs, of dinosaur tracks from the Yorkshire coast. In particular, Mr Cyril Ivens began recording prints in 1955, culminating in a valuable publication by Ivens & Watson (1994) in which he and Geoffrey Watson provided details of personnel, quotes and anecdotal accounts of early finds that give insight into Yorkshire dinosaur palaeoichnology between 1895 and 1993. Mr Ivens was still working in the field well into the 1990s. At this time most of the tracks figured in publications were either isolated finds of a single print or parts of a trackway consisting of only a few prints. In 1962, however, a trackway of eight prints was discovered in Scalby Bay (3.5 km north of Scarborough) by Mr C. Ivens, Mr A. Staniforth and Dr J. K. Wright (Dixon 1962; Ivens & Watson 1994). This was briefly recorded as a Letter in the New Scientist by Dixon (1962) under the heading of 'Reptilian footprints'. Unfortunately, the diagrams are rather schematic, and show a bird-like sketch of the trackway and a simplified drawing of a single print. Less than one year later the number of prints increased to nine as a slab of rock was loosened and finally removed by the sea to reveal an 11 m-long trackway of a bipedal dinosaur – the so-called 'Jackson's Bay' trackway (Fig. 11). Also of interest in Dixon's publication (Dixon 1962) is the mention of two tracks recorded by Mr S. Rowntree near to the 'Jackson's Bay' trackway, in which it is reported that on one of the specimens 'the scale marks and folds of skin on the sole of the beast's foot' can be seen. Unfortunately, according to Dixon (1962), the marks on the sole of the print are no longer visible and, although there is no record of the Plasticene cast made by Mr Rowntree (Dixon 1962), a plaster cast of the print exists in the Scarborough Museum collections (Ivens & Watson 1994).

A more modern approach to recording and interpreting tracks from the Middle Jurassic of the Cleveland Basin was initiated by William (Bill) Sarjeant, a graduate of the University of Sheffield, who specialized initially on dinoflagellate cysts

Fig. 11. Jackson's Bay Trackway, Scalby Bay, north of Scarborough. (**a**) View of trackway with individual prints highlighted by chalk outline. Length of individual prints is *c*. 40 cm. (**b**) Earthwatch volunteer team recording the Jackson's Bay Trackway as an overlay on a polythene sheet in September 1996. (**c**) Mr Cyril Ivens, co-finder of the Jackson's Bay Trackway, photographed close to the site in September 2000.

(marine phytoplankton). He was the first to assign a named ichnotaxon to a track from the Cleveland Basin (Sarjeant 1970). In this publication, Sarjeant figured, described and named *Satapliasaurus* cf. *dsocenidzei* Gabouniya from the 'Lower Deltaic Series' of the Peak Alum Quarries, near Ravenscar. For the first time, Sarjeant applied a formal systematic description to a fossil track from the Yorkshire region, and suggested the maker to be a bipedal, herbivorous ornithopod dinosaur. Recently, Lockley & Meyer (2000, p. 134) have expressed reservations about this assignment to the Lower Cretaceous Russian ichnotaxon, as they regarded the latter as 'not well known, and has not been described from a complete trackway.'

It was in the early 1980s that two of the present authors (M. A. Whyte and M. Romano) described a tridactyl print from just south of Scarborough (Whyte & Romano 1981). This paper was the first to consider the preservation and substrate relations in detail, as well as the morphology and possible maker, of a Yorkshire print. The 'Jackson Bay' trackway then made a reappearance 23 years after it was first published. It was partially figured in an oblique photograph by Delair & Sarjeant (1985, fig. 3c), and later as drawings by Ivens & Watson (1994) and Rawson & Wright (1992, 2000, fig. 26 showing five prints), and most recently by Romano & Whyte (2003, fig. 25) who reproduced the whole visible trackway as a drawing from an overlay made in the field. Although today the fourth track has disappeared, it remains the longest bipedal trackway known from the Cleveland Basin.

The second ichnotaxon to be formally named for a Yorkshire dinosaur track was *Deltapodus brodricki* (Fig. 12a); a track that was initially considered to have been made by a sauropod, but finally assigned to a stegosaurid maker (Whyte & Romano 1993, 1995, 2001). Between the naming of this ichnotaxon and the final interpretation, Lockley & Meyer (2000, fig. 6.3) had proposed the presence of the Central Asian ichnogenus *Ravatichnus* from the Cleveland Basin; but this print was later shown to be superimposed manus and pes tracks of *Deltapodus brodricki* (Whyte & Romano 2001). This ichnotaxon has been referred to in a number of publications since it was first named (Whyte & Romano 1995), and consequently it is worth noting that the ichnospecific name is frequently misspelled as *brodericki* (Lockley & Meyer 2000; McRea *et al.* 2001).

The next major step in Yorkshire dinosaur ichnology was the recognition and description of true sauropod tracks (Fig. 12b) from the Ravenscar Group (Romano *et al.* 1999). At least three different sauropod tracks were described, and these were possibly made by three different makers. That it took so long for sauropod tracks to be recognized is perhaps astonishing, as individual tracks may reach up to over 1 m in length (Romano *et al.* 1999, 2007) and 12 m trackways have subsequently been described (Romano & Whyte 2003). Perhaps it was all a matter of scale, and previous track hunters were focusing on the generally smaller tridactyl forms?

The productive years

By the early part of the twenty-first century publications were beginning to appear at a faster rate, and emphasis was placed more on preservation, classification, behaviour and community structure than morphology alone. The important aspect of preservation was approached by the Sheffield Dinosaur Track Research Group, with experimental work using models of dinosaur feet in laboratory simulations (Fig. 12c) on various substrates (Manning 2004; Romano *et al.* 2007; Jackson *et al.* 2009). The first serious attempt to classify all known print types from the Cleveland Basin was by Romano & Whyte (2003). These authors recognized 29 different morphotypes that were divided into three groups (Fig. 12d): those made by habitual quadrupeds (sauropods and stegosaurids); mesaxonic tridactyl tracks; and tracks made by swimming animals (behavioural group). At the time the authors were unwilling to assign ichnospecific names to most of the prints, but suggested that as few as 15 ichnospecies were represented, and between 7 and 10 animal makers. At this stage of dinosaur trace fossil studies these authors (Romano & Whyte 2003, pp. 208–209) designated the Middle Jurassic of the Cleveland Basin as a 'megatracksite' (*sensu* Lockley & Hunt 1995). The diversity and range of morphology of tridactyl tracks has been investigated by another Sheffield research student (Dr Danny Elvidge) using a biometric approach.

The behaviour of dinosaurs has always attracted attention, and the tracks of the Cleveland Basin have contributed to our understanding of this. An ichnocoenosis of mainly swimming forms (Fig. 12e) was first recognized in the mid-1990s (Romano & Whyte 1996), but it was not until 6 years later, when the prints had been investigated in detail and fully analysed, that information on animal size, swimming gait and water depth could all be ascertained (Whyte & Romano 2002). In this paper the second new vertebrate ichnotaxon from the Cleveland Basin, *Characichnos tridactylus*, was named for a trackway from the Saltwick Formation made by a swimming dinosaur. Unusual footprint shapes (Fig. 12f) with distinctive features resulting from animals living in environments characterized by ephemeral ponds were only really understood after studying modern tracks left by dogs and captive emus (Whyte & Romano 2008). Trackway Gauge (Farlow 1992) has been reinvestigated in the light of the dimensions of the trackways of habitual quadrupeds from Yorkshire (Romano *et al.* 2007); this led to the development of a quantitative measure (Trackway Ratio) to define gauges more accurately (Romano *et al.* 2007). The controversial subject of dinosaur communities, as deduced from footprint data, has been recently investigated for the Cleveland Basin dinosaurs (Whyte *et al.* 2007). These authors (Whyte *et al.* 2007) recognized the difficulty in applying the concept to the dinosaur-dominated sequences of the Middle Jurassic of Yorkshire by demonstrating spatial heterogeneity of coeval ichnofaunas. In addition to the more recent emphasis on preservation, classification, behaviour and community structure, isolated finds continue to add to our knowledge of dinosaur diversity; such as the latest discovery of a new morphotype, representing the largest known theropod from the Ravenscar Group (Whyte *et al.* 2006, 2007).

Finally, non-dinosaurian tracks provide evidence of other vertebrates in the dinosaur-dominated communities of the Middle Jurassic of Yorkshire. Following the original recording of 'probably crocodilian' tracks from Cayton Bay over 100 years earlier (Hargreaves 1913), other crocodilian, chelonian (pond turtles) and fish traces have been recognized (Romano & Whyte 2003; Whyte *et al.* 2007).

Other parts

Skeletal material and tracks and trackways may be the principal and most common dinosaur fossils, but there are other types of evidence of dinosaurs, including nests and eggs, skin impressions, feeding traces, stomach stones and coprolites (Thulborn 1990). Of these only the latter have been recorded from the Cleveland area, although it might be hoped that all might yet be found within the Ravenscar Group. The best record of coprolites came from low in the Saltwick Formation and the remains, a cluster of about 250 originally spherical, 8–18 mm-diameter pellets, are rich in plant cuticle (Hill 1976). These have been accepted as dinosaurian (Chin 1997, 2007; Weishampel *et al.* 2004) and

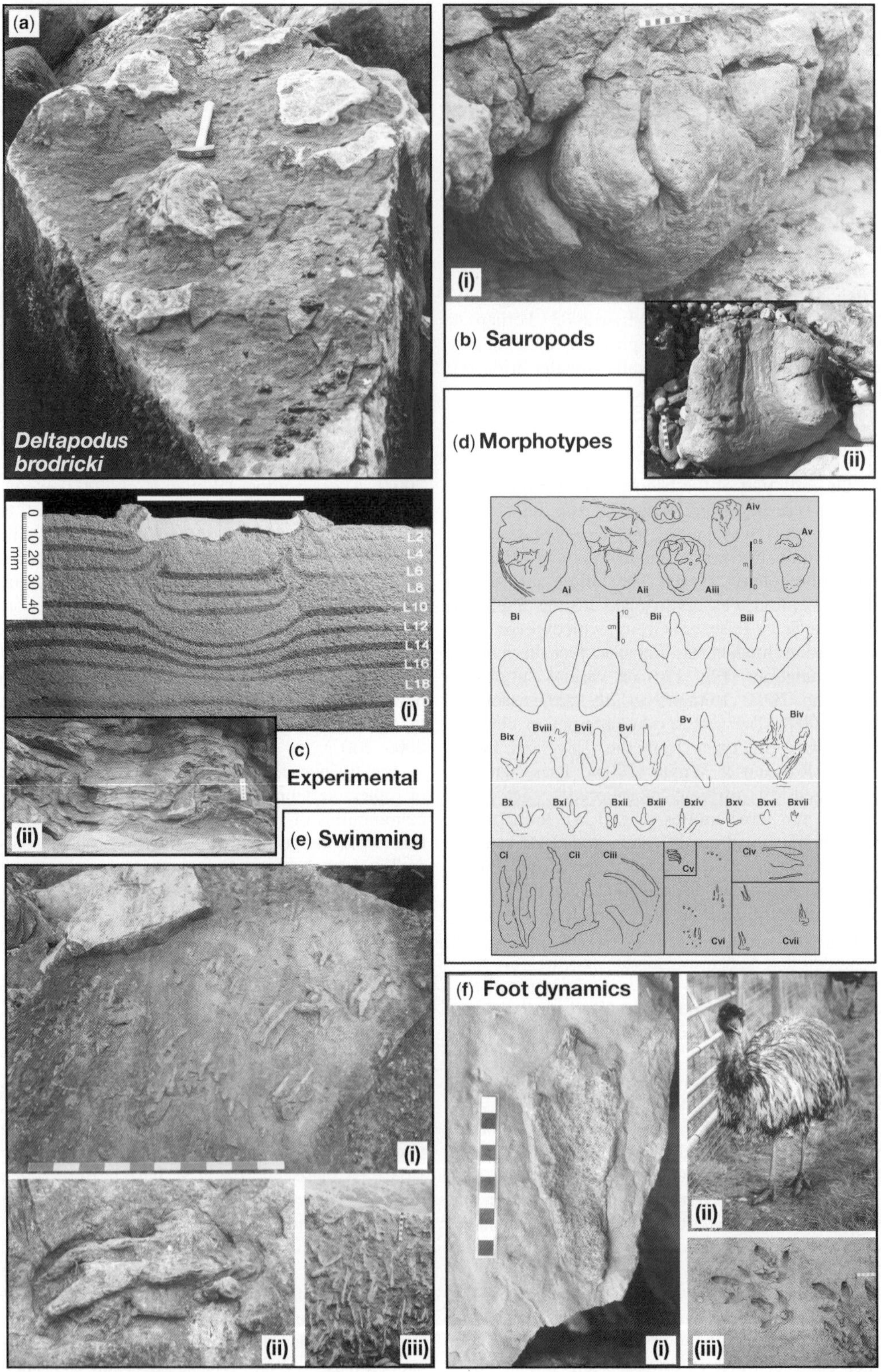
(a)
Deltapodus brodricki
(i)
(b) Sauropods
(ii)
(d) Morphotypes
Ai
Aii
Aiii
Aiv
Av
Bi
Bii
Biii
Biv
Bv
Bvi
Bvii
Bviii
Bix
Bx
Bxi
Bxii
Bxiii
Bxiv
Bxv
Bxvi
Bxvii
Ci
Cii
Ciii
Civ
Cv
Cvi
Cvii
0 10 20 30 40 mm
L2
L4
L6
L8
L10
L12
L14
L16
L18
(i)
(ii)
(c) Experimental
(e) Swimming
(i)
(ii)
(iii)
(f) Foot dynamics
(i)
(ii)
(iii)

Fig. 12.

provide evidence of dinosaur herbivory at a time when there appears to have been a major differentiation of the herbivorous dinosaurs to exploit different tiers of vegetation (Fastovsky & Smith 2004). Smaller clusters of smaller pellets rich in a variety of other sorts of plant material have been found at a few other sites (Harris 1946, 1951, 1956; Harris *et al.* 1974) but were probably not excreted by dinosaurs. In the unique ephemeral pool sequence (Whyte & Romano 2008), sideritized siltstone pellets infilled desiccation cracks and dinosaur footprints (Whyte & Romano 2008). These pellets help to reveal significant aspects of the footprint preservation and were interpreted as faecal in origin (Whyte & Romano 2008) but were most probably produced by invertebrates or by fish.

The apparently very limited preservation of dinosaur coprolites may, like the paucity of skeletal material, be the result of soil and sediment conditions coupled with vigorous recycling of nutrients. The differentiation of herbivorous dinosaurs was probably accompanied by physiological changes including the modification of digestive processes and the development of gut trituration (Farlow 1987; Fastovsky & Smith 2004). In this context the absence of stomach stones from the Ravenscar Group is perhaps surprising, especially as they would be expected to be obvious within sediments, which seldom exceed coarse sand size. As the Ravenscar Group could not have been a source of stomach stone material, any dinosaur employing gastroliths would have had to obtain the material from outside the depositional basin. Moving up the digestive process no evidence of feeding traces has yet been found. Although careful examination of the abundant plant fossils within the Ravenscar Group might yet add to the evidence of herbivory, the poor and selective preservation of skeletal evidence suggests that evidence of carnivory by marks on bone is probably extremely rare. Unfortunately, track-bearing surfaces are seldom exposed over the areal extent that would be needed to provide definite supporting evidence of dinosaur feeding habits of the types described by Chin (1997).

Some of the dinosaur tracks show evidence of padding on the maker's foot, and in a few cases there are features such as folds of skin (Dixon 1962) and groove marks (Romano & Whyte 2003; Whyte & Romano 2008), which give evidence of the character of the pedal skin. Otherwise, however, no skin impressions have yet been recorded.

The often waterlogged and acidic soils of the Cleveland Basin during Ravenscar Group times may have inhibited the dinosaurs from using the area as a breeding ground, and may thus explain the absence of eggs and nests. The dinosaurs may have moved to higher and drier ground around the margin of the basin for nesting, and this would be consistent with ichnological evidence suggestive of migratory habits (Romano & Whyte 2003; Whyte & Romano 2007). It should also be noted that there is, to date, only one published record of egg material from anywhere else in the world of this age (Garcia *et al.* 2006). The absence of any chelonian or crocodile eggs or nest structures is more surprising because, although the eggs would have been at best lightly calcified and susceptible to leaching, these creatures have a more riparian and non-migratory habit that would favour preservation.

International significance and the future

The long history of Yorkshire dinosaurs, in all its parts, is one that deserves to be more widely known, not only from a historical perspective but also because of the ongoing significance of the Yorkshire material for our better understanding of dinosaurs and other fossil saurians. As has already been indicated, the sparse records of dinosaurs and pterosaurs from the 'marine formations' each has its own importance or potential importance. While the great reduction in quarrying and exploitation of these formations means that future finds may be few and far between, it is likely that they too will each have their own imports and will underwrite the value of the earlier records.

Fig. 12. (*Continued*) Directions of ichnological research in Yorkshire over the past decade. (**a**) Trackway of *Deltapodus brodricki* Whyte & Romano 1995, the first new dinosaur ichnogenus and ichnospecies to be described from Yorkshire. The length of the hammer is 35 cm. (**b**) Sauropod tracks. Pes (i) and manus (ii) prints of types first recognized in 1999. Scale bar is 10 cm. (**c**) Experimental footprint simulation (i) compared to an example (ii) from the Scalby Formation, Scalby Bay. Scale bar in (ii) is 10 cm. (**d**) Diagrams, taken from actual specimens, showing the range of track morphotypes recognized from the non-marine rocks of the Ravenscar Group (Romano & Whyte 2003). The three principal groups (A, quadrupeds; B, tridactyl; C, swimmers) are discussed in the text. (**e**) Swimming tracks, Saltwick Formation, east of Whitby. (i) General view of large block showing swimming trackways (1 m scale bar). (ii) detail of single swimming track of *Characichnos tridactylus* Whyte & Romano 2002 from block. Print length is 22 cm. (iii) Surface dinoturbated by the action of swimming dinosaurs. Scale bar is 10 cm. (**f**) Foot dynamics. (i) Unusual track showing pronounced metatarsal extension, Saltwick Formation, Port Mulgrave. Scale bar is 10 cm. (ii) Captive emu (*Dromaius novaehollandiae*) used in replication of modern tracks. (iii) Tracks made by a captive emu in sand substrate. Scale bar is 10 cm.

The main body of dinosaur evidence comes from the Aalenian–Bathonian rocks of the Ravenscar Group and is of great significance on a global scale. The terrestrial Middle Jurassic has been called 'an enigmatic time due to a paucity of deposits of that age' (Fastovsky & Smith 2004). This is particularly true of the earlier parts of the Middle Jurassic, in the Aalenian and Bajocian, for which the skeletal records are particularly poor (Weishampel *et al.* 2004). Although the skeletal material from the lower part of the Ravenscar Group is not yet well identified, nearly as much bone has been recorded from the Aalenian Saltwick Formation as has been recorded in total from the Aalenian rocks of the rest of the world. When it has been better characterized, this material will contribute significantly to our understanding of Aalenian faunas and dinosaur evolution and biogeography. While the bone records from other parts of the Ravenscar Group are a smaller proportion of the global total for the Bajocian and Bathonian, they have a similar potential to contribute to the wider understanding of dinosaurs.

The interrelationships between the skeletal record and the ichnological record of the Ravenscar Group are also of great consequence. Although discovered rather late in the history of Yorkshire dinosaurs, it is these tracks and trackways that provide the evidence of greatest magnitude; evidence which is helping, and will continue to help, resolve the Middle Jurassic enigma. Thus, in addition to establishing the outline stratigraphy and occurrence of prints and ichnofaunas, the current renaissance in ichnological work has demonstrated the relationships between footprint preservation and substrate characters, a wide range of print morphotypes including the first stegosaur prints and prints revealing the swimming ability of dinosaurs. Current research is enhancing detailed knowledge of the stratigraphy, occurrence and preservation of prints. Occurences of prints on sloping surfaces are being investigated, and the different print types and their ontogenies are being characterized and classified. The level of knowledge reached is already at the stage where the Yorkshire material can be usefully compared with sites elsewhere both of the same and of different ages. Further integration of the ichnological record with the sedimentological, palaeobotanical and invertebrate palaeontological records will extend our knowledge of other aspects of dinosaur behaviour, including coprolites and, hopefully, even nests and eggs. The renaissance is far from over and there will yet be more parts to the history of Yorkshire dinosaurs!

We would like to thank Professor R. Moody for encouragement to contribute to the meeting. We are extremely indebted to P. Robinson, J. Hudson and R. Myerscough for bringing new finds to our attention and continuing the tradition of local involvement. We gratefully acknowledge the help given over the past 12 years by numerous volunteers belonging to Earthwatch International, as well as our past research students, Dr P. Manning, Dr S. Jackson and Dr D. Elvidge. Dr J. Wright (Royal Holloway & Bedford College), R. Osborne (Whitby Museum) and S. Ogilvy (York Museum) kindly supplied information on specimens and sources. Much appreciated technical assistance was received from P. Coles and R. Ashurst (University of Sheffield).

References

ANON. 1842. Association Britannique pour L'Avancement des Sciences. *L'Institut*, **10**, 11–14.

BENTON, M. 1996. *The Penguin Historical Atlas of the Dinosaurs*. Penguin Books, Harmondsworth, Middlesex.

BENTON, M. & SPENCER, P. S. 1995. *Fossil Reptiles of Great Britain*. Joint Nature Conservancy Committee, Chapman and Hall, London.

BENTON, M. & TAYLOR, M. 1984. Marine reptiles from the Upper Lias (Lower Toarcian, Lower Jurassic) of the Yorkshire coast. *Proceedings of the Yorkshire Geological Society*, **44**, 399–429.

BENTON, M. J. 1993. Reptilia. *In*: BENTON, M. J. (ed.) *The Fossil Record*, Volume 2. Chapman & Hall, London, 681–715.

BLACK, M., HEMINGWAY, J. E. & WILSON, V. 1934. Summer field meeting to North East Yorkshire, August 9th to 20th. *Proceedings of the Geologists' Association*, **45**, 298–299.

BRODRICK, H. 1907. A find!!! *Report of the Whitby Philosophical Society*, **85**, 8–9.

BRODRICK, H. 1908. Note on further footprint casts found in the Inferior Oolite at Saltwick. *Report of the Whitby Philosophical Society*, **86**, 6–7.

BRODRICK, H. 1909*a*. Note on Casts of Dinosaurian Footprints in the Lower Oolite at Whitby. *Report of the British Association for the Advancement of Science (Dublin 1908)*. John Murray, London, 707–708.

BRODRICK, H. 1909*b*. Note on Footprint casts from the Inferior Oolite near Whitby, Yorkshire. *Proceedings of the Liverpool Geological Society*, **10**, 327–335.

BUTLER, N., CHARNOCK, M. A., HAGER, K. O. & WATKINS, C. A. 2005. The Ravenscar Group: a coeval analogue for the Middle Jurassic reservoirs of the North Sea and offshore Mid-Norway. *In*: POWELL, A. J. & RIDING, J. B. *Recent Developments in Applied Biostratigraphy*. The Microplalaeontological Society, Special Publications, 43–53.

CADBURY, D. 2001. *The Dinosaur Hunters*. Fourth Estate, London.

CHIN, K. 1997. What did dinosaurs eat? Coprolites and other direct evidence of dinosaur diets. *In*: FARLOW, J. O. & BRETT-SURMAN, M. K. (eds) *The Complete Dinosaur*. Indiana University Press, Bloomington, IN, 264–290.

CHIN, K. 2007. The paleobiological implications of herbivorous dinosaur corolites from the Upper Cretaceous Two Medicine Formation of Montana: why eat wood? *Palaios*, **22**, 554–566.

CHURE, D. J. & MCINTOSH, J. S. 1989. *A Bibliography of the Dinosauria (Exclusive of the Aves) 1677–1986*. Museum of Western Colorado Palaeontology Series, **1**.

CLEEVELY, R. J. 1983. *World Palaeontological Collections*. British Museum (Natural History), Mansell Publishing, London.

COLBERT, E. H. 1961. *Dinosaurs: Their Discovery and Their World*. Dutton, New York.

COLBERT, E. H. 1983. *Dinosaurs: An Illustrated History*. Hammond, Maplewood, NJ.

DEAN, D. R. 1999. *Gideon Mantell and the Discovery of Dinosaurs*. Cambridge University Press, Cambridge.

DELAIR, J. B. & SARJEANT, W. A. S. 1975. The earliest discoveries of dinosaurs. *Isis*, **66**, 5–25.

DELAIR, J. B. & SARJEANT, W. A. S. 1985. History and bibliography of the study of fossil vertebrate footprints in the British Isles: Supplement 1973–1983. *Palaeogeography, Palaeoclimatology, Palaeoecology*, **49**, 123–160.

DELAIR, J. B. & SARJEANT, W. A. S. 2002. The earliest discoveries of dinosaur bones: the records re-examined. *Proceedings of the Geologists' Association*, **113**, 185–197.

DIXON, P. A. 1962. Reptilian footprints. *New Scientist*, **14**, 307.

ESCHARD, R., RAVENNE, C., HOUEL, P. & KNOX, R. 1991. Three-dimensional reservoir architecture of a valley-fill sequence and a deltaic aggredational sequence: influences of minor sea-level changes. *In*: MIALL, A. D. & TYLER, N. (eds) *The Three Dimensional Facies Architecture of Terrigenous Clastic Sediments and its Implications for Hydrocarbons Discovery and Recovery*. SEPM, Concepts in Sedimentology, **3**, 133–147.

FARLOW, J. O. 1987. Speculations about the diet and digestive physiology of herbivorous dinosaurs. *Paleobiology*, **13**, 60–72.

FARLOW, J. O. 1992. Sauropod tracks and track makers: integrating the ichnological and skeletal records. *Zubía*, **10**, 89–138.

FASTOVSKY, D. E. & SMITH, J. B. 2004. Dinosaur Paleoecology. *In*: WEISHAMPEL, D. B., DODSON, P. & OSMOLSKA, H. (eds) *The Dinosauria*, 2nd edn. University of California Press, Berkeley, CA, 614–626.

FILIPPELLI, G. M. 2002. The global phosphorus cycle. *In*: KOHN, M. J., RAKOVAN, J. & HUGHES, J. M. (eds) *Phosphates: Geochemical, Geobiological and Materials Importance. Reviews in Mineralogy and Geochemistry*, **48**, 391–425.

FOX-STRANGWAYS, C. 1892. *The Jurassic Rocks of Britain. Yorkshire*. Memoirs of the Geological Survey of the United Kingdom, London.

FOX-STRANGWAYS, C. & BARROW, G. 1915. *The Geology of the Country Between Whitby and Scarborough*, 2nd edn. Memoir of the Geological Survey, England and Wales, Sheets 35 and 44.

GALTON, P. M. 1980. *Priodontognathus phillipsii* (SEELEY), an ankylosaurian dinosaur from the Upper Jurassic (or possibly Lower Cretaceous) of England. *Neues Jahrbuch für Geologie und Paläontologie, Monatshefte*, **1980**, 477–489.

GALTON, P. M. 1983. A juvenile stegosaurian dinosaur, *Omosaurus phillipsi* Seeley from the Oxfordian (Upper Jurassic) of England. *Geobios*, **16**, 95–101.

GALTON, P. M. & UPCHURCH, P. 2004. Stegosauria. *In*: WEISHAMPEL, D. B., DODSON, P. & OSMOLSKA, H. (eds) *The Dinosauria*, 2nd edn. University of California Press, Berkeley, CA, 343–362.

GARCIA, G., MARIVAUX, L., PÉLISSIÉ, T. & VIANEY-LIAUD, M. 2006. Earliest Laurasian sauropod eggshells. *Acta Palaeontologica Polonica*, **51**, 99–104.

HALSTEAD, B. & HALSTEAD, J. 1981. *Dinosaurs*. Blandford Press, Poole, Dorset.

HANCOCK, N. J. & FISHER, M. J. 1981. Middle Jurassic North Sea deltas with particular reference to Yorkshire. *In*: ILLING, L. V. & HOBSON, G. D. (eds) *Petroleum Geology of the Continental Shelf of North-west Europe*. Institute of Petroleum, London, 186–195.

HARGREAVES, J. A. 1913. Fossil footprints near Scarborough. *The Naturalist*, **688**, 154–156.

HARGREAVES, J. A. 1914. Fossil footprints near Scarborough. *The Naturalist*, **673**, 92–95.

HARRIS, T. M. 1946. Notes on the Jurassic Flora of Yorkshire, 19–21. *Annals and Magazine of Natural History*, Series 11, **12**, 357–378.

HARRIS, T. M. 1951. Notes on the Yorkshire Flora, 4–51. *Annals and Magazine of Natural History*, Series 12, **4**, 915–937.

HARRIS, T. M. 1956. The investigation of a fossil plant. *Proceedings of the Royal Institution of Great Britain*, **36**, 1–11.

HARRIS, T. M., MILLINGTON, W. & MILLER, J. 1974. *The Yorkshire Flora, 4: Ginkgoales and Czekanowskiales*. British Musem (Natural History), London.

HESSELBO, S. P., MORGANS-BELL, H. S., MCELWAIN, J. C., REES, P. MCA., ROBINSON, S. A. & ROSS, C. E. 2003. Carbon-cycle perturbation in the Middle Jurassic and accompanying changes in the terrestrial environment. *Journal of Geology*, **111**, 259–276.

HILL, C. R. 1976. Coprolites of Ptilophyllum cuticles from the Middle Jurassic of North Yorkshire. *Bulletin of the British Museum (Natural History) Geology*, **27**, 289–294.

HOLTZ, T. R., MOLNAR, R. E. & CURRIE, P. J. 2004. Basal Tetanurae. *In*: WEISHAMPEL, D. B., DODSON, P. & OSMOLSKA, H. (eds) *The Dinosauria*, 2nd edn. University of California Press, Berkeley, CA, 71–110.

HUDLESTON, W. H. 1874. The Yorkshire Oolites. Part I. *Proceedings of the Geologists' Association*, **3**, 283–333.

HUDLESTON, W. H. 1878. The Yorkshire Oolites. Part II. Section 2. The Coralline Oolites, Coral Rag, and Supracoralline Beds. *Proceedings of the Geologists' Association*, **5**, 407–494.

HUENE, F. VON 1926. The carnivorous Saurischia in the Jura and Cretaceaous formations principlally in Europe. *Revista del Museo de La Plata*, **29**, 35–167.

IVENS, C. R. & WATSON, G. G. 1994. *Records of Dinosaur Footprints on the North East Yorkshire Coast 1895–1993*. Roseberry Publications, Middlesborough.

JACKSON, S., WHYTE, M. A. & ROMANO, M. 2009. Laboratory-controlled simulations of dinosaur footprints in sand: a key to understanding vertebrate track formation and preservation. *Palaios*, **24**, 222–238.

JANA, S. K. & DAS, S. S. 2002. A report of a 157.8 m.y.-old dinosaur bone from the Jurassic marine Chari Formation, Kutch, Gujarat and its taphonomic significance. *Current Science*, **82**, 85–88.

KENDALL, P. F. 1908. Reptilian Footprints in the lower Oolites at Saltwick. *The Naturalist*, **619**, 384.

KENDALL, P. F. & WROOT, H. E. 1924. *The Geology of Yorkshire*. Printed privately, Vienna.

LOCKLEY, M. & HUNT, A. P. 1995. *Dinosaur Tracks and other Fossil Footprints of the Western United States*. Columbia University Press, New York.

LOCKLEY, M. & MEYER, C. 2000. *Dinosaur Tracks and Other Fossil Footprints of Europe*. Columbia University Press, New York.

LYDEKKER, R. 1893. On the jaw of a new carnivorous dinosaur from the Oxford Clay of Peterborough. *Quarterly Journal of the Geological Society, London*, **49**, 284–287.

MANNING, P. L. 2004. A new approach to the analysis and interpretation of tracks: examples from the dinosauria. *In*: MCILROY, D. (ed.) *The Application of Ichnology to Palaeoenvironmental and Stratigraphic Analysis*. Geological Society, London, Special Publications, **228**, 93–123.

MCGOWAN, C. 2001. *The Dragon Seekers*. Perseus Publications, Cambridge, MA.

MCINTOSH, J. S. 1990. Sauropoda. *In*: WEISHAMPEL, D. B., DODSON, P. & OSMOLSKA, H. (eds) *The Dinosauria*. University of California Press, Berkeley, CA, 345–407.

MCINTOSH, J. S., BRETT-SURMAN, M. K. & FARLOW, J. O. 1997. Sauropods. *In*: FARLOW, J. O. & BRETT-SURMAN, M. K. (eds) *The Complete Dinosaur*. Indiana University Press, Bloomington, IN, 264–290.

MCRAE, R. T., LOCKLEY, M. G. & MEYER, C. A. 2001. Global distribution of purported ankylosaur track occurrences. *In*: CARPENTER, K. (ed.) *The Armoured Dinosaurs*. Indiana University Press, Bloomington, IN, 413–454.

NAISH, D. & MARTILL, D. M. 2007. Dinosaurs of Great Britain and the role of the Geological Society of London in their discovery: basal Dinosauria and Saurischia. *Journal of the Geological Society, London*, **164**, 493–510.

NAISH, D. & MARTILL, D. M. 2007. Dinosaurs of Great Britain and the role of the Geological Society of London in their discovery: Ornithischia. *Journal of the Geological Society, London*, **165**, 613–623.

NEWTON, E. T. 1888. On the skull, brain and auditory organ of a new species of pterosaurian (Scaphognathus purdoni) from the Upper Lias near Whitby, Yorkshire. *Philosphical Transactions of the Royal Society of London, Series B*, **179**, 503–537.

NORMAN, D. B. & BARRETT, P. M. 2002. Ornithiscian Dinosaurs from the Lower Cretaceous (Berriasian) of England. *Special Papers in Palaeontology*, **68**, 161–189.

OSBORNE, R. 1998. *The Floating Egg: Episodes in the Making of Geology*. Jonathan Cape, London.

OSBORNE, R. & BOWDEN, A. 2001. *The Dinosaur Coast: Yorkshire Rocks, Reptiles and Landscape*. North Yorks Moors National Park, Helmsley.

OWEN, R. 1841. A description of a portion of the skeleton of the Cetiosaurus, a gigantic extinct Saurian Reptile occurring in the Oolite formations of different portions of England. *Proceedings of the Geological Society, London*, **3**, 457–462.

OWEN, R. 1842. Report on British Fossil reptiles, Part II. *In*: *Report of the Eleventh Meeting of the British Association for the Advancement of Science*. Plymouth, England, July 1841. John Murray, London, 60–204.

OWEN, R. 1875. Monograph of the Fossil Reptilia of the Mesozoic formations. Part II. Monograph of the genus *Cetiosaurus*. *Monograph of the Palaeontographical Society*, **29**, 27–43.

OWEN, R. 1884. *A History of British Fossil Reptiles*. Cassell & Company, London.

PHILLIPS, J. 1871. *Geology of Oxford and the Valley of the Thames*. Clarendon Press, Oxford.

PHILLIPS, J. 1875. *Illustrations of the Geology of Yorkshire or a Description of the Strata and Organic Remains*, 3rd edn (R. Etheridge, ed.). John Murray, London.

RAWSON, P. & WRIGHT, J. K. 1992. *The Yorkshire Coast*. Geologists' Association Guide No. 34, London.

RAWSON, P. & WRIGHT, J. K. 1995. Jurassic of the Cleveland Basin, North Yorkshire. *In*: TAYLOR, P. D. (ed.) *Field Geology of the British Jurassic*. Geological Society, London, 173–208.

RAWSON, P. & WRIGHT, J. K. 2000. *The Yorkshire Coast*, 2nd edn. Geologists' Association Guide No. 34, London.

ROMANO, M. & WHYTE, M. A. 1996. Fossils explained 16: Trace Fossils 3 – dinosaur tracks. *Geology Today*, **12**, 75–79.

ROMANO, M. & WHYTE, M. A. 2003. Jurassic dinosaur tracks and trackways of the Cleveland basin, Yorkshire: preservation, diversity and distribution. *Proceedings of the Yorkshire Geological Society*, **54**, 185–215.

ROMANO, M., WHYTE, M. A. & JACKSON, S. J. 2007. Trackway Ratio: a new look at Trackway Gauge in the analysis of quadrupedal dinosaur trackways and its implications for ichnotaxonomy. *Ichnos*, **14**, 257–270.

ROMANO, M., WHYTE, M. A. & MANNING, P. L. 1999. New sauropod dinosaur prints from the Saltwick Formation (Middle Jurassic) of the Cleveland basin, Yorkshire. *Proceedings of the Yorkshire Geological Society*, **52**, 361–369.

SADLEIR, R., BARRETT, P. M. & POWELL, H. P. 2008. The anatomy and systematics of *Eustreptospondylus oxoniensis*, a theropod dinosaur from the Middle Jurassic of Oxfordshire, England. *Monograph of the Palaeontographical Society (Publication 627)*, **160**, 1–82.

SARJEANT, W. A. S. 1970. Fossil footprints from the middle Triassic of Nottinghamshire and the middle Jurassic of Yorkshire. *Mercian Geologist*, **3**, 269–282.

SARJEANT, W. A. S. 1974. A history and bibliography of the study of fossil vertebrate footprints in the British Isles. *Palaeogeography, Palaeoclimatology, Palaeoecology*, **16**, 265–378.

SARJEANT, W. A. S. 1987. The study of fossil vertebrate footprints: a short history and selective bibliography. *In*: LEONARDI, G. (ed.) *Glossary and Manual of Tetrapod Footprint Palaeoichnology*. Departamento Nacional da Produção Mineral, Brasilia, 1–19 (in English, with glossary in eight languages).

SARJEANT, W. A. S. 1997*a*. The earliest discoveries. *In*: FARLOW, J. O. & BRETT-SURMAN, M. K. (eds) *The Complete Dinosaur*. Indiana University Press, Bloomington, IN, 3–11.

SARJEANT, W. A. S. 1997*b*. History of dinosaur discoveries: early discoveries. *In*: CURRIE, P. J. &

PADIAN, K. (eds) *Encyclopedia of Dinosaurs*. Academic Press, New York, 341–347.

SCARBOROUGH PHILOSOPHICAL SOCIETY 1837. *Eighth Report of the Scarborogh Philospohical Society to August XXXI 1837*. Scarborough Philosophical Society, C.R. Todd, Scarborough.

SCHÄFER, W. 1972. *Ecology and Palaeoecology of Marine Environments*. Oliver & Boyd, Edinburgh.

SEELEY, H. G. 1869. *Index to the Fossil Remains of Aves, Ornithosauria, and Reptilia from the Secondary System of Strata Arranged in the Woodwardian Museum of the University of Cambridge*. Deighton, Bell and Co., Cambridge.

SEELEY, H. G. 1875. On the maxilliary bone of a new dinosaur (*Priodontognathus phillipsii*), contained in the Woodwardian Museum of the University of Cambridge. *Quarterly Journal of the Geological Society, London*, **31**, 439–443.

SEELEY, H. G. 1893. On *Omosaurus phillipsi* (Sealey). *Annual Report of the Yorkshire Philosophical Society*, **1892**, 52–57.

SHEPPARD, T. 1908. Footprints in a Yorkshire Sandstone. *The Naturalist*, **619**, 300–301.

THULBORN, A. 1990. *Dinosaur Tracks*. Chapman & Hall, London.

TORRENS, H. 1997. Politics and palaeontology: Richard Owen and the invention of dinosaurs. *In*: FARLOW, J. O. & BRETT-SURMAN, M. K. (eds) *The Complete Dinosaur*. Indiana University Press, Bloomington, IN, 175–190.

UPCHURCH, P. & MARTIN, J. 2003. The anatomy and taxonomy of Cetiosaurus (Saurischia, Sauropoda) from the Middle Jurassic of England. *Journal of Vertebrate Paleontology*, **23**, 208–231.

UNDERHILL, J. R. & PARTINGTON, M. A. 1993. Jurassic thermal doming and deflation in the North Sea: implications of the sequence stratigraphic evidence. *In*: PARKER, J. R. (ed.) *Petroleum Geology of Northwest Europe: Proceedings of the 4th Conference*. Geological Society, London, 337–345.

UPCHURCH, P., BARRETT, P. M. & DODSON, P. 2004. Sauropoda. *In*: WEISHAMPEL, D. B., DODSON, P. & OSMOLSKA, H. (eds) *The Dinosauria*, 2nd edn. University of California Press, Berkeley, CA, 259–322.

VICKARYOUS, M. K., MARYAŃSKA, T. & WEISHAMPEL, D. B. 2004. Ankylosauria. *In*: WEISHAMPEL, D. B., DODSON, P. & OSMOLSKA, H. (eds) *The Dinosauria*, 2nd edn. University of California Press, Berkeley, CA, 363–392.

WEISHAMPEL, D. B. 1990. Dinosaurian distribution. *In*: WEISHAMPEL, D. B., DODSON, P. & OSMOLSKA, H. (eds) *The Dinosauria*. University of California Press, Berkeley, 63–139.

WEISHAMPEL, D. B., DODSON, P. & OSMOLSKA, H. 1990. Introduction. *In*: WEISHAMPEL, D. B., DODSON, P. & OSMOLSKA, H. (eds) *The Dinosauria*. University of California Press, Berkeley, CA, 1–7.

WEISHAMPEL, D. B., BARRETT, P. M. *ET AL*. 2004. Dinosaur distribution. *In*: WEISHAMPEL, D. B., DODSON, P. & OSMOLSKA, H. (eds) *The Dinosauria*, 2nd edn. University of California Press, Berkeley, CA, 517–606.

WHYTE, M. A. & ROMANO, M. 1981. A footprint in the sands of time. *Journal of the University of Sheffield Geological Society*, **7**, 323–330.

WHYTE, M. A. & ROMANO, M. 1993. Footprints of a sauropod dinosaur from the middle Jurassic of Yorkshire. *Proceedings of the Geologists' Association*, **104**, 195–199.

WHYTE, M. A. & ROMANO, M. 1995. Probable sauropod footprints from the middle Jurassic of Yorkshire, England. *Gaia*, **10**, 15–26.

WHYTE, M. A. & ROMANO, M. 2001. Probable stegosaurian dinosaur tracks from the Saltwick Formation (Middle Jurassic) of Yorkshire, England. *Proceedings of the Geologists' Association*, **112**, 45–54.

WHYTE, M. A. & ROMANO, M. 2002 (for 2001). A dinosaur ichnocoenosis from the Middle Jurassic of Yorkshire, UK. *Ichnos*, **8**, 223–234.

WHYTE, M. A. & ROMANO, M. 2007. Reconstruction of Middle Jurassic dinosaur-dominated communities from the vertebrate ichnofauna of the Cleveland Basin of Yorkshire, UK. *Ichnos*, **14**, 117–129.

WHYTE, M. A. & ROMANO, M. 2008. Dinosaur footprints associated with an ephemeral pool in the Middle Jurassic of Yorkshire, UK. *Oryctos*, **8**, 15–27.

WHYTE, M. A., ROMANO, M. & ELVIDGE, D. J. 2007. Reconstruction of Middle Jurassic dinosaur communities from the vertebrate ichnofauna of the Cleveland Basin of Yorkshire, UK. *Ichnos*, **14**, 117–129.

WHYTE, M. A., ROMANO, M., HUDSON, J. G. & WATTS, W. 2006. Discovery of the largest theropod dinosaur track known from the Middle Jurassic of Yorkshire. *Proceedings of the Yorkshire Geological Society*, **56**, 77–80.

WILLIAMSON, W. C. 1834. On the distribution of organic remains in the Lias Series of Yorkshire, with a view to facilitate its identification by giving the situation of its fossils. *Proceedings of the Geological Society, London*, **2**, 82–83.

WILLIAMSON, W. C. 1836. On the distribution of Organic Remains in the Oolitic formations on the coast of Yorkshire. *Proceedings of the Geological Society, London*, **2**, 429–432.

WILLIAMSON, W. C. 1837. On the distribution of fossil remains on the Yorkshire Coast, from the Lower Lias to the Bath Oolite. *Transactions of the Geological Society, London*, Series 2, **5**, 223–242.

WILLIAMSON, W. C. 1867. On a cheirotherian footprint from the Keuper sandstone of Daresbury, Cheshire. *Quarterly Journal of the Geological Society, London*, **23**, 56–57.

WILLIAMSON, W. C. 1884. Bibliographical Notices of Eminent Geologists; III. 'John Williamson'. *Proceedings of the Yorkshire Geological and Polytechnic Society*, **8**, 295–313.

WILLIAMSON, W. C. 1896. *Reminiscences of a Yorkshire Naturalist*. George Redway, London.

WRIGHT, J. K. 1978. The Corallian succession in the Malton Bypass. *Geologists' Association Circular*, **807**, 9–10.

WRIGHT, T. 1860. On the subdivisions of the Inferior Oolite in the South of England, compared with the equivalent beds of the formation on the Yorkshire Coast. *Quarterly Journal of the Geological Society, London*, **16**, 1–48.

YOUNG, G. & BIRD, J. 1828. *A Geological Survey of the Yorkshire Coast: Describing the Strata and Fossils Occurring Between the Humber and the Tees, from the German Ocean to the Plain of York*, 2nd edn. R. Kirby, Whitby.

Chirotherium, the Liverpool footprint hunters and their interpretation of the Middle Trias environment

A. J. BOWDEN*, G. R. TRESISE & W. SIMKISS

Earth Sciences, National Museums Liverpool, William Brown Street, Liverpool L38EN, UK

**Correspondence author (e-mail: alan.bowden@liverpoolmuseums.org.uk)*

Abstract: The footprints called '*Chirotherium*', because of their resemblance to human hands, were found in Triassic sandstones from Germany in 1834 and Cheshire in 1838. As no bones or other fossil remains were found at either locality, the trackmaker's identity was a mystery. Marsupial mammals were first suggested but in 1842 Richard Owen confidently identified the prints as those of labyrinthodont amphibians. Later discoveries in Cheshire and elsewhere indicated that the trackmakers were more likely to have been pseudosuchian reptiles. In 1965 strong confirmation of this view came from the discovery in Switzerland of the skeleton of *Ticinosuchus ferox*.

The absence of fossil remains associated with the footprints has always been ascribed to the arid climate of Triassic times – a view reinforced by Henry Charles Beasley in 1907. A more moderate viewpoint was put forward by George Highfield Morton in 1898, who took note of the traces of flora found in the local Triassic strata. Pictorial representations of the Anisian through the late nineteenth and twentieth centuries indicate varying interpretations of the degree of aridity from sparsely vegetated landscapes to sand sea desert. Recent work shows that the environment in a local context was more richly vegetated and humid than had previously been supposed and that the historical interpretation of aridity has probably been overstated. A modern context may, perhaps, be seen in the river valleys of the Atacama Desert in northern Chile. Here, permanent fertile fluvial systems support a mixed indigenous flora of giant horsetails and conifers. The flora displays an adaptation to high groundwater salinity, which may have lessons in interpretation of the Anisian environment.

In the 1830s the study of fossil footprints was in its infancy. The first British discovery had been made 10 years earlier in 1824, when a fossil trackway was discovered in Permian sandstones being quarried at Corncockle Muir in Dumfriesshire. Mr Carruthers of Dormont in Dumfriesshire visited the quarry and noticed the fossil track of a quadrupedal animal. He arranged for the track to be extracted and then presented it to a local clergyman, the Reverend Henry Duncan (1774–1846). Duncan was sufficiently interested to make plaster casts of the footprints, which he sent to the Reverend William Buckland (1784–1856) at Oxford University.

Buckland, one of the foremost palaeontologists of the day, was not a man to theorize when he could experiment. He wrote back: 'I made a crocodile walk over soft pye crust, and took impressions of his feet, which shew decidedly that your sandstone footmarks are not crocodile'. He then repeated the experiment with tortoises 'of three distinct species' and concluded that the tracks from Corncockle Muir were, indeed, the footprints of tortoises.

Ten years later in 1834 came a more dramatic discovery from Germany – more dramatic because the prints found in Triassic sandstones at Hildburghausen in Thuringia were said to resemble 'a large man's hand in a thick fur glove' (Fig. 1).

Sarjeant (in Tresise & Sarjeant 1997, pp. 5–7) has described the convoluted process by which they were named. The prints were first reported in a *Sendschrieben* sent by Friedrich K. L. Sickler (1773–1836) to the German anatomist Johann Friedrich Blumenbach (1752–1840). The German palaeontologist Johann Jakob Kaup (1803–1873) provided the priority for the Linnaean binomial naming of the print. In a communication he wrote:

Darmstadt, 2 February 1835

> You have read of the large, so-called four handed footprints from Hildburghausen. I, myself, own a stone slab with something similar. The footprints are in a form, as if made by hands and raised, namely in that the soft sandstone has filtered into the mould that lies below – this mould is also sandstone with a fine clay layer. To me the animal appears to be an enormous marsupial with thumbs on the rear and front feet. In the aforementioned quarry [Hildburghausen] bone remains are also said to be found, which might provide further clarification. The historical context of the discovery is recorded in an open letter from Official Councillor SICKLER to BLUMENBACH. Since the animal is heretofore unknown, I have named it Chirotherium Barthii [sic] and reserve the right – if it should be an amphibian, which is unlikely in view of its gait - to change the name to Chirosaurus.

(Kaup 1835, pp. 327–328)

From: Moody, R. T. J., Buffetaut, E., Naish, D. & Martill, D. M. (eds) *Dinosaurs and Other Extinct Saurians: A Historical Perspective*. Geological Society, London, Special Publications, **343**, 209–228.
DOI: 10.1144/SP343.12 0305-8719/10/$15.00

Fig. 1. Slab showing *Chirotherium barthi* track from Hessburg, Hildburghausen, Germany (NHM specimen R.728).

Thus, the prints were named *Chirotherium* – from two Greek words meaning 'hand animal'. However, classical scholars questioned the orthography of Kaup's name, pointing out the Greek for hand was *cheiros* and therefore it should be named *Cheirotherium*. This was the usage adopted by Buckland and most nineteenth century geologists. However, the rules laid down by the International Code of Zoological Nomenclature (Ride *et al.* 1985) emphasized priority and, thus, Kaup's spelling was formally adopted. The identity of the *Chirotherium* animal was a mystery for over a century because the sandstone in which the footprints were found yielded no fossil remains of the animals that had left them: there were no bones, no teeth, no skeletal material of any kind. No living animal, nor any in the then sketchily known fossil record, could have left such prints. So only the footprints survived as proof that *Chirotherium* had ever existed.

Buckland described and illustrated these strange footprints from Germany in a new volume of the series of scientific textbooks known as the 'Bridgewater Treatises' (Buckland 1836). Two years later he would be shown similar footprints in a quarry on Storeton Hill in Cheshire.

The Storeton Hill discoveries

In the quarries at Storeton Hill, the massive yellow and white Triassic sandstones were worked for building stone. About 40 ft down in the quarry face were three thin seams of clay, some 2 ft apart. Because of these clay seams, the sandstone at this level tended to break into thin slabs that were useless for building.

It was on the underside of such worthless slabs that the Storeton workmen discovered these hand-like prints in June 1838. They had, in fact, found similar prints in the past but had always explained them as being those of the victims of Noah's Flood. They were, they believed, the handprints of adults and children, together with smaller prints left by domestic animals like cats, dogs and chickens, all of them caught up in the swirling floodwaters and leaving their prints in the mud as they tried desperately to scramble to safety.

But that theory could hardly account for the new find (Fig. 2). The workmen could trace the line of footprints for a distance of almost 30 ft across the rock surface. These prints could not be attributed to the drowning victims of the Flood. It was clear that something had walked across the mud – some animal that had forefeet which were only half the size of the hind feet, and which left the prints of right and left feet in a straight line.

By a lucky chance the quarry was visited by the Liverpool architect John Cunningham (1799–1873), who had a keen interest in geology. Some 20 years later, on 13 December 1858, he described, in a letter to the vertebrate palaeontologist Richard Owen (1804–1892), how he had recognized the prints:

> In the spring of 1838 I went across to Storeton quarry to select some blocks of stone ... I pointed out to the Foreman several beds or seams of clay between the strata and requested when he lifted the strata reposing on the clay beds he would examine the under surfaces of the slabs that rested on the clay beds and if he found

Fig. 2. Slab showing *Chirotherium storetonense*, found at Storeton Quarry in June 1838 (Bootle Museum specimen 10).

any impressions of vegetables or animals he would immediately communicate to me the circumstance. In the course of 10–12 days after I had made the request he sent a person over to my office in hot haste with the intelligence that he had found the impressions of 'a man's hands and knees'. I of course lost no time in getting over to the Quarry and was much gratified with the spectacle presented by the slab which I saw at once were the impressions of the animal called by Professor Kaup the cheirotherium similar to those found at Hilburghausen.

(Cunningham 1858, in the NHM archives)

Cunningham had read Buckland's Bridgewater Treatise with its description of the hand-like footprints from Germany and wrote to Buckland to tell him of the new find. His letter was luckily timed because, 2 months later in August, Buckland was to attend the annual meeting of the British Association for the Advancement of Science, which that year was held in Newcastle-on-Tyne. So on his way north from Oxford he was able to make a detour to visit Storeton Quarry in Cunningham's company. He was thus able to carry news of the find to the British Association meeting held at Newcastle-on-Tyne from 20 to 25 August 1838, confirming that the footprints did, indeed, resemble the *Chirotherium* prints from Germany:

Dr Buckland remarked that, having visited Storeton Hill on his way to Newcastle, he found the closest resemblance between the phenomena of these quarries and those of Hesseberg near Hilburghausen from whence he has seen many large slabs bearing casts of footsteps of Cheirotherium and of several small reptiles. The cause of their preservation in each case seems to have been the same, namely the deposition of a bed of thin greenish clay between the two beds of sandstone. This clay retained the impressions or marks made on it by feet until the next succeeding deposit of sand filled them with casts . . .

Dr Buckland considered the sandstone of Storeton Hill to be referable to the same portion of the New Red Sandstone formation as the strata near Hilburghausen and also the strata containing footsteps at Corn Cockle Muir in Dumfrieshire. Mr Hugh Strickland has discovered the track of a reptile near Warwick in sandstone which he refers to the Cuyper [Keuper] formation.

Dr Buckland expressed his acknowledgements of the scientific zeal and exirtions of Mr Cunningham and Mr Tomkinson in bringing the discoveries before the Natural History Society of Liverpool, and causing splendid specimens of slabs covered with footmarks to be preserved in the Museum of that Society, and accurate engravings to be taken from them.

Some of the slabs had their surface covered by veins of sandstone similar to those which in the slabs from Hessberg have been mistaken for inter-tangled roots. In both cases they originate from cracks in the thin bed of clay, like those at the bottom of a dry pond, which were filled with sand.

([Buckland] 1839, p. 85)

He also suggested that Cunningham should prepare a paper on the finds which Buckland offered to read to the Geological Society of London. Cunningham wrote back to Buckland on 5 September 1838 stating:

We will certainly avail ourselves of the honor of your proffered services to bring the subject in a more extended form before the Geological Society of London . . . At the same time I trust you will excuse me for stating that I cannot consent to the communication being made a personal matter as it would be doing a great injustice to my friends above mentioned [the Reverend Mr Dwyer and Dr Sutherland] and other members of the Society who have taken a lively interest in the discovery. I would therefore beg as a favour that you will bring it before the Geological Society of London as a communication from the Natural History Society of Liverpool.

(Cunningham 1838 in the Oxford University Museum Archives).

It was originally intended that Cunningham's paper be read before the Geological Society on 21 November 1838. However, the Society Secretary, William Lonsdale, heard that Sir Phillip Grey Egerton was also preparing a paper on *Chirotherium.* Therefore it was agreed to postpone Cunningham's paper so that it can be read alongside Egerton's paper. Buckland read Cunningham's paper on the Storeton finds to the Geological

Society on 5 December 1838, although not quite in the form that Cunningham had written it. Buckland was evidently prepared to substitute his own views whenever he disagreed with Cunningham's conclusions.

With the benefit of hindsight, it can be seen that some of these changes were justified. It was Buckland's suggestion that the footprints were those of reptiles, rather than mammals as Cunningham had assumed. He also recognized that if the thumb-like digit was indeed the first (innermost) toe, as Cunningham believed, then the animal must have crossed its legs while walking because the right-hand prints lay a little to the left and the left-hand prints a little to the right. Buckland was understandably doubtful if this could be the case. Conversely, Cunningham had suggested that the clay layers in which the prints were impressed had been subsequently buried under wind-blown sand. Buckland, however, insisted that they must have been left on a beach to be subsequently buried by the incoming tide. As the Triassic sandstones were thought to have formed in an arid environment, Cunningham's suggestion seems eminently reasonable and Buckland's amendment over-reliant on the ripple-marking seen on the slabs.

The final point made in the paper was that the *Chirotherium* footprints were not the only, nor indeed the most numerous, tracks in the sandstone. Many of the slabs were crowded with footprints. 'It is clear' wrote Cunningham 'that the clay beds on which they rested must have been traversed by multitudes of animals' ([Cunningham] 1838, p. 14).

To emphasis this final point, Buckland showed tracings made by James Yates of four of the smaller footprints from the lower footprint bed. The paper by Egerton that followed Buckland's presentation described two footprints from his own collection, which he named *Chirotherium Herculis* (Egerton 1838). He provided measurements contrasting these giant prints with both the Hessburg prints and the prints from Storeton. The problems posed by these '*herculis*' prints have been discussed in detail elsewhere (see Tresise 1991; Tresise & Sarjeant 1997) and need not be reiterated here. Suffice to say that they led King *et al.* to recommend 'that the use of the name *herculis* be discontinued' (King *et al.* 2005, p. 260).

In addition, Egerton's careful measurements to differentiate between the Hessberg and Storeton footprints were unintentionally misleading as one crucial type of Storeton footprint had gone unrecorded. It was not until 12 December, a week after the meeting, that Cunningham wrote to Buckland:

> In my opinion we have impressions of several species of *Chirotherium* on Storeton hill. Some hands are broad, having short phalanges and spread out very much, others again have long tapering fingers, compressed and altogether like a lady's hand.

It was the latter type that formed the trackway on which Egerton had based his measurements. However, there can be little doubt that the broader 'spread out' prints must have resembled those from Germany more closely than did the narrower 'lady's hand' forms. Unfortunately, this crucial letter from Cunningham (preserved in the Oxford University Museum archives) was never published or publicized, and the existence of these broader *Chirotherium* prints at Storeton went unrecorded in the nineteenth-century literature.

Cunningham had, moreover, referred to 'several species of *Cheirotherium* on Storeton hill', implying more than two. Three species are now recognized by King *et al.* (2005), distinguished both by their size and by the proportions and spread of their digits. In increasing size, they are *Chirotherium sickleri* Kaup, *Chirotherium storetonense* Morton and *Chirotherium barthii* Kaup. The authors admit, however, that 'tracks founds in the same area will almost certainly be representative of . . . different ages of animals at different stages of growth' (King *et al.* 2005, p. 241). In other words, it is possible that supposedly different ichnospecies may represent no more than the differences between juvenile and adult forms.

The Liverpool Natural History Society certainly believed this; in the autumn of 1838 they published four lithographs to illustrate the Storeton finds. Plate 2 showed the slab presented to the British Museum (now NHM specimen R729) on which the 'lady's hand' trackway (i.e. *Chirotherium storetonense*) is crossed by *C. sickleri* prints, which the plate's caption confidently claims are 'the best examples of the *young* animal's feet yet obtained'. *C. storetonense* and *C. sickleri* were clearly regarded as adult and juvenile forms of the same animal.

Later finds in Cheshire

Once footprints had been described from Cheshire, they began to be reported from other localities in the area: in 1840 from a quarry in Rathbone Street, Liverpool (Yates 1841); in 1842 from Lymm near Warrington (Hawkshaw 1843); in 1843 from Delamere Forest and from Weston, near Runcorn (Ormerod 1843, republished 1868); and in 1848 from Flaybrick Hill, Birkenhead (Cunningham 1848).

The quarries at Lymm would initially rival Storeton as rich sources of footprints. The Triassic sandstones worked there are now known to be younger than those quarried at Storeton – they occurred within the Tarporley Siltstone Formation, which overlies the Helsby Sandstone of Storeton.

The Lymm Sandstone was also very different in appearance. In contrast to the white and yellow sandstone found at Storeton, the Lymm rocks were a dark brownish red (the colour of dried blood). They were coloured by iron oxides but these were patchily distributed, and those parts of the sandstone where ferric iron was lacking were greenish-grey in colour. Suncracks, seldom seen in the ripple-marked sandstones of Storeton, were usually present at Lymm.

Perhaps reflecting the difference in age, the two localities also produced different assemblages of footprints. The 'lady's hand' prints so characteristic of Storeton were never found at Lymm where the prints were always broader. Like the *Chirotherium barthii* prints from Germany, they resembled a man's hand rather than a woman's. However, the initial reports on the Lymm quarries (Hawkshaw 1843; Rawlinson 1853) made no mention of this.

It was not until 1863 that George Highfield Morton (1826–1900), (Fig. 3), the founder of the Liverpool Geological Society, noted this distinction. It is greatly to be regretted that this crucial paper was published only as a two-paragraph abstract (Morton 1863*a*). Morton pointed out that no specific name had hitherto been given to the 'lady's hand' tracks from Storeton and proposed the name *Chirotherium storetonense.* He noted that this was the smallest of the three forms found in Cheshire, the others being *C. Kaupii* from Lymm and Egerton's *C. herculis* supposedly from Tarporley. Thus, a quarter of a century after Cunningham's paper, the Storeton trackways at last had a distinctive identity There was, however, still no mention of the occurrence of broader prints at Storeton nor whether these, like those from Lymm, could be equated with the *C. barthii* prints from Germany.

Fig. 3. George Highfield Morton (1826–1900), photographed on Bidston Hill, 1886 (LGS Archive, NML).

The Lymm quarries proved to be only short lived, and by the 1860s had been abandoned and infilled leaving Storeton as the only local source of *Chirotherium* prints. Storeton was, however, no longer so prolific a source as it had been in the 1830s. On 15 August 1838, only 2 months after the first trackway discoveries, the Storeton tramway was opened. This connected the quarry with Bromborough Pool, a tidal creek of the River Mersey, some 3 km to the east. For much of the distance, the stone-laden wagons ran downhill under the influence of gravity and speeds of over 20 miles an hour could be reached. Roads on the Wirral were notoriously poor at the time and it was claimed that the tramway allowed stone to be carried to the Mersey in as many minutes as it had formerly taken days (see Jermy 1981).

The tramway, moreover, ran through the South Quarry (the source of the footprint finds) to continue along the western side of Storeton Hill until it reached a smaller quarry, which lay 1 km to the north. Once the tramway was opened, it was the North Quarry that became the main supplier of Storeton stone. Work continued in the South Quarry on a small scale but it was the North Quarry that provided the stone for the civic buildings in the centre of Birkenhead, the Birkenhead docks and even for the first Philharmonic Hall in Liverpool – a building which John Cunningham designed and in which he took great pride. There are no records of footprints being found in the North Quarry. A photograph (see Sarjeant 1974, fig. 9; Tresise & Sarjeant 1997, fig. 14.15) allegedly shows the footprint bed at the top of the North Quarry, but it is likely that for most of its length the sandstone worked there came from the lower levels so that the footprint bed was not exposed in the quarry face.

By the 1890s neither the North or South quarries at Storeton were still in operation. The only quarry still working was the small Higher Bebington White Freestone Quarry, which lay immediately to the north of the disused South Quarry. Despite this, the decade was marked by a revival of interest in the Cheshire footprints, which can be jointly credited to two local geologists. In 1891 G. H. Morton published the second edition of his book *The*

Geology of the Country Around Liverpool. This edition (Morton 1891) was more than four times the length of the original (Morton 1863*b*) and the section on the Storeton quarries was illustrated by the first published photographs of the *Chirotherium storetonense* footprints.

It seems likely that it was the reappearance of Morton's book which stimulated the interest of Henry Charles Beasley (1836–1919), who has rightly been called 'by far the most important figure in the history of British vertebrate ichnology' (Sarjeant 1974, p. 295). Beasley realized that, as yet, there had been no systematic attempt to classify the Triassic footprints found in Britain and he was to devote the rest of his life to rectifying this omission. His first classification (Beasley 1896) listed eight types of print, which he did not name but denoted by the letters A–H. There can be little doubt that it was Beasley's paper which persuaded Morton, in turn, to attempt a classification of his own. An appendix to the third edition of *The Geology of the Country Around Liverpool* (Morton 1897) listed six types of print, as opposed to Beasley's eight. Unlike Beasley, however, Morton was prepared to allocate scientific names to the six. This would prove to be Morton's final contribution to the footprint literature, prior to his death in March 1900.

Beasley's work continued into the new century. In 1903 the British Association for the Advancement of Science (BAAS) met in Southport and set up a committee to study the fauna and flora of the British Trias. The Committee's Secretary was Joseph Lomas (1860–1908), a part-time lecturer in geology at University College Liverpool. The original members of this Committee were all academics but Lomas ensured that Beasley became a co-opted member (see Fig. 4). Beasley would produce annual reports for the Committee over the next 6 years. In the first two (Beasley 1904, 1905), he extended and refined his footprint classification, subdividing the alphabetical groups he had proposed 10 years before.

It was also in 1905 that the Higher Bebington White Freestone Quarry was purchased by Charles

Fig. 4. Liverpool Geological Society field trip, Flaybrick Hill Quarry, 1885. Members include: Henry Beasley (second from the left); Osmund W. Jeffs (third from the left); T. Mellard Reade, President (fourth from the left); Joseph Lomas (at the rear, fifth from the right); and Charles Ricketts (at the front, third from the right) (LGS Archive, NML).

Wells, a quarry master whose family firm was based in Bootle, and who equipped the quarry with mobile cranes to facilitate the operations. Beasley was quick to take advantage of this. The following year he reported:

> The Quarry having lately changed hands, a suggestion was made to Mr Charles Wells, the new proprietor, that he would much assist geologists if he would allow his men to preserve uninjured any good footprints which might be found. This he readily agreed to do, with the result that, on reaching the footprint bed, the slabs were carefully raised and every facility given for their inspection.
>
> (Beasley, undated manuscript note in a British Association Committee ledger, p. 37, in the Beasley Archive, National Museums Liverpool)

More than 20 slabs were raised in 1906, and these were stood on end and allowed to weather naturally so that the clay coating flaked away without injury to even the most delicate markings. Like Cunningham in 1838, Beasley was impressed by the diversity of tracks present:

> On some 400 square feet of surface, we have footprints of at least 10 quite distinguishable varieties, probably made by as many different species of animals, most certainly, all of them probably reptiles.
>
> (Beasley 1907, p. 170)

Chirotherium storetonense was well represented among these 10 varieties but there was also a superb trail of footprints of a different type of *Chirotherium*. These were best seen on a slab 11 ft long, which was crossed by a trail of 15 footprints (Fig. 5). Unlike *Chirotherium storetonense*, which left footprints pointing straight forward, this animal walked with its feet splayed outward. However, the most striking difference was in the size of the forefeet – those of *Chirotherium storetonense* were about half the size of the hindfeet, whereas the forefeet of the new form, later named *Isochirotherium lomasi* (Haubold), were exceptionally tiny and made only the lightest of impressions. So faint are they that the German palaeontologist Othenio Abel (1875–1946) misnamed these tracks *Chirotherium bipedale*, claiming that the trackmaker must have been a biped as no trace of the manus can be seen (Abel 1935).

Lomas described these tracks to the BAAS meeting in Leicester in 1907 (Lomas 1908) but his main interest was in the sedimentology of the Trias sediments. He had spoken on the subject to the Liverpool Geological Society (Lomas 1907) and in 1908 travelled to Algeria to study the desert sandstones there on behalf of the BAAS Committee. The trip ended in disaster on 16 December 1908, when the train he was travelling in crashed and Lomas was among a number of passengers killed. The death of their energetic Secretary also proved to be the death blow of the BAAS Committee. Beasley had little time to prepare one final report before it was disbanded. He had hoped that in this report he would be able to allocate scientific names to his footprint types. A classification was drafted (see Tresise & Sarjeant 1997, p. 118) but was never published. In the end Beasley concluded: 'The reasons for not giving generic and specific names to the various forms ... still hold good' (Beasley 1910, p. 152). He was to publish one final paper on footprints (Beasley 1914), which extended his alphabetical classification to type Q. Later, in 1914, he fell seriously ill and was thereafter housebound until his death in December 1919.

The Storeton quarries were now nearing the end of their productive life. Quarrying was cut back severely during World War I and ceased completely in the 1920s. There was then a long hiatus in the British literature on Triassic footprints. Not until 1960 did W.E. Swinton publish *The History of Chirotherium* (Swinton 1960) to mark the centenary of the Liverpool Geological Society. In the interim, as noted above, Othenio Abel had misidentified *Isochirotherium lomasi* as *Chirotherium bipedale* (Abel 1935). The 1960s would see a more serious challenge from continental Europe with Hartmut Haubold's assertion (Haubold 1969) that *Chirotherium storetonense* was merely a synonym of *Chirotherium barthii* – junior and so invalid. British geologists were far from convinced. Sarjeant was sceptical, regarding Haubold's many reattributions as 'highly questionable' (Sarjeant 1974, p. 311). Tresise (1996) defended *Chirotherium storetonense* but suggested that the footprints from both Storeton and Hessberg might show sexual dimorphism, blurring their differences. Most recently, King *et al.* (2005) considered *Chirotherium barthii* and *Chirotherium storetonense* to be distinct ichnospecies that were both present in the Helsby Sandstone of Storeton Hill.

The search for an originator

British workers had not always agreed with their German counterparts on matters of nomenclature. What is in no doubt is that it was in Germany that the mystery of the footprint maker's identity was finally resolved in the mid-twentieth century. The long search for the trackmaker has been described before (e.g. in Tresise 1989; Tresise & Sarjeant 1997) but it is a classic story of geological detection that merits summarizing here.

Since their discovery in Germany in the 1830s, the footprints had been found over and over again – not just in England, but in France, Spain, Italy and, in the twentieth century, across the Atlantic, in Arizona and Argentina. The trackmaker had clearly been both common and widespread in

Fig. 5. Type trackway of *Isochirotherium lomasi* (Beasley's type A4), 1906 slab 7, Storeton Quarry (LIVCM 1986.206.A).

Triassic times, and yet the print-bearing sandstones had never yielded any skeletal remains of the animal responsible.

From the very first, there had been no lack of speculation about what kind of animal might have left the tracks. The first suggestion, that the giant bears known from their remains in German caves might be responsible, was quickly ruled out. The Triassic period seemed too early in the Earth's history for such advanced mammals. The giant marsupials favoured by Kaup (1835) were a more plausible suggestion – the marsupials were regarded as a primitive group of mammals and the prints did appear to resemble the feet of the opossum with their grasping thumbs.

However this theory too was soon discarded. In 1842 Richard Owen identified the *Chirotherium* prints as those of an extinct group of amphibians. His main evidence was a single tooth found at Guy's Cliffe in Warwickshire, which he correctly identified as an amphibian tooth of a hitherto unknown type. Because the dental enamel was very intricately folded, he named these amphibians Labyrinthodonts – 'labyrinth toothed' (Owen 1842). Elsewhere in the Midlands, a few bones had been found in Triassic rocks – today they are recognized to be those of early dinosaurs. 1842 was also the year in which Owen proposed the name 'Dinosaur' for a group of giant, land-living reptiles, but the only dinosaurs he knew had lived in the Jurassic and Cretaceous periods and so he did not connect them with the bones from the Triassic. Instead, he assumed that the Triassic bones must be those of his labyrinthodont amphibians and, as these were the only large land animals then known from Triassic rocks, he deduced that they must also have been the originators of the *Chirotherium* tracks (Fig. 6).

This is an oversimplification of a thesis, which, in its original form, was so skilfully argued that it carried general conviction. Charles Lyell (1797–1875), an equally eminent geologist whose views were often violently opposed to Owen's, agreed with him on this occasion. Lyell even drew a reconstruction of a rather toad-like labyrinthodont to show how such an animal could cross its legs while walking, as *Chirotherium* appeared to have done, arguing that only an amphibian would have been able to walk in this extraordinary way (Fig. 7).

Owen reiterated his labyrinthodont theory in his famous textbook *Palaeontology*, published in 1860, although the reasoning that had seemed impeccably logical 20 years earlier was, by then, demonstrably false. Much more was now known about the Triassic fauna that had included many different land vertebrates. Some were labyrinthodonts, but the heyday of that group had been during the Carboniferous period, some 100 Ma earlier. By Triassic times the dominant land animals were reptiles, not giant amphibians.

Thus, in terms of numbers alone, it seemed most likely that the prints were reptilian. Then, too, the best-preserved casts showed that the skin on the base of the foot was scaly – not out of the question in amphibians, but much more likely in reptiles. The dinosaurs, an up and coming group in Triassic times, seemed likely candidates. The *Chirotherium* prints showed that the hindfoot was larger and supported the bulk of the animal's weight. Similarly, the dinosaurs were characterized by hindlegs that were larger and more powerful than their front legs.

So with Owen's amphibians ruled out, dinosaurs seemed the most plausible alternative. But it was not until 1925 that the riddle of *Chirotherium's* identity really began to be solved. This was thanks to Wolfgang Soergel (1887–1946), a German palaeontologist who worked at Tübingen University in Germany.

Soergel started by making one very simple assumption: that the footprints' similarity to the human hand was deceptive and that the digit resembling the thumb was, in fact, that on the outside of the foot – an unusually large 'little toe'. This immediately solved one problem: it was no longer necessary to assume that the animal had crossed its legs while walking. Now the prints on the left were those of the left feet, the prints on the right those of the right feet.

This, of course, was not a new idea. Both Buckland and Owen had suggested as much. Soergel, however, went one crucial step further. Were there, he wondered, any Triassic reptiles that had a large outer toe set at an angle to the others? After a careful search of the literature he found that there were: a group of reptiles from the Triassic rocks of South Africa known as Pseudosuchians (a name meaning 'false crocodiles').

Fig. 6. The mid-nineteenth century view of the trackmakers: a labyrinthodont amphibian (centre) leaves a *Chirotherium* trackway watched by dicynodonts (left) and rhynchosaurs (right) (B.W. Hawkins archive, © The Natural History Museum, London).

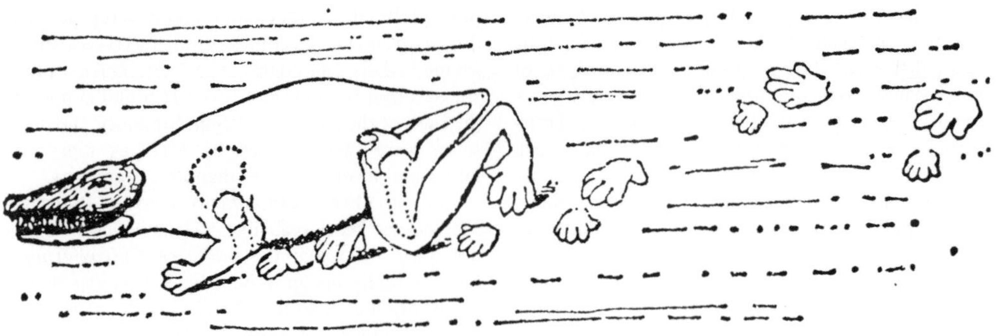

Fig. 7. *Chirotherium* shown as a labyrinthodont with a cross-legged gait. From Lyell (1855).

Among these pseudosuchians was a form called *Euparkeria*, which grew up to 1 m in length; it had a long tail, strong hindlegs and exactly the right shape of foot. However, there were problems – not only were the fossils found on the wrong continent, but *Euparkeria* was much too small, it had a foot only 5 cm long compared with over 20 cm for *Chirotherium*.

Nevertheless, Soergel was convinced that he was right. In 1925 he published his conclusions, claiming that the *Chirotherium* prints must be those of a large pseudosuchian up to 3 m in length. He reconstructed the animal's appearance (Fig. 8), deducing that *Chirotherium* had a narrow body, a short neck and a small head. The tail, however, would have been about twice as long as the body. Although the hands were small, the forelegs would be relatively long, but not as long as the hindlegs, which were kept bent while walking whereas the forelegs would have been stretched to their full extent.

Soergel's arguments were convincing and were soon widely accepted, but it would be another 30 years before the clinching evidence was forthcoming. But then, in 1965, the skeleton of a new species of pseudosuchian was found from the Grenzbitumen zone (Anisian–Landian boundary) in the marine Triassic rocks exposed near the Tessin River, Monte San Giorgio, Canton Tessin in Switzerland. The vertebrate palaeontologist Bernard Krebs (1934–2001) described the skeleton (Fig. 9). It was given the name *Ticinosuchus ferox* (Krebs 1966), but it was also pointed out that it looked very much like Soergel's reconstruction of *Chirotherium*.

Ticinosuchus ferox was about 2.5 m long. It had a long skull with a predator's pointed teeth. It was slim-bodied with a long tail. The hindlegs were half as long again as the front, while the hindfoot was very much larger than the forefoot and had an outer digit separated from the other four. The prints it would have left must have been very like those of *Chirotherium*.

So here at last, it seemed, was a possible originator for the *Chirotherium* tracks. Subsequent research has shown that, although the hindfoot had an obtrusive outer digit, the front foot did not. This suggests that *Ticinosuchus ferox* could not, itself, be the originator of the *Chirotherium* tracks. Nevertheless, the resemblance is sufficiently close to demonstrate beyond all doubt that Soergel's pseudosuchian identification had been correct.

Fig. 8. Soergel's (1925) reconstruction of *Chirotherium*.

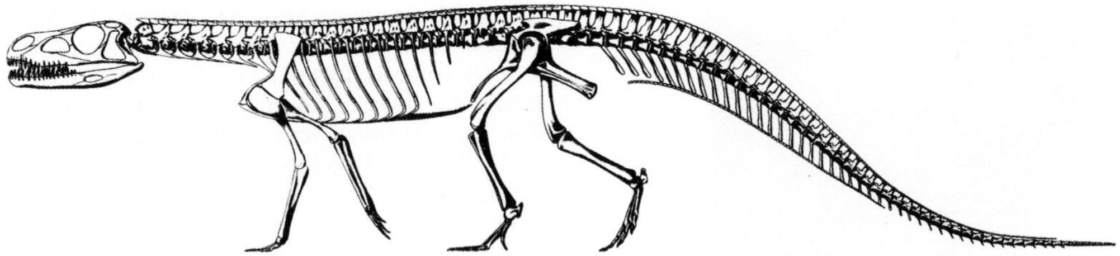

Fig. 9. Kreb's (1965) reconstruction of the *Ticinosuchus ferox* skeleton © Bernard Krebs.

It had taken a century and a quarter to identify the *Chirotherium* trackmaker. The problem had, of course, been the lack of any material remains in association with the footprints. The reason for their absence had always seemed to be that the environment was one of desert sands not conducive to the preservation of fossil remains. Current research has, however, suggested that this may be too simplistic an explanation.

The Liverpool footprint hunters and their interpretations of the trackmaker's environment

Henry Beasley (1907) in a Presidential Address given to the 48th session of the Liverpool Geological Society on 18 November 1906 discussed the Storeton Chirotherium footprints finds; in particular, the display mounted by Mr Charles Wells, the quarry proprietor. The recent finds had occupied Beasley for the best part of the year and he stated that he was able to study several hundred square feet of prints. From this research he was able to make some determinations of the possible environment and climate at the time the trackmakers were walking across the landscape. He stated:

> The work of recording and describing the various forms of footprints as they come to light during the weathering of the slabs is still in progress and incomplete, but many facts have presented themselves and suggest the reconsideration of older theories and the genesis of new ones.
>
> (Beasley 1907, p. 159)

Beasley's careful analysis of the footprint bearing beds led him to conclude that:

> There is no proof of the footprint beds in the various quarries in Wirral and Liverpool being parts of one continuous bed, nor is there any proof that they were synchronous. From the evident shallowness of the water one could hardly expect them to be the former, or, except within a very wide limit, the latter. It is probable that in each district there was a period during the accumulation of these sands when the climatic conditions were such as to favour the formation of these shallow 'slacks', but these conditions were not necessarily present at the same time in each.
>
> (Beasley 1907, p. 160)

He continued to speculate what the environment may have been like during the Triassic:

> Probably we were removed many hundreds of miles from the ocean, the continental land extending far to the westward. Imagine also a range or ranges of mountains to the west and south between us and the sea. What would then be our condition regarding climate? Shut off by the mountains from the moisture-bearing winds and the moderating influence of the sea upon the temperature – we should have an arid climate, clear sky, and consequently a considerable diurnal variation of temperature that would disintegrate the rocks as rapidly as rain or ice, and the wind would redistribute the resulting débris. This description may be correct – there is no geological evidence that I know of to disprove it – and if true, goes a long way to explain some of the peculiarities of our Triassic sandstones.
>
> (Beasley 1907, p. 162)

Further speculation upon the Storeton finds led Beasley to conclude that:

> Probably the animals were attracted to this spot by the near presence of water, but making every allowance for that, we cannot fail but to be impressed by the fact that there was an abundant fauna in the district.
>
> These must have required eventually a supply of vegetable food, however much they may have preyed upon each other, and a flora of some kind must have been within reach, but of this the recent finds at Storeton give us no indication. Probably the conditions were such as to destroy all trace of its existence.
>
> (Beasley 1907, p. 171)

This last statement from Beasley indicated that he had overlooked some evidence of flora present in the Storeton strata. The type specimen of *Equisetites keuperina* Morton 1863 was first found in 1838 and presented to the Royal Institution Museum on 10 September 1838 and later to Liverpool Museum by the Royal Institution Museum in 1889 (Fig. 10). Described as a reed in the Liverpool Natural History Plate 4 Lithograph, issued in August 1838, the Cambridge botanist John Stevens

Fig. 10. *Equisetites keuperina* Morton, found at Storeton Quarry in 1838 (LIVCM 1969.131).

Henslow (1796–1861) identified the fossil plant stem as a horsetail (*Equisetum*). It was subsequently designated as the holotype for this species by Morton in a paper given to the Liverpool Geological Society on 17 March 1863 and subsequently published Morton (1863*a*). In this published abstract Morton proposed the name *Equisetites keuperina* stating:

> About the same time the footprints were discovered the reed-like stem of a plant was found in the same place. Lithographs of both were published by the late Natural History Society of Liverpool. The fossil reed is now in the museum of the Royal Institution. It has been examined by Mr F.M.Webb, who described it as the upper portion of an Equisetum, but without any remains of fructification. The stem is simple, sulcate, grooves $1\frac{3}{4}$ lines in breadth. The teeth of sheaths are triangular, measuring when perfect, $1\frac{1}{4}$ lines in length. It is drawn half the natural size, the specimen being about 14 inches long. In Professor Morris's catalogue of British fossils there is no species of the genus, but one from the Keuper of Wurtemburg is inserted. The author proposed the name Equisetites Keuperina.
>
> (Morton, 1863*a*, p. 19).

Beasley was certainly aware of this specimen but overlooked its significance in his interpretation of the Trias environment. A Storeton specimen, now in the Lancashire Museum service LANMS 1998.12.1521 and described by Batty (2008), has recently come to light that clearly shows a stem of *Equisetites keuperina* overstepped by the manus of *Chirotherium storetonense* (Fig. 11a, b).

Morton noted evidence of an equisetalean flora stating that he has found 'long stems resembling those of Equisitites keuperina, but with the nodes further apart, being probably the lower portion, at Flaybrick' (Morton 1891, p. 114).

The Birkenhead medical practitioner Dr Charles Ricketts (1818–1904) briefly described (Ricketts 1886) the discovery of plant remains in a section exposed during the making of a sewer trench on Oxton Heath, Birkenhead. In slabs of sandstone containing the prints of rhynchosaurs he noted the occurrence of moulds of leaves, some of which clearly displayed a central midrib or rachis. Sadly, these specimens have been lost. However, his sketchy description of the finds seems to indicate a similarity in morpho-genera to that described by Wills (1907*a*, *b*, 1909) of the Waterstones flora found at Bromsgrove, Worcestershire. Lomas (1901) similarly described a Trias flora being exposed during building work at Oxton Heath. Here he makes the observation that so little is known of desert plants that 'in all probability the Triassic plants were such as grew under conditions more or less approximating to those now found in deserts' (Lomas 1901, p. 79).

These observations, apart from Lomas's later comments, probably enabled Morton to provide a slightly different view of the environment based on his own interpretations of the geology and finds of fossil flora. He stated:

> The general opinion is that it was deposited in a series of lakes, for no fossils indicating marine conditions have been found, and locally only a few land plants at Flaybrick and Storeton. There were shores, or banks, of sand and clay, and the occurrence of ripple-marks, rain marks, sun cracks, worm tracks, and footprints, indicate changes that might be expected in such situations.
>
> (Morton 1891, p. 140)

However, in an earlier passage in the work (Morton 1891), he alludes to a marine setting for the deposition of the print-bearing strata. In a discussion about the discovery of the *Chirotherium* and rhynchosaur footprints found at Flaybrick Hill and in a quarry in Rathbone Street, Liverpool around 1848 by a Mr Alfred Higginson (1808–1884), who was Secretary of the Liverpool Natural History Society and later became one of the leading medical practitioners in Liverpool, Morton stated:

> The occurrence of these footprints along a single horizon is of interest as it seems to indicate a pause

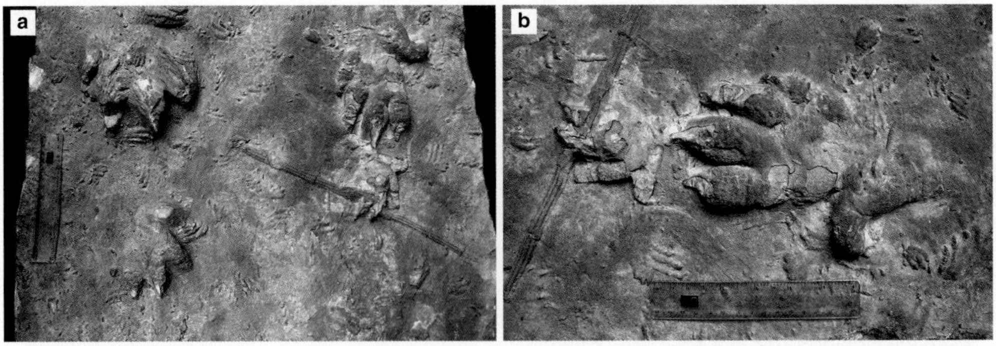

Fig. 11. *Equisetites keuperina* overstepped by the manus of *Chirotherium storetonense*, Lancashire Museums Service 1998.12.1521. (**a**) General view of the slab showing *Chirotherium* and Rhynchosaur prints. (**b**) Close-up of the overstepped *Equisetites keuperina* stem. Photographs reproduced courtesy of Mike Batty.

> in the subsidence of the sea bottom, or perhaps an extensive sand-bank uncovered at intervals between spring tides, during which the impressions of batrachian and reptilian feet were successively imprinted and covered by a deposit of sand, so as to be preserved.
>
> (Morton 1891, p. 110)

This view may have been prompted by noting earlier work by Cunningham who presented his ideas to the Liverpool Natural History Society on 5 February 1839 and, via Buckland, to the Geological Society on 27 February 1839. In his 1839 Liverpool paper Cunningham stated that the clay seams 'were laid down in a great freshwater lake or the delta of an immense river'. An alternative view was put forward in the version read to the Geological Society on 5 December 1838 by Buckland where it was changed to read:

> The author adds that Dr Buckland has suggested . . . the rise and fall of tides over extensive sandbanks, the surface of which was between the level of high and low water.
>
> [Cunningham 1838 p. 12]

It is already apparent that there is a certain amount of cyclicity in the arguments for the environment inhabited by *Chirotherium*.

Lomas concluded that:

> The animal and plant associations, and their adaptations to the peculiar circumstances under which they live in the desert, should find their counterparts in the Trias, if arid conditions existed during their formation.
>
> Although material is rapidly accumulating regarding the fauna and flora of the Trias, it must be acknowledged that we know too little to make useful comparisons, and we must wait for fuller information both in respect to the life of the Trias and the life of existing deserts.
>
> (Lomas 1907, p. 197)

Tragically, Lomas's premature death whilst on his way to study salt lakes in an attempt to further his understanding of the environment represented in the British Trias dealt a blow to furthering the understanding of the local palaeoenvironment for several years. Following the loss of Lomas, a further blow was dealt to local footprint researches by the illness of Beasley in 1914 that caused him to withdraw from active geological work. This, coupled with a decline in interest in the Storeton Quarry finds after the 1912 operations failed to find anything of significance from a collector's standpoint, caused a hiatus in local work until the 1990s. The 'golden age' of Trias footprint discovery in the NW of England spanned most of the nineteenth century and into the first decade of the twentieth. Today, the quarries have long gone, filled in with debris from the Mersey tunnel construction or covered over by building developments.

The Liverpool footprint hunters as a group did not appear to indulge in pictorial representations of the Trias environment. Their focus was on descriptions of the vertebrate footprint finds and prose speculation of possible environments in which the trackmakers lived. For a pictorial representation of the Trias it is necessary to look towards the popular accounts offered by continental authors. Of these, the most widely available was the popular work by Figuier (1863) and it is possible that the Liverpool Group was aware of pictorial reconstructions in his book.

Nineteenth–twentieth century pictorial representations of the Trias environment

Earlier European interpretations of the Anisian environment showed it to be more vegetative, with less emphasis on desert conditions. The Austrian botanist Franz Xavier Unger (1800–1870) teamed up with the Graz landscape artist Josef Kuwasseg (1799–1859) to produce a folio atlas entitled *Die Urwelt in ihren verschiedenen Bildungsperioden*, 1851 (translated as *The Primitive World in Its Different Periods of Formation*). In this atlas he portrayed the Keuper as being more humid than the time preceding it. His plate (Fig. 12) showed that the:

> flat and level banks of a large lake are extended before us. The dry and sandy downs are still completely barren; vegetation has been able to establish itself only on the marshy lowlands that the water fertilizes.
> (translated from Unger 1851, taf 7)

This vegetation is made up of the arboreal equisetalean *Calamites arenaceous*, with ferns alongside the marshy margins of the lake. The fauna is represented by a labyrinthodont crawling towards the giant horsetail forest. Here Kuwasseg, the artist, has loosely used Owen's interpretation of the *Chirotherium* trackmaker in his interpretation of Unger's text. Interestingly he has portrayed the footprints preceding the amphibian (Fig. 12).

Another early portrayal of the period is shown in a work by the Frenchman Guillame Louis Figuier (1819–1894), Professor at the School of Pharmacy in Paris, who teamed up with the Parisian landscape painter Edouard Riou (1833–1900). His interpretation of the Keuper in his book *Earth before the Deluge*, first published in 1863, is an interesting mix of graphic landscape portrayal borrowing heavily from Kuwasseg's engraving in Unger's *Primitive World* (Fig. 13). The artist, Riou, has depicted Owen's labyrinthodont and its tracks as it leaves the shore of a saliferous lagoon towards a stand of arboreal *Calamites* and other equisetalean plants. Below the landscape Figuier has depicted a fictitious geological section indicating the formation of halite deposits (Figuier 1863, p. 198). Here we see indications of the connection that Lomas was trying to make on his fateful journey to visit modern salt lakes and understand their depositional processes.

Pictorial depiction of the period appeared to lapse until the mid-twentieth century when the Czech artist Zdeněk Burian (1905–1981) teamed up with the Czech palaeontologist Joseph Augusta (1903–1968) to produce some of the most lifelike representations of geological 'Deep Time', which set a standard for much of the illustrative work found today. Burian's depiction of *Chirotherium*, painted in 1955, is based upon the reconstruction of Soergel and is set in a panoramic vista with a xerophytic flora typical of that found in the

Fig. 12. Unger and Kuwasseg's interpretation of the mid-Trias environment (Unger 1851).

Fig. 13. Figuiers and Riou's interpretation of the mid-Trias environment (Figuier 1863).

Anisian rocks of Germany (Fig. 14). Here we have stands of the lycopod *Pleuromeia* fringing the edge of a lake whilst the equisetalean *Schizoneura* grew in the water-saturated substrates of the lake margin. On drier ground conifers referred to *Voltzia* are shown. Augusta's notes that accompany the published painting provide a slightly romantic and almost poetic view:

> Only the horse-tail Schizoneura grew from the shallow water at the shores of the lakes; but even here it had to struggle for existence when the burning rays of the Lower Triassic sun dried out the lakes, and the coastal shallows often turned into swampy land. More than once the mysterious saurian *Chirotherium* waddled on to the boggy ground and imprinted indelible footprints, preserved for ages.
>
> (Augusta & Burian 1960, facing plate 16)

Was Augusta's description of *Chirotherium* waddling onto boggy ground a hangover from Owen's description of labryinthodont locomotion in his analysis of the *Chirotherium* prints? He continued to state, whilst referring to Soergel's reconstruction of the Chirotherium animal:

> The palaeontologists did not surrender even when faced with the mystery of the Chirotherium but on the contrary, with the tenacity proper to them, they used all their knowledge and experience in order to determine just from the footprints which animal had made them and how it looked. It would be a great victory for the human intellect should the find of a real skeleton confirm all the conclusions which the palaeontologists have drawn on the basis of mere footprints.
>
> (Augusta & Burian 1960, facing plate 16)

That conclusion was not long in coming with the find of *Ticinosuchus* in 1965, and Krebs (1965) published a diagrammatic reconstruction of the environment. Here *Chirotherium* is placed in a near shoreline or lagoonal setting amidst a stand of *Pleuromeia* with low growing neuropterid ferns and the occasional equisetalean *Schizoneura*. Krebs (1965) similarly depicted a xerophytic flora but with a higher localized vegetation density and a less arid setting than that portrayed by Burian (Fig. 15).

A return to a more arid depiction of the Anisian is reflected in the artist Tony Swift's painting (Fig. 16). This was commissioned by National Museums and Galleries on Merseyside in 1987 when the type specimen of *Isochirotherium lomasi* (Fig. 5) was acquired from the University of Liverpool and placed on display in what is now the World Museum Liverpool, part of National Museums Liverpool. It provides an interpretation of the local environment that closely reflects the views of Beasley (1907). In this interpretation a pair of pseudosuchians is seen crossing a sandy waste around a

Fig. 14. Burian's (1955) interpretation of the mid Trias environment (Augusta & Burian 1955) © Zdeněk Burian.

Fig. 15. Kreb's pictorial (1965) reconstruction of *Chirotherium* in its environment © Bernard Krebs.

Fig. 16. Triassic landscape with *Chirotherium*: painting by Tony Swift (commissioned by National Museums and Galleries on Merseyside in 1987) and reproduced by permission of the Board of Trustees, National Museums Liverpool.

seasonal pool fringed by a few diminutive horsetails representing *Equisetites keuperina*. The apparent lack of an extensive local fossil flora, compared with the Trias sites in Germany, reflected the views of Lomas, Beasley and Morton that the environment was generally unsuitable for the preservation of plant material or that conditions were too extreme for it to have flourished to any great extent.

A more recent pictorial depiction of the Sherwood Sandstone Anisian palaeoenvironment is that portrayed by King & Thompson (2000). In their view they have summed up the palaeontological and sedimentological evidence to show medium-sized archosaurs and small diapsids by the margins of slack-water pools along a braided river flood plain at low discharge levels. The vegetation consists of small equisetalean plants, some growing *in situ* along the pool margins whilst others are drifting in the slow current to be deposited away from their point of origin. The evidence for this is left as 'tool marks' in the substrate.

One of the problems in depicting the local palaeoenvironment is the relatively poor quality of chronostratigraphic control in the NW region. King & Thomson's (2000) composite interpretation may represent a view of the environment around the formation interval covering the Storeton finds but not necessarily of the same chronostratigraphic horizon. In this context, recent work in the succeeding Mercia Mudstone Group, Tarporley Siltstones, may reveal a refinement of the overall pictorial interpretation as regards the flora.

Recent environmental intepretations

Recent work in the Merseyside area (currently unpublished) conducted by National Museums Liverpool staff has revealed a diverse flora that enables a refinement in interpretation from the arid view depicted by the Swift painting (Fig. 17). Although at a higher, and therefore younger, chronostratigraphic horizon than the Storeton finds, the sites under investigation (Dungeon SSSI & Harrock Wood on the Wirral and St James's Cemetery, Liverpool) yield a fragmentary flora that is worthy of more detailed investigation. To date, some 454 fossil fragments (accessioned as LIV 2006.69) have been recovered from different levels within the Tarporley Siltstones. The fragments range in size from 0.5 to 20 mm, strongly indicating taphonomic selection or stunted floras due to stressed environmental conditions or a combination of both effects. The flora recovered indicates at least two species of *Equisetites* were present along with an indeterminate lycopsid (which may belong to either the Pleuromeiales or Isoetales), bryophytes, ferns and shrubby conifers. Poorly preserved fragmentary fossil specimens hint at the suggestions that representatives of the Cycadophytes and Pteridosperms were also present. In addition to the plant fragments, small diapsid footprints have been recorded (LIV 2003.68.A) along with a possible poorly preserved chirotheroid manus, now lost as a result of winter erosion.

Thompson in King *et al.* (2005) sums up the palaeoenvironment of the Anisian Tarporely Siltstones as being represented by 'coastal plains with sinuous rivers, lakes, estuaries, intertidal areas, sabkhas and salinas which provided challenging environments for colonization by *Chirotherium* and allied ichnospecies'. It is suggested that watery pools and vegetated channel margins of abandoned anabranches of the braided rivers, along with interdune corridors and the margins of playa lakes in semi-arid–arid plains, would have been the best places for footprint moulds to be made and eventually preserved.

The palaeobotanical finds made at the local sites bear out this interpretation but indicate that there may have been periods of climatic amelioration with humid intervals that made it more conducive to developing a restricted terrestrial flora, dominated by *Equisetites* species along the margins of pools and water courses with very rare lycopods, bryophytes and ferns.

Fragmentary evidence from carbonized films show that representatives of the Charales may have been present in brackish pools, although gryogonites have not been recorded as fossils. This could be indicative of high local salinities where the production of Oogonia is much reduced or halted. The existence of a brackish aquatic flora alongside

Fig. 17. Recent interpretation of a more richly vegetated Anisian landscape, water-colour illustration based on fossil evidence recovered from Anisian sites in the Merseyside area. © F. L. J. Bowden.

the limited terrestrial flora would have provided herbivorous reptiles with an easily digestible, although seasonal, food source. Small fragments of indeterminate conifer wood indicate that they may have grown on drier ground. Here the palaeobotanical evidence seems to be more in keeping with the diagrammatic environmental picture provided by Krebs (1965) rather than King & Thompson (2000), although the equisetalean *Schizoneura* appears to be absent.

Are we able to identify an environment today that may shed further light on the palaeobotanical evidence for the Middle Trias palaeoenvironments as depicted by workers who have tried to interpret the fossil evidence? Lomas was keen to try to understand modern desert environments in order to assess how analogous they may be to those interpreted for the Trias from the researches conducted by Morton, Beasley and others into the local Trias succession. One of the questions he posed was whether we can learn from understanding the conditions under which animal and plant associations live in modern-day desert environments and see how this relates to adaptations for the Trias environment? Moody (pers. comm.) noted salt-rich perch lakes in the dune fields at Mandara, Libya. These are characterized by well-vegetated angiosperm margins. We offer up an alternative environmental setting that may be worthy of future consideration. The river valley systems of northern Chile seem to offer potential as possible modern-day Trias analogues in as much as they present osmo-regulatory challenges to the indigenous flora, representatives of which would also have been present during the time of the *Chirotherium* trackmaker. The near-barren Atacama Desert flanks fertile valley systems that support an indigenous vegetation of rather primitive gymnosperm aspect, the most important of which are the basal pteridophytes and species of the sphenopsid *Equisetum*. Most notable of these valleys are the Lluta, Tana and Tarapacá valley systems where the native flora is noted for monoculture stands of the South American horsetail *Equisetum giganteum* along with ferns and conifers. These plants display an apparent adaptation to highly saliferous groundwaters that include the evolution of osmotic regulatory patterns which maintain a suitable K/Na (potassium/sodium) ratio conducive to surviving in a stressed environment. Husby *et al.*, in an abstract presented to the Botany 2006 conference, noted that *Equisetum giganteum* effectively maintains low Na concentrations in its xylem fluid and cytoplasm when soil water Na is at a high level (Husby *et al.* 2006). Equally, they found that this particular species was able to maintain a high K/Na ratio in its xylem fluid and cytoplasm when the soil water exhibited a low K/Na ratio. The authors conclude by suggesting that *Equisetum giganteum* is well adapted to cope with salinity stress, and that the efficient K uptake and Na exclusion may be important to the evolution of stress adaptations in desert environments. Understanding these adaptations may help in achieving an improved interpretation of the local Anisian environment and the vegetative response to it as the base of the food chain for the diapsid fauna and predatory archosaurs.

The authors wish to thank D. Thompson of Keele University for his kind comments and insight whilst reading an early draft of this paper. We also wish to thank M. Whyte and M. Romano without whose advice this paper would have been much the poorer.

References

ABEL, O. 1935. *Vorzeitliche Lebensspuren.* Fischer, Jena, Germany.

AUGUSTA, J. & BURIAN, Z. 1960. *Prehistoric Animals.* Artia, Spring Books, London.

BATTY, M. 2008. *Chirotherium* and its domain: a description of rediscovered specimens from northwest England. *The Geological Curator*, **8**, 437–454.

BEASLEY, H. C. 1896. An attempt to classify the footprints found in the New Red Sandstone of this district. *Proceedings of the Liverpool Geological Society*, **7**, 391–409.

BEASLEY, H. C. 1904. Report on footprints from the Trias, Part 1. *In*: *Report of the British Association for the Advancement of Science* (Southport 1903). John Murray, London, 219–230.

BEASLEY, H. C. 1905. Report on the footprints from the Trias, Part 2. *In*: *Report of the British Association for the Advancement of Science* (Cambridge 1904). John Murray, London, 275–282.

BEASLEY, H. C. 1907. Some results of the recent finds at Storeton. *Proceedings of the Liverpool Geological Society*, **10**, 157–171.

BEASLEY, H. C. 1910. Report on footprints from the Trias, Part 6. *In*: *Report of the British Association for the Advancement of Science* (Winnipeg 1909). John Murray, London, 151–155.

BEASLEY, H. C. 1914. Description of a footprint recently found in the Lower Keuper Sandstone of Runcorn Hill. *Proceedings of the Liverpool Geological Society*, **12**, 32–34.

BUCKLAND, W. 1836. *Geology and Mineralogy Considered with Reference to Natural Theology*, Volume 1. Bridgewater Treatises, **6**. Pickering, London.

BUCKLAND, W. 1839. Account of the footsteps of the Cheirotherium and five or six smaller animals in the stone quarries of Storeton Hill, near Liverpool, communicated by the Natural History Society of Liverpool, through Dr Buckland. *In*: *Report of the British Association for the Advancement of Science (Newcastle-upon-Tyne, 1838) Transactions*, Volume 7, Murray, London, 85.

CUNNINGHAM, J. 1838. An account of the footsteps of the Chirotherium, and other unknown animals lately discovered in the quarries of Storeton Hill, in the

peninsular of Wirral between the Mersey and the Dee. *Proceedings of the Geological Society, London*, 3, 12–14.
CUNNINGHAM, J. 1848. Description of plates. *Proceedings of the Literary & Philosophical Society of Liverpool*, 4, 128–130.
EGERTON, P. G. 1838. Two casts in sandstone of the impressions of the hind foot of a gigantic *Chirotherium* from the New Red Sandstone of Cheshire. *Proceedings of the Geological Society, London*, **3**, 14–15.
FIGUIER, L. 1863. *The World Before the Deluge*. Newly edited & revised by Bristow, H. W. Cassell, Petter, Galpin & Co., London.
HAUBOLD, H. 1969. Parallelisierung terrestrischer Ablagerungen der tieferen Trias mit Pseudosuchier-Fahten. *Geologie*, **18**, 836–843.
HAUBOLD, H. 1971. Ichnia, Amphibiorum et Reptiliorum fossilum. *In*: *Handbuch der Palaoherpetologie, Part 18* (KUHN, O. ed.) Gustav Fischer, Stuttgart.
HAWKSHAW, J. 1843. Notice of the Fossil Footsteps in the New Red Sandstone Quarry at Lymm, in Cheshire. *In*: *British Association for the Advancement of Science Transactions* (Manchester 1842), 56–57.
HUSBY, C., OBERBAUER, S., DELATORRE, J. & ORESTE, V. 2006. Salinity, tolerance, ecophysiology of the giant horsetail, Equisetum giganteum, in the Atacama Desert, Chile. *In*: *Botany 2006 Abstracts, Botanical Society of America. California State University*.
JERMY, R. C. 1981. *The Storeton Tramway*. Avon Anglia, Weston-super-Mare.
KAUP, J. J. 1835. Mitteilung über Tierfärhrten von Hildburghausen. *Neues Jahrbuch für Mineralogy, Geognosie, Geologie und Petrefaktenkunde*, 327–328.
KING, M. J. & THOMPSON, D. B. 2000. Triassic vertebrate footprints from the Sherwood Sandstone Group, Hilbre, Wirral, northwest England. *Proceedings of the Geologists' Association*, **111**, 111–132.
KING, M. J., SARJEANT, W. A. S., THOMPSON, D. B. & TRESISE, G. 2005. Return of the 'Hand Beast'. A revised systematic ichnotaxonomy and review of the vertebrate footprint Ichnofamily Chirotheriidae from the British Triassic. *Ichnos*, **12**, 241–299.
KREBS, B. 1965. Die Triasfauna der Tessiner Kalkapen. XIX. *Ticinosuchus ferox* nov.gen.nov.sp. *Schweizerische Paläontologische Abhandlungen i Mémoirs suisses de Paléontologie*, **81**, 1–140.
KREBS, B. 1966. Zur Deutung der Chirotherium-Fahten. *Natur und Museum*, **96**, 389–396.
LOMAS, J. 1901. The occurrence of Estheria and plant remains in the Keuper Marls at Oxton, Birkenhead. *Proceedings of the Liverpool Geological Society*, **9**, 75–80.
LOMAS, J. 1907. Desert conditions and the origin of the British Trias. *Proceedings of the Liverpool Geological Society*, **10**, 172–197.
LOMAS, J. 1908. On a footprint slab in the Museum of Zoology, University of Liverpool. *In*: *Report of the British Association for the Advancement of Science* (Leicester 1907), 304–306.
LYALL, C. 1855. *Marvel of Element Geology*, 5th edn. Murray, London.
MORTON, G. H. 1863*a*. On the footsteps of *Cheirotherium* and *Equisetum* found at Storeton, Cheshire. *Proceedings of the Liverpool Geological Society*, **1**, (4th session), 17.
MORTON, G. H. 1863*b*. *The Geology of the Country Around Liverpool*. Smith, Liverpool.
MORTON, G. H. 1891. *Geology of the Country Around Liverpool Including the North of Flintshire*, 2nd edn. George Phillip & Son, Liverpool.
MORTON, G. H. 1897. *Geology of the Country Around Liverpool Including the North of Flintshire*, 3rd edn. George Phillip & Son, Liverpool.
ORMEROD, G. W. 1868. On the salt field and the New Red Sandstone of Cheshire. *Manchester Geological & Mineralogical Society Transactions*, **8**, 26–30.
OWEN, R. 1842. Description of parts of the skeleton and teeth of five species of the genus *Labyrinthodon* with remarks on the probable identity of the *Cheirotherium* with this genus of extinct Batrachians. *Transactions of the Geological Society, London*, **6**, 515–543.
OWEN, R. 1860. *Palaeontology*, Black, Edinburgh.
RAWLINSON, R. 1853. On foot-tracks found in the New Red Sandstone at Lymm, Cheshire. *Quarterly Journal of the Geological Society, London*, **9**, 37–40.
RICKETTS, C. 1886. On footprints and plants in the Trias of Oxton Heath. *Proceedings of the Liverpool Geological Society*, **5**, 168–169.
RIDE, W. D. L., SABROSKY, C. W., BERNARDI, G., CORLISS, J. O., FOREST, J., KEY, K. H. L. & WRIGHT, C. W. 1985. *International Code of Zoological Nomenclature*, 3rd edn. University of California Press, Berkeley, CA.
SARJEANT, W. A. S. 1974. A history and bibliography of the study of fossil vertebrate footprints in the British Isles. *Palaeogeography, Palaeoclimatology, Palaeoecology*, **16**, 265–378.
SOERGEL, W. 1925. *Die Fahrten des Chirotheria, Eine palaobiologische Studie*. Fischer, Jura, Germany.
SWINTON, W. E. 1960. The History of *Chirotherium*. *Liverpool and Manchester Geological Journal*, **2**, 443–473.
TRESISE, G. R. 1989. *The Invisible Dinosaur*. National Museums & Galleries on Merseyside, Liverpool.
TRESISE, G. R. 1991. '*Chirotherium herculis*' – Problems posed by the first finds. *Annals of Science*, **48**, 565–576.
TRESISE, G. R. 1996. Sex in the footprint bed. *Geology Today*, **12**, 22–26.
TRESISE, G. R. & SARJEANT, W. A. S. 1997. *The Tracks of Triassic Vertebrates*. H. M Stationery Office, London.
UNGER, F. X. 1851. *Die Urwelt in ihren verschiendenen Bildungsperioden. 14 landschaftliche Darstellungen mit erlauternden Text. Le Monde primitive à ses differentes époques de formation. 14 paysages avec texte explicatif.* Beck, Vienna.
WILLS, L. J. 1907*a*. Fossiliferous Keuper Rocks at Bromsgrove (Worcs). *Geological Magazine*, **4**, 28–34.
WILLS, L. J. 1907*b*. Note on the fossils of the Lower Keuper of Bromsgrove. *In*: *Report of the British Association for the Advancement of Science*. John Murray, London, 505–506.
WILLS, L. J. 1909. On the Fossiliferous Lower Keuper Rocks of Worcestershire. *Proceedings of the Geologists' Association*, **21**, 249–331.
YATES, J. 1841. Footsteps of extinct animals observed in a quarry at Rathbone Street, Liverpool. *In*: *Report of the British Association for the Advancement of Science* (Glasgow 1840). John Murray, London, 99–100.

Pneumaticity, the early years: Wealden Supergroup dinosaurs and the hypothesis of saurischian pneumaticity

DARREN NAISH

School of Earth & Environmental Sciences, Burnaby Building, Burnaby Road, University of Portsmouth, Portsmouth PO1 3QL, UK (e-mail: eotyrannus@gmail.com)

Abstract: Saurischian dinosaurs were pneumatic animals. The presence of invasive skeletal foramina leading to large internal chambers within the skeleton strongly indicate the presence of avian-style skeletal pneumaticity of the skeleton in sauropodomorphs and non-avian theropods. While the hypothesis of skeletal pneumaticity has undergone a renaissance in recent years, it was initially promoted during the late 1800s after dinosaur fossils from the English Lower Cretaceous Wealden Supergroup led Richard Owen and Harry Seeley to note the pneumatic, bird-like features of the vertebrae they described (Hermann von Meyer had also briefly alluded to skeletal pneumaticity in dinosaurs during the 1830s). In describing the theropod *Becklespinax altispinax* from the Hastings Beds Group (at the time referred to *Megalosaurus*), Richard Owen proposed that the laminae on the neural arch served to house 'parts of the lungs'. He evidently imagined *Becklespinax* to exhibit avian-style post-cranial skeletal pneumaticity. In 1870 Harry Seeley described two sauropod vertebrae from the Wealden Supergroup, naming them *Ornithopsis hulkei*. Contrary to what is often stated, Seeley did not identify *Ornithopsis* as a pterosaur, but as an animal that might 'bridge over' the gap between birds and pterosaurs, while at the same time having some affinity with dinosaurs. The lateral foramina and internal bony cavities of one of these specimens were regarded by Seeley as allowing 'the prolongation of the peculiarly avian respiratory system into the bones', and he emphasized 'the lightest and airiest plan' of the specimen. In 1876 Owen described the Wessex Formation sauropod *Chondrosteosaurus gigas*. While regarding the lateral fossae as probably having 'lodged a saccular process of the lung', Owen now took the opportunity to attack Seeley's claims of pneumaticity in *Ornithopsis*, arguing that the internal cavities in *Chondrosteosaurus* 'were occupied in the living reptile by unossified cartilage, or chondrine'. The name *Chondrosteosaurus gigas* ('giant cartilage and bone lizard') also looks like a direct assault on Seeley's proposal of a pneumatic vertebral interior. Owen's actions seem odd given that he was familiar with the internal morphology of avian vertebrae (which are often strikingly similar to those of sauropods). However, both authors have proved insighful in correctly identifying skeletal pneumaticity during this early phase of dinosaur research. A thorough historical review of early ideas on dinosaurian pneumaticity is still required.

In terms of its significance for early dinosaur discoveries, the Lower Cretaceous Wealden Supergroup of southern England must rank as one of the most important geological units. It yielded Mantell's original *Iguanodon* material during the 1820s, the armoured dinosaur *Hylaeosaurus armatus* during the 1830s, the earliest sauropod discoveries during the 1840s, and what proved to be a pivotal form in early ideas on the evolutionary relationship between dinosaurs and birds, *Hypsilophodon*, in 1869. Despite the fact that Wealden exposures have been well explored and extensively studied since the early 1800s, they continue to yield new dinosaurs, with recently described taxa including the spinosauroid *Baryonyx walkeri* (Charig & Milner 1986), the ankylosaur *Polacanthus rudgwickensis* (Blows 1996), the allosauroid *Neovenator salerii* (Hutt *et al.* 1996), the basal tyrannosauroid *Eotyrannus lengi* (Hutt *et al.* 2001), the extremely unusual neosauropod *Xenoposeidon proneneukos* (Taylor & Naish 2007) and a large (as yet unnamed) tetanuran theropod of uncertain affinities (Benson *et al.* 2009).

The term 'Wealden' refers to a series of non-marine mudstones, sandstones and other strata that were deposited in two sub-basins located in what is now SE England: the Weald sub-basin of the English mainland; and the Wessex sub-basin of the Isle of Wight and Dorset (Martill & Naish 2001; Radley 2004, 2006*a*, *b*). While the strata of both the Weald and Wessex sub-basins were previously referred to as 'the Wealden Group', they are now known as the Wealden Supergroup (Fig. 1). Within the Weald sub-basin, the oldest unit is the Berriasian–Valanginian Hastings Beds Group. Younger than the Hastings Beds Group, but also occurring within the Weald sub-basin, is the Weald Clay Group: this unit is mostly Hauterivian and Barremian, but might extend into the Aptian as well (Allen & Wimbledon 1991). Finally, within the Wessex sub-basin, the Wealden Group (*sensu stricto*) is mostly Barremian and

From: Moody, R. T. J., Buffetaut, E., Naish, D. & Martill, D. M. (eds) *Dinosaurs and Other Extinct Saurians: A Historical Perspective*. Geological Society, London, Special Publications, **343**, 229–236.
DOI: 10.1144/SP343.13 0305-8719/10/$15.00

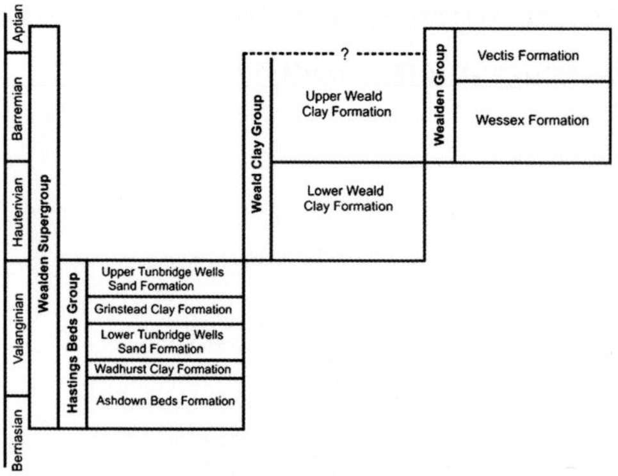

Fig. 1. Stratigraphic diagram showing the approximate correlations between the Weald sub-basin units of the English mainland and the Wessex sub-basin units of the Isle of Wight and Dorset. Based on Kerth and Hailwood (1988), Allen and Wimbledon (1991), Martill & Naish (2001) and Radley (2004, 2006*a*, *b*).

extends into the Aptian (Kerth & Hailwood 1988). It includes the Wessex and Vectis formations, both of which crop out on the Isle of Wight.

While the Wealden Supergroup is often noted as an important unit for discoveries that have shed new light on dinosaur diversity, less well appreciated is that dinosaurs from the Wealden have also proved important in terms of shaping our views on dinosaur palaeobiology. Among the most interesting and vexing, and arguably most important, aspect of dinosaur palaeobiology is the fact that saurischians (and not ornithischians so far as we know) exhibited skeletal pneumaticity: a system of air sacs and pneumatic diverticula were present in at least some of the vertebrae, with basal forms exhibiting shallow pneumatic fossae on their vertebral centra and derived forms possessing internalized pneumatic cavities connected to foramina located within the fossae (Britt 1993; Wedel 2003*a*, *b*, 2004, 2007; O'Connor 2006). Pterosaurs also exhibited skeletal pneumaticity, raising the possibility that it was ancestral for ornithodirans and secondarily lost in ornithischians (Bonde & Christiansen 2003; Butler *et al.* 2009). Skeletal pneumaticity has also been inferred for some basal archosauriforms (*Erythrosuchus africanus*) and crocodile-group archosaurs, which could suggest that it was primitive for crown-group archosaurs or even for a more inclusive clade (Gower 2001). However, the bony vertebral fossae present in these taxa do not communicate with internal chambers, and were argued by O'Connor (2006) to resemble structures that, in crocodilians and other extant reptiles, contain adipose tissue and are not pneumatic. While it can be argued that we are still in the early stages in our understanding of the distribution, phylogeny and function of pneumaticity, there are indications that its presence may correlate not only with pulmonary structure and function but also with metabolism and growth rates (Bonde & Christiansen 2003; Wedel 2003*b*; O'Connor 2006).

A thorough review on the history of thoughts about saurischian pneumaticity has yet to appear. Here, I examine the role that Wealden Supergroup dinosaurs had in early ideas on skeletal pneumaticity.

Institutional abbreviations: HASMG, Hastings Museum and Art Gallery, Hastings, UK; NHM UK, Natural History Museum, London, UK (formerly the British Musuem (Natural History)).

Becklespinax, the 'first' pneumatic theropod

Among the few theropods that are known from the Hastings Beds Group is NHMUK R1828, currently known as *Becklespinax altispinax* (Paul 1988). Represented only by three articulated dorsal vertebrae discovered by Samuel Beckles some time prior to 1855 (Owen 1855), these three vertebrae are all that we have of this dinosaur. However, in describing the specimen, Owen (1856) referred to some other material (another two vertebrae and two ribs) that apparently belonged to it but have since been lost. The proximal end of the robust right tibia HASM G.378 from the Hastings Beds Group, identified as Allosauroidea indet., was suggested by Naish (2003) to perhaps be referable to *B. altispinax*. It remains impossible to evaluate this in the absence of better *B. altispinax* remains.

Like many Wealden Supergroup dinosaurs, *B. altispinax* has had a tumultuous nomenclatural history, and I have largely avoided this area here (a full revision of *B. altispinax* is in preparation). However, Rauhut (2000) argued that Huene (1923) proposed the generic name *Altispinax* for NHMUK R1828, and not for the indeterminate tooth regarded as the type of *Megalosaurus dunkeri* by Kuhn (1939) and Olshevsky (1991). Rauhut therefore concluded that *B. altispinax* should be referred to as *Altispinax altispinax*. This can be interpreted as contradicting key statements in the literature. On naming *Altispinax*, Huene (1923) included *Megalosaurus dunkeri* and *M. oweni* within the genus. He stated that *Altispinax dunkeri* 'is distinguished from *Megalosaurus* by its enormously high neural spines in the dorsal region' (p. 453), and thus by implication included NHMUK R1828 within *A. dunkeri*. No specimen numbers were mentioned nor type species allocated. Huene later referred to NHMUK R1828 specifically when discussing *Altispinax* (Huene 1926*a*, p. 483) and wrote 'if it were certain that [these] dorsal vertebrae belong to *Megalosaurus dunkeri*, it would be necessary to put it into a distinct genus, for which the name *Altispinax*, gen. nov., might be reserved'. Obviously it is *not* possible to be certain that these vertebrae belong to *M. dunkeri*. Because Huene (1923) did not indicate a type species for *Altispinax*, Kuhn (1939) nominated *M. dunkeri* for this role. Because the type specimen for *M. dunkeri* is a single indeterminate tooth, this therefore becomes the type for *Altispinax*.

While Huene (1923, 1926*a*, *b*) clearly intended *Altispinax* to be attached to NHMUK R1828, his ambiguous wording and the inappropriate decision of Kuhn (1939) have complicated the matter. In the present work it is accepted that: (1) the name *Altispinax* shares the fate of *M. dunkeri*; and (2) NHMUK R1828 cannot be referred to this species and therefore retains Olshevsky's (1991) name *Becklespinax*. However, it is also recognized that Kuhn's allocation of *M. dunkeri* as the type species for *Altispinax* was counter to the spirit of the name and the content of the genus favoured by Huene (1923, 1926*a*, *b*). The name *Becklespinax* has been widely used in the literature in recent years and is now quite well known. Accordingly, it would be unwise to replace it; nevertheless, it may be appropriate for the International Commission on Zoological Nomenclature (ICZN to be petitioned in future regarding this issue. The affinities of *B. altispinax* remain uncertain beyond Tetanurae: Britt's (1993) suggestion that a close affinity with *Ceratosaurus* is evident are rejected, as some of the characters he used to support this proposal are either not present in NHMUK R1828 (e.g. small pneumatic paraphophyses borne on pedicles) or are more widely distributed within Theropoda (e.g. elongate neural spines). Nevertheless, *B. altispinax* should be regarded as a valid, diagnosable taxon, possessing elongate neural spines (more than four times taller than the articular surface of the centrum) in which the apices are robust and mediolaterally thick.

Owen (1855, 1856) assumed that the *Becklespinax* vertebrae belonged to the only large theropod that had been named from Britain at the time, *Megalosaurus*, and he also misidentified the vertebrae as anterior dorsals; a reasonable mistake given how poorly known theropods were at this time. Because the parapophyses are located on the neural arches and are close to the diapophyses, they are, in fact, posterior dorsals. Given Owen's identification of the vertebrae as anterior dorsals, the presence of tall, robust neural spines indicated to Owen that – like a mammal with tall neural spines in the shoulder region – *Megalosaurus* had massive muscles and ligaments supporting its head. Owen wrote 'The extraordinary size and strength of the spines of these anterior dorsal vertebrae, indicate the great force with which the head and jaws of the *Megalosaurus* must have been used' (Owen 1855, Tab. XIX caption).

The identification of these Lower Cretaceous tall-spined vertebrae as the anterior dorsals of *Megalosaurus* explains why the Crystal Palace *Megalosaurus* has a shoulder hump: it incorporates Owen's idea that the *Becklespinax* vertebrae were anterior dorsal vertebrae, and that they belonged to the same animal as did the remains from the Stonesfield Slate. The idea that the dorsal vertebrae of *Becklespinax* were anterior dorsals persisted until relatively recently: in a 1979 painting by Peter Snowball (included in Charig 1979), the *Becklespinax* in the near distance has a low sail over its shoulders, indicating that this is the part of the body where the tall-spined vertebrae belonged.

Like the vertebrae of many other saurischian dinosaurs, the *Becklespinax* holotype (NHMUK R1828) exhibits deep lateral fossae (the infraprezygapophyseal fossa, the infradiapophyseal fossa and the infrapostzygapophyseal fossa) on the sides of the neural arches (Fig. 2a). In the infradiapophyseal fossa of the second vertebra, what appears to be a pneumatic foramen perforates the medial wall of the fossa, invading the vertebral interior (Fig. 2b). It is possible that this is a genuine foramen and that others were present in the other fossae but are currently obscured by matrix. However, the ragged edges of the foramen raise the possibility that it is the result of breakage (M. Wedel pers. comm. 2008). While it is well known today that vertebral fossae and foramina demonstrate skeletal pneumaticity, this was not appreciated when Owen was writing about *Becklespinax* during the 1850s. Realizing that these fossae were probably pneumatic as they are in birds, Owen wrote of *Megalosaurus* that 'Three deep depressions, probably receiving parts of the lungs in the living animal, divide these lamelliform butresses from each other' (Owen 1856, p. 5). His 'lamelliform butresses' correspond to what we today call laminae. Britt (1993) identified this as the very first reference to pneumaticity in any Mesozoic dinosaur, making *Becklespinax* the first non-avian dinosaur for which pneumaticity was ever suggested. However, O'Connor (2006) has since noted that von Meyer (1837) alluded to skeletal pneumaticity in saurischians, and thereby predated Owen.

Ornithopsis and *Chondrosteosaurus*: the 'first' pneumatic sauropods

The next milestone in pneumaticity came from Harry Seeley (1839–1909) in his description of

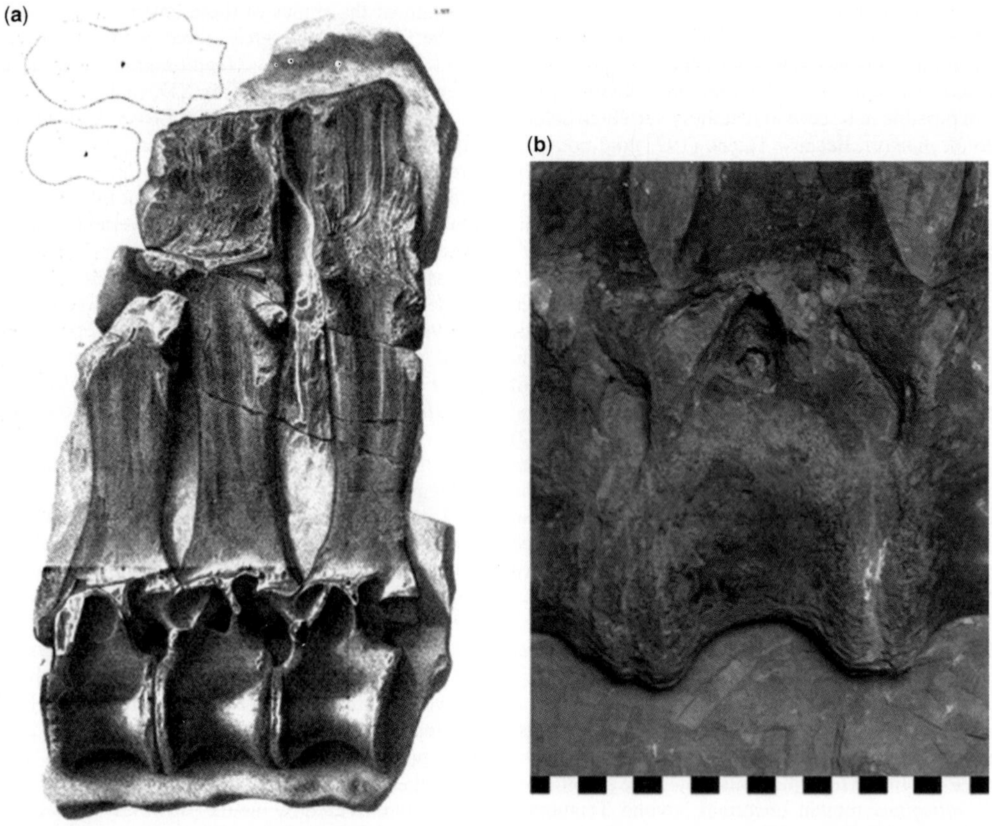

Fig. 2. NHMUK R1828, the holotype dorsal vertebrae of *Becklespinax altispinax* (Paul 1988) from the Hastings Beds Group of Battle, East Sussex. (**a**) As illustrated in left lateral view (anterior is to the left) by Owen (1855). (**b**) Detail of the neural arch fossae of the second vertebra showing (from left to right) infraprezygapophyseal fossa, infradiapophyseal fossa and infrapostzygapophyseal fossa. What appears to be a pneumatic foramen is present in the infradiapophyseal fossa, but this might be the result of breakage.

the Wealden Group sauropod *Ornithopsis hulkei* (Seeley 1870). *O. hulkei* was named for two dorsal vertebrae: NHMUK R2239 from East Sussex and NHMUK R28632 from the Wessex Formation of the Isle of Wight. The former was later removed from *O. hulkei* (then becoming the type for *Bothriospondylus elongatus* Owen 1875), leaving NHMUK R28632 alone associated with this name and as the lectotype. The strong opisthocoely, large lateral foramina and camellate internal anatomy show that NHMUK R28632 is from a titanosauriform (Fig. 3), although it cannot be identified more precisely than that and whether the specimen is diagnostic is arguable (see Naish & Martill 2007). It has sometimes been noted that Seeley (1870) suggested that these vertebrae belonged to an animal 'of the Pterodactyle kind', and hence to a pterosaur (Wilson 1999; Naish & Martill 2001). However, he did not think that these vertebrae belonged to a giant pterosaur: rather, he thought that *O. hulkei* represented something entirely new, the first member of a 'new order of animals which will bridge over something of the interval between birds and Pterodactyles, and probably manifest some affinity with the Dinosaurs' (Seeley 1870, p. 280).

Seeley – who has been described as 'the most defiant' of Victorian palaeontologists, of exhibiting 'anarchic tendencies' and of being considered 'strikingly individualistic', even in his own day (Desmond 1982) – has been criticized by modern palaeontologists (Pereda Suberbiola & Barrett 1999; Unwin 2001, 2006), in particular for his rampant taxonomic splitting and naming of new dinosaur and pterosaur species, and also for his unusual views on how vertebrate groups were related to one another. But his conclusions on life-styles and comments on palaeobiology were often not unreasonable in view of current hypotheses, and in fact often seem far-sighted.

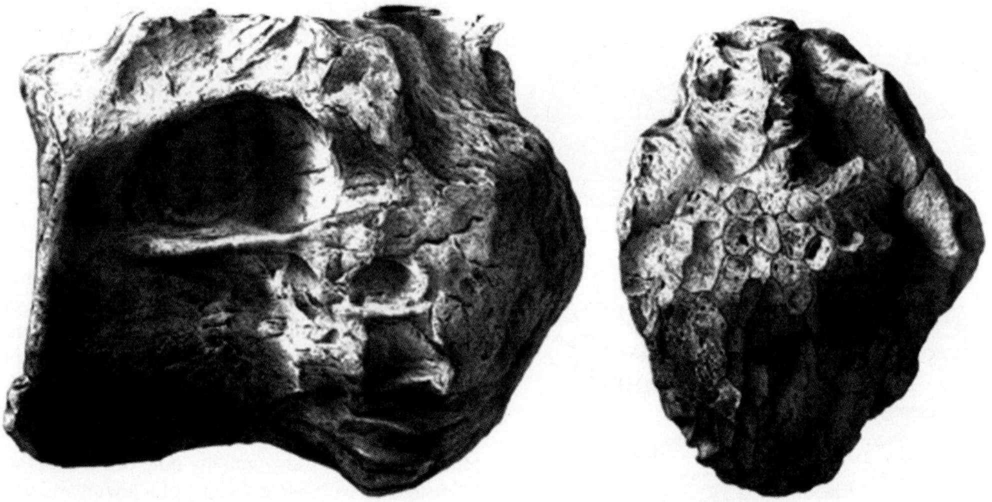

Fig. 3. NHMUK R28632, the lectotype dorsal vertebra of *Ornithopsis hulkei*, a titanosauriform sauropod from the Wessex Formation of the Isle of Wight, shown in right lateral and anterior view. The large lateral cavity on the centrum and numerous internal cavities of this specimen led Seeley (1870) to propose skeletal pneumaticity in this animal. From Seeley (1870). The specimen is 223 mm long, and has a maximum height of 230 mm and maximum width of 190 mm.

Seeley (1870) was impressed with the enormous lateral foramina present in *O. hulkei* (these were the main feature that led him to regard *O. hulkei* as allied to pterosaurs and birds), and wrote: 'Seeing that in living animals these foramina exist for the prolongation of the peculiarly avian respiratory system into the bones, and that no other function is known for them, we are compelled to infer for this animal bird-like heart and lungs and brain' (Seeley 1870, p. 280). In describing the worn anterior condyle of NHMUK R28632, Seeley noted the presence within the bone of 'enormous honeycomb-like cells of irregular polygonal form ... divided by exceedingly thin and compact films of bone' (Seeley 1870, p. 281). Elsewhere in the paper, he referred to the internal cavities as 'air-cells', and he also wrote of the *Ornithopsis* vertebrae (both NHMUK R2239 and NHMUK R28632) as 'being constructed after the lightest and airiest plan'. He never explicitly stated it, but it seems reasonable to infer from these statements that Seeley imagined the internal cavities of the centrum to be pneumatic: he was describing what today we call the camellae (that is, the numerous small pneumatic cavities that occupy the centrum in mamenchisaurs and titanosauriforms). In conclusion, Seeley can be congratulated for correctly inferring vertebral pneumaticity in *O. hulkei*.

Like several of this colleagues, Seeley did not get on particularly well with Owen. In 1876 Owen described another Wealden sauropod and, like the *O. hulkei* lectotype (NHMUK R28632), it was from the Wessex Formation of the Isle of Wight: it is based on two cervical vertebrae (NHMUK R46869 and NHMUK R46870) that Naish & Martill (2001) regarded as syntypes or as members of a type sequence. Today, it is obvious that these vertebrae are from sauropods, and their enormous lateral foramina and camellate internal anatomy (Fig. 4) show that they are from titanosauriforms (and not from camarasaurs as has been suggested in the past: see Naish & Martill 2001, 2007). However, Owen (1876) could not be this confident and identified the material as 'Dinosauria (?)'.

Of these vertebrae, NHMUK R46869 has massive lateral fossae housing large lateral foramina (Fig. 4a) and, again, Owen correctly interpreted them as pneumatic, writing: 'The whole of the side of the centrum is occupied by a deep oblong depression which, probably, lodged a saccular process of the lung' (Owen 1876, p. 6). Owen had the second specimen sectioned to reveal its camellate interior (Fig. 4b). This is specimen NHMUK R46870, although its catalogue number is incorrectly transcribed on one label in the collection as '46780', a mistake repeated by Naish & Martill (2001, p. 197). To date only one half of NHMUK R46870 has been published (Owen 1876, plate V; Naish & Martill 2001, text-fig. 8.4), on both occasions as a mirror-image of the actual specimen. Previously unreported is that both halves of the specimen were polished, and both are in the museum's collection today. They are similar in

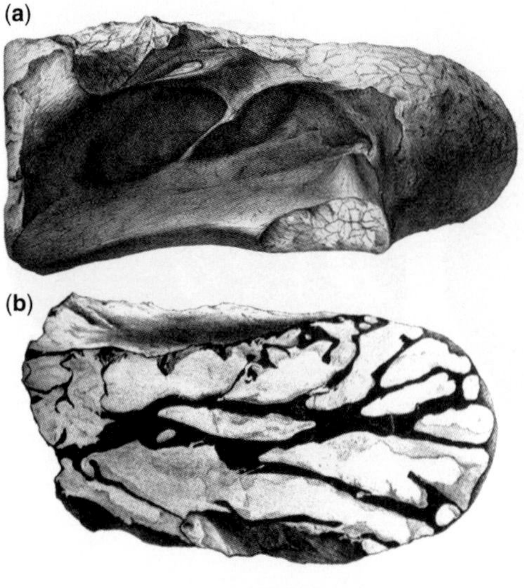

Fig. 4. Cervical vertebrae of the titanosauriform sauropod *Chondrosteosaurus gigas* from the Wessex Formation of the Isle of Wight. (**a**) NHMUK R46869 in right lateral view and (**b**) one half of NHMUK R46870 as longitudinally sectioned, showing internal cavities. In total length, NHMUK R46869 is 330 mm long, and has a preserved height of 170 mm and a preserved width of 230 mm; the half of NHMUK R46870 shown here (as a mirror-image of the actual specimen) is 225 mm long. From Owen (1876).

length (225 mm for the half figured in the literature and 227 mm for the other half) and similar overall, bar the fact that the unfigured half has a more eroded external surface and lacks its periosteum. As a result, the thin and eroded bony boundaries of the camellae are visible on the specimen's lateral surface.

While Seeley had implied that camellae were pneumatic, Owen interpreted those of NHMUK R46869 quite differently. He wrote 'I deem it much more probable that the large cancelli obvious at every fractured surface of this vertebra were occupied in the living reptile by unossified cartilage, or chondrine, than by air from the lungs, and consequently have no grounds for inferring that the whale-like Saurian, of which the present vertebrae equals in length the largest one of any Cetacean recent or fossil, had the power of flight, or belonged to either Pterosauria or Aves' (Owen 1876, p. 6). To reflect the presence of 'chondrine-filled' spaces in the vertebrae of this animal, Owen coined the new name *Chondrosteosaurus gigas* for NHMUK R46869 and R46870, meaning 'giant cartilage and bone lizard'.

Quite why Owen was happy with pneumatic lateral fossae, but not with pneumaticity within the body of the centrum itself, seems odd, especially when Owen was very familiar with avian anatomy (he specifically referred to the internal anatomy of avian vertebrae in, for example, his 1859 article on pterosaur vertebrae: Owen 1859). Indeed, the internal anatomy of bird and sauropod centra are so similar that it is difficult not to conclude that what applies for one applies for the other. However, it is clear from Owen's quote given above that, when interpreting *C. gigas*, he was not just producing an objective description, but also had an axe to grind: he was specifically refuting Seeley's statements on *O. hulkei*, hence the rejection of the idea that *C. gigas* might have been capable of flight, or that it might be allied to pterosaurs or birds. For whatever reason, Owen was also making note of the fact that he disagreed with Seeley's idea of a pneumatic vertebral interior: the name *Chondrosteosaurus* itself almost seeming like a snub to Seeley.

Despite this one-upmanship, ultimately, both Seeley and Owen emerge from this early phase in research quite well, as both workers still win citations for having made key early statements on saurischian pneumaticity (e.g. Wedel 2003*a*, *b*; O'Connor 2006). In the decades that followed, both Edward Cope and Othniel Marsh were to make statements about the probable pneumaticity of sauropod vertebrae (Cope 1877; Marsh 1877), and workers such as Werner Janensch kept the idea alive during the twentieth century (e.g. Janensch 1947). Today, as CT (computerized tomography)-scanning and other technological advancements allow the interiors of bones to be better understood, the pneumatic nature of saurischian vertebrae is unarguable and increasingly well documented.

I thank S. Chapman and P. Barrett for access to specimens in the NHM collections and for arranging photography of NHMUK R1828; J. Radley for discussion of Wealden Supergroup stratigraphy; and R. Benson, M. P. Taylor, D. Unwin and M. Wedel for data and discussion on pterosaurs, theropods, sauropods and pneumaticity. D. Schwarz-Wings and D. Martill made helpful comments and suggestions that improved the manuscript. Some of the text used here previously appeared on the blog site SV-POW! (available at http://svpow.wordpress.com/).

References

Allen, P. & Wimbledon, W. A. 1991. Correlation of NW European Purbeck–Wealden (nonmarine Lower Cretaceous) as seen from the English type areas. *Cretaceous Research*, **12**, 511–526.

Benson, R. B. J., Brusatte, S. L., Hutt, S. & Naish, D. 2009. A new large basal tetanuran (Dinosauria: Theropoda) from the Wessex Formation (Barremian) of the

Isle of Wight, England. *Journal of Vertebrate Paleontology*, **29**, 612–615.
BLOWS, W. T. 1996. A new species of *Polacanthus* (Ornithischia; Ankylosauria) from the Lower Cretaceous of Sussex, England. *Geological Magazine*, **133**, 671–682.
BRITT, B. B. 1993. *Pneumatic Postcranial Bones in Dinosaurs and Other Archosaurs*. PhD thesis, University of Calgary, Canada.
BONDE, N. & CHRISTIANSEN, P. 2003. The detailed anatomy of *Rhamphorhynchus*: axial pneumaticity and its implications. *In*: BUFFETAUT, E. & MAZIN, J.-M. (eds) *Evolution and Palaeobiology of Pterosaurs*. Geological Society, London, Special Publications, **217**, 217–232.
BUTLER, R. J., BARRETT, P. M. & GOWER, D. J. 2009. Postcranial skeletal pneumaticity and air-sacs in the earliest pterosaurs. *Biology Letters*, **5**, 557–560; doi: 10.1098/rsbl.2009.0139.
CHARIG, A. J. 1979. *A New Look at the Dinosaurs*. Heinemann, London, and the British Museum (Natural History), London.
CHARIG, A. J. & MILNER, A. C. 1986. *Baryonyx*, a remarkable new theropod dinosaur. *Nature*, **324**, 359–361.
COPE, E. D. 1877. On a gigantic saurian from the Dakota Epoch of Colorado. *Palaeontological Bulletin*, **25**, 5–10.
DESMOND, A. J. 1982. *Archetypes and Ancestors: Palaeontology in Victorian London 1850–1875*. Blond & Briggs, London.
GOWER, D. J. 2001. Possible postcranial pneumaticity in the last common ancestor of birds and crocodilians: evidence from *Erythrosuchus* and other Mesozoic archosaurs. *Naturwissenschaften*, **88**, 119–122.
HUENE, F. VON 1923. Carnivorous Saurischia in Europe since the Triassic. *Bulletin of the Geological Society of America*, **34**, 449–458.
HUENE, F. VON 1926*a*. On several known and unknown reptiles of the order Saurischia from England and France. *The Annals and Magazine of Natural History*, Series 9, **17**, 473–489.
HUENE, F. VON 1926*b*. The carnivorous Saurischia in the Jura and Cretaceous formations. *Revista del Museo de La Plata*, **29**, 35–167.
HUTT, S., MARTILL, D. M. & BARKER, M. J. 1996. The first European allosaurid dinosaur (Lower Cretaceous, Wealden Group, England). *Neues Jahrbuch fur Geologie und Paläontologie, Monatshefte*, **1996**, 635–644.
HUTT, S., NAISH, D., MARTILL, D. M., BARKER, M. J. & NEWBERY, P. 2001. A preliminary account of a new tyrannosauroid theropod from the Wessex Formation (Early Cretaceous) of southern England. *Cretaceous Research*, **22**, 227–242.
JANENSCH, W. 1947. Pneumatizität bei Wirbeln von Sauropoden und anderen Saurischiern. *Palaeontographica*, **3**, (Suppl. 7), 1–25.
KERTH, M. & HAILWOOD, E. A. 1988. Magnetostratigraphy of the Lower Cretaceous Vectis Formation (Wealden Group) on the Isle of Wight, southern England. *Journal of the Geological Society, London*, **145**, 351–360.
KUHN, O. 1939. *Saurischia, Fossilium Catalogus I: Animalia, Pars 87*. W. Quenstedt, Munich.
MARSH, O. C. 1877. Notice of new dinosaurian reptiles from the Jurassic Formation. *American Journal of Science*, **14**, 89–94.
MARTILL, D. M. & NAISH, D. 2001. The geology of the Isle of Wight. *In*: MARTILL, D. M. & NAISH, D. (eds) *Dinosaurs of the Isle of Wight*. The Palaeontological Association, London, 25–43.
NAISH, D. 2003. A definitive allosauroid (Dinosauria; Theropoda) from the Lower Cretaceous of East Sussex. *Proceedings of the Geologists' Association*, **114**, 319–326.
NAISH, D. & MARTILL, D. M. 2001. Saurischian dinosaurs 1: Sauropods. *In*: MARTILL, D. M. & NAISH, D. (eds) *Dinosaurs of the Isle of Wight*. The Palaeontological Association, London, 185–241.
NAISH, D. & MARTILL, D. M. 2007. Dinosaurs of Great Britain and the role of the Geological Society of London in their discovery: basal Dinosauria and Saurischia. *Journal of the Geological Society, London*, **164**, 493–510.
O'CONNOR, P. M. 2006. Postcranial pneumaticity: an evaluation of soft-tissue influences on the postcranial skeleton and the reconstruction of pulmonary anatomy in archosaurs. *Journal of Morphology*, **267**, 1199–1226.
OLSHEVSKY, G. 1991. *A Revision of the Parainfraclass Archosauria Cope, 1869, Excluding the Advanced Crocodylia*. Publications Requiring Research, San Diego, CA.
OWEN, R. 1855. *Monograph on the Fossil Reptilia of the Wealden and Purbeck formations. Part II. Dinosauria* (Iguanodon) (*Wealden*). Palaeontographical Society Monographs, **8**, 1–54.
OWEN, R. 1856. *Monograph on the fossil Reptilia of the Wealden and Purbeck Formations. Part III. Dinosauria* (Megalosaurus). Palaeontographical Society Monographs, **9**, 1–26.
OWEN, R. 1859. On the vertebral characters of the Order Pterosauria, as exexmplified in the genera *Pterodactylus* (Cuvier) and *Dimorphodon* (Owen). *Philosophical Transactions of the Royal Society of London*, **149**, 161–169.
OWEN, R. 1876. *Monograph on the fossil Reptilia of the Wealden and Purbeck Formations. Supplement 7. Crocodilia* (Poikilopleuron). *Dinosauria* (Chondrosteosaurus). Palaeontographical Society Monographs, **30**, 1–7.
PAUL, G. S. 1988. *Predatory Dinosaurs of the World*. Simon & Schuster, New York.
PEREDA SUBERBIOLA, X. & BARRETT, P. M. 1999. A systematic review of ankylosaurian dinosaur remains from the Albian-Cenomanian of England. *Special Papers in Palaeontology*, **60**, 177–208.
RADLEY, J. 2004. Demystifying the Wealden of the Weald (Lower Cretaceous, south-east England). *OUGS Journal*, **25**, 6–16.
RADLEY, J. 2006*a*. A Wealden guide I: the Weald sub-basin. *Geology Today*, **22**, 109–118.
RADLEY, J. 2006*b*. A Wealden guide II: the Wessex sub-basin. *Geology Today*, **22**, 187–193.
RAUHUT, O. W. M. 2000. *The Interrelationships and Evolution of Basal Theropods (Dinosauria, Saurischia)*. Unpublished PhD thesis, University of Bristol.

SEELEY, H. G. 1870. On *Ornithopsis*, a gigantic animal of the pterodactyle kind from the Wealden. *Annals and Magazine of Natural History*, Series 4, **5**, 279–283.

TAYLOR, M. P. & NAISH, D. 2007. An unusual new neosauropod dinosaur from the Lower Cretaceous Hastings Beds Group of East Sussex, England. *Palaeontology*, **50**, 1547–1564.

UNWIN, D. M. 2001. An overview of the pterosaur assemblage from the Cambrige Greensand (Cretaceous) of eastern England. *Mitteilungen aus dem Museum für Naturkunde in Berlin, Geowissenschaftliche Reihe*, **4**, 189–221.

UNWIN, D. M. 2006. *The Pterosaurs From Deep Time*. Pi Press, New York.

VON MEYER, H. 1837. Die Bayreuthen Petrefakten-Sammlungen. *Neues Jahrbuch Mineralogie, Geol Geol Petrefakten-Kunde*, **1837**, 314–316.

WEDEL, M. J. 2003*a*. The evolution of vertebral pneumaticity in sauropod dinosaurs. *Journal of Vertebrate Paleontology*, **23**, 344–357.

WEDEL, M. J. 2003*b*. Vertebral pneumaticity, air sacs, and the physiology of sauropod dinosaurs. *Paleobiology*, **29**, 243–255.

WEDEL, M. J. 2004. The origin of postcranial skeletal pneumaticity in dinosaurs. *In*: BUCKERIDGE, J. & CHEN, Y. (eds) *Proceedings of the 19th International Congress of Zoology*. China Zoological Society, Beijing, 443–445.

WEDEL, M. J. 2007. What pneumaticity tells us about 'prosauropods', and vice versa. *Special Papers in Palaeontology*, **77**, 207–222.

WILSON, J. A. 1999. A nomenclature for vertebral laminae in sauropods and other saurischian dinosaurs. *Journal of Vertebrate Paleontology*, **19**, 639–653.

A short history of research on *Archaeopteryx* and its relationship with dinosaurs

PETER WELLNHOFER

Gelbenholzener Strasse 36, D-82256 Fürstenfeldbruck, Germany (e-mail: p.wellnhofer@t-online.de)

Abstract: *Archaeopteryx*, first discovered in 1861 from the Solnhofen lithographic limestone of Bavaria, is the oldest feathered animal in the fossil record. Since its discovery it has been the focus of discussions about avian ancestry. Its mosaic of saurian and avian skeletal characters made it the classical 'missing link' of the Darwinian Theory of evolution. Even as early as 1868 Huxley advocated a close dinosaurian relationship of birds, a position followed later by such palaeontological luminaries as Marsh, Baur, Nopcsa and Abel, among others. Only in 1926, when Gerhard Heilmann published his seminal work, *The Origin of Birds*, was a 'thecodontian' origin of birds favoured. This book dominated perceptions of avian origins for the next half century, until John H. Ostrom reinvigorated the hypothesis of a dinosaurian ancestry for birds based on more *Archaeopteryx* specimens and new discoveries of theropod dinosaurs. Finally, the advent of cladistic methodology was instrumental in supporting *Archaeopteryx* and Aves within the theropod clade Maniraptora, a view almost ubiquitous today.

Since its initial discovery in 1861 in the Upper Jurassic Solnhofen lithographic limestone of southern Germany, *Archaeopteryx* has been the subject of debate and controversy because of its mix of classically 'reptilian' and 'avian' characters, and because it was the oldest feathered animal in the fossil record. Early discussions about this peculiar animal centred around the question of whether *Archaeopteryx* was optimally classified as a bird or a saurian, or was instead a transitional form between the two categories. Although a 'reptilian' origin of birds was generally accepted, conflicting hypotheses developed about the specific relationships of *Archaeopteryx* to various ancestral groups, predominantly 'thecodonts', crocodylomorphs and theropod dinosaurs.

The *Archaeopteryx* specimens – the fossil evidence

Archaeopteryx discoveries are rare events. The 10 skeletal specimens presently known and an isolated feather derive from the Upper Jurassic Plattenkalk, the Solnhofen lithographic limestone, of Bavaria; no other fossil Lagerstätte has produced one.

The single feather

The *Archaeopteryx* story began in the Solnhofen Community Quarry in the summer of 1861 with the discovery of a single feather, preserved in all its details as an imprint on a plate of limestone. Although seemingly insignificant, this fossil became a scientific sensation, receiving the highest level of attention from palaeontologists. Frankfurt palaeontologist Hermann von Meyer created the scientific name, *Archaeopteryx* ('ancient feather'), in 1861. To record the fossil's origin from the lithographic limestone, he erected the species name, *lithographica*. He referred to the fossil feather as 'the first remnant of a bird from pre-Tertiary times' (Meyer 1861*a*, 1862). It was the first indication of the existence of birds in the Jurassic, and was likewise evidence of the oldest known bird in the fossil record. Both counter slabs of the original fossil are housed today in the museums of Berlin and Munich, respectively.

The London specimen

In the very same year, 1861, in a Langenaltheim quarry near Solnhofen the first skeleton of *Archaeopteryx* was found, showing clear impressions of wing and tail feathers but seemingly lacking the skull (Fig. 1). The specimen was first described by Owen (1863*a*, *b*), who named it *Archaeopteryx macrura*. Designated as the 'London specimen' today, it was bought by the British Museum, London, where it is housed in the Natural History Museum. de Beer (1954) assigned it to *Archaeopteryx lithographica*.

The Berlin specimen

The second skeleton (and still the best *Archaeopteryx* specimen) showing the skull for the first time and displaying the plumage in perfect preservation was found near Eichstätt in 1876. It went to the Mineralogical Museum of Berlin University,

From: Moody, R. T. J., Buffetaut, E., Naish, D. & Martill, D. M. (eds) *Dinosaurs and Other Extinct Saurians: A Historical Perspective*. Geological Society, London, Special Publications, **343**, 237–250.
DOI: 10.1144/SP343.14 0305-8719/10/$15.00

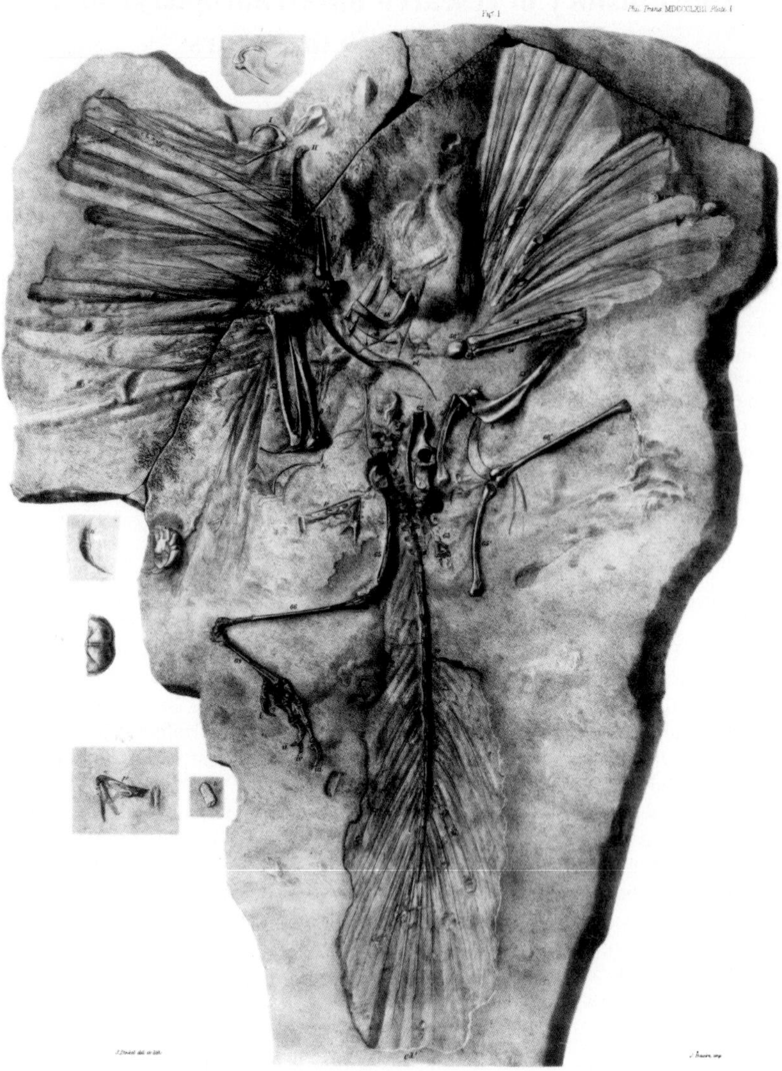

Fig. 1. The London specimen of *Archaeopteryx*, found near Solnhofen in 1861, was figured as a folded lithograph in natural size published by Richard Owen (1863*b*).

later to become the Museum für Naturkunde of Humboldt University, and is known as the 'Berlin specimen'. It was studied first by Dames (1884). Later, in 1897, he named it *Archaeopteryx siemensii*, and Petronievics (1921) gave it a distinct genus, *Archaeornis*, a separation that has not been generally accepted.

The Maxberg specimen

The third specimen, a disarticulated, incomplete skeleton with feather imprints lacking the skull and the tail, was found in 1956, not far from the locality of the London specimen. It had been called the 'Maxberg specimen' because it was on display in the local museum on the Maxberg near Solnhofen. After its owner had withdrawn it from display in 1974, it disappeared and is considered to be lost. The specimen was first described by Heller (1959) as *Archaeopteryx lithographica*.

The Haarlem specimen

Even as early as 1855, a rather fragmentary, partial specimen was found in a Plattenkalk quarry near Riedenburg that was originally identified as a pterodactyl by Meyer (1857, 1859–1860). It was only in 1970 that John Ostrom recognized it in the collections of the Teyler Museum in Haarlem, The Netherlands, as the skeletal remains of an *Archaeopteryx*. He described it in detail and assigned it to *Archaeopteryx lithographica* (Ostrom 1972). It is known as the 'Haarlem specimen' today.

The Eichstätt specimen

The fifth skeletal specimen of *Archaeopteryx* came to light in 1973 when F. X. Mayr announced its existence (Mayr 1973). However, it had actually been found in 1951 in the vicinity of Eichstätt, but not recognized at that time. It is an almost complete skeleton with feather imprints and with a perfectly preserved skull. It is the smallest individual so far known and was taken to be a juvenile of *Archaeopteryx lithographica* by Wellnhofer (1974). However, it was assigned to a new taxon, *Jurapteryx recurva* by Howgate (1985). This 'Eichstätt specimen' is housed in the Jura-Museum in Eichstätt.

The Solnhofen specimen

In 1987 the sixth *Archaeopteryx* specimen, a not quite complete skeleton, became known to the public. It originated from a private collection in Solnhofen and was purchased by the community of Solnhofen for display in the Bürgermeister-Müller-Museum, there. Its original locality and time of discovery have not been disclosed. After the location of its depository, it is called the 'Solnhofen specimen'. The largest individual so far known, it was first described by Wellnhofer (1988) as *Archaeopteryx lithographica*, but was assigned to a new taxon, *Wellnhoferia grandis*, by Elzanowski (2001*a*).

The Munich specimen

Not far from the quarries in which the London and Maxberg specimens had been found, a seventh skeletal specimen of *Archaeopteryx* was discovered in 1992 showing feather impressions and new osteological details. It was secured by the Bavarian State Collection of Palaeontology and Geology in Munich, and is thus called the 'Munich specimen'. It was first described by Wellnhofer (1993) and assigned to a new species, *Archaeopteryx bavarica*.

The eighth specimen

A very fragmentary, badly preserved specimen including skull and a few long bones was obtained from the Mörnsheim Formation overlying the Solnhofen limestone at a quarry near Daiting. It is in private ownership and has recently been deposited in the Munich State Collection. After a preliminary description published by Mäuser (1997) a detailed study has been carried out by Tischlinger (2009). He called it the *Daiting* specimen of *Archaeopteryx*.

The ninth specimen

In 2004 an isolated wing skeleton of an *Archaeopteryx* was found in the oldest Solnhofen quarry. It is in private ownership, but is on public display in the Solnhofen Museum on a permanent loan basis. This 'Ninth specimen' was first described by Wellnhofer & Röper (2005) as *Archaeopteryx lithographica*.

The Thermopolis specimen

Finally, in 2001, a 10th skeletal specimen of *Archaeopteryx* turned up in a private collection in Switzerland, and has been purchased by an anonymous donor for deposition and public display in the Wyoming Dinosaur Center in Thermopolis, Wyoming, USA. Therefore called the 'Thermopolis specimen', it was studied in detail by Mayr *et al.* (2005, 2007) and designated as *Archaeopteryx siemensii*. It is one of the best preserved and most complete *Archaeopteryx* specimens known. Its original locality and horizon were not made public, but it seems to have originated from the Eichstätt quarry district.

Detailed descriptions and the history of all of the *Archaeopteryx* specimens can be found in Wellnhofer (2008, 2009).

Early scientific debates and controversies between 1861 and 1876

Until the discovery of the 'feathered dinosaurs' from China in the 1990s, feathers had been a significant character, diagnostic exclusively for birds. In the traditional Linnaean classification based on extant animals there was a clear separation of the Class Aves from all other vertebrates. The same applied to the Class Reptilia, composed of the extant orders Testudines, Sphenodonta, Squamata and Crocodylia. The boundaries between these discreet categories were rather clear but inflexible, and fossils such as *Archaeopteryx* that exhibit a mosaic of features traditionally identified with different groups posed unique problems. Today, of course, it is widely recognized that evolutionary entities do not naturally occur in discreet groups but instead along a continuous spectrum that is poorly encapsulated by categorization. But even in Linnaean terms, this is especially well exemplified by the continuing debate of whether *Archaeopteryx* was a dinosaur-like bird or a feathered, bird-like dinosaur.

According to modern 'phylogenetic systematics' the traditional class Reptilia is no longer tenable as representing a phylogenetically unified, monophyletic, group. It is considered a paraphyletic association of tetrapods that are not monophyletic, i.e. do not share a common ancestor. However, in this historical context, using the terms 'Reptilia', 'reptiles' and 'reptilian' is justifiable.

Archaeopteryx – bird, saurian or intermediate?

In 1861, even more than the isolated feather, the first *Archaeopteryx* skeleton with feather imprints, the London specimen, aroused emotions. Indeed, it inflamed learned disputation as to whether this animal was a bird with reptilian characteristics, a saurian with bird-like feathers, or some kind of intermediate or transitional form between the reptiles and the birds.

To comprehend the controversies, one must remember the disturbance caused by Charles Darwin, who had recently (November 1859) published his book *The Origin of Species by means of Natural Selection. Or the Preservation of Favoured Races in the Struggle for Life*. Therein Darwin presented his Theory of Evolution, which proposed that all forms of life were related insofar as they ultimately descended from a single organism. With his theory of descent Darwin especially offended believers in biblical creation. One of the first objections to Darwin's theory concerned the so-called missing links. If, indeed, life on Earth had a single origin and all later species have evolved from one another, then there must have been intermediates or transitional forms in the fossil record; and these links seemed to be missing.

Andreas Wagner

Munich palaeontologist Andreas Wagner was one of the first who recognized the meaning of *Archaeopteryx* as a 'missing link' for the Darwinian Theory:

> I must add a few words to ward off Darwinian misinterpretations of our new saurian. At the first glance ... we might certainly form a notion that we had before us an intermediate creature, engaged in the transition from the saurian to the bird. Darwin and his adherents will probably employ the new discovery as an exceedingly welcome occurrence for the justification of their strange views upon the transformations of animals.
>
> (Wagner 1862b, p. 266)

He concluded that the vertebrate was not a bird but a saurian, which he christened *Griphosaurus* (Greek: *griphos*, enigma). Being an orthodox Protestant, he tried to bring the observations of geology and palaeontology into agreement with the biblical narrative of the Creation. There was no place in Wagner's system of the animal kingdom for an intermediate form. A bird, in his view, could not have existed as early as the Jurassic. Consequently, for Wagner, the feather-like imprints on the *Archaeopteryx* skeleton were no proof that they were produced by the real feathers of a bird. He interpreted them instead as 'peculiar adornments' of the *Griphosaurus* that merely possessed the external appearance of bird feathers. But even at his time Andreas Wagner stood rather alone with such ideas.

Hermann von Meyer

However, the avian nature of *Archaeopteryx* was not generally accepted. Hermann von Meyer, after having identified the single feather as definitely avian, was more cautious in his judgement on the feathered skeleton. When first notified of the creature, he described it as 'a feathered animal which differs from our birds essentially' (Meyer 1861*a*, *b*; Wellnhofer 2001). In a letter to London geologist John Evans, who had discovered isolated cranial fragments including teeth on the London *Archaeopteryx* plate, Hermann von Meyer had something more detailed to say:

> An arming of the jaw with teeth would contradict the view of the *Archaeopteryx* being a bird or an embryonic form of bird. But after all, I do not believe that God formed his creatures after the systems devised by our philosophical wisdom ... The *Archaeopteryx* is of its kind just as perfect a creature as other creatures, and if we are not able to include this fossil animal in our system, our short-sightedness is alone to blame.
>
> (Meyer in Evans 1865, p. 415)

Ernst Friedrich Witte

Knowledgeable amateur palaeontologist Ernst Friedrich Witte from Hannover considered (Witte 1863) the problem of whether *Archaeopteryx* was a bird or a reptile as a 'fruitless controversy'. In a, perhaps, Solomonic attempt at solution, he pointed out that as the animal had characters of both reptiles and birds then it was actually neither: 'Rather there arises the question which characters predominate, and to which class it has to be assigned to, provisionally' (p. 568). Obviously, Witte expected that tallies would be made of its avian and its reptilian characteristics by the professionals, and whichever tally had more entries should determine how it was classified. Such statements indicate that facets of the debate about whether *Archaeopteryx* was a bird or a reptile were concerned more with the classification of *Archaeopteryx* itself than they had to do with avian evolution.

Richard Owen

The first to study and formally describe the London *Archaeopteryx* specimen was Richard Owen (1863*a*, *b*). From the title of his monograph, it is already obvious that Owen regarded *Archaeopteryx* as a bird, despite the long tail with 20 vertebrae 'resembling in structure and proportions those of a squirrel'. He compared the tail with the embryonic stage of modern birds, and stated that in the young ostrich 18–20 vertebrae could also be counted. Thus, he concluded that in *Archaeopteryx* an embryonic condition was preserved in the adult individual, and that it was closer to the general vertebrate type. This idea was quite in agreement with his concept of archetypes. As an opponent of the evolutionary theory of Charles Darwin, Owen was convinced that all animals within each larger systematic group were only variations of a single theme, the 'ideal archetype', and that the 'divine spirit' who had planned the archetype knew in advance of all its modifications. Of course, such an explanation of the diversity of all life forms, according to a divine plan, was in sharp contrast to the theory of species transformations, a result of natural selection factors in the 'struggle for life' as proposed by Darwin. Thus, he called it a 'long-tailed' bird, albeit a very primitive one, with true feathers, rather than an intermediate form. However, Owen pointed also to structures that are not bird-like, like the long tail and the claws on both preserved fingers. His conclusion was:

> The best-determinable parts of its preserved structure declare it unequivocally to be a bird, with rare peculiarities indicative of a distinct order in that class. By the law of correlation we infer that the mouth was devoid of lips, and was a beak-like instrument fitted for the preening of the plumage of *Archeopteryx*. A broad and keeled breast-bone was doubtless associated in the living bird with the great pectoral ridge of the humerus, with the furculum, and with the other evidences of feathered instruments for flight.
>
> (Owen 1863*b*, p. 46).

However, Owen's speculations on the presence of a beak and a keeled sternum could not be confirmed after the more complete second skeleton that included the skull, the Berlin specimen, became known about 20 years later. But even before, many of Owen's interpretations and conclusions were heavily criticized by Huxley (1868*a*).

Charles Darwin and Thomas Henry Huxley

The London specimen of *Archaeopteryx* was discovered 2 years after the first edition (1859) of Darwin's *Origin of Species*, so it could not be incorporated into Darwin's initial evolutionary formulations. Yet, even in later editions, Darwin definitely showed noticeable restraint with regard to *Archaeopteryx*. In only two places of his 'Origin' did he mention it:

> that strange bird, *Archaeopteryx*, with a long lizard-like tail, bearing a pair of feathers on each joint, and with its wings furnished with two free claws ... Hardly any recent discovery shows more forcibly than this, how little we as yet know of the former inhabitants of the world.
>
> (p. 284).

Then some pages later:

> Even the wide interval between birds and reptiles has been shown ... to be partly bridged over in the most unexpected manner, on the one hand, by the ostrich and extinct *Archaeopteryx*, and on the other hand, by the *Compsognathus*, one of the Dinosaurians – that group which includes the most gigantic of all terrestrial reptiles.
>
> (Darwin 1878, p. 302)

He mentioned *Archaeopteryx* one more time in his book *The Descent of Man* (1871) as: 'that strange bird with a long, lizard-like tail', as an example of an intermediate form.

Darwin apparently accepted the ideas of his friend and advocate of his theory, Thomas Henry Huxley, who, in 1868, had postulated a close relationship between dinosaurs and birds for the first time. But Huxley's conclusions were based not on *Archaeopteryx* but on the small bipedal Solnhofen dinosaur *Compsognathus*, which he regarded as 'still more bird-like than any of the animals ... included in that group', representing a near approximation to the 'missing link' between reptiles and birds (Huxley 1868*b*, p. 73) (Fig. 2). (Incidentally, it is in this discussion that the phrase 'missing link' seems to have been published for the first time.)

It is surprising to read his statement about *Archaeopteryx:* 'In many respects, *Archaeopteryx* is more remote from the boundary-line between birds and reptiles than some living Ratitae are' (Huxley 1868*a*, p. 248). He concluded that the nearest approximation to reptiles was represented among the ostriches and their allies in the flightless Ratitae. Huxley compared the Dinosauria, including *Iguanodon*, *Hadrosaurus*, *Megalosaurus*, *Plateosaurus* and some others known at his time, with the living ratites and concluded that 'the hind quarters of the Dinosauria wonderfully approached those of birds in their general structure, and therefore that these extinct reptiles were more closely allied to birds than any which now live' (Huxley 1868*b*, p. 73).

Nevertheless, Huxley (1868*b*, p. 75) considered both *Compsognathus* and *Archaeopteryx* as

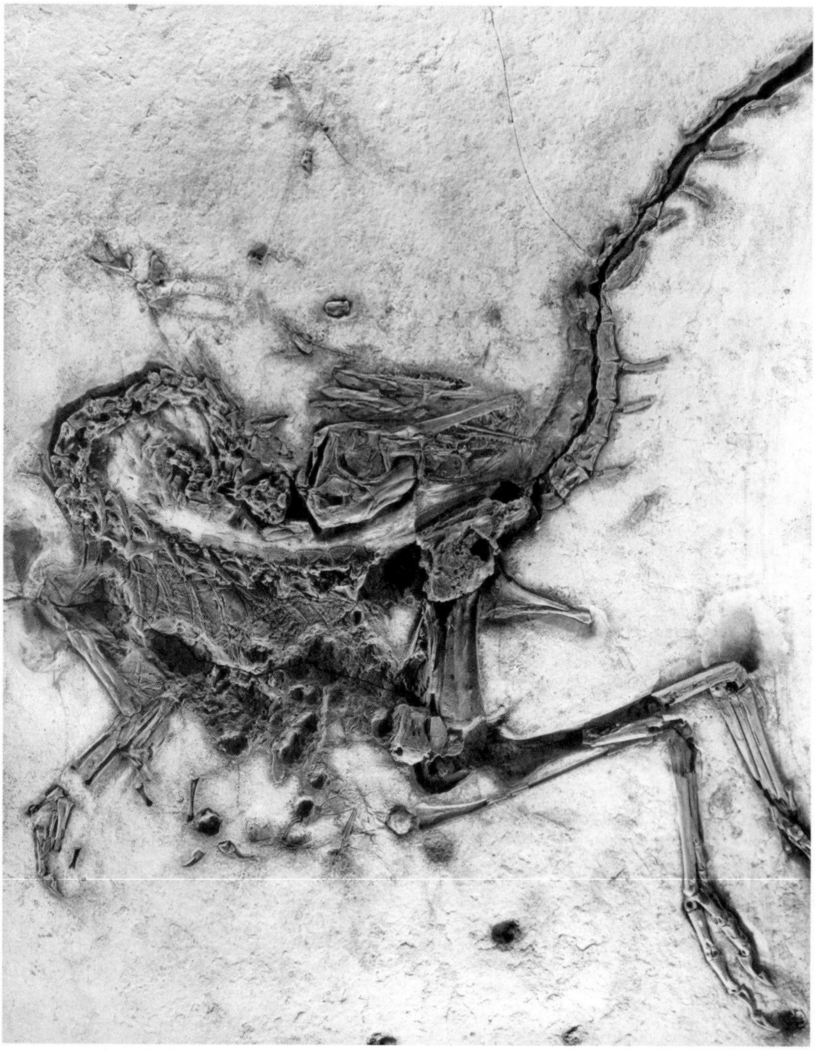

Fig. 2. *Compsognathus longipes* Wagner, from the Upper Jurassic lithographic limestone of Bavaria. This small theropod dinosaur was perceived as the most bird-like reptile by Huxley and was critical to his hypothesis of dinosaur–bird relationships (Bavarian State Collection of Palaeontology and Geology, Munich, BSP AS I 563).

'intermediate forms' and favoured the hypothesis that birds may have been evolved from dinosaurs, although not indicating a particular group. But he was cautious about the position of *Archaeopteryx* because the skull was thought to be missing from the only known (London) specimen at the time, and he was confused by the presence of a furcula in *Archaeopteryx*, which was not then known in any other dinosaur. However, it must be remembered that only a few dinosaur taxa were known, mostly based on fragmentary skeletal material. The concept of the Theropoda for the bipedal, carnivorous saurischians was not established until 1881 by Marsh.

Research after the discovery of the second *Archaeopteryx* specimen: 1876–1926

Wilhelm Dames

A second *Archaeopteryx* skeleton, the 'Berlin specimen' (Fig. 3), included the skull and perfectly preserved feather imprints. Wilhelm Dames, then Curator of the geological–palaeontological collections of the Mineralogical Museum in Berlin, was entrusted with the scientific investigation (Dames 1884). Two years earlier, he had already published a short paper on the skull. He was forced to this premature publication, since Carl Vogt, in 1879,

Fig. 3. The Berlin specimen of *Archaeopteryx*, found near Eichstätt in 1876, was figured as a coloured lithograph in the monograph of Wilhelm Dames (1884).

and O. C. Marsh, in 1881, had already described details of the skull which, after further preparation, turned out to be partly incorrect. Later, Dames (1897) also discussed evolutionary problems and concluded that *Archaeopteryx* was a primitive bird. He also seems to have given up his former caution against the Darwinian evolutionary theory. However, he qualified this by writing that *Archaeopteryx* was no longer a transitional or intermediate link between the classes of reptiles and birds, but was in the series of birds and already far from the point of separation of both branches of the sauropsids (Dames 1897).

Carl Vogt

Carl Vogt, Professor of Geology at the University of Geneva, was a passionate defender of the evolutionary theory and came to the conclusion that *Archaeopteryx* could be interpreted as a flying reptile furnished with bird's feathers and bird-like hind limbs. Actually, he considered it neither a bird nor a reptile, but that it formed a marked intermediate type. He confirmed the idea of Huxley who had combined classes Reptilia and Aves as 'Sauropsida', but did not agree with Huxley's view that the dinosaurs might be ancestral to all birds. Rather, he suggested that the Class Aves was not monophyletic, but rather polyphyletic, originating from different groups, the ratites from dinosaurs and the carinates from *Archaeopteryx*. He speculated that *Archaeopteryx* might have descended from terrestrial, lizard-like saurians covered with rudimentary feathers similar to those of bird embryos (Vogt 1879, 1880).

Harry Govier Seeley

London palaeontologist Harry Govier Seeley refuted most of Vogt's conclusions, since, in his view, he had overestimated the similarity of *Archaeopteryx* to reptiles (Seeley 1881). Seeley considered it a primitive bird, explicitly confirming Owen's interpretation. He argued: 'It would have been reversing of one of the oldest canons of natural history to find well-developed plumage associated with a reptilian skeleton' and 'There would have been no transition here, but an incongruity' (Seeley 1881, p. 305). With such a statement Seeley also criticized Huxley in arguing that obligatory bipedalism in both dinosaurs and birds was the result of convergence rather than indicating a closer relationship. However, he offered no alternative for the ancestry of birds. Comparing the Berlin and London *Archaeopteryx* skeletons, he concluded also that they might be assigned to different species, if not genera; a conclusion followed by Dames (1897) and Petronievics (1921), respectively.

Othniel Charles Marsh

In 1881 Othniel Charles Marsh, had the opportunity to study both the London and Berlin specimens, and reported on his investigations in a lecture at a meeting of the British Association for the Advancement of Science in York, UK. He had found hitherto unknown features of *Archaeopteryx*, such as real teeth, and concluded that *Archaeopteryx* was a bird, but the most reptilian one. He suspected the ancestors of birds to be among more primitive and older dinosaur-like reptiles, still unknown from the fossil record (Marsh 1881).

Fürbringer, Gegenbauer, Williston, Baur, Nopcsa and Abel

In Germany, Fürbringer (1888) argued also that *Archaeopteryx* was a true bird far beyond the reptilian–avian transition, originating from a long series of feathered ancestors without indicating a particular group. He was unable to decide whether it might have been ancestral to modern birds or belonged rather to a line long extinct.

Yet, Huxley's idea of a close dinosaurian relationship of birds (Huxley 1869*a*, *b*) was not dead, but maintained by Gegenbaur (1878), Williston (1879), Baur (1883, 1885*a*, *b*) and others. Baur (1885*b*) supported an ornithopod, rather than theropod, origin of birds based largely on the alleged opisthopubic pelvis of the Berlin specimen of *Archaeopteryx*. (This concept was briefly revived by Galton 1970, although he more broadly examined ornithischian dinosaurs as a whole, rather than just ornithopods. This view was refuted in detail by Charig 1972 on the basis of functional studies of the pelvis and hind limbs of archosaurs.)

Often, research on *Archaeopteryx* and its phylogenetic origin has also included the problem of the origin of flight or, most commonly, was coupled with it. It centred on the problem of whether *Archaeopteryx* could climb tree trunks and was thus an arboreal animal, or was adapted to bipedal running on the ground and was thus a cursorial animal. The idea of modern 'cursorial theory' of the origin of flight from the ground up, goes back to Hungarian Baron Franz Nopcsa who introduced his famous 'running *Proavis*' hypothesis arguing that birds originated from bipedal dinosaur-like running forms in which the anterior extremities, on account of flapping movements, gradually transmuted elongated feathers into wings without thereby affecting terrestrial locomotion (Nopcsa 1907). Viennese palaeobiologist Othenio Abel agreed with Nopcsa insofar as he argued that of all dinosaurs it is the theropods sharing a common ancestor that have the closest similarity to birds. But he disagreed with Nopcsa in suggesting that this ancestor was arboreal (Abel 1911, 1912). However, Abel was not the first who combined the 'arboreal theory' of the origin of flight, from the trees down, with the dinosaurian origin of birds. In 1900 Osborn had already preferred a conjecture about a 'Dinosaur–Avian stem' and urged an arboreal origin of flight (Osborn 1900).

Research on *Archaeopteryx* from Heilmann (1926) to de Beer (1954)

The idea of the dinosaurian ancestry of *Archaeopteryx* and birds was abandoned following Gerhard Heilmann's (1926) landmark monograph *The Origin of Birds*. While Huxley may have created the term 'missing link' when discussing the positions of various reptiles and *Archaeopteryx* with regard to avian origins, Heilmann clearly was able to balance the mosaic of reptilian and avian features, and dismissed the concept, at least for *Archaeopteryx*:

> We may now stop talking about the *missing link* between birds and reptiles. So much so is *Archaeopteryx* this link that we may term it a warm-blooded reptile disguised as a bird.
>
> (Heilmann 1926, p. 36)

He carried out a most comprehensive comparative study of all anatomical details of the skeleton of *Archaeopteryx* (especially the Berlin specimen), as well as of 'thecodonts', 'coelurosaur' dinosaurs (small, gracile theropods, not in the sense of the currently recognized monophyletic Coelurosauria) and extant birds, and concluded:

> From this it would seem a rather obvious conclusion that it is amongst the coelurosaurs that we are to look for the bird-ancestor.

and further:

> The striking points of similarity between coelurosaurs and birds pertained to nearly all the parts of the skeleton.
>
> (Heilmann 1926, p. 182).

Nevertheless, he ultimately decided not to pursue this evidence to its logical conclusion because he felt it was all negated by a single character: the absence in 'coelurosaurs' of ossified clavicles. Clavicles are fused medially to form the furcula in birds, a structure present in *Archaeopteryx* but unknown in theropods at that time. Consequently, he concluded that, according to Dollo's law of evolutionary irreversibility, a bird ancestor simply could not lack clavicles, and as they lacked these bones 'coelurosaurian' dinosaurs could be, at best, distant relatives of birds.

Heilmann perceived that the best possible candidacy for avian ancestry lay somewhere among the Triassic 'thecodonts', probably the 'Pseudosuchia', a theory first explicitly suggested by Broom (1913). They were documented in primitive, generalized forms like *Ornithosuchus* and *Euparkeria*, and Heilmann compared *Archaeopteryx* especially with the Ornithosuchia. Thus, he used the same arguments as Huxley to distance dinosaurs from *Archaeopteryx* because of the presence of a furcula in the latter. However, given his statements concerning the otherwise great similarity between 'coelurosaurs' and birds, had Heilmann known that many theropods indeed possessed ossified clavicles in the form of a median furcula (now known in many taxa, including dromaeosaurids), he would unquestionably have favoured a theropod origin of birds, and the subsequent 'great debate' about bird origins would probably never have transpired (Sereno 2004; Ries 2007). The influence of Heilmann's book, however, was so great that his hypothesis of a 'pseudosuchian' origin was almost universally accepted for almost 50 years.

Relying on the data of Heilmann, the position of *Archaeopteryx* was analysed among others by Lowe (1935, 1944). He interpreted the morphology of the skull as reptilian rather than intermediate between birds and reptiles. He even went so far as to claim that *Archaeopteryx* was not a bird at all, but was an 'arboreal climbing dinosaur with the power to glide'. George Gaylord Simpson, the influential American palaeontologist of the twentieth century, defended Heilmann's position against Lowe's view, which he called 'nothing short of fantastic' (Simpson 1946). In Simpson's view the skull of *Archaeopteryx* was intermediate, 'almost ideally so', between a pseudosuchian reptile-like *Euparkeria* and an advanced bird such as *Columba*. All the resemblances of saurischian dinosaurs to birds were nothing but 'parallelisms and convergences'.

> Birds arose as feathered fliers, even if this development occurred (contrary to probability and without known evidence) in more than one line and if *Archaeopteryx* ... was not in the successful particular line that did give rise to the later Aves as a whole.
>
> (Simpson 1946, p. 95)

In his great monograph on the London *Archaeopteryx* specimen, Gavin de Beer (1954), then Director of the British Museum (Natural History) in London, also discussed in detail its nature and relationships. He argued that *Archaeopteryx* was a bird close to the main line of evolution to modern birds. He accepted Heilmann's view to consider Triassic 'thecodonts', like *Euparkeria* and *Ornithosuchus*, to have been ancestral to birds. He recognized *Archaeopteryx* as an excellent example of a transitionalal form between one group and another. He also applied the principle of the 'mosaic of characters', as proposed by D. M. S. Watson (1919), to *Archaeopteryx*. With regard to the origin of avian flight, de Beer regarded the structures of *Archaeopteryx* of the greatest importance, concluding that 'all the evidence is in favour of the arboreal ... theory' (de Beer 1954, p. 52). With such an authoritative statement the controversial discussions about the meaning of *Archaeopteryx* for the origin and early evolution of birds seemed to be settled once and forever.

The revival of the dinosaurian ancestry of *Archaeopteryx* and birds after 1970

John H. Ostrom

The 'old' idea of a close relationship of birds to dinosaurs underwent a revival beginning 40 years ago with the work of John H. Ostrom. Purely by serendipity, Ostrom 'rediscovered' the fourth *Archaeopteryx* specimen in the Teyler Museum in Haarlem (mislabelled as a specimen of the pterosaur *Pterodactylus*) in 1970, shortly after describing a new theropod dinosaur, *Deinonychus antirrhopus*, from the Lower Cretaceous of Montana. In terms of its skeletal anatomy, *Deinonychus* was a mirror of *Archaeopteryx*, and Ostrom noticed these similarities immediately. These enabled him to hypothesize that the dromaeosaurid *Deinonychus* was one of the closest relatives of *Archaeopteryx* (Ostrom 1969, 1970, 1972, 1973). Ostrom penned a short letter on this subject to *Nature* that was published on 9 of March 1973, entitled 'The ancestry of birds', and ignited an intense reaction from the scientific community. Ostrom, however, laid out his evidence: a series of characters that he considered strong evidence of a coelurosaurian (theropod) ancestry of birds. He was convinced that, were it not for the feather imprints, today the *Archaeopteryx* specimens 'would be identified

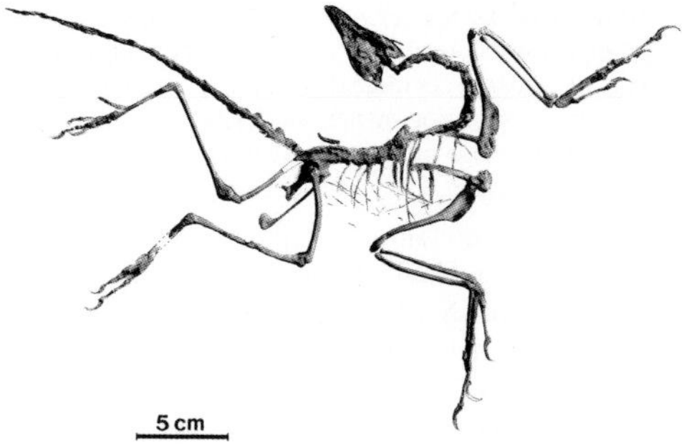

Fig. 4. The Berlin specimen of *Archaeopteryx*, with the plumage removed. Were it not for the feathers, the early authors would probably have identified the skeleton alone as that of a small theropod dinosaur. (Photograph prepared by Frank Haase.)

unquestionably as coelurosaurian theropods' (Ostrom 1976, p. 109) (Fig. 4).

Ostrom's new-found data inspired some adherents, such as Bakker & Galton (1974), who developed rather revolutionary ideas about the classification of the Aves, including *Archaeopteryx*, in general. The argument that birds evolved from small theropod dinosaurs prompted inferences that these possible bird ancestors may also have had an advanced physiology as opposed to that of other reptiles. The idea was entertained especially by Bakker (1975). It was stated that the successful radiation of birds was enabled by their use of aerial space, and that this was, in turn, enabled by a fundamentally theropod physiology and structure. Consequently, 'Dinosauria' was established as a new class of vertebrates and Aves was demoted to a subclass rank within it. Thulborn (1975) took this idea to a different extreme, suggesting that avian ancestors, that is, the entire Suborder Theropoda, should be transferred to the Class Aves, to which Alan Charig (1976, p. 65), in his typically humorous manner, commented 'just as the layman will refuse to accept Bakker and Galton's suggestion that a sparrow is a dinosaur, so will he balk at Thulborn's idea of *Tyrannosaurus rex* as a bird'. Ostrom (1985, p. 163) pragmatically suggested that these 'proposed re-alignments of birds and various archosaurs fail to meet the requirements of a utilitarian and stable systematic framework. I recommend that the class Aves be left where it is and include *Archaeopteryx* as its most archaic member'.

The hypothesis of a theropod origin of birds as advocated by Ostrom was opposed by certain camps of thought, those who argued for a crocodilian – avian relationship, first proposed by Walker (1972) and adopted by Martin *et al.* (1980), and those who argued for a 'pseudosuchian' origin of birds, advocated by Tarsitano & Hecht (1980 and subsequent papers) and others. These two different hypotheses, each using characters of *Archaeopteryx*, were critically discussed in detail by Ostrom (1985) and defeated by Gauthier & Padian (1985). The arguments are lengthy and need not be repeated in the context of this paper.

Classification of *Archaeopteryx* in the light of modern cladistics after 1982

Many of these issues were and are purely semantic, dependent wholly on the lack of rigorous definition and solidity inherent in the Linnaean classification system and its ranks: evidence for a close dinosaur–bird relationship was gaining adherents from the Heilmannian viewpoint, and ensuing quibbles were not about the validity of this relationship but about how to classify the grouping. It required the overhaul of the process for analysing phylogenies and classifying organisms based more solidly on evolutionary relationships to end this debate. On the basis of cladistic character analyses, Padian (1982) and Gauthier (1986) suggested that, in a purely evolutionary sense, birds were nested deeply within the Theropoda – birds, in short, were indeed coelurosaurian dinosaurs, just as they were theropods, saurischians, dinosaurs and archosaurs. Specifically, in this system Aves is a clade within the more inclusive theropod clade Maniraptora. This systematic arrangement, based on ever-increasing amounts of evidence, is nearly universally accepted today (e.g. Padian & Chiappe 1998; Witmer 2002; Chiappe 2007). However, nomenclatural debates have by no means ceased, and *Archaeopteryx* retains a central role in these debates. Pursuing such questions would by far exceed the limits set for this historical approach. Aves, traditionally a class in the Linnaean system, was restricted by Gauthier (1986) to the 'crown group', meaning only extant birds and all descendants of the most recent common ancestor of all extant birds (Fig. 5). To encompass the group including both extant birds and *Archaeopteryx*, he introduced the name Avialae with the intent that the term 'bird' would be a colloquialism not for Aves but for Avialae – *Archaeopteryx* was thus a bird, but not an avian. The Avialae, in turn, is the sister group of the Deinonychosauria, the clade that includes *Deinonychus* and all theropods closer to it than to the Avialae. However, there are other concepts differing in details from the one just mentioned, such as proposed by Clark *et al.* (2002), Sereno (2004) and others.

Some palaeornithologists, however, remain opposed to the idea of birds as derived theropods (e.g. Feduccia 2002) and interpret some of the

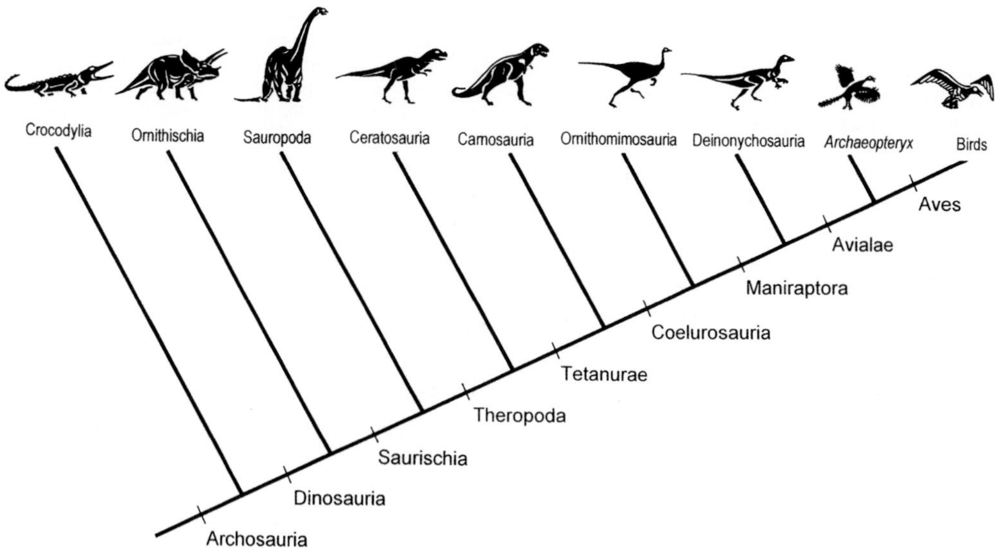

Fig. 5. Phylogenetic relationships of *Archaeopteryx* in a simplified cladogram of the Archosauria after Gauthier (1986) and others, showing its relationship within the Dinosauria.

'feathered dinosaurs' from the Lower Cretaceous of China (Chang 2003) as flightless birds that bear osteological similarities to theropod dinosaurs only due to convergent evolution for functional, but not phylogenetic, reasons, an idea harkening back to that voiced by Seeley (1881). Paul (2002), although not refuting the proposition that birds were dinosaurs, also considered many of these Cretaceous taxa 'neo-flightless birds', apostrophized by some as 'Mesozoic kiwis'.

The problem of a clear-cut distinction between birds and dinosaurs is often circumvented using the informal designations 'non-avian theropods' versus 'avian theropods', that is, in a rank-less nomenclatural system based on phylogenetic systematics. If we then ask 'what is a bird?' we are in danger of mixing up Linnaean and cladistic principles. It seems to be rather a problem of human perception, which has always been influenced by subjective opinions and traditions. Nevertheless, *Archaeopteryx*, now documented by 10 skeletons and a single feather from the Solnhofen limestone of Bavaria, will remain a key taxon in these debates. Possibly, it might best be characterized as 'a theropod dinosaur disguised as a bird', in modification of Heilmann's statement of 1926.

Discussion and conclusion

For almost 150 years, beginning in 1861 up to the present, the significance of *Archaeopteryx* has generated an overwhelming number of scientific publications that could not all be considered within the context of this paper. A short summary up to the 1970s was given by Ostrom (1976). In historical retrospect, research on *Archaeopteryx* has concentrated on three principal points of emphasis: (1) its taxonomic position; (2) its phylogenetic position; and (3) its meaning for the origin of avian flight.

The initial discussions centred on the question of whether *Archaeopteryx* was a saurian, a bird or an intermediate form in between them. Ironically, its meaning as a potential transitional form was recognized first by prominent anti-Darwinist Andreas Wagner (1862*a*, *b*), but not by Darwin's 'bulldog', Thomas Henry Huxley, and following him by Darwin himself. Huxley had introduced the popular term of the 'missing link', in 1868, for the small, bipedal dinosaur *Compsognathus* rather than for *Archaeopteryx*. It seems as if only Gerhard Heilmann (1926) has elevated *Archaeopteryx* to the rank of a 'missing link' par excellence, a label that has been attached to *Archaeopteryx* as the classical textbook example, until today.

With regard to the phylogenetic position of *Archaeopteryx*, different contradictory hypotheses have been developed. Although Huxley recognized a close dinosaurian–bird relationship, the predominant view until the 1970s was Heilmann's conclusion of a 'thecodontian' relationship and the suggestion that the Aves, including *Archaeopteryx* as the oldest member of that class, have descended from Triassic pseudosuchians. Despite the simultaneously developed hypotheses of a crocodylomorph and pseudosuchian (or basal archosaurian) origin, from the early 1980s onwards the theropodan ancestry of *Archaeopteryx* and the birds has been confirmed using cladistic methodology, a hypothesis that is almost universally accepted today.

First ideas about the origin of avian flight were published by Nopcsa (1907, 1923), whose 'running *Proavis*' model initiated the recently prevailing cursorial theory – the beginning of flight 'from the ground up.' This was also in agreement with the theropod-like skeletal morphology of *Archaeopteryx*, indicating its principally bipedal terrestrial locomotion. The opposite view was put forward by the authors who favoured a scenario for the beginning of flight 'from the trees down', called the arboreal theory. Again, *Archaeopteryx* had to support this idea on the basis of other features, as the shape and size of the finger claws, suggesting climbing abilities and arboreal lifestyle. This, in turn, was used as evidence that *Archaeopteryx*, and the birds, could not have descended from bipedally running theropods (Feduccia 1996, 2nd edn in 1999).

These controversies have shown how close these conclusions are to the danger of circular reasoning, according to the pattern: *Archaeopteryx* could climb tree trunks. Thus, it could not have descended from bipedal terrestrial, but from climbing arboreal ancestors; therefore, flight originated from the trees down. Leaving aside that there are no possible candidates for such arboreal ancestors in the fossil record, the entire reasoning can also be read in reverse. The proponents of the cursorial theory have the same problem, of course. But they have the decisive advantage of being able to present possible candidates for avian ancestors that are well documented in the fossil record. These are the dromaeosaurid theropod dinosaurs whose skeletal characters have survived in the skeletons of *Archaeopteryx*.

A fourth problem of avian evolution discussed in the past has been the origin of feathers. It was not stressed here, because *Archaeopteryx* already had well-developed feathers and an advanced, 'modern' plumage. Thus, it cannot contribute to the recent debate that has been initiated by the discoveries of the 'feathered dinosaurs' in China in the mid-1990s.

Many other aspects of research on *Archaeopteryx* have been carried out, such as its flying ability, its physiology, its lifestyle and habitat. These and many other interesting subjects have been treated in several comprehensive publications, such as Feduccia (1996, 1999), Elzanowski (2001*b*, 2002*a*, *b*), Chatterjee (1997), Chiappe (2007) and, last, by the present author (Wellnhofer 2008, 2009).

I would like to thank the organizers of the meeting 'Dinosaurs (and Other Extinct Saurians) – A Historical Perspective' held in London on 6–7 May 2008 – R. Moody, E. Buffetaut, D. Martill and D. Naish. They have made possible the presentation of quite different aspects of this wide field of research during a very interesting, well-organized meeting, and a field excursion to the Isle of Wight. This paper is an extended version of my oral presentation at this meeting, and has been considerably improved by many helpful suggestions from S. Hartmann and an anonymous reviewer. My thanks are extended to F. Haase, who reviewed the final version of the manuscript and corrected my English text.

References

ABEL, O. 1911. Die Vorfahren der Vögel und ihre Lebensweise. *Verhandlungen der k. k. zoologisch-botanischen Gesellschaft in Wien*, **61**, 144–191.

ABEL, O. 1912. Über den Erwerb des Flugvermögens. *Schriften des Vereins zur Verbreitung naturwissenschaftlicher Kenntnisse*, Wien, **52**, 1–22.

BAKKER, R. T. 1975. Dinosaur renaissance. *Scientific American*, **232**, 58–78.

BAKKER, R. T. & GALTON, P. M. 1974. Dinosaur monophyly and a new class of vertebrates. *Nature*, **248**, 168–172.

BAUR, J. G. 1883. Der Tarsus der Vögel und Dinosaurier. *Morphologisches Jahrbuch*, **8**, 417–456.

BAUR, J. G. 1885*a*. Dinosaurier und Vögel. Eine Erwiderung an Herrn Prof. W. Dames in Berlin. *Morphologisches Jahrbuch*, **10**, 446–454.

BAUR, J. G. 1885*b*. Bemerkungen über das Becken der Vögel und Dinosaurier. *Morphologisches Jahrbuch*, **10**, 613–616.

BROOM, R. 1913. On the South African pseudosuchian *Euparkeria* and allied genera. *Proceedings of the Zoological Society, London*, **1913**, 916–933.

CHANG, M.-M. (ed.) 2003. *The Jehol Biota. The Emergence of Feathered Dinosaurs, Beaked Birds and Flowering Plants*. Shanghai Scientific & Technical Publishers, Shanghai.

CHARIG, A. J. 1972. The evolution of the archosaur pelvis and hindlimb: an explanation in functional terms. *In*: JOYSEY, K. A. & KEMP, T. S. (eds) *Studies in Vertebrate Evolution*. Oliver & Boyd, Edinburgh, 121–155.

CHARIG, A. J. 1976. 'Dinosaur monophyly and a new class of vertebrates': a critical review. *In*: BELLAIRS, A. D'A. & COX, C. B. (eds) *Morphology and Biology of Reptiles*. Academic Press, New York, 65–104.

CHATTERJEE, S. 1997. *The Rise of Birds*. Johns Hopkins University Press, Baltimore, MD.

CHIAPPE, L. M. 2007. *Glorified Dinosaurs. The Origin and early Evolution of Birds*. John Wiley, London.

CLARK, J. M., NORELL, M. A. & MAKOVICKY, P. J. 2002. Cladistic approaches to the relationships of birds to other theropod dinosaurs. *In*: CHIAPPE, L. M. & WITMER, L. M. (eds) *Mesozoic Birds. Above the Heads of Dinosaurs*. University of California Press, Berkeley, CA, 31–61.

DAMES, W. 1884. Über *Archaeopteryx*. *Palaeontologische Abhandlungen*, **2**, 119–196.

DAMES, W. 1897. Über Brustbein, Schulter- und Beckengürtel der *Archaeopteryx*. *Sitzungsberichte der königlich-preussischen Akademie der Wissenschaften zu Berlin*, **38**, 818–834.

DARWIN, C. 1859. *On the Origin of Species by Means of Natural Selection: or the Preservation of Favoured Races in the Struggle for Life*. John Murray, London (2nd edn published in January 1860; 3rd edn published in April 1861; 4th edn published in June 1866; 5th edn published in July 1869; 6th edn published in January 1872, revised in 1878).

DARWIN, C. 1871. *The Descent of Man and Selection in Relation to Sex*. John Murray, London (2nd edition revised, 1885).

DE BEER, G. 1954. *Archaeopteryx lithographica*. A study based upon the British Museum specimen. Trustees of the British Museum (Natural History), London, 68 pp.

ELZANOWSKI, A. 2001*a*. A new genus and species for the largest specimen of *Archaeopteryx*. *Acta Palaeontologica Polonica*, **46**, 519–532.

ELZANOWSKI, A. 2001*b*. The life style of *Archaeopteryx* (Aves). *Publicación Especial de la Asociación Paleontológica Argentina*, **7**, 91–99.

ELZANOWSKI, A. 2002*a*. Biology of basal birds and the origin of avian flight. *In*: ZHOU, Z. & ZHANG, F. (eds) *Proceedings of the 5th Symposium of the Society of Avian Paleontology and Evolution, Beijing*, 1–4 June 2000. Science Press, Marrickville, NSW, 211–226.

ELZANOWSKI, A. 2002*b*. Archaeopterygidae (Upper Jurassic of Germany). *In*: CHIAPPE, L. M. & WITMER, L. M. (eds) *Mesozoic Birds: Above the Heads of Dinosaurs*. University of California Press, Berkeley, CA, 129–159.

EVANS, J. 1865. On portions of a cranium and of a jaw, in the slab containing the fossil remains of *Archaeopteryx*. *Natural History Review*, **5**, 415–421.

FEDUCCIA, A. 1996. *On the Origin and Evolution of Birds*. Yale University Press, New Haven, CT (2nd edn published in 1999).

FEDUCCIA, A. 2002. Birds are dinosaurs: simple answer to a complex problem. *Auk*, **119**, 187–201.

FÜRBRINGER, M. 1888. *Untersuchungen zur Morphologie und Systematik der Vögel*. Holkema, Amsterdam.

GALTON, P. M. 1970. Ornithischian dinosaurs and the origin of birds. *Evolution*, **24**, 448–462.

GAUTHIER, J. 1986. Saurischian monophyly and the origin of birds. *In*: PADIAN, K. (ed.) *The Origin of Birds and the Evolution of Flight*. Memoirs of the Californian Academy of Sciences, **8**, 1–55.

GAUTHIER, J. & PADIAN, K. 1985. Phylogenetic, functional, and aerodynamic analyses of the origin of birds and their flight. *In*: HECHT, M. K., OSTROM, J. H., VIOHL, G. & WELLNHOFER, P. (eds) *The Beginnings of Birds*. Freunde des Jura-Museums Eichstätt, 185–197.

GEGENBAUR, C. 1878. *Grundriss der vergleichenden Anatomie*. Engelmann, Leipzig.

HEILMANN, G. 1926. *The Origin of Birds*. F. & G. Witherby, London.

HELLER, F. 1959. Ein dritter *Archaeopteryx* – Fund aus den Solnhofener Plattenkalken von Langenaltheim/ Mfr. *Erlanger Geologische Abhandlungen*, **31**, 1–25.

HOWGATE, M. E. 1985. Problems of the osteology of *Archaeopteryx*. Is the Eichstätt specimen a distinct genus? *In*: HECHT, M. K., OSTROM, J. H., VIOHL, G. & WELLNHOFER, P. (eds) *The Beginnings of Birds*. Freunde des Jura-Museums, Eichstätt, 105–112.

HUXLEY, T. H. 1868*a*. Remarks upon *Archaeopteryx lithographica*. *Proceedings of the Royal Society of London*, **16**, 243–248.

HUXLEY, T. H. 1868*b*. On the animals which are most nearly intermediate between the birds and reptiles. *Annals and Magazine of Natural History*, **4**, 66–75.

HUXLEY, T. H. 1869*a*. Further evidence of the affinity between the dinosaurian reptiles and birds. *Quarterly Journal of the Geological Society, London*, **26**, 12–31.

HUXLEY, T. H. 1869*b*. The classification and affinities of the Dinosauria. *Quarterly Journal of the Geological Society, London*, **26**, 32–51.

LOWE, P. R. 1935. On the relationship of the Struthiones to the dinosaurs and to the rest of the avian class, with special reference to the position of *Archaeopteryx*. *Ibis*, **5**, 398–432.

LOWE, P. R. 1944. An analysis of the characters of *Archaeopteryx* and *Archaeornis* . Were they reptiles or birds? *Ibis*, **86**, 517–543.

MARSH, O. C. 1881. Jurassic birds and their allies. *American Journal of Science*, **22** , 337–340.

MARTIN, L. D., STEWART, J. D. & WHETSTONE, K. N. 1980. The origin of birds: structure of the tarsus and teeth. *Auk*, **97**, 86–93.

MÄUSER, M. 1997. Der achte *Archaeopteryx*. *Fossilien*, **3**, 156–157.

MAYR, F. X. 1973. Ein neuer *Archaeopteryx*-Fund. *Paläontologische Zeitschrift*, **47**, 17–24.

MAYR, G., POHL, B. & PETERS, D. S. 2005. A well-preserved *Archaeopteryx* specimen with theropod features. *Science*, **310**, 1483–1486.

MAYR, G., POHL, B., HARTMAN, S. & PETERS, D. S. 2007. The tenth skeletal specimen of *Archaeopteryx*. *Zoological Journal of the Linnean Society*, **149**, 97–116.

MEYER, H. VON 1857. Beiträge zur näheren Kenntnis fossiler Reptilien. *Neues Jahrbuch für Mineralogie, Geologie, Geognosie und Petrefakten-Kunde*, **1857**, 532–543.

MEYER, H. VON 1859–1860. *Zur Fauna der Vorwelt. Vierte Abteilung: Reptilien aus dem lithographischen Schiefer des Jura in Deutschland und Frankreich*, Frankfurt.

MEYER, H. VON 1861*a*. Vogel-Feder und *Palpipes priscus* von Solenhofen. *Neues Jahrbuch für Mineralogie, Geognosie, Geologie und Petrefakten-Kunde*, **1861**, 561.

MEYER, H. VON 1861*b*. *Archaeopterix lithographica* (Vogel-Feder) und *Pterodactylus* von Solenhofen. *Neues Jahrbuch für Mineralogie, Geognosie, Geologie und Petrefakten-Kunde*, **1861**, 678–679.

MEYER, H. VON 1862. *Archaeopteryx lithographica* aus dem lithographischen Schiefer von Solnhofen. *Palaeontographica*, **10**, 53–56.

NOPCSA, F. 1907. Ideas on the origin of flight. *Proceedings of the Zoological Society, London*, **1907**, 223–236.

NOPCSA, F. 1923. On the origin of flight in birds. *Proceedings of the Zoological Society, London*, **1923**, 463–477.

OSBORN, H. F. 1900. Reconsideration of the evidence for a common dinosaur–avian stem in the Permian. *American Naturalist*, **34**, 777–799.

OSTROM, J. H. 1969. *Osteology of Deinonychus antirrhopus, an* Unusual Theropod from the Lower Cretaceous of Montana. Peabody Museum Bulletin, Yale University, New Haven, CT, **30**, 1–165.

OSTROM, J. H. 1970. *Archaeopteryx*: notice of a 'new' specimen. *Science*, **170**, 537–538.

OSTROM, J. H. 1972. Description of the *Archaeopteryx* specimen in the Teyler Museum, Haarlem. *Proceedings Koninklijk Nederlandse Akademie van Wetenschappen, B*, **75**, 289–305.

OSTROM, J. H. 1973. The ancestry of birds. *Nature*, **242**, 136.

OSTROM, J. H. 1976. *Archaeopteryx* and the origin of birds. *Biological Journal of the Linnean Society, London*, **8**, 91–182.

OSTROM, J. H. 1985. The meaning of *Archaeopteryx*. *In*: HECHT, M. K., OSTROM, J. H., VIOHL, G. & WELLNHOFER, P. (eds) *The Beginnings of Birds*. Freunde des Jura-Museums, Eichstätt, 161–176.

OWEN, R. 1863*a*. On the fossil remains of a long-tailed bird (*Archeopteryx macrurus* Ow.) from the lithographic slate of Solenhofen (Abstract). *Proceedings of the Royal Society of London*, **12**, 272–273.

OWEN, R. 1863*b*. On the *Archeopteryx* of von Meyer with a description of the fossil remains of a long-tailed species, from the lithographic stone of Solenhofen. *Philosophical Transactions of the Royal Society of London*, **153**, 33–47.

PADIAN, K. 1982. Macroevolution and the origin of major adaptations: vertebrate flight as a paradigm for the analysis of patterns. *American Paleontological Convention, Proceedings*, **2**, 387–392.

PADIAN, K. & CHIAPPE, L. M. 1998. The origin and early evolution of birds. *Biological Review*, **73**, 1–42.

PAUL, G. S. 2002. *Dinosaurs of the Air. The Evolution and Loss of Flight in Dinosaurs and Birds*. Johns Hopkins University Press, Baltimore, MD.

PETRONIEVICS, B. 1921. Über das Becken, den Schultergürtel und einige andere Teile der Londoner *Archaeopteryx*. Georg and Co., Genf.

RIES, C. J. 2007. Creating the proavis: bird origins in the art and science of Gerhard Heilmann 1913–1926. *Archives of Natural History*, **34**, 1–19.

SEELEY, H. G. 1881. Prof. Carl Vogt on the *Archaeopteryx*. *Geological Magazine*, Series 2, **8**, 300–309.

SERENO, P. K. 2004. Birds as dinosaurs. *Acta Zoologica Sinica*, **50**, 991–1001.

SIMPSON, G. G. 1946. Fossil Penguins. *Bulletin of the American Museum of Natural History*, **87**, 1–99.

TARSITANO, S. & HECHT, M. K. 1980. A reconsideration of the reptilian relationships of *Archaeopteryx*. *Zoological Journal of the Linnean Society*, **69**, 149–182.

THULBORN, R. A. 1975. Dinosaur polyphyly and the classification of dinosaurs and birds. *Australian Journal of Zoology*, **23**, 249–270.

TISCHLINGER, H. 2009. Der achte *Archaeopteryx* – das Daitinger Exemplar. *Archaeopteryx*, **27**, 1–20.

VOGT, C. 1879. *Archaeopteryx macrura*, an intermediate form between birds and reptiles. *Annals and Magazine of Natural History*, Series 5, **5**, 185–188.

VOGT, C. 1880. *Archaeopteryx macroura*, an intermediate form between birds and reptiles. *Ibis*, **4**, 434–456.

WAGNER, J. A. 1862*a*. Über ein neues, angeblich mit Vogelfedern versehenes Reptil aus den Solenhofener lithographischen Schiefern. *Sitzungsberichte der Bayerischen Akademie der Wissenschaften, mathematisch-physikalische Classe*, Sitzung vom 9. November, München, **1861**, 146–154.

WAGNER, J. A. 1862*b*. On a new Fossil Reptile supposed to be furnished with Feathers. *Annals and Magazine of Natural History*, Series 3, **9**, 261–267. (Translation of Wagner 1862*a* by W. S. Dallas).

WALKER, A. D. 1972. New light on the origin of birds and crocodiles. *Nature*, **237**, 257–263.

WATSON, D. M. S. 1919. On *Seymouria* the most primitive known reptile. *Proceedings of the Zoological Society London*, **1919**, 267–301.

WELLNHOFER, P. 1974. Das fünfte Skelettexemplar von *Archaeopteryx*. The fifth skeletal specimen of *Archaeopteryx*. *Palaeontographica, A*, **147**, 169–216.

WELLNHOFER, P. 1988. Ein neues Exemplar von *Archaeopteryx*. *Archaeopteryx*, **6**, 1–30.

WELLNHOFER, P. 1993. Das siebte Exemplar von *Archaeopteryx* aus den Solnhofener Schichten. *Archaeopteryx*, **11**, 1–48.

WELLNHOFER, P. 2001. Hermann von Meyer und der Solnhofener Urvogel *Archaeopteryx lithographica*. *In*: KELLER, T. & STORCH, G. (eds), *Hermann von Meyer – Frankfurter Bürger und Begründer der Wirbeltierpaläontologie in Deutschland. Kleine Senckenberg-Reihe*, **40**, 11–18.

WELLNHOFER, P. 2008. *Archaeopteryx. Der Urvogel von Solnhofen*. Dr. F. Pfeil-Verlag, München.

WELLNHOFER, P. 2009. *Archaeopteryx. The Icon of Evolution*. Dr. F. Pfeil-Verlag, München.

WELLNHOFER, P. & RÖPER, M. 2005. Das neunte *Archaeopteryx* – Exemplar von Solnhofen. *Archaeopteryx*, **23**, 3–21.

WILLISTON, S. W. 1879. Are birds derived from dinosaurs? *Kansas City Revue of Sciences*, **3**, 457–460.

WITMER, L. M. 2002. The debate on avian ancestry. Phylogeny, function, and fossils. *In*: CHIAPPE, L. M. & WITMER, L. M. (eds) *Mesozoic Birds. Above the Heads of Dinosaurs*. University of California Press, Berkeley, CA, 3–30.

WITTE, F. E. 1863. Die *Archaeopteryx lithographica* (Briefliche Mitteilung an Prof. H. B. Geinitz). *Neues Jahrbuch für Mineralogie, Geologie und Palaeontologie*, **1863**, 567–568.

Thomas Henry Huxley and the reptile to bird transition

BRIAN SWITEK

Rutgers University, New Brunswick, NJ 08901, USA (e-mail: evogeek@gmail.com)

Abstract: The overwhelming evidence that birds evolved from maniraptoran theropod dinosaurs has rekindled an interest in the work of the Victorian anatomist Thomas Henry Huxley. Many popular and technical accounts credit Huxley with being the first to propose that birds evolved from dinosaurs, but this is a misinterpretation of Huxley's work. During the 1860s Huxley was preoccupied with identifying the basic 'groundplans' that united vertebrate forms. Birds and reptiles were two groups united by a shared body plan, with dinosaurs representing an intermediate form. Huxley did not begin to cast dinosaurs as transitional forms between birds and earlier reptiles until he read Ernst Haeckel's *Generelle Morphologie*, at which time Huxley amassed ample anatomical evidence to illustrate how birds could have evolved from something dinosaur-like. Even then, however, Huxley did not say that birds had evolved from dinosaurs. As he explicitly stated in public addresses during the 1870s, small bird-like dinosaurs like *Compsognathus* only represented the form of what the true ancestors of birds might have looked like. Bird-like dinosaurs chiefly served to show that such a transition was possible. Thus, Huxley's views on the evolution of birds were much more complex than many modern authors appreciate.

During the 1860s and early 1870s Huxley contributed many papers on the relationship between reptiles and birds, coining the term Sauropsida to unite both groups as early as 1863 (Huxley 1869*b*, 1871). This arrangement was initially based on similarities between living representatives of both groups, but palaeontological discoveries provided new evidence that bolstered Huxley's argument.

When *Hadrosaurus* was first described (Foulke & Leidy 1858), the disparity in fore- and hindlimb length led the authors to suggest that it may have adopted a 'kangaroo-like' posture, and Cope came to similar conclusions about the theropod dinosaur '*Laelaps*' (=*Dryptosaurus* (Marsh 1877)) (Cope 1867*a*, 1868). From this Huxley inferred similar bipedal postures for *Iguanodon* and *Megalosaurus*, but the description of *Compsognathus* (Wagner 1861*c*) and *Hypsilophidon* (Huxley 1870*a*) were more important to Huxley's hypothesis that birds had evolved from reptiles. While it was difficult to imagine birds arising from something as monstrous as a *Megalosaurus*, the smaller dinosaurs more closely resembled the hypothetical reptilian ancestor of birds.

Strangely, *Archaeopteryx* had little significance to Huxley even though he had published on it in 1868 (Huxley 1868*b*). Huxley's minimal interest in *Archaeopteryx* probably stemmed from his view that most evolution had occurred during ancient 'non-geologic time', and the consensus that the three-toed tracks from the Triassic of New England (Hitchcock 1836, 1858) were those of birds made the Jurassic *Archaeopteryx* far too young to be a bird ancestor. Even when Huxley later modified his views on persistence and transitional forms, as reflected in his 1876 lecture tour of America, *Archaeopteryx* was placed on an evolutionary side branch and he doubted that it resembled a stage in the reptile–bird transition (Huxley 1877). The direct ancestors of birds were also unlikely to be found among the most bird-like of the dinosaurs, and Huxley considered them the 'modified descendants of Palaeozoic forms through which the transition was actually affected' (Huxley 1877, p. 67). Marsh's recently discovered Cretaceous toothed birds *Hesperornis* and *Ichthyornis*, however, were marshalled as evidence of the relationship between birds and reptiles, and, although Huxley could not identify a direct line of descent, there were enough intermediates to defend the evolution of birds from reptiles.

Huxley's work on this problem was never so simple as to assert that birds evolved from dinosaurs, and the evolution of his arguments about the relationship of birds and reptiles marks a transition in his own thinking (Di Gregorio 1982; Lyons 1993) as well as a period of change in the discipline of vertebrate palaeontology.

When Charles Darwin published *On the Origin of Species by Means of Natural Selection, or the Preservation of Favoured Races in the Struggle for Life* (Darwin 1859) palaeontology presented major problems for his still-nascent evolutionary hypothesis. Although palaeontology was still a relatively young science, it was generally believed that the geological strata had been sampled adequately enough by 1859 to reveal the diversity of ancient life in each age (Rudwick 1976). If transitional forms had not yet been discovered there was little chance that they existed. What was present in one

From: Moody, R. T. J., Buffetaut, E., Naish, D. & Martill, D. M. (eds) *Dinosaurs and Other Extinct Saurians: A Historical Perspective*. Geological Society, London, Special Publications, **343**, 251–263.
DOI: 10.1144/SP343.15 0305-8719/10/$15.00

locality seemed to be present in all, and it appeared that well-studied fossil sites in Europe were representative of the entire record of life on Earth (Rudwick 1976, pp. 228–229).

Darwin's hypothesis was primarily derived from observations of living organisms (population growth, artificial selection, etc.), but his evolutionary mechanism did make predictions about ancient life. If all of life on Earth shared a common ancestor in the distant past, with evolution branching gradually instead of making 'jumps', then the fossil record should provide graded intermediate forms. Unfortunately, such forms were rare and failed to bridge major gaps between groups of animals. Darwin attempted to explain the negative evidence through the imperfection of the fossil record. That any ancient creature, particularly a soft-bodied animal, should be preserved as a fossil seemed unlikely, and many animals that became fossilized were only known from fragmentary remains.

In order for an evolutionary series to be preserved a group of organisms would have to live in a place with regular sedimentation events over huge expanses of time – a doubtful scenario. The problem was further compounded by the fact that the span of geological time contained gaps, blank spots in the history of life on Earth, and there were too many unpredictable factors required to preserve an evolutionary series (Darwin 1859, pp. 310–311):

> For my part, following out Lyell's metaphor, I look at the natural geological record, as a history of the world imperfectly kept, and written in a changing dialect; of this history we possess the last volume alone, relating only to two or three countries. Of this volume, only here and there a short chapter has been preserved; and of each page, only here and there a few lines. Each word of the slowly-changing language, in which the history is supposed to be written, being more or less different in the interrupted succession of chapters, may represent the apparently abruptly changed forms of life, entombed in our consecutive, but widely separated formations. On this view, the difficulties above discussed are greatly diminished, or even disappear.

One of the first major responses by the palaeontological community to Darwin's work was *Life on Earth* by geologist John Phillips (1860). Phillips found little evidence of the gradual evolutionary series predicted by Darwin's hypothesis. Some of the oldest known fossils from the Cambrian and Silurian, for instance, already represented complex forms of life that provided no clues as to their ancestors. Phillips regarded them as new creations consistent across multiple localities generated by some unknown law of nature. As Phillips (1860, p. 214) incredulously asked, 'How is it conceivable that the second stage should be everywhere preserved, but the first nowhere?'.

Many found Darwin's theory intriguing, a 'secondary law' for the creation of species worthy of consideration, but overall it received a mixed reception (Bowler 2007). Of those who were more impressed by Darwin's work, however, perhaps none is as well known as the British anatomist Thomas Henry Huxley. Today, Huxley is often referred to as 'Darwin's Bulldog', the 'General' who fought Darwin's battles while the elder naturalist remained at his estate, but vertebrate palaeontologists often cite Huxley for a different reason. Since the 1960s an overwhelming flood of evidence has illustrated that birds are living dinosaurs (Zhou 2004; Norell & Xu 2005; Chiappe & Dyke 2007), and Huxley is often credited in both the technical and popular literature as being the first to propose that birds evolved from dinosaurs (e.g. Osborn 1900; Olson & Thomas 1980; Bakker 1986; Paul 1988; Norman 1991; Psihoyos & Knoebber 1994; Norell *et al.* 1995; Weishampel & Young 1996; Chatterjee 1997; Shipman 1998; Feduccia 1999; Larson & Donnan 2002; Zhou 2004; Norell & Xu 2005; Farmer 2006; Chiappe 2007; Codd *et al.* 2008).

Much like the overblown claim that Huxley trounced Bishop Samuel Wilberforce in a debate at Oxford in 1860 (Gould 1991), however, the idea that Huxley perfectly anticipated the modern confirmation that birds are living dinosaurs is an example of 'textbook cardboard' (*sensu* Gould 1987). This can be defined as a past notion that appears to have predicted recent discoveries but is, in reality, abstracted and ripped from their proper context, a technique often used to lend weight to a particular idea or deconstruct unfavourable notions. In this particular case, authors and researchers have cited Huxley's work to support the idea that birds were thought to have evolved from dinosaurs as soon as *Archaeopteryx* was discovered, and that recently discovered evidence confirms what Huxley had hypothesized nearly 150 years ago. A survey of Huxley's work, however, does not bear out such gross summation.

Owen and *Archaeopteryx*

Although human interest in fossils has a long history (Mayor 2000), it was not until the late eighteenth century that palaeontology became a systematic study of ancient life (Rudwick 1976). With a scientific framework combining geology and comparative anatomy in place, the bones of dinosaurs began to be recognized as belonging to ancient, nonmythological beasts that had lived and died during some past era. The first fragmentary fossils found were most similar to those of living reptiles, so it was reasonable that their first describers assumed that the creatures resembled enormous versions of extant lizards and crocodiles (Buckland 1824; Mantell 1825). *Iguanodon*, in particular, was thought to be a gargantuan lizard, nearly identical to the living reptile from which the name of the taxon had been derived. The lizard-like interpretation did not last long. When Richard Owen coined the term '*Dinosauria*' (Owen 1842) he created a new, mammal-like image for the group. Rather than being gigantic lizards, dinosaurs were more like living 'pachyderms', the 'highest' of the reptiles. Owen's revised interpretation of dinosaurs was given physical form in the sculptures created by Benjamin Waterhouse Hawkins, and Owen's role as scientific advisor to Hawkins allowed him to create lasting monuments of his particular palaeontological vision (Desmond 1982).

It was Owen's interpretation of dinosaurs that was at the fore when the first skeleton of *Archaeopteryx* was discovered in 1861. At the time the fossil record of birds was thought to stretch back into the Triassic (Hitchcock 1836, 1858) based on fossil tracks, and in 1860 a single feather impression was found from the Jurassic rock of a German limestone quarry. This feather was named *Archaeopteryx lithographica* by palaeontologist Hermann von Meyer (1861*a*, *b*, 1862), and in 1861 a fossil skeleton representing the rest of the animal was recovered from a similar quarry. This is the fossil that would become known as the 'London specimen' of *Archaeopteryx*, and it was the oldest skeleton of a bird yet discovered. *Archaeopteryx* was no common sparrow or finch, however: it possessed both avian and reptilian characters. As such it was precisely the sort of transitional form that Darwin's theory predicted. In a letter dated 3 January 1863, palaeontologist Hugh Falconer wrote to Darwin about the fossil (Falconer 1863), beaming:

> Had the Solenhofen quarries been commissioned – by august command – to turn out a strange being à la Darwin – it could not have executed the behest more handsomely – than in the *Archaeopteryx*.

Darwin (1863*a*) replied that he longed to see the fossil, and in a letter to American palaeontologist J.D. Dana wrote: 'Oh how I wish a skeleton could be found in your so-called Red Sandstone footstep-beds', from which the footprints of Triassic 'birds' were already known (Darwin 1863*b*). Not everyone shared Darwin's enthusiasm, however. One of the earliest descriptions of the fossil, based on the verbal report of a Mr Witte who had seen the fossil while in the possession of its first owner Dr Haberlein, was made by the German palaeontologist Johann Andreas Wagner. Wagner's publications about the fossil (Wagner 1861*a*, 1862) warned against evolutionary interpretations and he unequivocally deemed *Archaeopteryx* as a long-tailed pterosaur with feathers. Even if it was a transitional fossil, Wagner argued, it was but one isolated form; where were the other intermediates predicted by Darwin's theory? (Wagner 1861*b*).

Wagner died shortly after voicing his concerns in 1861, but the debate over *Archaeopteryx* continued. The fossil was purchased from Haberlein by the British Museum, where it was described by Richard Owen in 1862 (Owen 1863). Owen recognized that the single feather discovered in 1860 which von Meyer used to name *Archaeopteryx* may not have come from the same kind of animal represented by the skeleton, but he retained von Meyer's appellation and identification. *Archaeopteryx* was a bird, the 'by-fossil-remains-oldest known feathered Vertebrate' (Owen 1863, p. 46). Moreover, the caudal vertebrae of *Archaeopteryx* closely resembled those of living birds during embryonic development, and this allowed Owen to make reference to his notion of morphological archetypes because the bird exhibited 'a retention of a structure embryonal and transitory in the modern representatives of the class, and a closer adhesion to the general vertebrate type' (Owen 1863, p. 46). Unfortunately, the head of the London *Archaeopteryx* was thought to be missing, and its conspicuous absence caused the bird to be depicted without one in *The World Before the Deluge* (Figuier 1866) (Fig. 1.). This did not bring into question the affinities made clear by the available remains, however, and Owen proposed that when the skull was found it would be much like those of living birds: 'By the law of correlation we infer that the mouth was devoid of lips, and was a beak-like instrument fitted for preening the plumage of *Archaeopteryx*' (Owen 1863, p. 47).

Huxley's sojourn into palaeontology

Huxley critiqued Owen's description of *Archaeopteryx*, motivated at least in part by his grievances with the elder anatomist, but he did not do so until 1868. This delay must be understood in the greater context of Huxley's sojourn into palaeontology. As a young man Huxley got his scientific start studying cnidarians and other invertebrates collected during his voyage as an assistant surgeon in the Royal Navy aboard the HMS *Rattlesnake* (1846–1850). Influenced by the German school of anatomical science (Di Gregorio 1982), he was most concerned with finding the common denominator of form, an abstract archetype to rival Owen's Platonic one (Desmond 1997). Palaeontology in and of itself was of little interest, particularly as Huxley viewed it as being tied to notions of 'Progress'. That Christian theology could co-opt the succession of forms

Fig. 1. 'Ideal landscape of the upper oolitic period' from Figuier (1866). A headless *Archaeopteryx* flies above the scene. It was not drawn with a head as the skull was not known at the time of illustration.

seen in the fossil record for its own philosophical ends was anathema to Huxley, and the invocation of the Divine in nature become ever more distasteful to him as he moved among the circles of the learned and avant-garde (Desmond 1997).

In 1859 Huxley changed scientific course and described a number of fossil creatures that had been imported from South Africa, and he would soon extend his research to pterosaurs, 'labyrinthodont' amphibians, crocodylians and South American fossil mammals. Combined with the influence of *On the Origin of Species*, this research programme got Huxley thinking about what the fossil record had to say about evolution. Although struck by *On the Origin of Species*, Huxley's vision of evolution was starkly different from Darwin's (Lyons 1993). This is best represented by his paper 'On the persistent types of animal life' (Huxley 1859). Taking a cue from Lyell's uniformitarian philosophy, Huxley recited the consensus view that the Earth had changed little from the Cambrian or Silurian era, and the same geological forces acted then as they did now. Nothing could be said of what occurred during the ages preceding the known strata, however, and the Earth was assuredly older than even the most ancient rocks then known. Huxley applied this programme to palaeontology, and explained that many fossil animals had living representatives with the extant and extinct forms differing little from one another. This showed that many groups had survived for enormous amounts of time and such examples could be called 'persistent types'.

Citing numerous 'living fossils', from crocodylians to conifers, Huxley saw a fossil record that revealed little change. Yet, the concept of persistent types created problems for evolution by natural selection ('a hypothesis which, though unproven and sadly damaged by some of its supporters, is yet the only one to which physiology lends any countenance' (Huxley 1859, p. 153)) as it did not answer the question of when certain groups of organisms had evolved. Pre-geological time held the answer, and Huxley supposed that the evolutionary changes that took place before known geological time were far greater than any actually recorded in the known fossil record. Three years later Huxley reiterated these views, using many of the same examples, during an address to the Geological Society on the state of palaeontology (Huxley 1862).

Even though he was still thinking in terms of shared anatomical form, Huxley began to attempt to demonstrate the close relationship between reptiles and birds as early as 1863. Lecturing to students at the Royal College of Surgeons, he applied the designation 'Sauroids' to both reptiles and birds (later changed to 'Sauropsida' (Huxley 1869*b*), meaning 'reptile faced'), and explained that birds were 'so essentially similar to Reptiles in all the most essential features of their organization, that these animals may be said to be merely an extremely modified and aberrant Reptilian type' (Huxley 1863, 1869*b*). On the other side of the divide, dinosaurs showed the closest approximation to birds: '[t]he pelvis and bones of the hind limb are in many respects very like those of birds' (Huxley 1863, 1869*b*). Huxley used much the same reasoning, albeit more explicitly, in his survey of bird classification (1867, p. 415):

> The members of the class Aves so nearly approach the Reptilia in all the essential and fundamental points of their structure, that the phrase 'Birds and greatly modified Reptiles' would hardly be an exaggerated expression of the closeness of that resemblance.
>
> In perfect strictness, no doubt, it is true that Birds are no more modified Reptiles than Reptiles are modified Birds, the reptilian and the ornithic types being both, in reality, somewhat different superstructures raised upon one and the same ground-plan; but it is also true that some Reptiles deviate so very much less from the groundplan than any Bird does, that they might be taken to represent that which is common to both classes without any serious error.

In Huxley's view, both birds and reptiles were derived from a common 'superstructure' from which birds deviated further than reptiles did. This was not an evolutionary system but an anatomical one. A shared 'groundplan' did not necessarily reveal an evolutionary relationship, yet some fossil specimens proved exceptions to Huxley's morphological delineations. The vertebrae of *Archaeopteryx* were more reptile-like than bird-like and, as had previously been noted by the German anatomist Carl Gegenbaur (Gegenbaur 1864), the hind limbs of the small dinosaur *Compsognathus* approximated those of birds.

Although *Archaeopteryx* gained most of the press, *Compsognathus* was another exceptional fossil recovered from the Solnhofen quarries in 1861. Wagner was the first to note the very bird-like form of *Compsognathus* in his description of the fossil (Wagner 1861*c*), and, although he denied any actual kinship between reptiles and birds, Huxley would use the same similarities to pull the groups into close association. In addition, Huxley used shared characteristics between birds, pterosaurs and dinosaurs to make some striking predictions about the metabolism of dinosaurs, perhaps taking a cue from H.G. Seeley (1864). Although the form of the circulatory systems in birds and bats differed, their shared way of life led them to be physiologically similar. Using this concept, Huxley reasoned that even if dinosaurs had a slightly different circulatory set-up than birds they were similar enough to birds morphologically that they too might have been 'hot-blooded' (Huxley 1867, p. 418):

> Birds have hot blood, a muscular valve in the right ventricle, a single aortic arch, and remarkably modified respiratory organs; but it is, to say the least, highly probable that the *Pterosauria*, if not the *Dinosauria*, shared some of these characters with them.

Huxley's search for ancestors

The publication of Ernst Haeckel's *Generelle Morphologie* (1866) marked a major shift in Huxley's thinking. Although Huxley rejected Owen's Platonic Archetype, the equivalent of a translated idea from the mind of a Creator, he was more concerned with groundplans than evolutionary branching lineages. Haeckel's work caused him to change direction and start looking for real ancestors (Di Gregorio 1982; Desmond 1997). In January of 1868, the year that would see Huxley dive head-long into his work on dinosaurs and birds, he wrote to Haeckel stating (quoted in Di Gregorio 1982, p. 415):

> In scientific work the main thing just now about which I am engaged is a revision of the *Dinosauria* – with an eye to the *Descendenz Theorie*! The road from Reptiles to Birds is by way of *Dinosauria* to the *Ratitae* – the Bird 'Phylum' was Struthious, and wings grew out of rudimentary fore limbs. You see that among other things I have been reading Ernst Haeckel's *Morphologie*.

That same year Huxley published 'On the animals which are most nearly intermediate between birds and reptiles' (Huxley 1868*a*). Although he had treaded carefully over the validity of evolution by natural selection in the past, the opening salvo of the paper reveals Huxley's zeal; the whole of the universe attested to evolution. Yet, evolution was still plagued by a conspicuous lack of transitional forms. If Darwin's uniformitarian theory was correct – that evolution acted in the past just as it did today – then transitional fossils linking major groups of organisms should have been discovered. Huxley (1868*a*, p. 358) likened the state of affairs to a landowner who is not able to come up with any title deeds to his properties:

> If a landed proprietor is asked to produce the title-deeds of his estate, and is obliged to reply that some of them were destroyed in a fire a century ago, that some were carried off by a dishonest attorney, and that the rest are in a safe somewhere, but that he really cannot lay his hands upon them; he cannot, I think, feel pleasantly secure, though all his allegations may be correct and his ownership indisputable. But a doctrine is a

scientific estate, and the holder must always be able to produce his title-deeds, in a way of direct evidence, or take the penalty of that peculiar discomfort to which I have referred.

Huxley had to admit that his petrified 'title deeds' were largely missing, but he did have 'a considerable piece of parchment' (Huxley 1868*a*, p. 359) that offered a confirmation of his claims. This tattered piece of evidence had 'Sauropsida' written on it, and he stated that while 'a Stork seems to have little animality in common with the Snake it swallows' (Huxley 1868*a*, p. 359) there could be little doubt that birds had evolved from reptiles (Fig. 2). The best evidence among birds was to be found among flightless birds like the kiwi (*Apteryx*), the moa (*Dinornis*) and the ostrich (*Struthio*). Rather than being degenerate birds, these were persistent types that approximated the appearance of the earliest birds. *Archaeopteryx*, bearing claws and a long tail, brought birds even closer to reptiles. It was not a direct ancestor of modern birds, Huxley explained, but an illustration that birds had evolved from reptiles. Thus, *Archaeopteryx* marked the limit of the avian side of the divide, and with no earlier reptile-like bird for Huxley to jump to he started to work from the bottom up. For Huxley the closest 'reptilian' relatives to birds were to be found on the ground among the Dinosauria.

Richard Owen had envisioned dinosaurs as immense, mammal-like quadrupeds, but his interpretation began to be overturned by new discoveries in North America that sparked the first 'Dinosaur Renaissance'. The indication that *Hadrosaurus* was at least facultatively bipedal (Foulke & Leidy 1858; Leidy 1865) was crucial in revising the image of the dinosaur into a form that would fit Huxley's programme. If the North American *Hadrosaurus* was bipedal then there was little reason to think *Iguanodon* differed in the way it walked, especially if the large, bird-like tracks discovered in the Wealden (Beckles 1854) were really those of dinosaurs. The hips of dinosaurs were bird-like, their feet were bird-like and the tracks they left were bird-like; it was the dinosaurs that most 'wonderfully approached' birds (Huxley 1868*a*, p. 365). Most of the dinosaurs then known were far too immense to have given rise to birds, however. Huxley avoided this problem by pointing to the diminutive *Compsognathus*. Although Huxley was not sure whether to place *Compsognathus* within the Dinosauria or in a new, closely allied category, the avian characteristics of the fossil brought the reptiles close enough to touch the birds (see Fig. 3). Speculating on the appearance of *Compsognathus* in life Huxley (1868*a*, p. 365) wrote:

It is impossible to look at the conformation of this strange reptile and to doubt that it hopped or walked, in an erect or semi-erect position, after the manner of a bird, to which its long neck, slight head, and small anterior limbs must have given it an extraordinary resemblance.

Yet, *Compsognathus* was of the same age as *Archaeopteryx*, too young to be a real ancestor.

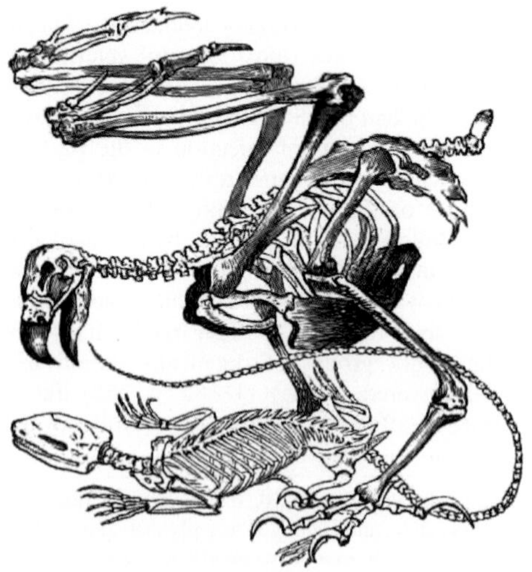

Fig. 2. The skeletons of an eagle and a lizard. As different as they might appear to be, Huxley thought that birds and reptiles shared a common body plan. He placed both within the group 'Sauropsida'. From Bell (1852).

Fig. 3. A restoration of *Compsognathus.* Huxley wondered if, had such a creature had been covered in feathers, we would call it a bird. From Huxley (1877).

The presence of 'bird' tracks in Connecticut also suggested to Huxley that it would be in Triassic strata that 'birds so much more reptilian than *Archaeopteryx*, and reptiles so much more ornithic than *Compsognathus*, as to obliterate completely the gap which they still leave between reptiles and birds' (Huxley 1868*a*, p. 366) would be found. Despite this, Huxley did not think it 'wild' or 'illegitimate' to propose that 'the class *Aves* has its root in the Dinosaurian reptiles' (Huxley 1868*a*, p. 366). Thus, *Compsongnathus* was a persistent form of an actual creature in the line of descent from reptile to bird, leading up to the flightless ratites from which the carinate birds would then be derived. The hypothetical evolutionary arc approximated by *Compsognathus* → ratites → carinates provided an illustration that confirmed Darwin's theory.

No scientific programme aimed at studying avian evolution could ignore *Archaeopteryx*; yet, as has been illustrated, it was of little importance to Huxley's hypothetical evolutionary series. Huxley's description of the fossil bird, read before the Royal Society on 30 January 1868 (Huxley 1868*b*), was more of a swipe at Owen than an elucidation of the evolution of birds. Huxley opened by asserting that Owen had confused the ventral side of the London specimen with the dorsal side, and the left leg for the right. If the sides were not properly identified then the anatomy of the animal could not be understood. Huxley further charged that Owen had made mistakes about the hips and shoulder girdles of the animal – the younger anatomist characterized Owen's interpretation as upside-down and inside-out. As the *coup de grâce*, Huxley attacked Owen's hypothesis that the head, when found, would bear a toothless beak, using turtles and the pterosaur *Rhamphorhynchus* to express the variability and diversity found within reptiles. Huxley (1868*b*, p. 248) quipped:

> If when the head of *Archaeopteryx* is discovered, its jaws contain teeth, it will not the more, to my mind, cease to be a bird, then turtles cease to be reptiles because they have beaks.

Given his previous work, it might be expected that Huxley would devote some section of his description to finding a place for *Archaeopteryx* in his reptile to bird series, but no such explanation was undertaken. The bird was simply too derived to be close to the transition from reptiles, being 'more remote from the boundary-line between birds and reptiles than some living *Ratitae* are' (Huxley 1868*b*, p. 248). The evidence Huxley was looking for would have to be found elsewhere.

In a paper read before the Geological Society in May of 1869 (Huxley 1869*a*) Huxley described part of the upper jaw of *Megalosaurus* (see Benson *et al.* 2008 for a current reassessment of the material referable to this taxon). The specimen was only part of the skull, and a fracture at the front of the skull that did not appear to run along a defined suture hinted that there was more to the skull than Huxley had to work with. Based on the material available, however, Huxley entertained three options: that (1) the premaxilla and maxilla were fused; (2) the premaxilla became detached from the maxilla; or (3) the entire upper jaw was the premaxilla, an option with the potential to further connect dinosaurs and birds. Without more evidence no determination could be made about which of these hypotheses was correct, but the ornithischian dinosaur *Hypsilophodon* would soon provide Huxley with a different piece of his evolutionary puzzle. *Hypsilophodon* was recognized as being closely related to *Iguanodon* (it was initially thought to be a new, miniature species of that genus) and Huxley described it before the Geological Society in November of the same year (Huxley 1870*a*). Much like his earlier *Archaeopteryx* paper, the description generally lacked evolutionary interpretations, but the small skeleton did reveal at least one important feature; the ischium and pubis were preserved, and both pointed backwards in a fashion similar to that seen in birds.

If Huxley held back his evolutionary considerations in the *Hypsilophodon* description, he opened the floodgates with a paper read at the same meeting entitled 'Further evidence of the affinity between the dinosaurian reptiles and birds' (Huxley 1870*b*). As described in the introduction of the paper, Huxley had coincidentally met up with John Phillips in October of 1867 and Phillips had encouraged Huxley to view the geological collection under his care at Oxford. There Huxley noticed something strange about the *Megalosaurus* bones in the collection: the 'scapula' was truly part of the ilium. When he realized this the bird-like traits of the skeleton suddenly became more apparent, and another bone (previously identified as a clavicle) appeared to be part of the ischium. (According to a letter by Phillips included in the paper it seems that the Oxford scientist had already suspected that some of the bones were not correctly identified – Huxley made his visit in the midst of Phillips' reinvestigation.)

The rearranged bones reflected a creature with small forelimbs and a more bird-like hip, an image of *Megalosaurus* that departed from Owen's elephantine vision. Huxley resolved to undertake a study of how the anatomy of *Megalosaurus* corresponded to those of other dinosaurs, but what Huxley did not know was that on the other side of the Atlantic the American palaeontologist Edward Drinker Cope was coming to similar conclusions about birds and reptiles (Cope 1866, 1867*a*, 1868) based on the bipedal predatory dinosaur *Laelaps* (later changed to *Dryptosaurus* (Marsh 1877)). Cope thought that the ankle joint of the terror of the ancient New Jersey coast resembled that of an embryonic chick, and he also recognized the avian character of the ankle joint in *Compsognathus* as initially pointed out by Gegenbaur (Cope 1867*b*, 1869). Just as Huxley was doing in his own research, Cope used flightless birds to bring reptiles and birds together, although he favoured penguins as the birds morphologically closest to reptilian ancestors.

Although impressed with Cope's views, Huxley disagreed on a few points, particularly the shape of the dinosaurian pelvis. Bones identified as the 'clavicles' of dinosaurs, for instance, often turned out to be part of the hip – Cope thinking that they were forward-oriented pubes and Huxley insisting that they were rear-pointing ischia. Huxley marshalled the hips of *Hypsilophodon* in support of his view, but it was the whole of the hip, leg and foot morphology that provided the best evidence for a reptile–bird connection (Huxley 1870*b*, p. 31):

> if the whole hind quarters, from the ilium to the toes, of a half-hatched chicken could be suddenly enlarged, ossified, and fossilized as they are, they would furnish us with the last step of the transition between Birds and Reptiles; for there would be nothing in their characters to prevent us from referring them to the *Dinosauria*.

Not everyone present for the reading of Huxley's paper was impressed by the similarities, however. Harry Seeley, a young expert on pterosaurs, thought the hindlimb characteristics Huxley used to support a close relationship between dinosaurs and birds were only signs of a shared mode of life. Furthermore, Seeley argued, dinosaurs were so different from birds, mammals and reptiles that they should be separated into a new, distinct group. Huxley disagreed with Seeley, opining that the study of nature revealed a blurring of lineages rather than sharp divisions.

Huxley reinvents the Dinosauria

Huxley was now ready to unveil his revised taxonomic groupings of dinosaurs within the Sauropsida (Huxley 1870*c*). His first step was to permanently tear down the vision of dinosaurs characterized in the works of other authorities like Owen and von Meyer. In so doing Huxley had to rediagnose the entire group, setting out a 12-point list (including two–six sacral vertebrae, thecodont teeth and a bird-like astragalus, among other characters) with which to give the Dinosauria a firm foundation. Under this system he placed the '*Megalosauridae*', '*Scelidosauridae*' and '*Iguanodontidae*' within the Dinosauria, but *Compsognathus* did not appear to naturally fit into any of these groups even though all were 'ornithic modification[s] of the Saurian type' (Huxley 1870*c*, p. 36). Instead, he placed *Compsognathus* in a separate group, the '*Compsognatha*'. Cope had previously created a similar classification, setting *Compsognathus* aside in his 'Ornithopoda' while he placed the rest of the Dinosauria in the 'Goniopoda', but Huxley disagreed with Cope's reliance on an ankylosed astragalus as a definitive character and so erected his own groups.

Using terminology to his advantage, Huxley then grouped the Dinosauria and '*Compsognatha*' together in the new group '*Ornithoscelida*', thus recognizing a group of 'bird-legged reptiles' within the larger, more inclusive, 'Sauropsida'. Among his reptilian groups, organized by characteristics of the vertebrae, the '*Ornithoscelida*' was grouped with crocodylians, dicynodonts and pterosaurs under the '*Suchospondylia*'. Huxley proposed that the dicynodonts and crocodylians were the closest relatives of the dinosaurs, and he predicted that lizard-like ancestral forms for each group might be found during the Permian or some earlier period.

Huxley's comparison of the '*Ornithoscelida*' with birds, however, was much more important. Huxley ruled out pterosaurs as bird relatives because their similarities arose from common 'physiological action and not ... affinity' (Huxley 1870*c*, p. 39). In contrast, the similar leg and hip characteristics of the '*Ornithoscelida*' were seen in all birds, both flying and non-flying, but Seeley's objection about convergence had left a mark on Huxley. Although bipedal dinosaurs were a major part of his new vision for the '*Ornithoscelida*', Huxley deemed the large members of the Dinosauria to be facultative bipeds, doubting that they 'stood more habitually upon their hind limbs than Kangaroos or Jerboas do' (Huxley 1870*c*, p. 39). If all birds always stood on their hind legs but members of the Dinosauria could switch between bipedal and quadrupedal motion then the resemblances in their limb morphology could truly be said to illustrate a 'genetic connexion' and not just convergence due to shared habits (Huxley 1870*c*, p. 39).

With a quick note of how the 'breast bone' of dinosaurs resembled the sternum of birds, Huxley dived into a review of Triassic dinosaurs known from Europe, India and North America, but it was again his presentation on the relationship of birds to the '*Ornithoscelida*' that stirred the most commentary. Roderick Murchison, the eminent geologist who established the hotly debated Silurian system, asked of the oldest known strata from which bird-like dinosaurs were known. The reply pointed to the Triassic, if not even older, strata. It was Seeley who, again, challenged Huxley, however, noting that a common morphological plan for all reptiles had to be identified before a classification could stand. Citing his own work that was shortly to be published (Seeley 1870), Seeley stated that his own classification came out differently. Unfortunately, the transcript of the discussion does not illuminate details, noting only that Huxley 'was pleased to find that there was such a diversity of opinion between Mr. Seeley and himself, as it was by discussion of opposite views that the truth was to be attained' (Huxley 1870*c*, p. 50).

What did Huxley mean by a 'genetic connexion' between birds and the *Ornithoscelida*? Were dinosaurs the progenitors of birds? Although Huxley (1870*d*, p. 24) called the Dinosauria 'the links between reptiles and birds', in a short review of Triassic dinosaurs in *Nature* his views on the subject were more explicitly laid out in an address to the Geological Society (Huxley 1870*e*). Huxley still maintained his notion of persistent types, and his palaeontological work reinforced the concept that he had outlined before the same society years before. If evidence for evolution was to be found, it was amongst the 'higher' groups of vertebrates, but Huxley urged caution in teasing out the details. Simply because lineages of intermediates could be constructed connecting one form to another did not automatically mean that evolution occurred in such a sequence. Huxley warned 'it is always probably that one may not hit upon the exact line of filiation, and, in dealing with fossils, may mistake uncles and nephews for fathers and sons' (Huxley 1870*d*, p. xlix) The creatures representing the expected intermediate form, the 'uncles and nephews', could be called *intercalary types*, while those that could be proven to be on the direct line, the 'fathers and sons', were dubbed *linear types* (Huxley 1870*d*, p. xlix). Despite the amount of effort he put into pulling birds and dinosaurs together, the members of the '*Ornithoscelida*' could only be considered evolutionary 'uncles and nephews' (Huxley 1870*d*, p. li):

> At the present moment we have, in the *Ornithoscelida* the intercalary type, which proves that transition ['from the type of the lizard to that of the ostrich'] to be something more than a possibility; but it is very doubtful whether any of the genera of *Ornithoscelida* with which we are at present acquainted are the actual linear types by which the transition from the lizard to the bird was effected. These, very probably, are still hidden from us in the older formations.

While a known direct line of descent might have been defensible for horses (from *Anchitherium* to *Hipparion* to *Equus*), no such line could be drawn from dinosaurs to birds. The 'ornithichnites' from the Triassic sandstone of the Connecticut Valley and the hypothetical existence of dinosaurs during the Permian further complicated matters. If there were Triassic birds and Permian dinosaurs then the creatures from which birds evolved must have been even older still, but their location and age were a mystery. This ran counter to the notion that the geological strata were well sampled and represented a good approximation of the succession of life, and Huxley urged that there was more to discover.

Reptiles into birds: a popular transition

After 1870 Huxley's research into the relationship between birds and reptiles, and palaeontology in general, slowed. His focus shifted towards bringing nature in from the field to be cut up under the microscope, and he overworked himself to the point that, by the beginning of 1872, his wife Nettie sent him on vacation to Egypt to recuperate (Desmond 1997). When he returned he threw himself back into his work but was more concerned with establishing a sound morphological programme than continuing to pick at gigantic bones. Huxley did not simply drop the subject, however, and the relationship between reptiles and birds ranked as one of his primary illustrations of evolution during his 1876 tour of the United States.

In a lecture delivered in New York on 20 September 1876 (Huxley 1877) Huxley reiterated the presence of persistent types, but with a twist. Darwin's theory of evolution by natural selection, in which the environment acts upon variation, would cause creatures to evolve if environmental conditions changed. If conditions were stable then the organisms, too, would undergo little change. This made sense of both evolution and persistence, thus negating the problem of lineages that seemed to show little or no evolutionary change. The explanation that the fossil record was an imperfect one further defused objections to Huxley's arguments; the Triassic red sandstone 'bird tracks' were perfect examples of the vagaries of preservation. Although the tracks were seemingly innumerable, no skeletons of the trackmakers had been found.

With living birds and reptiles divided by an anatomical gulf, Huxley set out to connect the two for his audience as he had done in his technical works. The research of O.C. Marsh provided Huxley with extra ammunition: the toothed birds *Hesperornis* and *Ichthyornis* (Marsh 1875) were avians with a classic reptilian characteristic, and raised the possibility that the still-headless *Archaeopteryx* may have had a mouth full of teeth. Still, Marsh's birds and *Archaeopteryx* chiefly served to show that taxonomic boundaries erected through the study of extant organisms alone could be broken by evolution, and that fossil creatures featuring a mix of characters from different groups did exist. *Archaeopteryx* was still, at best, an intercalary type. Echoing his caveats about 'uncles and nephews' from his 1870 Geological Society address Huxley told the audience (Huxley 1877, p. 59):

> But it by no means follows, because the *Palaeotherium* has much in common with the Horse, on the one hand, and with the Rhinoceros on the other, that it is the intermediate form through which Rhinoceroses have passed to become Horses, or *vice versa*; on the contrary, any such supposition would certainly be erroneous. Nor do I think it likely that the transition from the reptile to the bird has been effected by such a form as *Archaeopteryx*.

Indeed, it was the '*Ornithoscelida*' that held the key to the evolutionary puzzle. Using a diagram first printed in his 1871 textbook on vertebrate anatomy (Huxley 1871), Huxley compared the legs and hips of a bird, a generalized dinosaur and a crocodile made to 'stand up' (see Fig. 4). The leg of the 'ornithoscelidan' more closely resembled that of the bird, but was still intermediate between the bird and crocodile. (This diagram was of sufficient use that it was still being used in Harvard anatomy classes in 1890: Pick & Sloan 2004). The 'ornithoscelidan' form, based on *Hypsilophodon*, seemed to perfectly link the representation of the living bird and reptile, yet it was *Compsognathus* that Huxley considered to be the most bird-like. The anatomist opined, 'There is no evidence that *Compsognathus* possessed feathers; but, if it did, it would be hard indeed to say whether it should be called a reptilian bird or an avian reptile' (Huxley 1877, p. 66). (Interestingly, compsognathids with 'protofeathers', like *Sinosauropteryx*, have since been discovered: Chen *et al.* 1998).

Huxley also wavered on the notion that the famous Triassic tracks from New England were made by birds. As at least some members of the '*Ornithoscelida*' were considered to walk bipedally, and dinosaurs had been found in the same strata as immense three-toed tracks from the Wealden, it was possible that the New England tracks were also made by dinosaurs. (This would soon turn out to be the correct interpretation.) Huxley refrained from coming down on one side or the other, but he did think that if the trackmakers could be identified, they would help naturalists to understand the evolution of birds (Huxley 1877, p. 66):

> it becomes a very important question whether the tracks in the Trias of Massachusetts, to which I referred some time ago, and which formerly used to be unhesitatingly ascribed to birds, may not all have been made by Ornithoscelidan reptiles; and whether, if we could obtain the skeletons of the animals which made these tracks, we should not find in them the actual steps of the evolutional process by which reptiles gave rise to birds.

Still, even the Triassic creatures might have been too young, and Huxley proposed that birds may have already been present at the beginning of the Mesozoic. The known members of the '*Ornithoscelida*' may have only been persistent types, descendants of earlier creatures that lived when reptiles evolved into birds (Huxley 1877, p. 67):

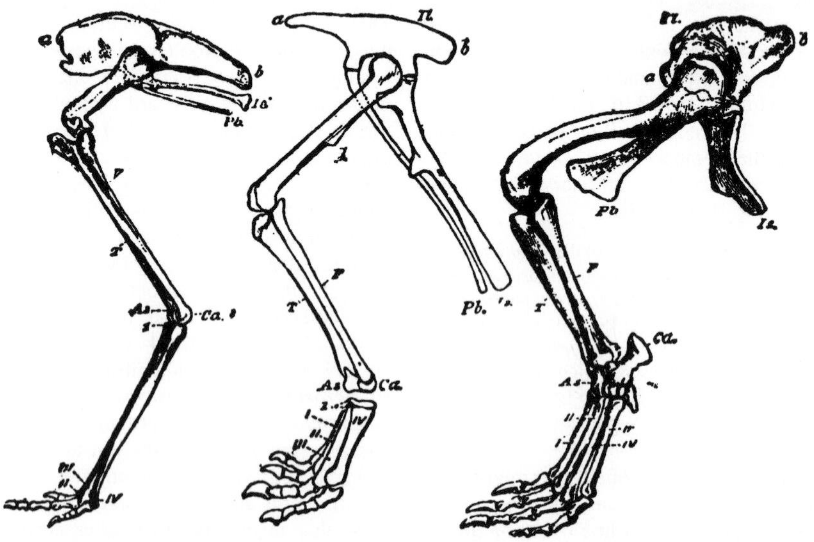

FIG. 6.—BIRD. ORNITHOSCELIDAN. CROCODILE.

Fig. 4. A comparison of the hips and legs of a bird, a generalized 'ornithoscelidan' and a crocodile. This figure was meant to illustrate the similarity between the legs and pelves of dinosaurs and birds. From Huxley (1877).

> It is, in fact, quite possible that all these more or less avi-form reptiles of the Mesozoic epoch are not terms in the series of progression from birds to reptiles at all, but simply the more or less modified descendants of Palaeozoic forms through which that transition was actually effected.

> We are not in a position to say that the known *Ornithoscelida* are intermediate in the order of their appearance on the earth between reptiles and birds. All that can be said is that if independent evidence of the actual occurrence of evolution is producible, then these intercalary forms remove every difficulty in the way of understanding what the actual steps of the process, in the case of birds, may have been.

Huxley would reiterate similar statements in a series of notes on the origins of major vertebrate groups published the same year in *Nature* (Huxley 1876*a*, *b*). His reptilian and avian intercalary types were more important for illustrating that evolution by natural selection occurred than solving all the questions about the origin of birds. Huxley again took up this position in an 1880 lecture delivered to the Royal Institution on the state of evolution by natural selection (Huxley 1880) in which he stated that the evolution of birds from reptiles confirmed Darwin's predictions. Further resolution on the origin of birds proved elusive, however. Huxley had built the avian evolutionary groundwork, but very little had been added to it outside of Marsh's toothed Cretaceous birds.

Conclusion

Huxley (1882) briefly returned to the topic again in one of his last papers, 'On the respiratory organs of *Apteryx*'. After refuting the notion that the respiratory system of this bird closely resembled that of mammals, Huxley noted that pneumatic bones such as those possessed by birds are only seen elsewhere in crocodylians, pterosaurs and dinosaurs. Although the respiratory organs of dinosaurs were entirely missing, and there was no expectation of them being found, Huxley still proposed that the '*Ornithoscelida*' may have had a similar physiology (Huxley 1882, p. 569):

> Thus, notwithstanding all the points of difference, there is a fundamental resemblance between the respiratory organs of Birds and those of Crocodiles, pointing to some common form (doubtless exemplified by some of the extinct *Dinosauria*), of which both are modifications.

Such a statement could be easily misconstrued as proposing that dinosaurs were the ancestors of birds (or the intermediate type from which both crocodiles and birds evolved), but the vast amount of literature Huxley produced on this subject does not allow for such a conclusion. Huxley came so tantalizingly close to pinning dinosaurs as the ancestors of birds that later researchers have often posthumously put those words in his mouth, promulgating a 'textbook cardboard' version of his views. Even if Huxley privately entertained the idea that birds had evolved from a dinosaur like *Compsognathus*, as implied in his 1868 letter to Haeckel, he explicitly urged caution in his published scientific work. Dinosaurs and birds were linked by form, their morphology revealing a common ancestry, but in both his public lectures and scientific papers Huxley was agnostic as to precisely what might have existed at the evolutionary nexus between the groups. Despite such caveats, Huxley did more than any other naturalist of his era to popularize the close relationship between birds and reptiles. Wagner, Gegenbaur, Cope and others recognized the bird-like traits of dinosaurs contemporaneously, but it was Huxley who turned similarities in form into compelling evidence of evolution by natural selection. During a time when the fossil record appeared to be at odds with Darwin's theory, Huxley endeavoured to find examples of transitional forms and he found just that in the evolution of birds from reptiles.

I am grateful for the assistance of M. Taylor (University of Portsmouth), J. Harris (Dixie State College of Utah) and D. Naish, all of whom provided useful advice and guidance as I prepared this paper. I am also indebted to several anonymous persons who provided hard-to-find papers and other resources that formed the backbone of this work. Finally, I am most thankful to my wife, Tracey, whose unflagging support encouraged me throughout the writing process.

References

Bakker, R. T. 1986. *The Dinosaur Heresies*. Kensington, New York, 22.

Beckles, S. H. 1854. On the ornithoidichnites of the Wealden. *Quarterly Journal of the Geological Society, London*, **10**, 456–464.

Bell, C. 1852. *The Hand: Its Mechanism and Vital Endowments, As Evincing Design*, 5th edn. John Murray, London, 54.

Benson, R. B., Barrett, P. M., Powell, H. P. & Norman, D. B. 2008. The taxonomic status of *Megalosaurus bucklandii* (Dinosauria, Theropoda) from the Middle Jurassic of Oxfordshire, UK. *Palaeontology*, **51**, 419–424.

Bowler, P. J. 2007. *Monkey Trials and Gorilla Sermons*. Harvard University Press, Cambridge, MA.

Buckland, W. 1824. Notice on the *Megalosaurus* or great fossil lizard of Stonesfield. *Transactions of the Geological Society*, **I**, 390–396.

Chatterjee, S. 1997. *The Rise of Birds*. Johns Hopkins University Press, Baltimore, MD, 4.

Chen, P., Dong, Z. & Zhen, S. 1998. An exceptionally well-preserved theropod dinosaur from the Yixian Formation of China. *Nature*, **391**, 147–152.

Chiappe, L. M. 2007. *Glorified Dinosaurs*. John Wiley, Hoboken, NJ, 30.

CHIAPPE, L. M. & DYKE, G. J. 2007. The beginnings of birds: recent discoveries, ongoing arguments, and new directions. *In*: ANDERSON, J. S. & SUES, H. (eds) *Major Transitions in Vertebrate Evolution*, Indiana University Press, Bloomington, IN, 303–336.

CODD, J. R., MANNING, P. L., NORELL, M. A. & PERRY, S. F. 2008. Avian-like breathing mechanics in maniraptoran dinosaurs. *Proceedings of the Royal Society B*, **275**, 157–161.

COPE, E. D. 1866. On anatomical peculiarities in some Dinosauria. *Proceedings of the Academy of Natural Sciences of Philadelphia*, **18**, 316–317.

COPE, E. D. 1867*a*. The fossil reptiles of New Jersey. *The American Naturalist*, **1**, 23–30.

COPE, E. D. 1867*b*. *Proceedings of the Academy of Natural Sciences of Philadelphia*, **19**, 234–235.

COPE, E. D. 1868. On some Cretaceous Reptilia. *Proceedings of the Academy of Natural Sciences of Philadelphia*, **20**, 233–242.

COPE, E. D. 1869. *Proceedings of the Academy of Natural Sciences of Philadelphia*, **21**, 123.

DARWIN, C. 1859. *On the Origin of Species by Means of Natural Selection*. John Murray, London.

DARWIN, C. 1863*a*. Letter to H. Falconer via the Darwin Correspondence Project. World wide web address: http://www.darwinproject.ac.uk/darwinletters/calendar/entry-3901.html.

DARWIN, C. 1863*b*. Letter to J.D. Dana via the Darwin Correspondence Project. World wide web address: http://www.darwinproject.ac.uk/darwinletters/calendar/entry-3905.html.

DESMOND, A. 1979. Designing the dinosaur: Richard Owen's response to Robert Edmond Grant. *Isis*, **70**, 224–234.

DESMOND, A. 1982. *Archetypes and Ancestors*. University of Chicago Press, Chicago, IL.

DESMOND, A. 1997. *Huxley*. Addison-Wesley, Boston, MA.

DI GREGORIO, M. A. 1982. The dinosaur connection: a reinterpretation of T.H. Huxley's evolutionary view. *Journal of the History of Biology*, **15**, 397–418.

FALCONER, H. 1863. Letter to Charles Darwin via the Darwin Correspondence Project. World wide web address: http://www.darwinproject.ac.uk/darwinletters/calendar/entry-3899.html.

FARMER, C. G. 2006. On the origin of avian air sacs. *Respiratory Physiology & Neurobiology*, **154**, 89–106.

FEDUCCIA, A. 1999. *The Origin and Evolution of Birds*. Yale University Press, New Haven, CT.

FEDUCCIA, A. 2001. The problem of bird origins and early avian evolution. *Journal of Ornithology*, **142**, 139–147

FIGUIER, L. 1866. *The World Before the Deluge*. D. Appleton & Co., New York, 230–231.

FOULKE, W. P. & LEIDY, J. 1858. Remarks concerning *Hadrosaurus*. *Proceedings of the Academy of Natural Sciences of Philadelphia*, **10**, 215–218.

GEGENBAUR, C. 1864. *Untersuchungen zur vergleichenden Anatomie der Wirbelthiere erstes Heft. Carpus und Tarsus*. Wilhelm Engelmann, Leipzig.

GOULD, S. J. 1987. *Time's Arrow, Time's Cycle*. Cambridge University Press, Cambridge, 4–7.

GOULD, S. J. 1991. *Bully for Brontosaurus*. W.W. Norton & Co., New York, 385–401.

HAECKEL, E. 1866. *Generelle Morphologie der Organismen*. Reimer, Berlin.

HITCHCOCK, E. 1836. Ornithichnology: description of the foot marks of birds, (Ornithichnites) on new Red Sandstone in Massachusetts. *American Journal of Science and the Fine Arts*, **29**, 307–340.

HITCHCOCK, E. 1858. *Ichnology of New England*. William White, Boston.

HUXLEY, T. H. 1859. On the persistent types of animal life. *Proceedings of the Royal Institution of Great Britain*, **III**, 151–153.

HUXLEY, T. H. 1862. The Anniversary Address to the Geological Society. *Quarterly Journal of the Geological Society, London*, **XVIII**, xl.–liv.

HUXLEY, T. H. 1863. *Lectures on the Elements of Comparative Anatomy*. John Churchill, London, **69**, 74.

HUXLEY, T. H. 1867. On the classification of birds; and on the taxonomic value of the modifications of certain of the cranial bones observable in that class. *Proceedings of the Scientific Meetings of the Zoological Society of London*, 415–472.

HUXLEY, T. H. 1868*a*. On the animals which are most nearly intermediate between birds and reptiles. *Geological Magazine*, **V**, 357–365.

HUXLEY, T. H. 1868*b*. Remarks upon *Archaeopteryx lithographica*. *Proceedings of the Royal Society of London*, **XVI**, 243–248.

HUXLEY, T. H. 1869*a*. On the upper jaw of *Megalosaurus*. *Quarterly Journal of the Geological Society, London*, **XXV**, 311–314.

HUXLEY, T. H. 1869*b*. *An Introduction to the Classification of Animals*. John Churchill, London, 70, 76, 104, 111.

HUXLEY, T. H. 1870*a*. On *Hypsilophodon foxii*, a new dinosaurian from the Wealden of the Isle of Wight. *Quarterly Journal of the Geological Society, London*, **XXVI**, 3–12.

HUXLEY, T. H. 1870*b*. Further evidence of the affinity between the dinosaurian reptiles and birds. *Quarterly Journal of the Geological Society, London*, **XXVI**, 12–31.

HUXLEY, T. H. 1870*c*. On the classification of the Dinosauria with observations on the Dinosauria of the Trias. *Quarterly Journal of the Geological Society, London*, **XXVI**, 32–50.

HUXLEY, T. H. 1870*d*. Triassic Dinosauria. *Nature*, **I**, 23–24.

HUXLEY, T. H. 1870*e*. The anniversary address of the president. *Quarterly Journal of the Geological Society, London*, **XXVI**, xxix–lxiv.

HUXLEY, T. H. 1871. *A Manual of the Anatomy of Vertebrated Animals*. D. Appleton & Sons, New York, 223.

HUXLEY, T. H. 1876*a*. On the evidence as to the origin of existing vertebrate animals. *Nature*, **XIII**, 388–389, 410–412, 429–430, 467–469, 514–516.

HUXLEY, T. H. 1876*b*. On the evidence as to the origin of existing vertebrate animals. *Nature*, **XIII**, 33–34.

HUXLEY, T. H. 1877. *American Addresses*. D. Appleton & Co., New York, 43–67.

HUXLEY, T. H. 1880. The coming of age of the Origin of Species. *Nature*, **XXII**, 1–4.

HUXLEY, T. H. 1882. On the respiratory organs of *Apteryx*. *Proceedings of the Scientific Meetings of the*

Zoological Society of London for the Year 1882, 560–569.

LARSON, P. & DONNAN, K. 2002. *Rex Appeal*. Invisible Cities Press, Montpelier, 25.

LEIDY, J. 1865. Cretaceous reptiles of the United States. *Smithsonian Contributions to Knowledge*, **14**, 76–102.

LYONS, S. L. 1993. Thomas Huxley: fossils, persistence, and the argument from design. *Journal of the History of Biology*, **26**, 545–569.

MANTELL, G. A. 1825. Notice on the *Iguanodon*, a newly discovered fossil reptile, from the sandstone of Tilgate Forest, in Sussex. *Philosophical Transactions of the Royal Society of London*, **115**, 179–186.

MARSH, O. C. 1875. Odontornithes, or birds with teeth. *The American Naturalist*, **9**, 625–631 .

MARSH, O. C. 1877. Notice of a new and gigantic dinosaur. *American Journal of Science*, **3**, 87–88.

MAYOR, A. 2000. *The First Fossil Hunters*, Princeton University Press, Princeton, NJ.

MEYER, H. VON 1861*a*. *Archaeopteryx lithographica* (Vogel–Feder) und *Pterodactylus* von Solnhofen. *Neües Jahrbuch fur Mineralogie, Geologie und Palaontologie*, **1861**, 678–679.

MEYER, H. VON 1861*b*. *Archaeopteryx lithographica* aus dem lithographischen Schiefer von Solenhofen. *Palaeontographica*, **10**, 53–56.

MEYER, H. VON 1862. On the *Archaeopteryx lithographica*, from the lithographic slate of Solenhofen. *Annals and Magazine of Natural History*, **9**, 366–370.

NORELL, M. & XU, X. 2005. Feathered dinosaurs. *Annual Review of Earth and Planetary Sciences*, **33**, 277–299.

NORELL, M., DINGUS, L. & GAFFNEY, E. 1995. *Discovering Dinosaurs*. Knopf, New York, 11.

NORMAN, D. 1991. *Dinosaur!* Macmillan, New York, 93.

OLSON, E. C. & THOMAS, R. D. K. 1980. *A Cold Look at the Warm-blooded Dinosaurs*. Westview Press, Boulder, CO, 3.

OSBORN, H. F. 1900. Reconsideration of the evidence for a common dinosaur–avian stem in the Permian. Dinosaur Contributions, No. 4. *The American Naturalist*, **34**, 777–799.

OWEN, R. 1842. Report on British Fossil Reptiles, Part II. *In*: *Report of the Eleventh Meeting of the British Association for the Advancement of Science, Plymouth, England, July 1841*. John Murray, London, 60–204.

OWEN, R. 1863. On the *Archaeopteryx* of von Meyer, with a description of the fossil remains of a long-tailed species, from the lithographic stone of Solenhofen. *Philosophical Transactions of the Royal Society of London*, **153**, 33–47.

PAUL, G. S. 1988. *Predatory Dinosaurs of the World*. Simon & Schuster, New York, **195**, 353.

PHILLIPS, J. 1860. *Life on Earth*. Macmillan, London.

PICK, N. & SLOAN, M. 2004. *The Rarest of the Rare*. HarperCollins, New York, 6–7.

PSIHOYOS, L. & KNOEBBER, J. 1994. *Hunting Dinosaurs*. Random House, New York, 129.

RUDWICK, M. 1976. *The Meaning of Fossils*. Neal Washington Academic, New York.

SEELEY, H. G. 1864. On the pterodactyle as evidence of a new subclass of Vertebrata (Saurornia). *In*: *Report of the British Association of the Advancement of Science* (Bath Meeting). John Murray, London, 69.

SEELEY, H. G. 1870. *The Ornithosauria: An Elementary Study of the Bones of Pterodactyles*. Deighton, Bell, & Co., Cambridge.

SHIPMAN, P. S. 1998. *Taking Wing*. Simon & Schuster, New York, 202.

WAGNER, J. A. 1861*a*. Ein neues, angeblich mit vogelfedern versehenes Reptil. *Sitzungsberichte der königl. bayerischen Akademie der Wissenschaften zu München*, **2**, 146–154.

WAGNER, J. A. 1861*b*. Zur Feststellung des Artbegriffes, mit besonderer Bezugnahme auf die Ansichten von Nathusius, Darwin, Is. Geoffroy und Agassiz. *Sitzungsberichte der königl. bayerischen Akademie der Wissenschaften zu München*, **1**, 308–58.

WAGNER, J. A. 1861*c*. Schildkröten und Saurier aus dem lithographischen Schiefer: V. *Compsognathus longipes* Wagn. Neue Beiträge zur Kenntniss der urweltlichen Fauna des lithographischen Schiefers. *Abhandlungen der Mathemat.-Physikalischen Classe der Koeniglich Bayerischen Akademie der Wissenschaften*, **9**, 94–102.

WAGNER, J. A. 1862. On a new fossil reptile supposed to be furnished with feathers. *Annals and Magazine of Natural History*, **9**, 261–267.

WEISHAMPEL, D. B. & YOUNG, L. 1996. *Dinosaurs of the East Coast*. Johns Hopkins University Press, Baltimore, MD, 202.

ZHOU, Z. 2004. The origin and early evolution of birds: discoveries, disputes, and perspectives from fossil evidence. *Naturwissenschaften*, **91**, 455–471.

A history of digit identification in the manus of theropods (including Aves)

KASPER LYKKE HANSEN

Zoological Museum, Natural History Museum of Denmark, University of Copenhagen, Universitetsparken 15, DK-2100 Copenhagen Ø, Denmark
(e-mail: stenfisker@live.dk)

Abstract: The identification of avian and dinosaurian digits remains one of the major controversies in vertebrate evolution. A long history of morphological interpretations of fossil forms and studies of limb development in embryos has been given as evidence for two differing points of view. From an originally pentadactyl forelimb, either digits I, II and III form in the manus of birds and thus support a dinosaurian ancestry, or digits II, III and IV form in the manus supporting a more ancient ancestry or an evolutionary frame shift. A review of the history of research into the subject is presented here, dating from approximately 1825 to 2009.

The early investigations (1825–1934)

During the first 100 years or so the history of digit identification in theropods mostly concerned birds (Aves). Birds are now generally accepted as dinosaurs, with the dromaeosaurids and troodontids being their closest relatives (Gauthier 1986; Sereno 1999).

Sir Richard Owen (1804–1892), the first Director of London's Museum of Natural History, was a pioneering British comparative anatomist who, amongst other things, was famous for coining the term 'Dinosauria', after recognizing these large, extinct reptiles as a new suborder (Fig. 1). He had noticed that this particular group of fossils (which included remains of *Megalosaurus*, *Iguanodon* and *Hylaeosaurus*) had certain characteristics in common, including: column-like legs and five fused vertebrae fused to the pelvic girdle. Owen thus claimed:

> The combination of such characters, some, as it were, from groups now distinct from each other, and all manifested by creatures far surpassing in size the largest of existing reptiles, will, it is presumed, be deemed sufficient ground for establishing a distinct tribe or suborder of Saurian Reptiles, for which I would propose the name of Dinosauria.
>
> (Owen 1842)

Owen was also famed for his appropriation and initial description of the London specimen of *Archaeopteryx lithographica* in the early 1860s. But as an anatomist he also studied the embryology of birds (Owen 1836). He was one of the first to identify the digits in the manus of adult birds as numbers II–III–IV, out of an original five, in the pentadactyl ancestral forelimb. His conclusions were, in part, based on the early works of Dr J. F. Meckel (Fig 2.) on the anatomy of birds (Meckel 1825) in combination with his own observations of bird embryos. Owen, however, disagreed with Meckel, who identified the digits in birds as I–II–III.

During the next 100 years two dominant schools of thought emerged on the subject. Both were based on studies of various species of bird and reptile embryos, often supplemented by fossils including dinosaurs. Leighton (1894), Nopcsa (1894), Sieglbauer (1911) and Holmgren (1933) interpreted the digits of modern birds as II–III–IV, just as Owen had done previously, with digits I and V having been lost. Opposed to this view were Gegenbauer (1864), Rosenberg (1873), Parker (1888), Steiner (1922), Heilmann (1926) and others, who stated that the digits were numbers I–II–III (IV and V having been lost).

The differing points of view of these scientists can initially seem somewhat surprising, as they all, at least to some extent, studied digit anatomy in similar developmental stages in embryonic chicks using modern-day microscopes.

However, the two opposing lines of thought had been firmly established by the late 1800s, and proponents for both sides vigorously defended their positions. In W. K. Parker's paper on wing development, for example (Parker 1888 p. 386),

From: Moody, R. T. J., Buffetaut, E., Naish, D. & Martill, D. M. (eds) *Dinosaurs and Other Extinct Saurians: A Historical Perspective*. Geological Society, London, Special Publications, **343**, 265–275.
DOI: 10.1144/SP343.16 0305-8719/10/$15.00

Fig. 1. Richard Owen, the British anatomist (1804–1892), was famous for coining the term dinosauria and for appropriating the first specimen of *Archaeopteryx lithographica*. Owen also combined Cuvier's (1769–1832) anatomical work with German transcendental anatomy. (The photograph is public domain.)

Fig. 2. Johann Friedrich Meckel (1781–1833), sometimes referred to as Johann Friedrich Meckel, the Younger, was a German anatomist. After graduating from the University of Halle, Meckel spent time in Paris assisting Georges Cuvier with systematic analysis of anatomical and zoological specimens. In his later years Meckel was mostly concerned with the field of embryonic development, especially in birds. (The photograph is public domain.)

earlier work by Gegenbauer (1864) was strongly supported:

> Since Gegenbauer spoke the last weighty word upon the structure of the Bird's wing, no new facts have transpired to make us re-open the question of the homologies of the three digits with the pollex, index, and medius of other groups. Nothing in the skeleton, the muscles, or the development of the limb contradicts this acceptation, to the best of my knowledge. I take it for granted accordingly in this paper.

Richard Owen was equally unequivocal when describing the general pattern for loss of digits, in support of digits II–III–IV remaining:

> To sum up, then, the modifications of the digits: they never exceed five in number on each foot [limb] in any existing vertebrate animal above the rank of Fishes ... The first or innermost digit, as a general rule, is the first to disappear.
>
> (Owen 2007)

Only very few natural scientists dared to diverge from these two alternatives. Hurst (1893) identified the digits as III, IV and V, whereas Tschan (1889) concluded that they were digits I, II and IV. These studies, however, gained little or no support. It is important to mention that Owen's contemporaries within the field of Zoology were often trained in several different, but sometimes overlapping, fields of interest, such as general morphology, anatomy and embryology. It should also be noted that in the early stages of development in vertebrate embryos it is very difficult to identify the various digits and carpals, and following their development it can be extremely difficult even with modern technology. It is much more than the study of adult vertebrates with fully ossified bones in the manus.

It is also likely that some of these early studies were biased, for or against ideas based on evolution and/or natural selection after the recent emergence of Darwinian theory. Some did not adhere to classical and/or recognized scientific methods; others were also based on analyses performed with poor-quality microscopes (compared with today) (Fastovsky & Weishampel 2005).

In 1926 the ongoing debate was put to rest for a time when Danish amateur ornithologist and painter Gerhard Heilmann (1859–1946) published

The Origin of Birds (Heilmann 1926). In this lavishly illustrated and highly detailed work the entire history and evolution of birds was described in convincing terms. So convincingly, in fact, that virtually no one challenged the book for approximately 50 years! In the chapter dedicated to skeletal features in birds, the digits in the wing were clearly identified as I–II–III. Although this particular claim would only stand for 20 years.

Post-World War II research (1945–1979)

In 1945 a detailed study on chick digit development was published using current state-of-the-art technology (Montagna 1945) that challenged Gerhard Heilmann's I–II–III hypothesis. Serial sections of the wings were stained with haematoxylin and eosin, and camera lucida reconstructions were created from all critical stages of digit development. Montagna identified representations of all five distal carpals, and distal carpal I was seen without a metacarpal. Of the remaining metacarpals, II, III and IV develop fully, whereas number V eventually fuses into metacarpal IV. Thus, the digits of adult birds were numbers II–III–IV. A total of 13 embryonic carpals arranged in three rows were also identified (Fig. 3). The stalemate temporarily created by Gerhard Heilmann had now been broken and the controversy flared up again.

One person, who was not convinced by Montagna's work, was A. S. Romer (1894–1973). In his outstanding book *Vertebrate Palaeontology* (Romer 1966 p. 164–165) Romer wrote the following:

> We find a reduction in the hand [of birds] similar to that in dinosaurs, for only three fingers are represented. Despite some conflicting embryological evidence, these appear to be (as in some dinosaurs) the inner three; the fourth and fifth have vanished completely.

This was a fitting account of the disagreement surrounding the identification of birds' fingers. What was also highly interesting, in Romer's book, was that an entire chapter was devoted to dinosaurs (Fig. 4). Doubts on the monophyly of this group still existed, although a great deal of knowledge had been gained through increased studies on fossils in the post-World War II era. Within the next 40 years more and more fossils of dinosaurs were discovered, and this would force the debate on digit identity into a dispute between palaeontologists and developmental biologists.

Disagreement in Eichstätt

The International *Archaeopteryx* Conference held in the town of Eichstätt, Germany in September 1984 was hosted by palaeontologists John H. Ostrom (1928–2005) and Peter Wellnhofer

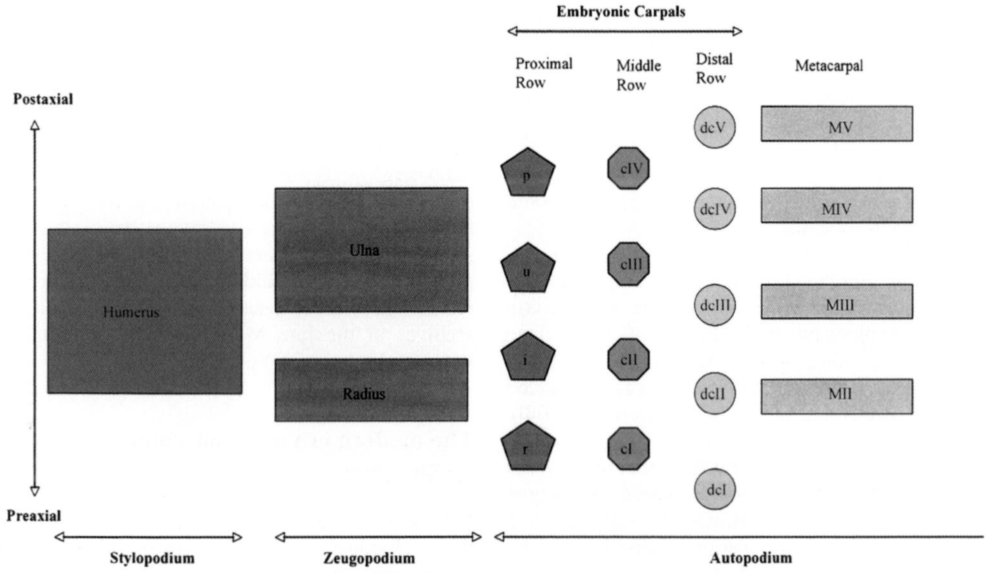

Fig. 3. Schematic representation of the possible full complement of the embryonic carpals of the manus of a chick (after Montagna 1945). Phalanges are not shown. The carpals are roughly arranged in three rows: (1) a proximal series that comprises a radiale (r), intermedium (i), ulnare (u) and pisiforme (p); (2) a middle series of four centralia (cI–cIV); and (3) a series of five distal carpals (dcI–dcV).

Fig. 4. *Allosaurus* on the move. This Late Jurassic theropod carried three digits (I–II–III) on the manus (reproduced with kind permission from Luis Rey).

(1936–). Ostrom was the father of the revised version of the hypothesis that birds were descended directly from dinosaurs (Ostrom 1969) and Wellnhofer an established authority on matters pertaining to *Archaeopteryx*. The conference lasted for 5 days and included a number of discussions on digit identity in the early Jurassic bird *Archaeopteryx lithographica* (Fig. 5) that could potentially resolve the issue.

During the conference, embryologist J. R. Hinchliffe presented results integrating evidence based on isotope labelling of the chondroitin sulphate component of the matrix of precartilage elements, together with a review of Montagna (1945) and Holmgren (1955). It was concluded that the digits on birds' hands were rightfully II–III–IV, but the identification of the various carpal elements was different from that of previous authors (Hinchcliffe 1984). Where Montagna had identified 13 carpals Hinchcliffe only saw five (Fig. 5); radiale, ulnare, pisiforme, distal carpal III and an element labelled 'X' (because of its unclear homology) (Fig. 6). The digits II–III–IV were described, together with a rudimentary digit V consisting of only the metacarpal. The numbering of digits was based on the relative position of the pisiforme. It was also proposed that the last digits to form during ontogeny were the first to be lost in during evolution.

In opposition to this standpoint, and to that of Tarsitano & Hecht (1980), Peter Wellnhofer verified the forelimb digits and phalangeal codes of the 'Maxberg' – Berlin and Eichstätt – specimens of *Archaeopteryx* as being homologous to those of theropods (Wellnhofer 1984).

No consensus was reached on the digit identity problem, but it should be mentioned that tape recordings of these discussions are still held in the archives of the Jura Museum (Eichstätt) and the Peabody Museum of Yale University.

The modern era and molecular genetics (1980–1998)

In the period 1980–1998 a wide array of new scientific techniques were applied to the digit identity controversy and several groundbreaking fossils were uncovered.

In the beginning of the 1980s developmental biologists described the development of limbs in vertebrates using molecular genetics and found

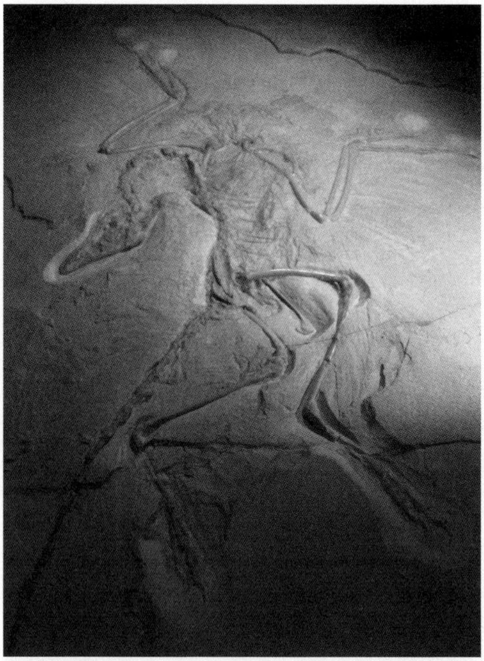

Fig. 5. *Archaeopteryx lithographica*, Berlin specimen. The Jurassic urvogel with a combination of avian and dinosaur character traits is central to the discussion regarding the origin of birds. (Photography, K. L. Hansen.)

that: (1) the positions where limbs emerge from the body axis depend on *Hox* gene expression; (2) as the limb grows, the stylopod (shoulder with humerus) forms first, then the zeugopod (radius and ulna) and the autopod (manus) is formed last. Again, each phase of these limb developments are governed by *Hox* gene expression; (3) the identity of each digit is specified by BMP (bone morphogenetic protein) activity in the interdigital region posterior to it; and (4) cell death in the limb is necessary for the formation of both digits and joints. Furthermore, it was discovered that differences in BMP expression could, for example, produce webbed feet in ducks or unwebbed feet in chickens. BMPs were also involved in differentiating mesenchymal cells into cartilage (Gilbert 2003).

Following the results generated by molecular geneticists, certain 'morphogenetic rules' regarding the ontogeny of the vertebrate limb were proposed and described (Shubin & Alberch 1986). The preliminary investigation utilized *Danio rerio* (the zebra fish) and amphibians *Ambystoma mexicanum* (an urodel) and *Xenopus laevis* (an anuran) as model organisms. Later on, amniotes were also investigated. *Hox* gene expression was examined in the limbs and a conserved developmental 'bauplan' of the pentadactyle limbs was presented. The following series of features were included: (1) proximo-distal development; (2) a preaxial axis of segmentation into radius and radiale; (3) a post-axial

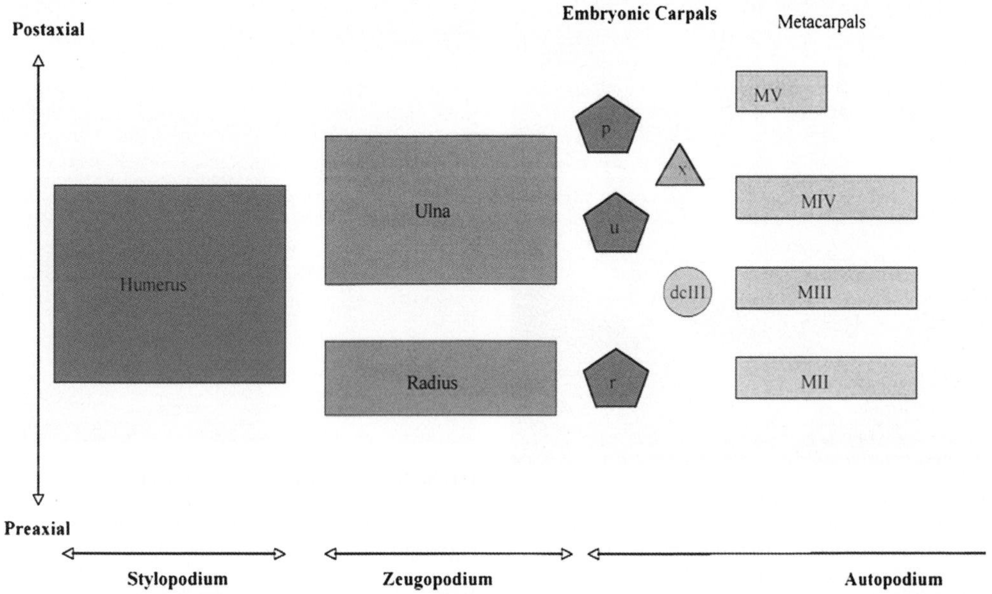

Fig. 6. Schematic representation of the manus of a chick with the embryonic carpals (after Hinchcliffe 1984). Phalanges are not shown. The embryonic carpals comprise a radiale (r), ulnare (u), pisiforme (p), distal carpal III and X (see text). Metacarpal V remains rudimentary.

axis of a single zeugopod element (ulna) running via ulnare into the digital arch that forms distal carpal elements which are the base for the apparent branching of the digits; (4) digit IV begins the posterior to anterior sequence of digit formation; (5) a maximum of five digit rays; and, finally, (6) connections of the prechodrogenic condensations are stereotyped.

This model seemed to fit most of the species that were examined; however, the urodeles seemed to follow a different pattern, where digit II (instead of IV) began the sequence of digit formation. Furthermore, it was proposed that digit III and not IV possibly begins the sequence of digit formation in birds because of developmental acceleration. In the end, the authors concluded, that their 'bauplan' was a good 'rule of the thumb' for vertebrate limb development, but it was not without exceptions.

In 1991 Stephen Jay Gould (Fig. 7) reflected on Shubin's (Fig. 8) morphogenetic rules and the newly discovered eight-fingered Devonian Tetrapod *Acantostega* (Coates & Clack 1990) in his article 'Eight (or fewer) little piggies' (Gould 1991). Discussing the urodeles' 'front to back' formation of digits, which, as previously mentioned, is totally opposite to all other tetrapods digit development, Gould wrote (p. 407):

> Some zoologists have used this basic difference to argue that urodeles form an entirely separate evolutionary line of tetrapods, perhaps even arising from a different group of fish ancestors. But most (including me) would respond that embryonic patterns are as subject to evolutionary change as adult form, and that an ancestor to the urodele-lineage – for some utterly unknown and undoubtedly fascinating reason – shucked an otherwise universal system in tetrapods and developed this 'backward' route to the formation of digits.

This quote underlines the problems of assuming total stability in pattern through time, not only with regards to the formation of digits, but also, with *Acantostega* in mind, with regards to the identity and number of digits in tetrapods.

Meanwhile, a number of very important dinosaur fossil discoveries were made in South America by Sereno *et al.* (1993), who described two very basal

Fig. 7. Stephen Jay Gould. S. J. Gould (1941–2002) was one of the most influential and most frequently cited scientists in the field of evolutionary theory. Together with N. Eldredge he developed the theory of punctuated equilibrium, in which evolutionary change occurs relatively rapidly compared to longer periods of relative evolutionary stability (Eldredge & Gould 1972). (Harvard University online.)

Fig. 8. Neil Shubin, Professor and Chairman of Organismal Biology and Anatomy at the University of Chicago. Shubin has used salamanders as model organisms for studying developmental systems and limb variation during ontogeny. With P. Alberch (1954–1998) he presented a conserved developmental 'bauplan' of the pentadactyle limbs utilizing *Hox* gene expression (reproduced with kind permission from John Easton, University of Chicago Medical Center).

dinosaurs *Herrerasaurus ischigualastensis* and *Eoraptor lunensis* (Fig. 8). There still exists today some doubt as to whether these were basal theropods or basal saurischians, but, as they each had five digits on the manus, they were important in the context of plotting the loss of digits in the hand in the series of fossils leading to living birds. One can observe the reduction of digits in a chronological series of fossil theropods from around the world beginning with five digits in the late Triassic *Herrerasaurus* and *Eoraptor* (Fig. 9), four digits (I–II–III–IV) in *Coelophysis* (Fig. 10) having lost digit V and three digits (I–II–III) in, for example, the late Jurassic *Allosaurus* (Fig. 4) and most later theropods. It is important to mention that the urvogel *Archaeopteryx* also has three digits with the exact same number of phalanges as *Allosaurus*. An even further reduction in digits is found in *Tyrannosaurus rex* with only two comparatively small functional digits on the manus. Finally, the alvaresaurid *Mononykus* retains only a single, but very powerfully built, digit.

Ichnological (the study of fossilized hand and footprints, and also nests and coprolites) evidence for digit reduction in various theropods was published in 1993. A series of Triassic theropod tracks from several taxons were presented, supposedly showing the reduction of first digit I and then digit V in the manus (Thulborn 1993). The study was criticized for being somewhat lacking in the amount and quality of prints used as evidence (J. Milan per. comm.). No further ichnological material has since entered the debate.

Fig 9. *Eoraptor* spots early mammal. The Triassic theropod *Eoraptor* is seen with five digits (of which the inner two are notably shorter), consisting of one metacarpal each and with a chain of at least one phalange on digits I–II–III–IV (reproduced with kind permission from Luis Rey).

In an article from 1997 the formation of 'digit condensations' in the manus of embryos of chicks (*Gallus sp.*), turtles (*Chelydra serpentina*) and alligators (*Alligator mississippiensis*) was described (Burke & Feduccia 1997). In the early developmental stages of the chick (stained with alcian blue) four condensations were observed with a primary axis through the fourth digit (IV), as described in Shubin's bauplan for vertebrate limb formation (Shubin & Alberch 1986). Later, but still in the relatively early stages of the chick embryo, digit V is reduced and eventually lost. The transient presence of the first digit could not be confirmed. In the turtles and in the alligator condensations of all five digits were observed and followed through to final digit ossification. The result was digits II–III–IV remaining in birds, and therefore the authors rejected the bird–dinosaur relationship altogether, because digit reduction could have happened twice during evolution and accordingly digits in birds and dinosaurs were not homologous.

In 1998 it was claimed that a shift in the primary axis had happened from the fourth to the third digit in birds (Chatterjee 1998). As previously noted, Shubin & Alberch (1986) had earlier described this as a probable scenario. The shift of axis could have taken place by modification of the expression of *Hox D* genes in the process of distal carpal elements' ossification.

The frame-shift hypothesis and the latest developments (1999–2009)

In the groundbreaking and controversial publication '1, 2, 3 = 2, 3, 4: A solution to the problem of the homology of the digits in the avian hand', the so-called 'frame-shift' hypothesis was presented (Wagner & Gauthier 1999).

Other authors had rightly identified the early condensations (C) in birds as numbers CII, CIII and CIV, but these did not ossify into adult digits (D) DII, DIII and DIV, rather into DI, DII and DIII. According to Gauthier (Fig. 11) and Wagner, the reason for this was because DV did not form because its condensation (CV) was reduced in the relatively early stages of the embryo. The condensation (CI) for DI was also lost owing to embryological constraints. This follows the pattern of reduction according to Morse's law (Morse 1872) that states that in the ontogeny of vertebrates, DI and DV are lost first. If CI was lost at the same

Fig. 10. Hunting *Coelophysis*. Four digits are carried on the manus (I–II–III–IV), digit V has been lost and only a rudimentary digit IV with a single phalange remains (reproduced with kind permission from Luis Rey).

point in time as the functional DIV then a so-called developmental frame-shift could have occurred, where the remaining CII–CIV would ossify as DI–DIII. In other words, CII–CIV would take form and function as DI–DIII (Fig. 12).

It is important to mention that in Wagner & Gauthier (1999) the results were based on natural experiments with Kiwis (*Apteryx sp.*). It was demonstrated that Kiwi hands develop from CIII and CIV, but can grow into either DI and DII, or DII and DIII, but never into DIII and DIV. In conclusion, Wagner & Gauthier (1999) claimed that there was a conflict between embryology and palaeontology only if one assumed a particular model of character evolution (viz. that C = D), which Kiwi's proved was not the case necessarily.

Comments on the frame-shift hypothesis were presented in the same journal issue as Wagner & Gauthier (Feduccia 1999). Lack of evidence in morphological character traits of theropods that could indicate frame shift through evolution was the main argument against this new idea.

The frame-shift hypothesis probably had few advocates in the beginning, but unexpected support for the theory emerged in Dahn & Fallon (2000). Experimenting with chick embryos, it was concluded that there was not necessarily a correlation between the numbering of digit condensations and ossified digits. *Hox* genes control the timing and patterning in the ossification process, and the gradient of BMP plays an active role in the specification of the final ossification of the digits. This could potentially explain Wagner and Gauthier's hypothesis, but further experiments were essential.

Experiments with transgenic mice showed frame shifts in the development of vertebrae (Drossopoulou *et al.* 2000). Importantly, the same author also showed that, by carefully manipulating the activity of the *Shh* gene (sonic hedgehog) and BMP2 (bone morphogenetic protein number 2), they produced phenotypes with the same number of digits but with differences in digit identity, thus showing that the identity of digits can be changed without a change in the number of digits.

Other new experiments gave different results. Chick wing buds were stained with HRP (horse radish peroxidase)-labelled peanut agglutinin to indicate skeletogenic condensations and it was concluded that five condensations CI–CV could be identified, out of which digits DII–DIV develop (Larsson & Wagner 2002). Later the same year

Fig. 11. Jacques Armand Gauthier, Professor of Geology and Geophysics, Curator of Vertebrate Paleontology and Vertebrate Zoology, Yale Peabody Museum. Gauthier is considered one of the founders of the use of cladistics in the field of biology. He contributed to the foundational phylogenetic studies of Archosauria and Lepidosauria, as well as the first major cladistic analysis of Diapsida (Gauthier 1984, 1988) (reproduced with kind permission from Jacques A. Gauthier).

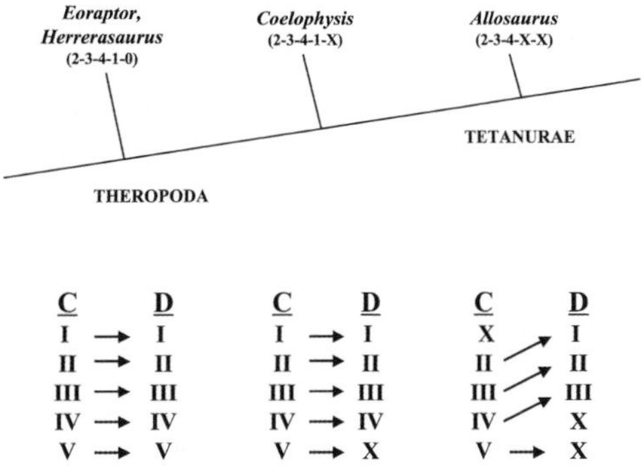

Fig. 12. Schematic representation of the frame-shift hypothesis combined with fossil evidence of the digit reduction in the manus of theropods. C, condensation; D, digit; phalangeal formula in parenthesis. *Herrerasaurus* and *Eoraptor* with five digits as the most basal configuration, *Coelophysis* with four digits and *Allosaurus* (including recent birds, but with a different phalangeal formula to *Allosaurus*: 1–2–1–X–X) with three digits. Somewhere before *Allosaurus* but after *Coelophysis* the proposed frame-shift took place; condensations CII–CIV took shape and function of digits DI–DIII (Wagner & Gauthier 1999). DV did not form in *Coelophysis* as its condensation (CV) was reduced in the relatively early stages of the embryo. In early Tetanureans, condensation (CI) for DI was also lost owing to embryological constraints. If CI was lost at the same point in time as the functional DIV was lost a so-called developmental frame shift could have occurred, where the remaining CII–CIV would ossify as DI–DIII (adapted from Wagner & Gauthier 1999).

results on early ostrich embryos were presented (Feduccia & Nowicki 2002). Observing embryos between 8 and 14 days old in detail, but also between days 15 and 28, Feduccia's earlier work (Burke & Feduccia 1997) was confirmed; birds still had digits DII–DIV as adults, based on the observation of five condensations CI–CV.

New molecular data arrived on the scene in 2005 when 'Birds have dinosaur wings: the molecular evidence' was published (Vargas & Fallon 2005). Here the expression of *Hox* genes in the manus of chicks and mice was studied. From the basal pentadactyl hand it could be shown that *Hox 13* was expressed in all digits, while *Hox 12* was not expressed in the first digit (DI) but in all other digits (DII–DV). In the chick embryos it was apparent that of the three digits that ossify there was no expression of *Hox 12* in the innermost digit, meaning that this digit could correspond to the basal digit I (DI) in the pentadactyle hand in amniotes. Digits DI–DIII in living birds must, therefore, be homologous with those of theropods.

The latest contributions to the digit identity controversy appeared at the 68th Annual Meeting of the Society of Vertebrate Palaeontology (Xu & Clark 2008) and later in *Nature* (Xu *et al.* 2009). Here studies of *Limusaurus inextricabilis*, a new basal ceratosaur (theropod group positioned between coelophysoids and tetanurans) from the Late Jurassic of China with a strongly reduced first digit (DI) and a distally asymmetrical metacarpal II, were introduced. From this new specimen a scenario that contradicts the generally accepted lateral digit reduction in theropods, in favour of a bilateral digit reduction that is more commonly observed in other tetrapod groups, was presented. In this scenario a sequence of events including the reduction of DI and the enlargement of DII in the cerato-saur–tetanuran common ancestor, followed by complete loss of DI and an enlargement of DIV early on in tetanuran evolution, were proposed (Fig. 13). The results were clearly in favour of recent birds and post-Coelophysidaen theropods sharing the 2–3–4 digit configuration. The new

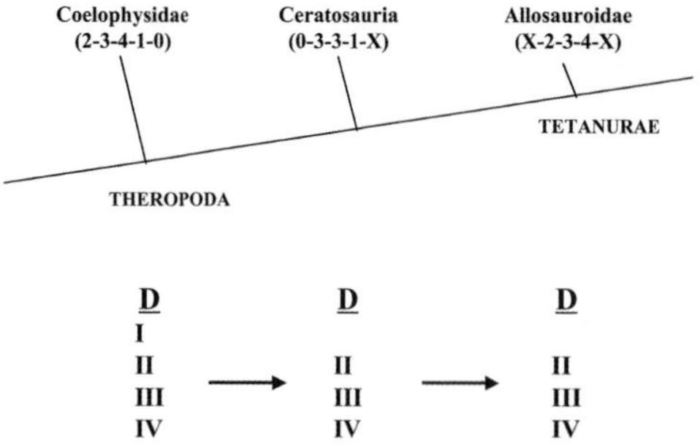

Fig. 13. Schematic representation of manual digital evolution in theropod dinosaurs. D, digit and phalangeal formula in parenthesis. Coelophysidae have the most basal configuration of digits (I–II–III–IV). Ceratosauria (including the newly described species *Limusaurus inextricabilis*) retain only the three middle digits (II–III–IV), as does Allosauridae (including recent birds). The reduction of DI and the enlargement of DII in the ceratosaur–tetanuran common ancestor, followed by a complete loss of DI and an enlargement of DIV early on in tetanuran evolution supports the II–III–IV hypothesis. It should be noted, that according to Xu *et al.* (2009), both Allosauridae and recent birds have different phalangeal formulae to Ceratosauria (Allosauridae, *X*–2–3–4–*X*; recent birds, *X*–1–2–1–*X*), compared with Gauthier (1984, 1988). (adapted from Xu *et al.* 2009).

scenario fitted reasonably well with the frame-shift hypothesis, both with regards to onset of the event and to the general manual morphological characters on the currently accepted theropod phylogeny. It does, however, have one weakness; it requires an increase in phalangeal counts. This increase is relatively rarely observed and therefore this particular issue needs further examination.

Conclusions

The history of investigation regarding digit identity in the manus of theropods (including Aves) is somewhat paradoxical. Almost from the beginning, more than 180 years ago, and right up to today two different branches of the scientific community (vertebrate palaeontology and embryology) continue to disagree on the subject at hand. But is it, in fact, possible to compare results observed in developing embryos with the findings from fossil analysis? No digit condensations have so far been found in any relevant fossil dinosaurs, and therefore a comparative analysis of developing digits in embryos of birds and other relevant theropods can only be theoretical and somewhat speculative. Fossilized eggs have been found with embryos inside, but unfortunately they have not disclosed any information on the identity of forming digits (Chiappe 2007). Until one or more fossil embryos of different stages in development (and of relevant theropod species) have been found, it is probably impossible to make a fair comparison between developments in the embryo.

The fossil record seems to hold the most promising potential to resolve the controversy at this time. New theropod species emerging from China, South America and elsewhere could very probably in the near future, put the digit homology controversy to rest beyond reasonable doubt once and fore all.

Until then, the long history of attempting to identify the digits in theropods (including Aves) that began in Richard Owens' time, more than 180 years ago, continues.

References

Burke, A. C. & Feduccia, A. 1997. Developmental patterns and the identification of homologies in the avian hand. *Science*, **278**, 666–668.

Chatterjee, S. 1998. Counting the fingers of birds and dinosaurs. *Science*, **280**, 355a.

Chiappe, L. M. 2007. *Glorified Dinosaurs*. John Wiley, Chichester.

Coates, M. I. & Clack, J. A. 1990. Polydactyly in the earliest known tetrapod limbs. *Nature*, **347**, 66–69.

Dahn, R. D. & Fallon, J. F. 2000. Interdigital regulation of digit identity and homeotic transformation by modulated BMP signaling. *Science*, **289**, 438–441.

Drossopoulou, G., Lewis, K. E., Sanz-Ezquerro, J. J., Nikbakht, N., McMahon, A. P., Hofmann, C. & Tickle, C. 2000. A model for anteroposterior patterning of the vertebrate limb based on sequential long- and short-range Shh signalling and Bmp signalling. *Development*, **127**, 1337–1348.

Eldredge, N. & Gould, S. J. 1972. Punctuated equilibria: an alternative to phyletic gradualism. *In*: Schopf, T. J. M. (ed.), *Models in Paleobiology*. Freeman, Cooper & Co., San Francisco, CA, 82–115.

Fastovsky, D. E. & Weishampel, D. B. 2005. *The Evolution and Extinction of the Dinosaurs*, 2nd Edn. Cambridge University Press, Cambridge.

Feduccia, A. 1999. 1, 2, 3 = 2, 3, 4 accommodating the cladogram. *Proceedings of the National Academy of Sciences, USA*, **96**, 4740–4742.

Feduccia, A. & Nowicki, J. 2002. The hand of birds revealed by early ostrich embryos. *Naturwissenschaften*, **89**, 391–393.

Gauthier, J. A. 1984. A Cladistic Analysis of the Higher Systematic Categories of the Diapsida. PhD dissertation. Available from University Microfilms International. Ann Arbor, MI #85-12825.

Gauthier, J. A. 1986. Saurischian monophyly and the origin of birds. *Memoirs of the California Academy of Sciences*, **8**, 1–55.

Gauthier, J. A., Kluge, A. & Rowe, T. 1988. Amniote phylogeny and the importance of fossils. *Cladistics*, **4**, 105–209.

Gegenbaur, C. 1864. *Untersuchungen zur vergleichenden Anatomie der Wirbeltiere. I.* Carpus und Tarsus, Leipzig, 6–127.

Gilbert, S. F. 2003. *Developmental Biology*, 7th edn. Sinauer Associates, Sunderland, MA.

GOULD, S. J. 1991. Eight (or fewer) little piggies. *Natural History*, **28**, 405–410.

HEILMANN, G. 1926. *The Origin of Birds*. Witherby, London.

HINCHCLIFFE, J. R. 1984. 'One, two, three' or 'two, three, four': an embryologist's view of the homologies of the digits and carpus of modern birds. *In*: HECHT, M. K., OSTROM, J. H., VIOHL, G. & WELLNHOFER, P. (eds) *The Beginnings of Birds*. Freunde des Jura-Museum, Eichstätt, 141–148.

HOLMGREN, N. 1955. On the origin of the tetrapod limb. *Acta Zoologica*, **14**, 185–295.

HURST, C. H. 1893. Biological theories, VIII. The digits in a bird's wing. *Natural Sciences*, **3**, 275–281.

LARSSON, H. C. E. & WAGNER, G. 2002. Pentadactyl ground state of the avian wing. *Journal of Experimental Zoology*, **294**, 146–151.

LEIGHTON, V. 1894. The development of the wing of *Sterna wilsonii*. *The American Naturalist*, **28**, 761–774.

MECKEL, J. F. 1825. *System der vergleichenden Anatomie*. Theil II, Abt. II. Rengersche, Halle.

MONTAGNA, W. 1945. A re-investigation of the development of the wing of the fowl. *Journal of Morphology*, **76**, 87–113.

MORSE, E. S. 1872. On the tarsus and carpus of birds. *Annals of the Lyceum of Natural History, New York*, **10**, 3–22.

NOPCSA, E. 1894. Aleune recherché sulla morfologia dei membri anteriori degli uccelli. *Richerche fatte nel Laborat Anatomico di Roma e alti laboratori biologici*, **4**, 137–156.

OSTROM, J. H. 1969. *Osteology of* Deinonychus antirrhopus, *an Unusual Theropod From the Lower Cretaceous of Montana*. Peabody Museum of Natural History, Yale University, New Haven, CT.

OWEN, R. 1836. 'Aves' *Todd's Cyclopedia of Anat. and Phys.*, Volume I, 265–358.

OWEN, R. 1842. Report on British Fossil Reptiles. Part II. *Report of the British Association for the Advancement of Science, Plymouth, England*. John Murray, London, 60–204.

OWEN, R. 2007. *On the Nature of Limbs, a Discourse*. Reprint. University of Chicago Press, Chicago, IL.

PARKER, W. K. 1888. On the structure and development of the wing in the common fowl. *Philosophical Transactions of the Royal Society of London. B*, **179**, 385–398.

ROMER, A. S. 1966. *Vertebrate Paleontology*. University of Chicago Press, Chicago, IL.

ROSENBERG, A. 1873. Über die Entwicklung des vorderen Extremitätenskelettes bei einigen durch Reduktion ihrer Gliedmassen charakteristischen Wirbeltiere. *Zeitschrift für wissenschaftliche Zoologie*, **23**, 116–166.

SERENO, P. C. 1999. The evolution of dinosaurs. *Science*, **284**, 2137–2147.

SERENO, P. C., FORSTER, C. A., ROGERS, R. R. & MONETTA, A. M. 1993. Primitive dinosaur skeleton from Argentina and the early evolution of Dinosauria. *Nature*, **361**, 64–66.

SHUBIN, N. & ALBERCH, P. 1986. A morphogenetic approach to the origin and basic organization of the tetrapod limb. *Evolutionary Biology*, **20**, 319–387.

SIEGLBAUER, F. 1911. Zur Entwicklung der Vogelextremität. *Zeitschrift für wissenschaftliche Zoologie*, **97**, 262–313.

STEINER, H. 1922. Die ontogenetische und phylogenetische Entwicklung des Vogelflüelskelettes. *Acta Zoologica*, **3**, 307–360.

TARSITANO, S. & HECHT, M. 1980. A reconsideration of the reptilian relationships of *Archaeopteryx*. *Zoological Journal of the Linnean Society*, **69**, 149–182.

THULBORN, R. A. 1993. A tale of three fingers: ichnological evidence revealing the homologies of manual digits in theropod dinosaurs. *New Mexico Museum of Natural History & Science Bulletin*, **3**, 461–463.

TSCHAN, A. 1889. *Reserches sur l'extremité anterieur des oiseaux et des reptiles*. Dissertation, université de Genève.

VARGAS, A. O. & FALLON, J. F. 2005. Birds have dinosaur wings: the molecular evidence. *Journal of Experimental Zoology*, **304B**, 86–90.

WAGNER, G. & GAUTHIER, J. A. 1999. 1, 2, 3 = 2, 3, 4: A solution to the problem of the homology of the digits in the avian hand. *Proceedings of the National Academy of Sciences, USA*, **96**, 5111–5116.

WELLNHOFER, P. 1984. Remarks on the digit and pubis problems of *Archaeopteryx*. *In*: HECHT, M. K., OSTROM, J. H., VIOHL, G. & WELLNHOFER, P. (eds) *The Beginnings of Birds*. Freunde des Jura-Museum, Eichstätt, 113–122.

XU, X. & CLARK, J. 2008. Homologies in the hand of theropods. *In*: *68th Annual Meeting, Journal of Vertebrate Paleontology, Program and Extracts*. Publisher, 163A.

XU, X., CLARK, J. M. ET AL. 2009. A Jurassic ceratosaur from China helps clarify avian digital homologies, *Nature*, **459**, 940–944.

The history of Late Jurassic pterosaurs housed in Hungarian collections and the revision of the holotype of *Pterodactylus micronyx* Meyer 1856 (a 'Pester Exemplar')

ATTILA ŐSI[1]*, EDINA PRONDVAI[2] & BARNABÁS GÉCZY[2]

[1]*Hungarian Academy of Sciences – Hungarian Natural History Museum, Research Group for Palaeontology, Ludovika tér 2, Budapest, 1083, Hungary*

[2]*Eötvös Loránd University, Department of Palaeontology, Pázmány Péter sétány 1/c, Budapest, 1117, Hungary*

**Corresponding author (e-mail: hungaros@freemail.hu)*

Abstract: The history and scientific significance of three Late Jurassic pterosaur specimens housed in different Hungarian palaeontological collections are described. One of these is the holotype of *Pterodactylus micronyx* Meyer 1856 that was thought to be lost, but with its rediscovery in the 1980s the 'Pester Exemplar' becomes the name-bearing type again. The second specimen is an articulated, partially three-dimensional skeleton of a *Rhamphorhynchus muensteri*; and the third is an articulated right hindlimb of a *Pterodactylus* sp. – both donated by Andor Semsey to the Hungarian Geological Institute. The anatomical revision of the holotype of *P. micronyx* indicated the osteological immaturity of the specimen; however, there is insufficient data on this taxon to assess its taxonomic validity.

Three specimens of Late Jurassic pterosaurs are housed in the palaeontological collections of different Hungarian institutes. All were collected from the Upper Jurassic Solnhofen Limestone in southern Germany. From a historical perspective, the most interesting specimen is the holotype of *Pterodactylus micronyx* Meyer 1856 (Meyer 1859) (Fig. 1).

This find, known as the 'Pester Exemplar' (ELTE V 265 – Eötvös University, Budapest, Hungary (ELTE)), is one of the earliest discoveries of pterosaur fossils and has an eventful history going back to second half of the eighteenth century (Meyer 1856, 1859; Géczy 1989, 1991). Meyer (1859, p. 59) stated that:

> diese Versteinerung fand sich unter altem Vorrath, wonach anzunehmen ist, dass sie schon zur Zeit der Kaiserin Maria Theresia (gest. 1780) in die Sammlung gekommen; sie gehört daher zu den wenigen Stücken von *Pterodactylus*, die so alt sind, dass man die Zeit ihrer Auffindung nicht mehr im Stande ist zu ermitteln. [this fossil was found in an old collection; by reason of that it presumably got into the collection at the time of Empress Maria Theresa (d. 1780), consequently it belongs to the few *Pterodactylus* specimens that are so old that their date of discovery cannot be determined.]

As was brought to light by Papp & Weiszburg (1985), originally this famous find was deposited in the private collection of Archduchess Maria Anna (1738–1789) (Fig. 2), daughter of Empress Maria Theresa, before Collini (1784) described the Mannheim specimen of *Pterodactylus antiquus*. This is also supported by a paper label on the back of the counterpart slab that includes the letters P.AI.e.4.M. (Fig. 3). Papp & Weiszburg (1985) pointed out that in the catalogue of the Maria Anna Collection these letters stand for the words 'Petrefacta' (fossil), 'Animalia', 'entomolithi' (arthropods), the serial number of the specimen in the collection and Maria Anna, respectively. The Mannheim specimen of *P. antiquus* has usually been regarded as the earliest pterosaur find in the world (Wellnhofer 1991). It was not mentioned in the catalogue of the Mannheim Collection in 1767 but was published in 1784, indicating that its discovery and deposition into the Mannheim Collection occurred during this period (Wellnhofer 1984). The 'Pester Exemplar' was found, however, probably after 1757 and certainly before its first study in 1779 (see below). The earlier date refers to the convalescence of Maria Anna from pneumonia and tuberculosis, after which she became interested in collecting minerals and fossils. This indicates that the 'Pester Exemplar' was one of the earliest, if not the earliest, pterosaur find in the world!

The first scientific contribution to the 'Pester Exemplar' was made by one of the most outstanding naturalists of the Middle European Enlightenment, Ignaz von Born (Fig. 4), who determined the specimen incorrectly as a decapod crustacean

From: MOODY, R. T. J., BUFFETAUT, E., NAISH, D. & MARTILL, D. M. (eds) *Dinosaurs and Other Extinct Saurians: A Historical Perspective*. Geological Society, London, Special Publications, **343**, 277–286.
DOI: 10.1144/SP343.17 0305-8719/10/$15.00

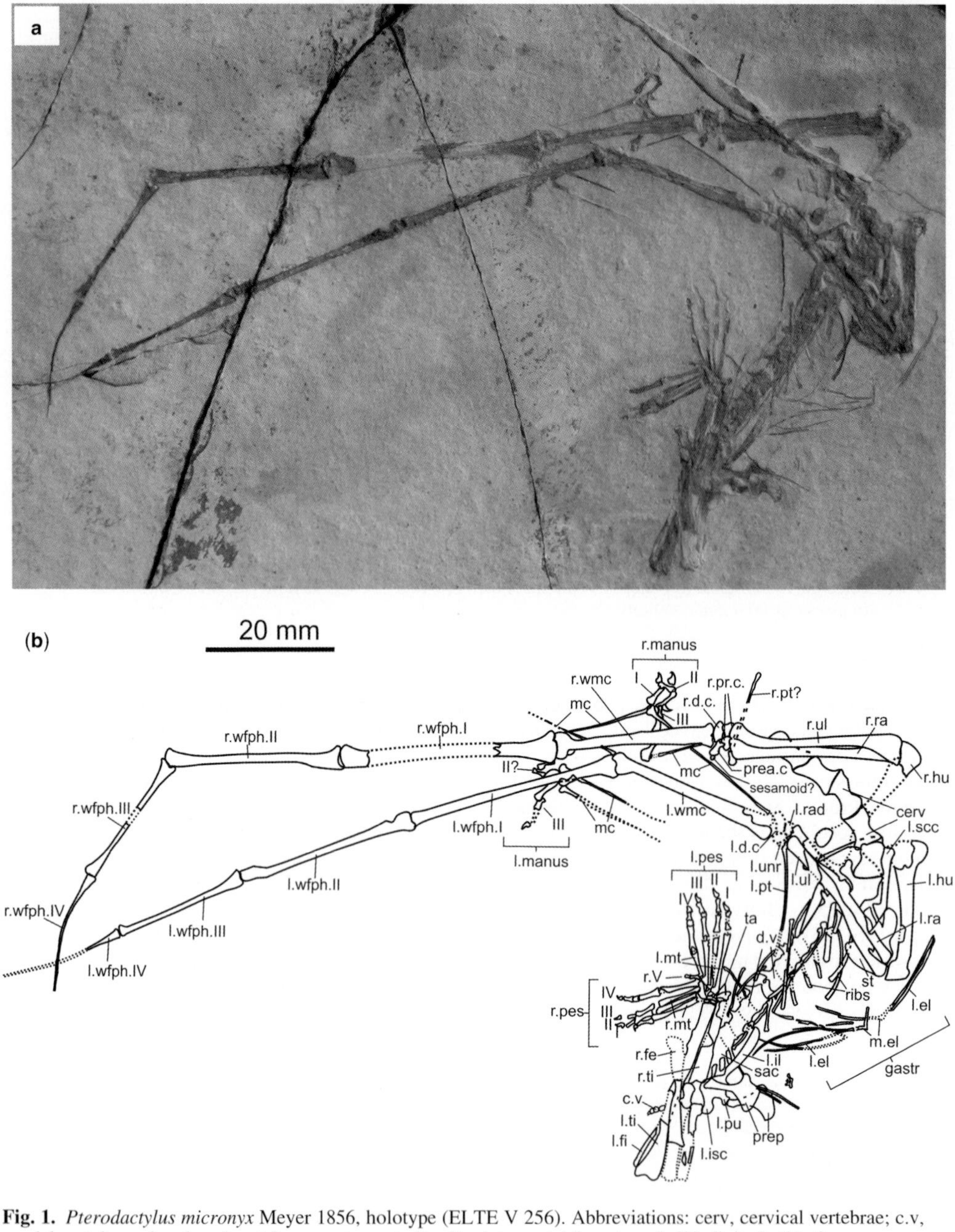

Fig. 1. *Pterodactylus micronyx* Meyer 1856, holotype (ELTE V 256). Abbreviations: cerv, cervical vertebrae; c.v, caudal vertebrae; d.v, dorsal vertebrae; gastr, gastralia; f.ic, intercostal fenestrae; I–IV, digits I–IV of manus or pes; l.d.c, left distal carpals; l.el, lateral elements of gastralia; l.fi, left fibula; l.hu, left humerus; l.il, left ilium; l.il.pr, preacetabular part of the left ilium; l.isc, left ischium, l.manus, left manus; l.mt.I–IV, left metatarsals I–IV; l.mt, left metatarsals; l.pd.I–IV, left pedal digits I–IV; l.pes, left pes; l.ph.I–V, left phalanges I–V of the pedal digits; l.pr.c, left proximal carpals; l.pu, left pubis; l.ra, left radius; l.rad, left radiale; l.scc, left scapulocoracoid; l.ti, left tibia; l.unr, left ulnare; l.wfphI–IV, left wing finger phalanges I–IV.; l.wmc, left wing metacarpal; m.el, medial elements of gastralia; mc, metacarpals; prea.c, preaxial carpal; prep, prepubes; pt, pteroid; r.d.c, right distal carpals; r.fe, right femur; r.hu, right humerus; r.isc, right ischium; r.manus, right manus; r.mt.I–V, right metatarsals I–V; r.mt, right metatarsals; r.pd.I–V, right pedal digits I–V; r.pes, right pes; r.ph.I–V, right phalanges I–V of the pedal digits; r.pr.c, right proximal carpals; r.ra, right radius; r.ti, right tibia; r.V, fith digit of the right pes; r.wfphI–IV, right wing finger phalanges I–IV.; r.wmc, right wing metacarpal; sac, sacrals; st, sternum; ta, tarsals.

Fig. 2. Archduchess Maria Anna Jozefa (1738–1789), who was the first owner of the holotype of *Pterodactylus micronyx*.

Fig. 4. Ignaz von Born (1742–1791) was the first to study the holotype specimen of *Pterodactylus micronyx*, but identified it incorrectly as a decapod crustacean.

(Born 1779). In 1781 the Maria Anna Collection (including other fossils, as well as minerals, and zoological and botanical specimens) was sold to the Royal Hungarian University of Buda for 25000 florins. In the following decades the specimen was housed in the collection of Pest University (in 1784 the university had to move from Buda to Pest: Papp & Weiszburg 1991), where in the 1850s professors Langer and Peters handed the specimen to the excellent German palaeontologist Hermann von Meyer. Meyer (1856) briefly described and later (1859) also figured the ‘Pester Exemplar’ as *Pterodactylus micronyx*.

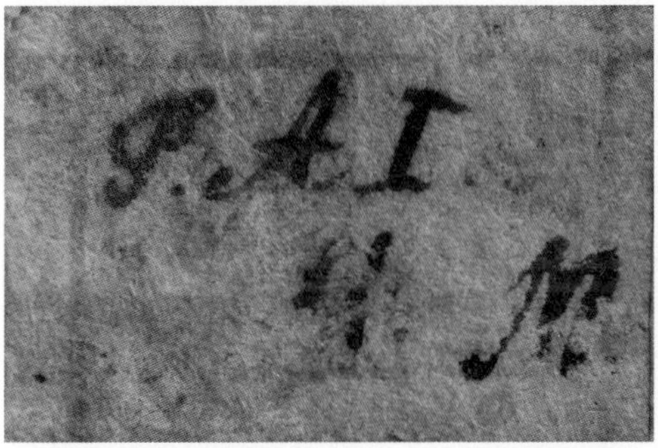

Fig. 3. The paper label preserved on the back of the counterpart slab of the holotype of *Pterodactylus micronyx*.

More than a century later, in 1968, Peter Wellnhofer asked Ilona Csepreghyné Meznerics, the Head of the Department of Palaeontology in the Hungarian Natural History Museum at that time, to provide information on the holotype of *P. micronyx* (Wellnhofer 1970; Géczy 1991). Unfortunately, however, the specimen could not be found either in the museum or at Eötvös University and was thought to be lost; therefore Wellnhofer (1970) established a neotype (specimen #42) for *P. micronyx*. In 1982, as the result of rearrangements of the collections in the Department of Palaeontology at Eötvös University, in preparation for a ceremony celebrating the centenary of the department, the ‘Pester Exemplar’ was found (Géczy 1987, 1989, 1991) and, thus, was again available as a holotype. Because of it having been mislaid nobody had studied the holotype specimen of *P. micronyx* in detail since Meyer (1859). In the 110 years following 1859, 15 additional specimens of *P. micronyx* had been discovered from the Upper Jurassic Lithographic Limestone of the Altmühl-Alb (for a review see Wellnhofer 1970). As a result of these finds much new information has been published on *P. micronyx* (Winkler 1870; Broili 1912; Wiman

1925; Wellnhofer 1970) that has greatly improved our knowledge of this taxon, especially of its skull, which is, unfortunately, missing in the holotype.

More recently, Bennett (1993, 1995, 1996) questioned the taxonomic diversity of the Solnhofen pterosaur fauna and, based on cranial characters, stated that '*Pterodactylus micronyx* and *Gnathosaurus subulatus* are juveniles and adults, respectively, of a single species' (Bennett 1996). Unfortunately, the missing skull of the holotype *P. micronyx* prevents a direct comparison with *Gnathosaurus subulatus*. Here we redescribe the holotype of *Pterodactylus micronyx* (see below) and include those features, especially characteristics of juveniles, that were not discussed by Meyer (1859).

The two other Hungarian specimens have apparently never been studied scientifically. One is a partially articulated, exquisitely preserved skeleton of a *Rhamphorhynchus sp.* (MTM V 2008.33.1.) (Fig. 5a). Originally, the specimen was bought in 1904 by one of the greatest patrons of Hungarian science, Andor Semsey, for 800 German Marks from Wilhelm Grimm, who was the supervisor of a Solnhofen quarry at that time. Only partially prepared, the specimen was on display in the exhibition of the Geological Institute of Hungary. Later, in the 1960s, it was transferred to the Hungarian Natural History Museum. Interestingly, Baron Franz Nopcsa, who was the director of the Geological Institute from 1925 to 1928, never worked on this superb specimen.

The third Late Jurassic pterosaur specimen (MÁFI V.08.823.1. (V. 27889)) is an articulated hindlimb of a pterodactyloid pterosaur housed in the Museum of the Geological Institute of Hungary (Fig. 5b). There are no data on its origin, but most probably it was also given by Semsey as a gift to the Geological Institute.

Today, these latter two pterosaur remains seem to have no particular taxonomic significance. In comparative anatomical, palaeobiological and also historical perspectives, however, they can provide important new information for pterosaur research.

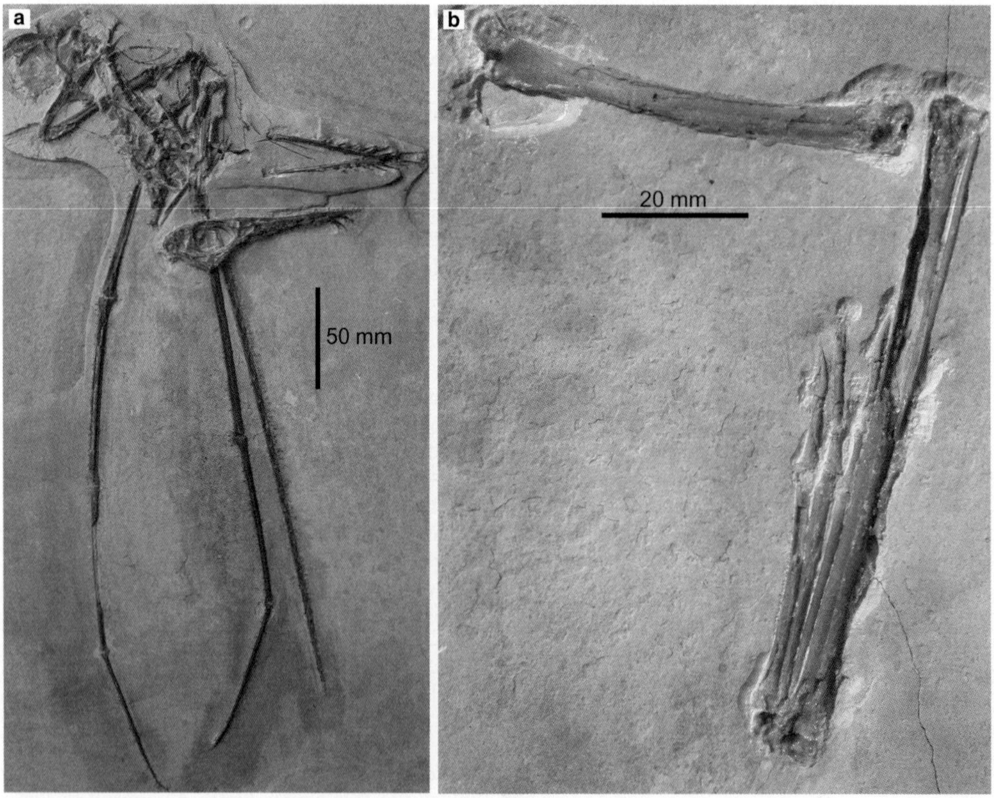

Fig. 5. Pterosaur specimens from different Hungarian palaeontological collections. (**a**) *Rhamphorhynchus muensteri* (Goldfuss 1831) (MTM V 2008.33.1). (**b**) *Pterodactylus* sp. (MAFI V.08.823.1. (V. 27889)).

Redescription of the holotype of *Pterodactylus micronyx* Meyer 1856

The holotype of *Pterodactylus micronyx* Meyer 1856 was described in more detail in 1859 (Meyer 1859). Since Meyer's study, however, some small parts of the holotype specimen have been eroded due as a result of the university and collection having been relocated on various occasions. Furthermore, since Meyer's work 15 additional specimens of *P. micronyx* have been published (Wellnhofer 1978). Thus, besides the rediscovery of the specimen, the above-mentioned circumstances led us to provide a new anatomical description of the specimen.

Systematic Palaeontology

Order Pterosauria Kaup 1834
Suborder Pterodactyloidea Plieninger 1901
Family Pterodactylidae Bonaparte 1838
Pterodactylus Cuvier 1809
Pterodactylus micronyx Meyer 1856

Holotype

ELTE V 265 (Fig. 1 and Table 1), housed in the Natural History Museum of Eötvös University. Corresponding to the International Code of Zoological Nomenclature (1999), with the rediscovery of the holotype in 1982, the established neotype by Wellnhofer (1970) is invalid and the rediscovered material becomes the name-bearing type again.

Type locality. The original inventory catalogue shows that the locality of the specimen is 'Eichstätt in Schwebischer Kreise', Bayern, southern Germany (Géczy 1991).

Type horizon. Solnhofen Beds, Lowermost Tithonian, Altmühl-Alb, southern Germany.

Table 1. Measurements of the skeletal elements of *Pterodactylus micronyx* Meyer 1856 holotype (ELTE V 256) from the Upper Jurassic of Eichstäat

Skeletal elements of the holotype of *Pterodacrylus micronyx* (ELTE V 256)	Length (in mm)
Atlas–axix	–
3rd	6.1
4th	6.1
5th	5.6
6th	6
7th	7.7
dorsal column	31.4
sacrum	–
caudal column	–
left coracoideum	11
Sternum	–
l. humerus	20.7
r. radius	25
r. ulna	25.5
r. carpus	2.8
r. pteroid	15.1
r. metacarpal IV	26.1
r. wingphalanx I	33.7
r. wingphalanx II	28.7
r. wingphalanx III	21.8
r. wingphalanx IV	19
r. wingfinger	103.2
Prepubis	7.2
l. illium	–
r. femur	22
l. tibia	28.9
r. metatarsal I	9
r. metatarsal II	8.2
r. metatarsal III	7.8
r. metatarsal IV	6.8
r. metatarsal V	1.6

l., left; r., right.

Description and comparisons

Meyer (1859) described the holotype of *P. micronyx* including most of the measurements of the identifiable bones and the phalanges formula of the foot (see also Wellnhofer 1970). The holotype of *Pterodactylus micronyx* is in a small (170 × 155 mm), 10 mm-thin slab that contains the more or less articulated skeleton. Except for the middle part of the first phalanx of the right wing finger and some parts of the epiphyses of various wing and limb elements, the counterpart contains only the impressions of the bones (Fig. 6). The specimen on the main slab lacks the skull and the mandible or any of their elements. The skeleton is fairly compressed and most of the bones are crushed. In some cases the actual bones or parts of the bones are missing, only their impressions can be seen. Most of the epiphyses of long bones are severely damaged. No traces of soft-tissue preservation have been observed on the holotype specimen.

Axial skeleton

The vertebral column appears to be well articulated but greatly damaged, and the identification of different vertebrae is not always possible (Figs 1 and 7). Of the cervical series, the last five vertebrae can be separated and appear to be well articulated to the dorsal series. Both Meyer (1862) and Wellnhofer (1970) described seven cervicals, indicating that of the holotype probably only the atlas and axis are not preserved. The first preserved cervical

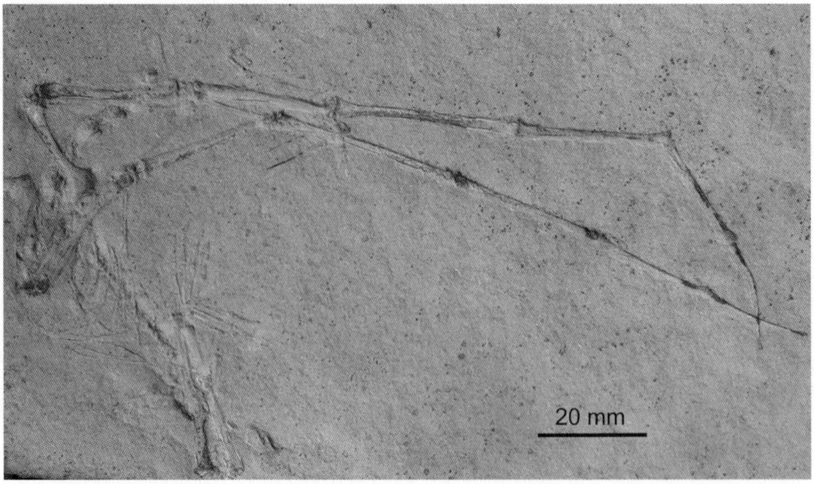

Fig. 6. The counterpart slab of holotype specimen *Pterodactylus micronyx* Meyer 1856 (ELTE V 256).

(3rd) is partially covered with the right ulna–radius complex. The cervicals are strongly eroded and only some parts of the centra or their outlines can be recognized. The poorly preserved right humerus is lying above the 6th cervical.

The dorsal series is better preserved, including probably 14 or 15 vertebrae depending on the last one that cannot be unambiguously separated from the sacrals. Meyer (1862) calculated 13–15 dorsal for specimen #41 and Wellnhofer (1970) described 15 dorsals in specimen #30. The right laterally exposed dorsals are strongly compressed; their centra are slightly concave and 1.5 times longer anteroposteriorly than high. Some of the left ribs are preserved attached to the dorsal vertebrae (?5th–7th) and some ribs are lying separately but

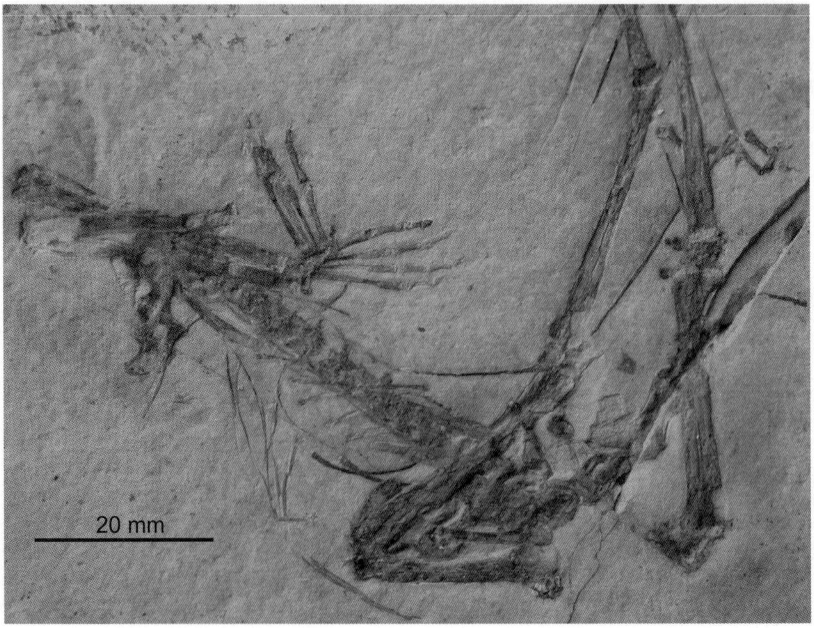

Fig. 7. Details of the body of *Pterodactylus micronyx* Meyer 1856, holotype (ELTE V 256).

close to the vertebral column. Numerous gastralia consisting of lateral and medial elements lie close to the dorsal vertebrae.

The sacrum is covered by the right tibia, thus only a small part of the first sacral and the first two right sacral ribs are seen (Figs 1 and 7). The sacral ribs are short and massive. As Meyer (1859) also noted, from the caudal series only the distal two or three can be seen because the right tibia and fibula cover the anterior ones.

Appendicular skeleton

The shape of the ventrally exposed sternum differs from those illustrated by Meyer (1862) and by Wellnhofer (1970, fig. 8) in having a sternal plate that is rather axe–shaped with a slightly rounded edge posteriorly (Figs 1 and 7). The sternal plate is partially covered by the left radius–ulna complex. The anterior part of the sternum is damaged, thus the cristospina cannot be observed.

One of the scapulocoracoids, probably the right, is completely crushed. The left one is also damaged but can be studied (Figs 1 and 7). The middle part of the coracoid shaft is circular in cross-section. The scapula is blade-like and the scapula–coracoid junction is covered by one of the cervical vertebrae.

Both forelimbs are preserved and almost completely articulated (Figs 1 and 7). The left humerus appears to be articulated to the glenoid of the scapulocoracoid but it is badly damaged. Of the right humerus, only some small pieces and its outline are preserved. The proximal epiphysis, especially the deltopectoral crest, is not wide, which is similar to other specimens of *Pterodactylus* (Wellnhofer 1970, 1978). The condyles of the distal ends of the humeri cannot be recognized. Both humeri were preserved as being connected to the lower arms. The ulnae and radii can be recognized on both sides, but they are better preserved on the right side. Although compressed, they are straight elongate bones.

Of the left carpals, only their impressions are preserved, which, however, better show the form and articulation of proximal and distal carpals than on the right side where they are almost completely crushed (Figs 1 and 7). On the left side the impression of the ulnare and radiale are very easily distinguished from the three distal carpals, as was also illustrated by Wellnhofer (1970, fig. 8c). This indicates the absence of fused proximal and distal syncarpals in the specimen. The left pteroid appears to be present but was rotated from its original position (Figs 1 and 7). On the right side, however, a thumb-shaped carpal, probably the preaxial carpal (also called as medial carpal by Unwin *et al.* 1996), appears to be present directed anteriorly from the distal carpals. There is a smaller rounded bone preserved anteriorly to the preaxial carpal, possibly the sesamoid (also called 'sesamoid A' by Bennett 2001) which normally sits in the dorsal pit of the preaxial carpal (Bennett 2001; Frey *et al.* 2006). This sesamoid was not mentioned by Wellnhofer (1970, 1978). A distal end of a thin needle-like bone, suggested here as the right pteroid bone, is preserved close to the carpals of the right wing which continues as an impression and ends proximal to the supposed sesamoid.

From the metacarpals, only the wing metacarpals are articulated on both sides. Metacarpals I–III are extremely thin bones with circular cross-section, and they are slightly crushed and disarticulated from the forearm. Whereas parts of digits I–III of the right manus are disarticulated but well-preserved, the left manus is incomplete and only the phalanges of the second and third digits are preserved. The wing fingers are in good condition, although some parts of the diaphyses of phalanges are lost. The last needle-like phalanx of the right wing finger is slightly curved, but it seems that this feature is not due to the compression.

The pelvic girdle is strongly compressed but some elements lying somewhat separated can be studied. The ventrally exposed left preacetabular iliac process is present, reaching cranially the level of the third last dorsal vertebra, similarly to specimen #30 (Wellnhofer 1970) (figs 1 and 7). It has slightly concave medial and slightly convex lateral edges, and its anterior end is rounded anterolaterally. A rugose, wrinkled surface, probably a muscle scar is present on its anteroventral surface, was probably the origin of the M. iliotibialis (Baumel 1993), the name of which refers only to its topographically corresponding position and not to its homology with the identical muscles in birds. The postacetabular processes cannot be clearly observed. The ischium and pubis are preserved on both sides. The pubis and the ischium are connected to each other, and on the left side a poorly preserved suture can be recognized between them. The pubes are mostly covered with other bones, but ventrally they have a 1.3 mm-long process for attachment of the prepubic plates. Both prepubic plates are well preserved and have a 3.5 mm-long dorsally oriented shaft and an axe-shaped ventral plate (figs 1 and 7).

The hindlimbs are preserved but, except for the pes, they are strongly compressed and damaged. The right hindlimb is almost completely articulated but does not connect to the acetabulum. Of the femora, the right one is present but its epiphyses are missing and only their impressions can be recognized. The left tibia and fibula are articulated, and the proximal end of the fibula is ball-like. Both feet are well preserved (Fig. 8) and the left one is nicely articulated with the tibia. The right pes is

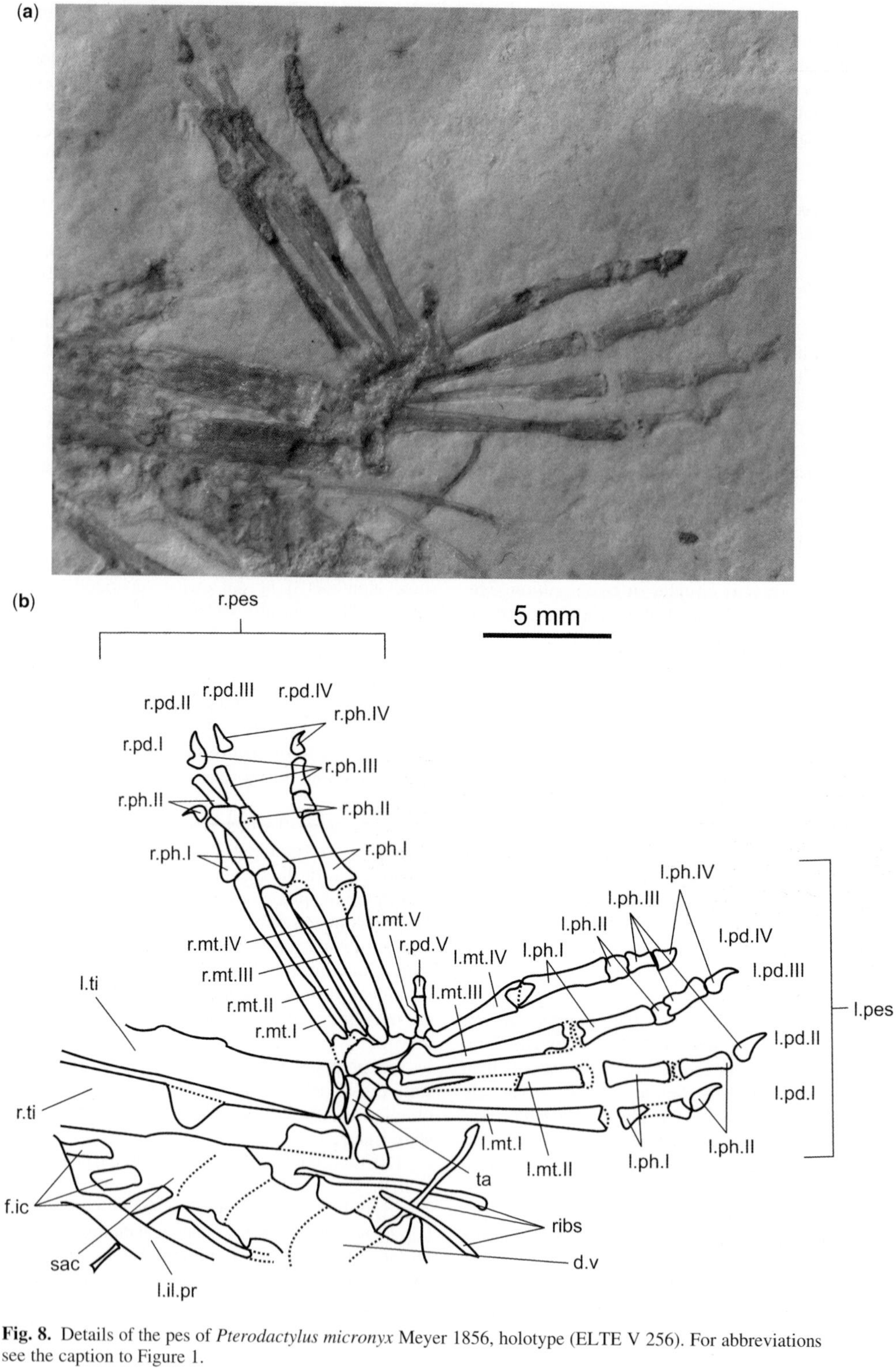

Fig. 8. Details of the pes of *Pterodactylus micronyx* Meyer 1856, holotype (ELTE V 256). For abbreviations see the caption to Figure 1.

close to the tibia but rotated almost 120° to the left. The tarsals are strongly damaged and only the proximal ones of the right pes can be recognized. Similar to specimen #30 (Wellnhofer 1970, fig. 8b), the first metatarsal is the longest and metatarsals II–IV gradually decrease in length, whereas the fifth is extremely short. The numbers of phalanges of digits I–V are 2–3–4–4–1, respectively, in contrast to the observation made by Meyer (1856) who described the formula 2–3–3–3–1. Meyer probably overlooked the very small second phalanges in both the third and fourth digits.

Ontogenetic stage and taxonomic position of the specimen

The 'Pester Exemplar' clearly represents a small specimen among the Solnhofen pterosaurs, with an estimated wingspan of about 38 cm, and some size-independent features listed by Bennett (1993) suggest its subadult nature. All epiphyses of the limb bones are damaged, preventing the study of the degree of epiphyseal ossification. The surface of limb bone shafts (e.g. both radii and ulnae, right wing metacarpal), however, possesses numerous vascular canals opening onto the external surface of the bones indicating skeletal immaturity. The fusion of the tibia with proximal tarsals cannot be studied owing to the poor preservation; however, the suture between the left ischium and pubis, and the distinguishable elements of the proximal and distal carpals of the left carpus, refer to a subadult ontogenetic stage.

Wellnhofer (1970) noted the increase in the number of the third and fourth hindlimb digits in *P. micronyx*, which he suggested were related with the size of the animal. Specimen #42, originally described by Broili (1912), is one of the largest of the *P. micronyx* specimens with the numbers of phalanges of foot digits I–V being 2–3–4–5–1, respectively (Wellnhofer 1970, fig. 19). However, in specimens #30, #32 and #33, with a smaller body size, this formula is 2–3–3–3–1 (Wellnhofer 1970). Concerning the size of the 'Pester Exemplar', it is intermediate between that of the smaller specimens, #30, #32 and #33, and the larger specimen, #42, and its phalangeal formula appears also to be transitional between those of the smaller and larger specimens.

As pointed out by Wellnhofer (1970), and later by Bennett (1996) and Jouve (2004), the majority of specimens referred to *Pterodactylus micronyx* represent juveniles. On the basis of dental and cranial characters, Bennett (1996) regarded *P. micronyx* (Meyer 1856) as the juvenile form of *Gnathosaurus subulatus* (Meyer 1834), which, in this case, would have priority. Jouve (2004), however, noted that *P. micronyx* could be the juvenile form of *G. subulatus*, as well as that of *Ctenochasma roemeri* and *Ctenochasma* sp., but there is not enough morphological data to determine which species is the adult form of *P. micronyx*. According to this the 'Pester Exemplar' is referred here to *Pterodactylus micronyx*, with the comment that additional material and future studies, particularly on the cranial characters of these species, may change this conception.

We are grateful to the organizers of the meeting 'Dinosaurs: Historical Perspective'. We thank T. Weiszburg and G. Zboray (ELTE) for access to the specimen and we are grateful to J. Pálfy (MTM) for critically reading the first draft of the manuscript. We are grateful to E. Buffetaut (CNRS), and to Á. Görög (ELTE) and R. Wernli (Université de Genève), for sending relevant reprints.

References

Baumel, J. J. 1993. *Handbook of Avian Anatomy: Nomina Anatomica Avium*, 2nd edn, Publications of the Ornithological Club, **23**.

Bennett, S. C. 1993. The ontogeny of *Pteranodon* and other pterosaurs. *Paleobiology*, **19**, 92–106.

Bennett, S. C. 1995. A statistical study of *Rhamphorhynchus* from the Solnhofen Limestone of Germany: year-classes of a single large species. *Journal of Paleontology*, **69**, 569–580.

Bennett, S. C. 1996. Year-classes of pterosaurs from the Solnhofen Limestone of Germany: taxonomic and systematic implications. *Journal of Vertebrate Paleontology*, **16**, 432–444.

Bennett, S. C. 2001. The osteology and functional morphology of the Late Cretaceous pterosaur *Pteranodon*. *Palaeontographica*, Abteilung A, **260**, 1–153.

Bonaparte, C. L. 1838. Synopsis vertebratorum systematis. Amphibiorum. *Nuovi Annali Science Naturali Bologna*, **2**, 391–397.

Born, I. 1779. Zufällige Gedanken über die Anwendung der Konchylien Petrefaktenkude auf die physikalische Erdbeschreibung. *Abhandlungen einer Privatgesellschafts*, **4**, 305–312.

Broili, F. 1912. Über *Pterodactylus micronyx* H. v. Meyer. *Zeitschrift der Deutschen Geologischen Gesellschaft*, **64**, 492–500.

Collini, A. C. 1784. Sur quelques zoolithes du cabinet d'histoire naturelle de S.A.S.E. Palatine et de Baviére, à Mannheim. *Acta Academiae Theodoro-Palatinae Mannheim*, **5**, *pars physica*, 58–103.

Cuvier, G. 1809. Mémoire sur le squelette fossile d'un reptile volant des environs d'Aichstedt, que quelques naturalistes ont pris pour un oiseau, et dont nous formons un genre de sauriens, sous le nom de Ptero-Dactyle. *Annales de Musée du Historie Naturales, Paris*, **13**, 424.

Frey, E., Buchy, M.-C., Stinnesbeck, W. & González, A. G. & di Stefano, A. 2006. *Muzquizopteryx coahuilensis* n.g., n. sp., a nyctosaurid pterosaur with soft tissue preservation from the Coniacian (Late

Cretaceous) of northeast Mexico (Coahuila). *Oryctos*, **6**, 19–39.

GÉCZY, B. 1987. An unrivalled *Pterodactylus* specimen. *Természet Világa*, **118**, 32–34 (in Hungarian).

GÉCZY, B. 1989. Ignace Born et le *Pterodactylus* dans le collection de l'archiduchesse Marianne. *In*: *Transactions of the Seventh International Congress on Enlightenment, Voltaire Centre, Taylor Institute, Oxford*, 808–810.

GÉCZY, B. 1991. History of the 'Pester Exemplar' of *Pterodactylus*. *In*: VITÁLIS, GY. & KECSKEMÉTI, T. (eds) *Museums and Collections in the History of Mineralogy, Geology and Paleontology in Hungary*. Hungarian Geological Society, Budapest, 159–167.

JOUVE, S. 2004. Description of the skull of *Ctenochasma* (Pterosauria) from the latest Jurassic of eastern France, with a taxonomic revision of European Tithonian Pterodactyloidea. *Journal of Vertebrate Paleontology*, **24**, 542–554.

KAUP, J. 1834. Versuch einer Eintheilung der Säugethiere in 6 Stämme und der Amphibien in 6 Ordnungen. *Isis von Oken*, **1834**, 311–324.

MEYER, H. VON 1834. Beiträge zur Petrefactenkunde. *Gnathosaurus subulatus*, ein Saurus aus dem lithographischen Schiefer von Solnhofen. *Museum Senckenbergianum*, **1**, 1–26.

MEYER, H. VON 1856. Letter on various fossil vertebrates. *Neues Jahrbuch für Mineralogie, Geognomie Geologie Petrefakt*, 826.

MEYER, H. VON 1859. *Zur Fauna der Vorwelt. Vierte Abt.: Reptilien aus dem lithographischen Schiefer des Jura in Deutschland und Frankreich*, Vol. 1. Lieferung, Frankfurt am Main, 59–60.

MEYER, H. VON 1862. *Pterodactylus micronyx* aus der lithographischen Schiefer von Solenhofen. *Palaeontographica*, **10**, 47–52.

PAPP, G. & WEISZBURG, T. 1985. *Two Centuries of the Mineralogical Collection of Budapest University*. Unpublished manuscript, Department of Mineralogy, Eötvös Loránd University, Budapest (in Hungarian).

PAPP, G. & WEISZBURG, T. 1991. The mineral collection of Archduchess Maria Anna. *In*: VITÁLIS, GY. & KECSKEMÉTI, T. (eds) *Museums and Collections in the History of Mineralogy, Geology and Paleontology in Hungary*. Hungarian Geological Society, Budapest, 135–143.

PLIENINGER, F. 1901. Beiträge zur Kenntnis der Flugsaurier. *Palaeontographica*, **48**, 65–90.

UNWIN, D. M., FREY, E., MARTILL, D. M., CLARKE, J. B. & RIESS, J. 1996. On the nature of the pteroid in pterosaurs. *Proceedings: Biological Sciences*, **263**, 45–52.

WELLNHOFER, P. 1970. Die Pterodactyloidea (Pterosauria) der Oberjura-Plattenkalke Süddeutschlands. *Bayerische Akademie der Wissenschaften, Mathematisch-Naturwissenschaftliche Klasse, Abhandlungen*, **141**, 1–133.

WELLNHOFER, P. 1978. Pterosauria, *Handbuch der Paleoherpetology. Teil 19. Pterosauria*. Gustav Fischer, Stuttgart.

WELLNHOFER, P. 1984. Cuvier and his influence on the first known pterosaur. *In*: BUFFETAUT, E., MAZIN, J.-M. & SALMON, E. (eds) *Actes du symposium paléontologique G. Cuvier*, Montbéliard, 525–538.

WELLNHOFER, P. 1991. *The Illustrated Encyclopedia of Pterosaurs*. Crescent Books, New York.

WIMAN, C. 1925. Über einige Flugsaurier. *Paläontologische Zeitschrift*, **7**, 15–20.

WINKLER, T. C. 1870. Description d'un nouvel exemplaire de *Pterodactylus micronyx* du Musée Teyler. *Archives du Musée Teyler*, **3**, 1–16.

The early history of pterosaur discovery in Great Britain

DAVID M. MARTILL

Palaeobiology Research Group, School of Earth and Environmental Sciences, University of Portsmouth, Portsmouth PO1 3QL, UK
(e-mail: david.martill@port.ac.uk)

Abstract: The first pterosaur fossil was described by Cosimo Alessandro Collini in 1784, but the epithet *ptero dactyle* was not applied until Georges Cuvier recognized the fossil as that of a volant animal in 1801. In eighteenth-century Britain, pterosaur bones had been discovered in Jurassic strata at Stonesfield, Oxfordshire but were considered to be bird bones, and largely went unnoticed. Bones of pterosaurs considerably larger than those of the first pterosaurs were discovered in the early nineteenth century by Gideon Mantell, but because of their comparatively large size were considered by Cuvier to also be the bones of birds. This perception by early nineteenth-century palaeontologists, including William Buckland and Gideon Mantell, that pterosaurs were relatively small animals was probably the reason their remains went unrecognized in British Jurassic and Cretaceous strata for several decades. Furthermore, the eighteenth- and early nineteenth-century dogmatic acceptance that fossil birds *were* present in the Jurassic Stonesfield 'slate' of Oxfordshire delayed the identification of medium-sized pterosaurs until the late 1820s, when Dean William Buckland described the Liassic *Pterodactylus* (= *Dimorphodon*) *macronyx* in 1829. Even after that date many fragmentary, but large, pterosaur bones were misidentified as avian, despite there being no convincing evidence for Mesozoic birds until the discovery of *Archaeopteryx* in the 1860s. Truly gigantic pterosaurs were first discovered in Great Britain some 20 years before *Pteranodon* was found in the Late Cretaceous of Kansas. However, the British material was so fragmentary that it was easily eclipsed by the spectacular, near-complete skeletons of *Pteranodon* found by O. C. Marsh and others from the 1870s onwards.

Pterosaurs were first described scientifically in 1784 by Cosimo Allesandro Collini (Fig. 1a) who, on having access to a unique specimen in the natural history collection of Karl Theodor, Elector of Palatinate and Bavaria, considered them to be a type of marine animal (the history of this discovery is reviewed and extensively illustrated by Wellnhofer 1991*a*, and the original specimen has been figured on numerous occasions: e.g. Cuvier 1801; Buckland 1836; Meyer 1859; Wellnhofer 1991*a*; Buffetaut & Mazin 2003) (see also Taquet & Padian 2004 for a note on the first, but unpublished, restorative drawing of a pterosaur by Herman *c.* 1800). In the following approximately 50 year period from 1780 to the early 1830s numerous and well-preserved pterosaurs came to light from the Late Jurassic Solnhofen Limestone of Bavaria (e.g. Soemmerring 1817; Cuvier 1819; Münster 1830, 1839; Theodori 1830; Goldfuss 1831; Meyer 1832, 1834, 1859), but an important specimen was also discovered in Lower Jurassic strata in southern England in 1828 (Buckland 1829), marking the beginning of the scientific study of pterosaurs in Britain.

The pterosaur fossil record in Britain is now known to be extensive, ranging from the Late Triassic (Fraser & Unwin 1990) to Late Cretaceous (Martill *et al.* 2008), and encompasses more than a dozen localities (Benton & Spencer 1995). However, excluding one or two examples of articulated specimens from the Lias of Dorset, most British specimens are highly fragmentary and often generically indeterminate. Despite this, they have fostered considerable scientific and popular interest, especially in the latter part of the nineteenth century, culminating in Harry Govier Seeley's scientific treatment of the group in his *The Ornithosauria: An Elementary Study of Pterodactyles* (Seeley 1870*a*) and his semi-popular *Dragons of the Air* (Seeley 1901). Numerous taxa were erected on the basis of this fragmentary material, especially by Richard Owen (Fig. 1g) and Harry Seeley (Fig. 1k), but recent discoveries of more complete specimens elsewhere, notably China and Brazil, and the analyses of Unwin (2001, 2003) has proved many of the British taxa to be *nomina dubia* or junior synonyms of other species. Nevertheless, despite their often fragmentary nature, the remains do reflect a diversity of form, and some specimens indicate the presence of relatively gigantic species in the British assemblage.

An anecdotal and anonymous account (Anon. 1757), noted in Benton & Spencer (1995, p. 140), of fossil bird bones occurring in the Stonesfield

From: Moody, R. T. J., Buffetaut, E., Naish, D. & Martill, D. M. (eds) *Dinosaurs and Other Extinct Saurians: a Historical Perspective*. Geological Society, London, Special Publications, **343**, 287–311.
DOI: 10.1144/SP343.18 0305-8719/10/$15.00

Fig. 1. Scientists involved in the early discovery and description of pterosaurs. (**a**) Cosimo Alessandro Collini described the first pterosaur fossil in 1784; (**b**) Samuel Thomas Soemmerring, German anatomist who described the second pterosaur to be discovered in 1817, but was the first to give a pterosaur a valid 'Linnean' binomial; (**c**) Baron Georges Cuvier, famous French anatomist who recognized pterosaurs were volant and reptilian; (**d**) Mary Anning, commercial fossil dealer and discoverer of the first British pterosaur; (**e**) William Buckland, described the first British pterosaur in 1829 and recognized that many so-called Stonesfield Slate birds were probably pterosaurian; (**f**) Gideon Algernon Mantell, first to figure Cretaceous pterosaurs, but thought they were the remains of fossil birds in 1827; (**g**) Sir Richard Owen, first to recognize truly gigantic pterosaurs; (**h**) Sir Charles Lyell, one time President of the Geological Society of London and good friend of Mantell; (**i**) James Scott Bowerbank, described the first pterosaur from the English Chalk as *Pt. giganteus*; (**j**) Frederick Dixon, his death provided Richard Owen with an opportunity to criticize Bowerbank when Owen posthumously published Dixon's book; (**k**) Harry Govier Seeley, who described numerous pterosaurs from the Cambridge Greensand; (**l**) Othniel Charles Marsh, who discovered skeletons of *Pteranodon* in Kansas and which drew attention from European pterosaurs for nearly a century.

Slate of Oxfordshire predates the discovery of pterosaurs by 27 years and might be the first hint of pterosaur bones in Britain. Unfortunately, the article is brief, is not illustrated and provides no details of the occurrence or the whereabouts of the specimens.

Likewise, the first hint of Cretaceous pterosaurs in Britain is a mention in 1824 by Gideon Mantell (Fig. 1f) of 'bird' bones in the Wealden (Wealden Supergroup of modern parlance) of Sussex. This casual notice post-dates the discovery of two complete pterosaurs in the German Solnhofen Limestone Formation in the late eighteenth and early nineteenth centuries (Collini 1784 and Soemmerring 1812, respectively), and their extensive description in the early nineteenth century by

Cuvier (1801, 1809) (Fig. 1c) and Soemmerring (1812, 1817) (Fig. 1b). It is thus intriguing to consider why British remains were not recognized as pterosaurian sooner. In this paper I examine the early history of British pterosaur palaeontology, and suggest that a psychological block prevented their recognition as part of the British fossil assemblage for at least 5 years, and possibly longer. In addition, it can be demonstrated that gigantic pterosaurs, perhaps with wingspans in excess of 6 m, were a part of this assemblage but became all but forgotten with the discovery by Othniel Charles Marsh (Fig. 1l) of more complete remains of *Pteranodon* in Kansas in the 1870s (Marsh 1871).

Pterosaurs large and small

Pretend for one moment that Cosimo Alessandro Collini, curator of the collection of Karl Theodor, Elector of Palatinate and Bavaria, had described the gigantic (wingspan, in excess of 9 m) *Quetzalcoatlus* of Texas in 1784. It would certainly have been considered an enormous animal, although quite whether Cuvier would later have recognized its flying capabilities is moot. All subsequent pterosaur discoveries of the nineteenth century would have seemed small by comparison, even those of *Pteranodon*. Scientific papers might have appeared with titles such as '*the World's smallest pterosaur*' or 'Microdactylus: *a diminutive pterosaur* . . . '. Indeed, in North America, where nearly all pterosaur discoveries for 100 years beginning in 1871 were of giant forms, exactly that happened: the discovery of small pterosaurs became as noteworthy as that of big ones (e.g. Jensen & Padian 1989; Jenkins *et al.* 2001). The concept of a giant animal is thus in part a matter of perspective: Minke are small baleen whales, but try moving a stranded example! The spectrum of pterosaur wingspans after more than 200 years of discovery ranges from as little as 0.3 m to upper estimates of 11 or even 12 m (Lawson 1975; Padian 1984; Buffetaut 2004; Buffetaut *et al.* 2003) (Fig. 2).

Several pterosaur taxa are now estimated to have achieved wingspans in excess of 7 m, including the azhdarchids *Quetzalcoatlus* Lawson 1975, *Arambourgiania* (Frey & Martill 1996) and *Hatzegopteryx* Buffetaut *et al.* 2002, 2003 and the pteranodontid *Pteranodon* (Eaton 1910; Bramwell & Whitfield 1974; Bennett 2001) and possibly some ornithocheirids (Dalla Vecchia & Ligabue 1993; Martill *et al.* 1996). From today's perspective, while a pterosaur with a wingspan of 5 or 6 m is considerably larger that any extant volant bird[1], it is no longer considered a giant, and Cretaceous pterosaurs with wingspans of between 3 and 6 m are generally considered the norm. This was not the case for the first three decades of the nineteenth century.

Calculating the wingspan of a pterosaur

The wingspan of pterosaurs can easily be calculated as it was realized very early on that the pterosaur wing has a supporting skeleton extending to the very tip of the flight surface, unlike birds where a significant component of the wing is comprised of feathers. Thus, for any complete skeleton of a pterosaur, determining the wingspan (at maximum stretch) requires merely the addition of the lengths of the individual wing elements and the width of the thorax. A simplified wing span formula is:

$$(a+b+c+d+e+f+g+h)\times 2+i = \text{wingspan}$$

where a is the length of the 4th phalanx digit IV; b is the length of the third phalanx digit IV; c is the length of the 2nd phalanx digit IV; d is the length of the 1st phalanx digit IV; e is the length metacarpal IV; f is the length of the carpal complex; g is the length of the radius/ulna; h is the length of the humerus; and i is the width of the thorax. However, this is effectively a 'stretched-out' pterosaur wingspan and it does not accurately reflect the *in vivo* wingspan where the elbow and wrist is slightly flexed, and the phalangeal elements of the wing digit are directed progressively more caudally (see the discussion by Bennett 2001).

Several problems arise in trying to determine the wingspans of large or gigantic pterosaurs. Complete specimens are almost unknown and a majority of taxa are known from fragmentary postcranial remains. It is unclear how different the linear dimensions of wing elements are between small and large forms, but it is clear that the ratios of the various components of the wing skeleton (humerus, radius/ulna, carpals, metacarpals and four – rarely three – phalanges) vary between major taxa, sometimes quite significantly. For example, the metacarpals of azhdarchoid pterosaurs such as *Quetzalcoatlus* form more of the wing length than do the same elements in

[1]The procellariforms *Diomedea exulans* and *D. epomorpha* achieve a wingspan of 3.5m, while the Andean Condor *Vultur gryphus* has a wingspan of 3.2 m and are thus the largest extant volant birds. The extinct *Argentavis* was a vulture-like bird with a wingspan estimated at approximately 7 m (Chatterjee *et al.* 2007).

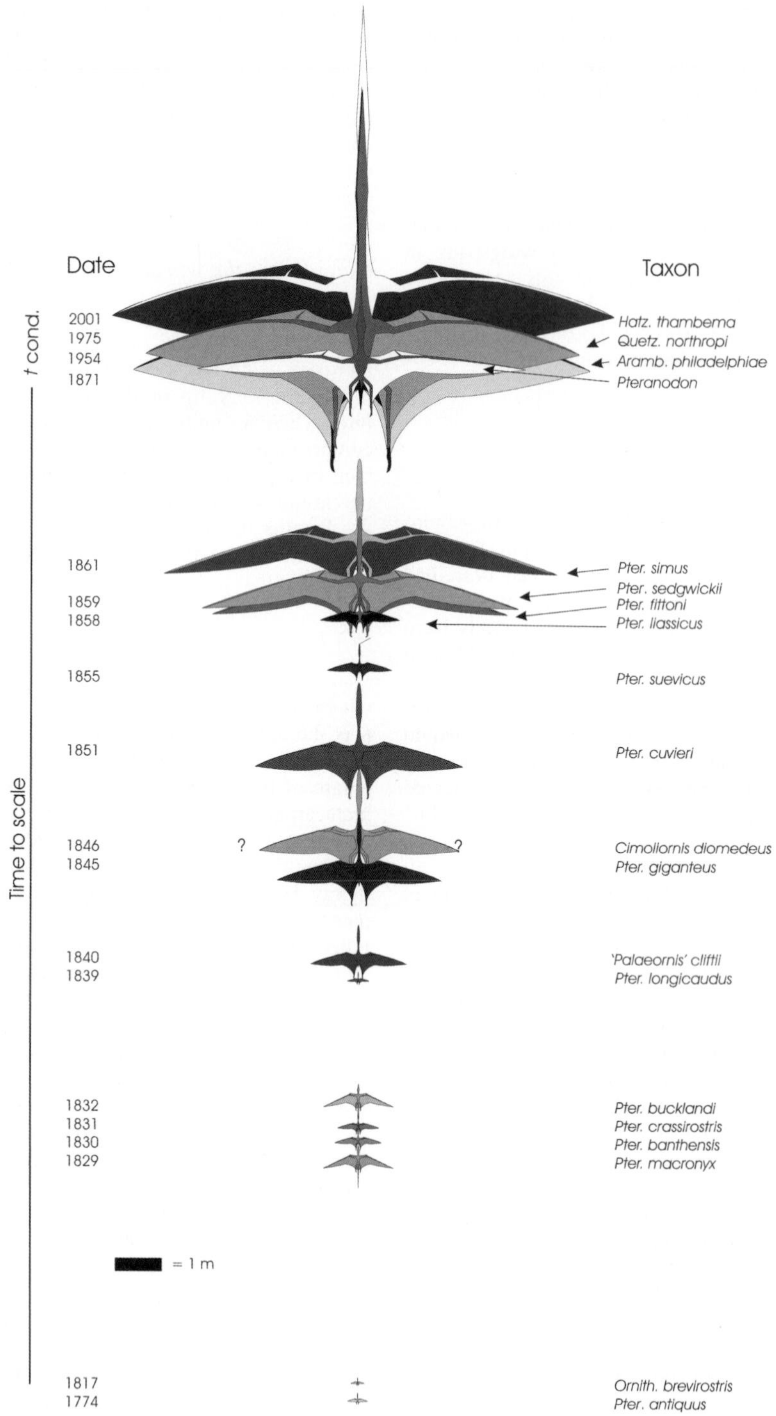

Fig. 2. Pterosaur wingspan plotted against time. The impression that pterosaur discoveries just kept on getting bigger is only true for the beginning of their palaeontological history.

Santanadactylus. Little is known of the growth allometry of large pterosaurs, although it is well studied for smaller forms such as *Rhamphorhynchus* and *Pterodactylus* (Bennett 1995, 1996). Given these problems, it is still possible to make reasonable estimates of the wingspan of pterosaurs, even from quite fragmentary material, but for some groups the error bars can be quite significant. During the early part of the nineteenth century even less was known of the growth and variation of pterosaurs, and workers rarely stated how they calculated the wingspan for incomplete specimens.

Setting the mould: the first three pterosaurs

Pterosaurs are such unusual animals that it is hardly surprising that their phylogenetic relationships and their palaeobiology cause so much heated debate. The first pterosaur described by Collini (1784) now goes under the name of *Pterodactylus antiquus* (Soemmerring 1812), and the history of its discovery and nomenclature has been discussed in detail by Wellnhofer (1970, 1991*a*) and Müller (1985). The holotype (Fig. 3) is an exquisite fossil from the Late Jurassic Solnhofen Limestone of Bavaria, with a wingspan of only 45 cm (Cuvier 1801, 1809). The second pterosaur to be discovered also came from the Solnhofen Limestone and was named *Ornithocephalus brevirostris* by Soemmerring (1817). This specimen was even smaller than *Pterodactylus antiquus*, with a wingspan of only 25 cm (Fig. 4), although it was later demonstrated to be a juvenile of that species (Wellnhofer 1991*a*). The third pterosaur to be named was found by Mary Anning (Fig. 1d) in the Lower Jurassic cliffs of Lyme Regis, Dorset in 1828[2]. Her specimen (Fig. 5) came to the attention of William Buckland (b. 1784, d. 1856) (Fig. 1e) in Oxford, who described it as a new species, *Pterodactylus macronyx*, in allusion to its large claws (Buckland 1829). Although not complete, and lacking a skull, the animal had a wingspan of around 1.4 m and, with its highly distinctive, elongate tail, it is surprising that Buckland did not erect a new genus to accommodate it: an action performed some 30 years later by Owen (1859*a*, *b*). Thus, despite Buckland's pterosaur being more than twice the size of *Pterodactylus antiquus*, and a giant by the standards of the day, by 1830 the perception was that pterosaurs were small, lightly built animals with delicate skeletons and with wingspans no greater than that of a raven or buzzard (Buckland 1836).

The Jurassic 'birds' of Stonesfield

Another hint of British pterosaurs is a casual mention of a bird bone in the Jurassic Stonesfield 'slate' of Oxfordshire by James Parkinson in his *Organic Remains of a Former World* (Parkinson 1811, Vol. 3, p. 307) but, as with the anonymous account mentioned earlier, this note lacks details or illustrations.

In their benchmark work on the *Outlines of the Geology of England and Wales* Conybeare & Phillips (1822)[3] record that leg and thigh bones of birds occur in the 'Calcareous slate of Stonesfield', and that they represent the only known examples of birds in strata of any antiquity. Subsequent workers, including Mantell (1827) and Buckland (1929, see personal comment on p. 219) initially accepted this as fact, and there was little reason at the time not to believe that birds might be present in Middle Jurassic strata (nor is there today). However, Buckland (1929) records that Mr I. S. Miller of Bristol, a naturalist who wrote a classic monograph on crinoids, had expressed an opinion in 1823 that some of the Stonesfield bird bones might be referred to the Pterodactyle. Certainly by 1829, having examined Mary Anning's discovery from the Lias of Lyme Regis, Buckland had concluded that *all* the bird bones of Stonesfield were pterodactyle, and in a footnote of his famous '*Bridgewater Treatise*' (Buckland 1836, Vol. 1, p. 86) further states that the 'bird' bones from Stonesfield are pterosaurs. It is slightly surprising that, despite their being good friends, Buckland fails to pass comment on the then oldest bird remains: those of a wader larger than a heron from the Tilgate Forest found by Gideon Mantell (see below). This is all the more surprising as Buckland supplied Mantell with engravings of 'bird' bones from Stonesfield for inclusion in Mantell's (1827) *Illustrations of the Geology of Sussex*. These few bones, figured on plate XIX, figs 3, 4, 5, 7, 10 and 13, are reproduced here (Fig. 6).

According to surviving personal correspondence between Charles Lyell (Fig. 1h) and Mantell (all correspondence between Lyell and Mantell is reproduced in Wennerbom 1999), the pioneering microscopist John Quekett, Professor of Histology

---

[2]It is probable that pterosaurs had been found some 20 years earlier at this locality, but they were not described (see Buckland 1829, p. 219).

[3]There is anecdotal evidence of a possibly slightly earlier occurrence in Buckland (1829, p. 219)

(a)

(b)

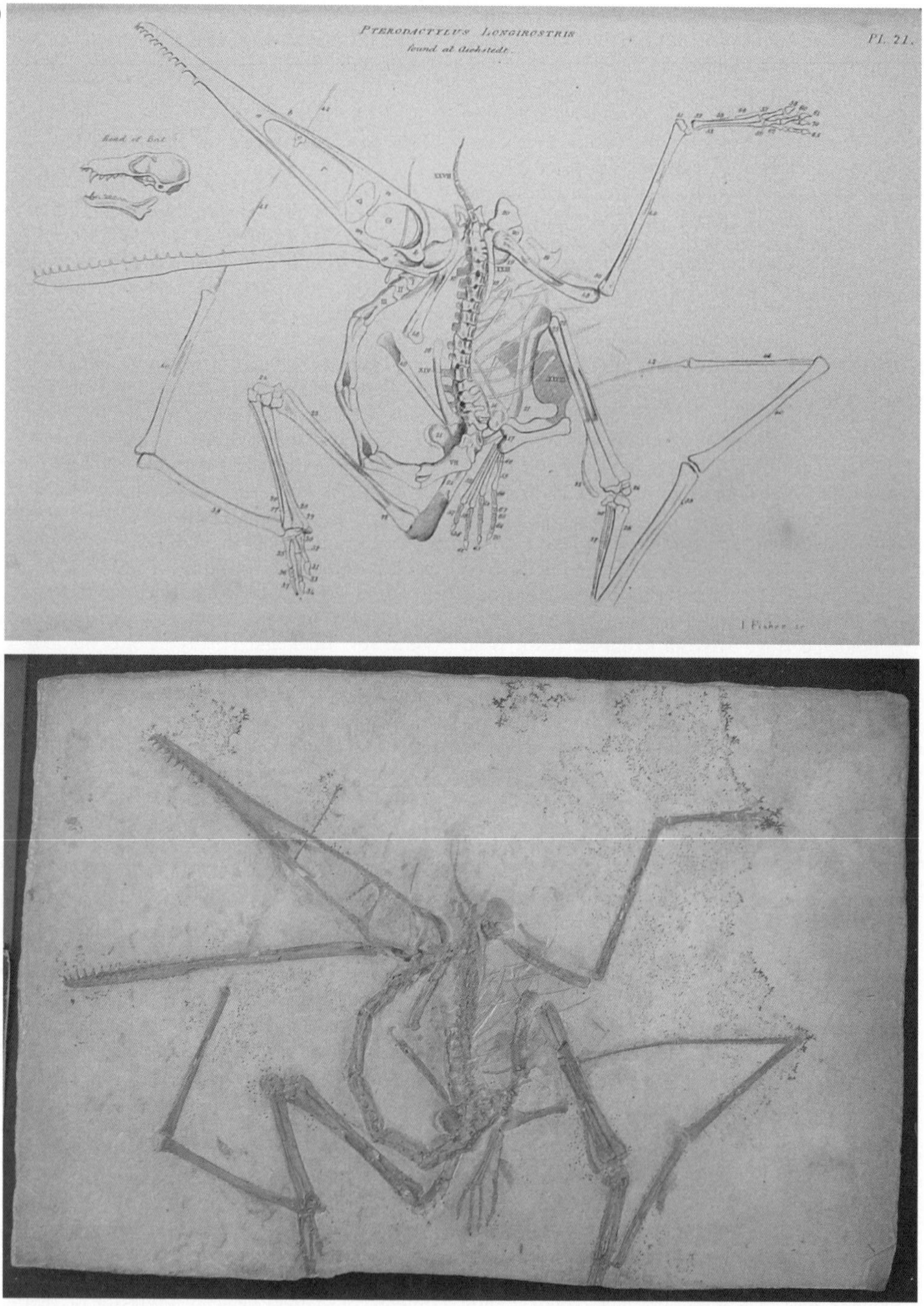

Fig. 3. The specimen now known as the holotype of *Pterodactylus antiquus* (Soemmerring 1812) was the first pterosaur to be scientifically described and the first to be named. It was also the first pterosaur specimen to be considered 'Volant'. With a wingspan of only 0.45 m, many early scientists regarded pterosaurs as small animals, perhaps transitional between mammals and birds. (**a**) Skeletal diagram of Cuvier as reproduced by Buckland (1836); (**b**) original specimen. Permission for photography from Bavarian State Collection of Palaeontology and Historical Geology is gratefully acknowledged.

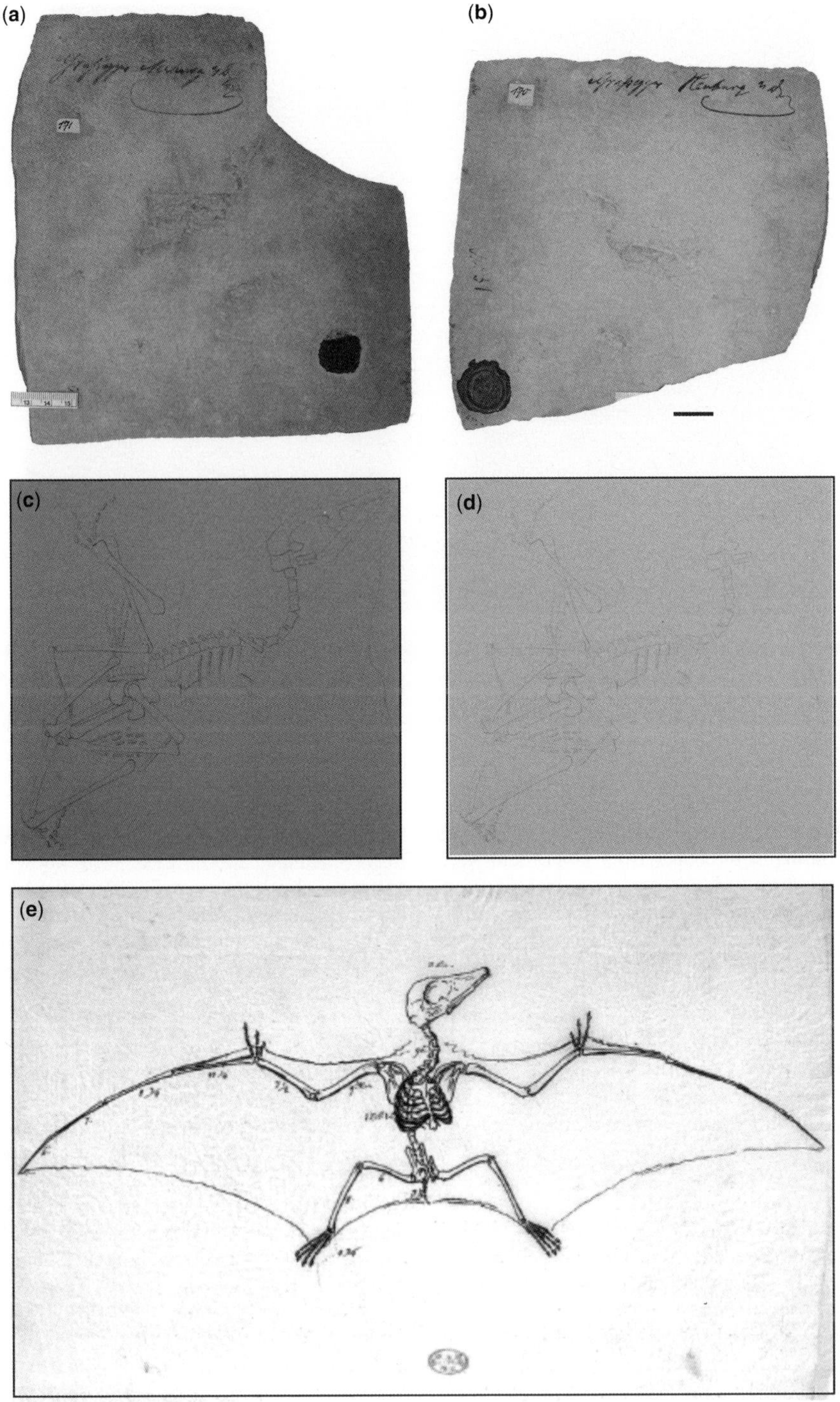

Fig. 4. '*Ornithocephalus*' *brevirostris* Soemmerring 1817 from the Solnhofen Limestone of Bavaria was only the second pterosaur specimen to be scientifically described. With a wingspan of only 25 cm, it reinforced the notion that pterosaurs were small animals. (**a**) and (**b**) Part and counterpart of holotype (Jura Museum, Eichstätt). Photographs by E. Endenburg and A. J Veldmeijer. (**c**) and (**d**) Outline sketch of the original specimen by Soemmerring taken from a reproduction in Meyer (1859), and lightened in (**d**). (**e**) Soemmerring's highly inaccurate skeletal reconstruction.

Fig. 5. The first substantial pterosaur skull discovered in England. This drawing is of the skull that was named *Dimorphodon* by Richard Owen. The specimen was obtained by Mary Anning of Lyme Regis, and the drawing executed by her brother Joseph using ink from the fossilized ink sacs of Lower Jurassic squids. The original is now in the archive of the Philpots Museum at Lyme Regis. Thanks to Paul Pursglove for permission to reproduce his photograph of the drawing, courtesy of Lyme Regis Philpot Museum.

to the Royal College of Surgeons, was still of the opinion that some bones from Stonesfield were from fossil birds, as too was Dennis (1856). A belief that seems to have been maintained at least until 1851, as Quekett had sought Lyell's help to procure a 'pterodactyle' bone from a hard matrix; a request that Lyell passed on to Mantell, to compare with 'bird' bones from Stonesfield slate (letter from Lyell to Mantell 31 October 1851 in Wennerbom 1999) (see also below). Quekett also lobbied Lyell to include Stonesfield 'birds' in the new edition of his *Principals of Geology*.

Mantell's Wealden 'birds'

Gideon Mantell (1790–1852) has received due recognition for his significant contributions to the early discovery of dinosaurs (*Iguanodon*, *Hylaeosaurus*, *Pelorosaurus*, *Regnosaurus*), the palaeontology and stratigraphy of southern England, the anatomy of New Zealand Moas, as well his numerous medical and humanitarian endeavours (Dean 1998, 1999). Such were his contributions that he not only received accolades in his own life time, including the prestigious Geological Society's Wollaston Medal, but is still revered as one of the founding fathers of British vertebrate palaeontology (Cadbury 2000). Less well known is that Mantell also discovered (Mantell 1824) and described (Mantell 1835, 1844, 1846) what were, at the time, the remains of 'gigantic' pterosaurs, but he was never truly aware of the significance of his discovery.

In his first palaeontological paper Mantell (1824, p. 422) mentions the presence of bird bones in a 'sandstone slate' in the Tilgate Forest of Cuckfield, Sussex. Three years later (Mantell 1827) he figures a number of 'bird' bones in his *Geology of Sussex*, some of which became accessions to the Mantell collection now held in the Natural History Museum, London (e.g. specimen numbers BMNH 2458, 8469, 2229, 2353 and 2353a) (Fig. 7). Considerably later, Mantell (1844) described and figured two of these specimens comprising the proximal and distal ends of a humerus lacking part of the diaphysis (BMNH 2353 and 2353a) (Fig. 8a, b), which at that time Mantell considered to be a tibiotarsus belonging to a species of wading bird close to herons (the history of this discovery is reviewed by Witton *et al.* 2009). For this specimen (the size and preservation indicates they are from the same bone) Mantell named a new taxon of 'bird', *Palaeornis*

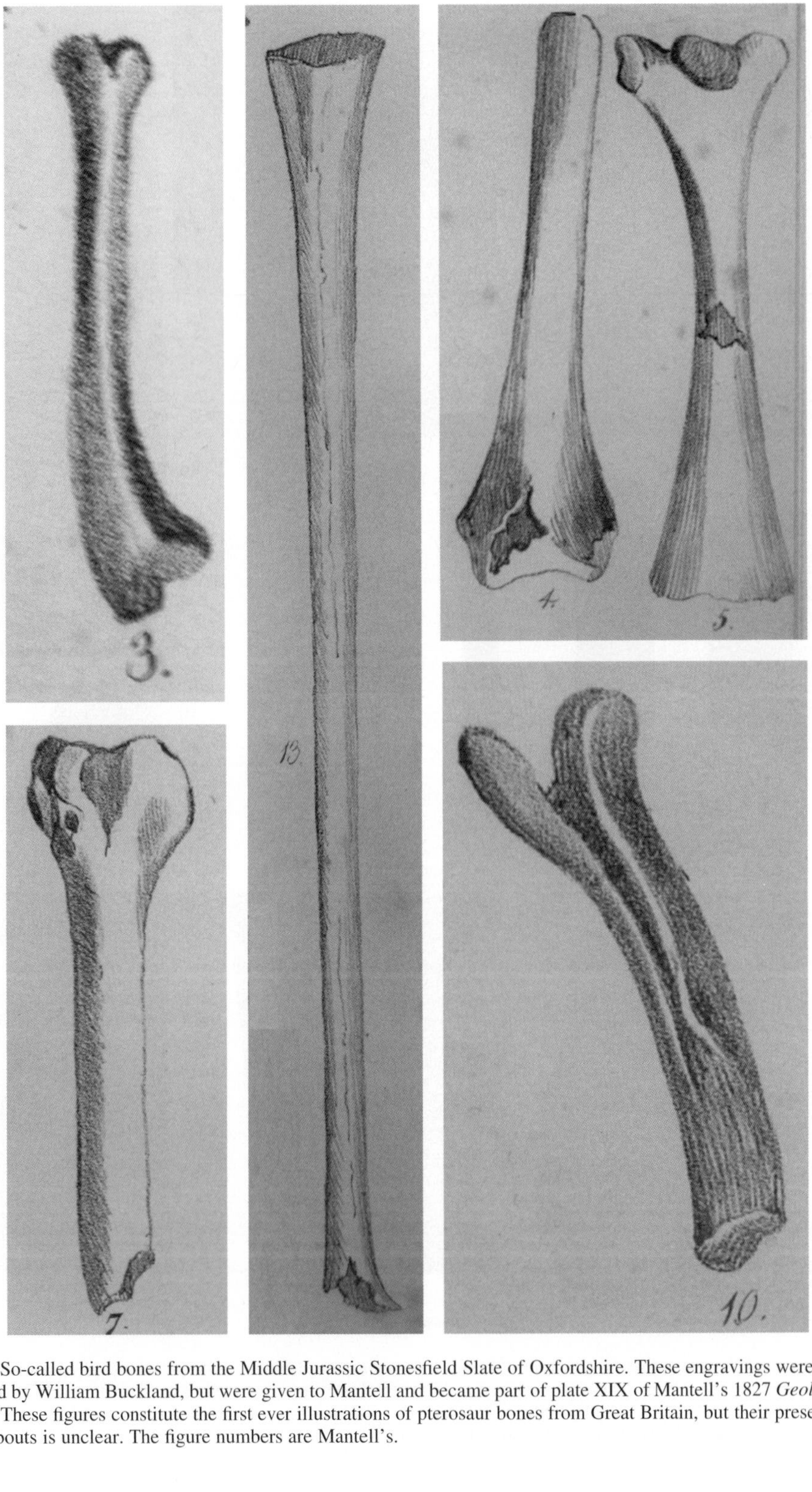

Fig. 6. So-called bird bones from the Middle Jurassic Stonesfield Slate of Oxfordshire. These engravings were part prepared by William Buckland, but were given to Mantell and became part of plate XIX of Mantell's 1827 *Geology of Sussex*. These figures constitute the first ever illustrations of pterosaur bones from Great Britain, but their present whereabouts is unclear. The figure numbers are Mantell's.

Fig. 7. Bones of pterosaurs from Tilgate Forest, Sussex. Mantell obtained numerous hollow, thin-walled bones that he thought were from fossil birds. The first was noted in 1824, but they were not described or figured until 1827. His material was controversially used by Bowerbank and Quekett to examine the microsctructure, and formed the basis of a bitter argument between Mantell and Owen. (**a**) Indeterminate fragment from which Mantell made a microscope

cliftii in honour of William Clift, the curator of the Royal College of Surgeons[4]. It was William Clift who had made material of Recent iguanas available for Mantell to compare with his newly discovered *Iguanodon* teeth (Dean 1999).

This generically indeterminate bone was referred to the Ornithosauria[5] (=Pterosauria) by Owen (1846*b*) who, strangely, when he redescribed Mantell's specimen as a pterosaur chose not to use the name *Palaeornis cliftii*, and later Owen (1851) in an act of taxonomic subterfuge tacitly replaced the name with *Pterodactylus sylvestris*, perhaps to emphasize the inappropriateness of the name for an animal that was clearly not a bird, but perhaps just as a snub to Mantell (Owen seems to have changed both the generic and specific epithets of other authors on a whim – see later). The name *Palaeornis* was, in any case, invalid for Mantell's specimen[6] as Lydekker (1888, p. 10) noted its pre-occupation (Lydekker 1888, p. 25), and referred *Palaeornis cliftii* to the genus *Ornithochirus* (sic) as *O.* (?) *clifti* (sic). However, with hindsight, Owen's referral to *Pterodactylus* was also inappropriate, as was Lydekker's tentative referral to *Ornithocheirus*, as the specimen is most probably from an azhdarchoid pterosaur (Witton *et al.* 2009). Owen (1846*b*) did, however, speculate on the size of '*Palaeornis*' when alive, suggesting it 'must have been about one-third larger than the *Pterodactylus macronyx* ... and probably as large as the pterodactyle from the Chalk exhibited by Mr. Bowerbank at the meeting of the Society in May last'. Bowerbank's 'pterodactyle' (see later) had been of an animal with an estimated wingspan of 8–9 ft (*c.* 2.5 m). Thus, Mantell had discovered, but was unaware of it at the time, fragments of the world's largest known prehistoric flying creature. In fact, it is doubtful if '*Palaeornis*' was this large, as a reappraisal of the holotype suggests very little of the shaft is missing and the humerus is not much larger than that of *Dimorphodon*, perhaps belonging to an animal with a 2 m wingspan.

Mantell may originally have been a little unsure of his identification of the specimen as a bird, and chose to include in its original description a bolstering of its identification by noting that Cuvier himself was of the opinion that it was avian. He also reproduced at length Owen's comments regarding its clearly avian affinities (Mantell 1837). Even when it was becoming clear that many of the so-called 'bird' bones from the English Cretaceous were proving to be pterosaurian, Mantell (1847) clung to the view that '*Palaeornis*' *cliftii* was a bird and was reluctant to accept Owen's (1846*b*) pterosaurian reidentification, maintaining that, whilst certainly a volant animal, its true affinities remained to be proven. James Bowerbank (1848, p. 7) noted that reservations had been expressed about the avian nature of Mantell's Wealden birds prior to publication of his (Mantell's 1835) paper, but Bowerbank does not credit these doubts to any individuals. Bowerbank does note, however, that he obtained fragments of Mantell's '*Palaeornis*' for microscopical examination and that in its microstructure it 'coincide(s) in every respect with those of the Pterodactyl' (Bowerbank 1848, p. 8). Mantell (1851) finally seems to have relented just a year or so before his death in 1852 and accepted '*Palaeornis*' as a pterosaur. This final change of heart seems to have surprised Charles Lyell who wrote in a letter to Mantell:

> I also am struck with what you say at p. 91 of your new book (*Petrifactions and Their Teachings*) for you seem

---

[4]In *Fossil Reptilia of the Cretaceous Formations*, Supplement 3 (Owen 1861*a*, p. 17) Owen erects the name *Pterodactylus ornis* for the proximal humerus of Mantell's *Palaeornis cliftii*, referring specifically to p. 99 and figure 5 of his own work. He cites his own paper incorrectly as Owen 1845. In fact, the paper was presented at the Geological Society in December 1845 but published in 1846 (Owen 1846*b*). Presumably Owen was unwilling to accept that the two pieces are from different individuals, but it seems slightly odd that Owen should suppress the specific name *cliftii*, as Mantell named it in honour of William Clift who became Owen's father-in-law when he married Caroline Clift in 1835. It also seems monumentally hypocritical of Owen to erect the name *ornis* for a specimen that he now knew to be pterosaurian, after having admonished Bowerbank (see later) for the inappropriate name *giganteus*.

[5]Owen had used the term Pterosauria of Kaup (1834) in his now classic essay for the British Association for the Advancement of Science in 1842.

[6]According to Lydekker (1888) the generic name *Palaeornis* had been used just 2 years previously by Lear (1832) for a parakeet. In fact *Palaeornis* was erected by Vigors (1825) for *P. alexandri* (Linne.).

Fig. 7. (*Continued*) section, MNH 36531; (**b**) indeterminate ulna, BMNH 2458; (**c**)–(**f**) long bone fragments, BMNH 3535 (probably equates to fig. 3 of Mantell's 1827, plate VII); (**g**) tooth probably from an ornithocheirid, BMNH 3322; (**h**) indet. long bone, BMNH 3477 (probably equates to fig. 4 of Mantell's 1827, plate VII); and (**i**) possible proximal femur, BMNH 2453. It is easy to see why, from this motley collection, it took some time for their pterosaurian nature to be established. Even now, some of the identifications are dubious, and the tooth of (**g**) may be from a plesiosaur.

> to give up fig. 6 Plate 13 Geol. Tans. Vol. 5. in which Wealden bone Bowerbank found ornithic structure.
>
> (C. Lyell 2 November 1851)

Mantell's reply to Lyell seems somewhat terse:

> I am not prepared to admit that microscopical structure alone (in the present state of our knowledge) is evidence sufficient to decide upon the ornithic or reptilian character of a fragment of bone: peruse the paragraph in my p. 192 to which you refer ....

But softens further down the page

> ... If Mr Quekett[7] & Tomes would come to me on Saturday evening, I should be delighted to see them & look over their sections & my own, & you could then see the evidence which microscopic structure really affords. I would strongly advise you not to rely upon the microscopic test alone: but adopt with reservation as I have done.
>
> (G. A. Mantell, probably 3 November 1851)

So, no reason for his change of heart was given. Mantell died in 1852 having discovered a pterosaur in the Wealden that, at that time of its discovery, represented an entirely new group of pterosaurs. With regard to the latter, Mantell never realized this, but then neither did his main critic, Sir Richard Owen.

One perplexing issue regarding Mantell's so-called bird bones of the Wealden is that in his 3rd and 4th editions of the extremely popular *The Wonders of Geology* Mantell (1st edn 1838; 3rd edn 1839; 4th edn 1840, Vol. 1, p. 403) notes that:

> The remains of thin and slender bones, evidently belonging to animals capable of flight, were among my earliest discoveries in the Strata of Tilgate Forest. Some of these bones appear to be referable to those singular extinct creatures called *pterodactyles*, or *wing-toed reptiles* ....

Mantell also includes a frontispiece by celebrated engraver John Martin of *the Country of the Iguanodon* (Fig. 9) depicting a very bat-like pterosaur perched with spread wings observing a titanic clash between several iguanodons. This brief note and illustration represent the first acknowledgement that pterosaurs were part of the Wealden assemblage. It is quite surprising that Mantell did not make more of this discovery: instead he was much more concerned with the fact that he thought some of the bones were avian, stating:

> The discovery of the *undoubted* [my emphasis] remains of birds in the grit of Tilgate Forest became, therefore, a fact of great interest and importance in the physical history of the globe ... after selecting the bones which appeared to belong to pterodactyls, several remained which bore so striking a resemblance to those of waders, that I ventured to describe them as such ....
>
> (Mantell 1840 6th edn p. 440)

Strangely, there is no mention in Mantell's 1837 paper where he describes these Wealden 'bird' bones of any associated pterodactyle material. Of course, had the remains truly been those of birds then Mantell's hyperbole would have been warranted. Alas, they too were pterosaurian and the realization of an authentic Mesozoic bird took another 32 years, with the discovery of an *Archaeopteryx* feather in the Solnhofen Limestone in 1860 (Meyer 1861).

It is possible that Mantell may have been beaten in discovering a Cretaceous pterosaur. In a paper describing the geology of the coast of Hastings, Sussex (Webster 1829, but read to the Geological Society in 1824), Thomas Webster figured a supposed 'bird' bone from the Hastings Beds Group (Fig. 10). This specimen now appears to be lost, and its avian or pterosaurian affinity cannot be tested. Nevertheless, it was announced to the scientific community in the same year that Mantell (1824) mentioned bird bones in the Tilgate Forest, but its publication appeared 2 years after Mantell figured his first 'bird' bone discoveries (Mantell 1827).

James Scott Bowerbank and the not-so-giant *Pterodactylus giganteus*

Because Mantell, not surprisingly, failed to recognize the Wealden 'bird' bones as pterosaurian, the first claim for discovering a gigantic pterosaur was made by James Scott Bowerbank (b. 1797, d. 1877). An acknowledged expert on sponges on which he wrote extensive monographs, Bowerbank was the first to describe pterosaurs from the English Chalk Formation (Bowerbank 1846, 1851), and the first to claim that they attained gigantic sizes (Bowerbank 1852*a*); achievements for which history has accorded him only scant recognition. Bowerbank also wrote short notes on a giant bird from the Eocene London Clay and a giant shark from the Red Crag, and clearly was fascinated by gigantism in fossils (Bowerbank 1852*a*–*c*, 1854).

In 1845 Bowerbank exhibited a portion of the snout of 'a new and gigantic species of Pterodactyl' at a meeting of the Geological Society of London (Bowerbank 1846) (Fig. 11). For this material, which includes fragments of jaws, scapulocoracoid and other broken elements, Bowerbank had no hesitation in erecting the name *Pterodactylus giganteus*, estimating its wingspan at 6 ft 7 in (2.02 m). Bowerbank (additional note in the same paper

[7] See Steel (2003) for a discussion on the survival of some of Quekett's thin sections.

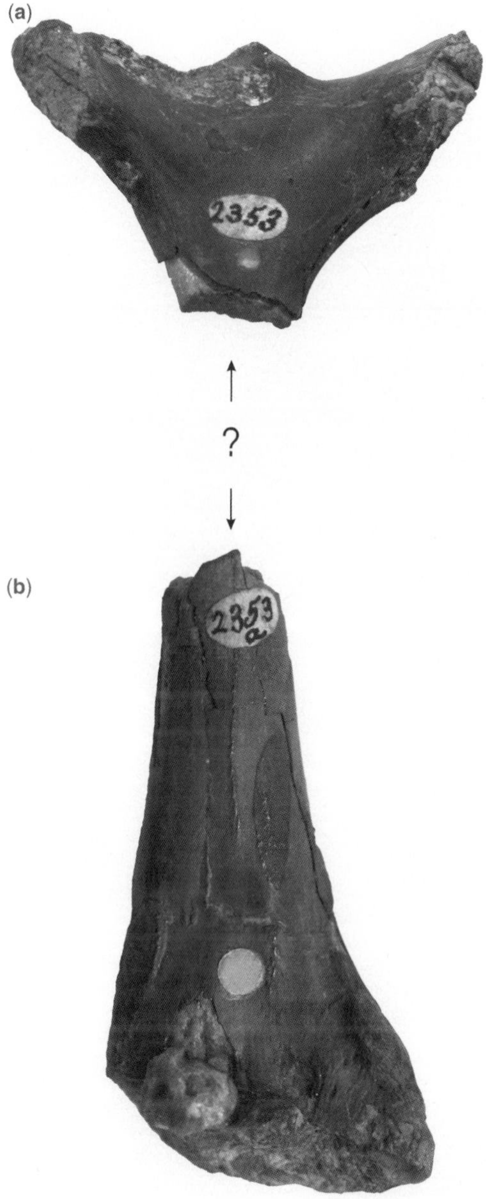

Fig. 8. Holotype of '*Palaeornis*' *cliftii* Mantell 1844. (**a**) BMNH 2353 and (**b**) 2353a. There is some confusion as to when Mantell discovered this bone, which eventually proved to be a pterosaurian humerus. Because of the lack of a fit and because Mantell did not know the distance between the two pieces he was unsure that they were from the same element or, if they were from the same bone, its original length. However, Mantell believed it was from a heron-like bird, as did Cuvier, and so, for a while, did Owen. Today it is considered to be a non-ornithocheiroid pterodactyloid, and a *nomen dubium*. Scale bars, 10 mm.

dated December 1845 in Bowerbank 1846) also considered that many of the bones described as avian by Owen (see later) were most likely to be from 'pterodactyls', which led him to suppose that there were even larger pterosaurs in the English Chalk, perhaps with wingspans of 8 or 9 ft (*c.* 2.5 m). Later, Bowerbank (1848, 1852*b*) described the remains of even larger forms from the chalk for which he suggested even greater wingspans, at 16 ft 6 in (*c.* 5.04 m) for *Pterodactylus cuvieri* and a 15 ft (*c.* 4.5 m) span for *Pt. compressirostris* (Bowerbank 1852). These were gigantic estimates, and signified animals almost four times larger than Buckland's *Dimorphodon*.

Owen (1850, 1852) was highly critical of Bowerbank's work and, in a monumental snub that attracted the ire of Gideon Mantell, chose to replace the name *Pterodactylus giganteus* with *Pterodactylus conirostris* when he posthumous published Frederick Dixon's work *The Geology and Fossils of the Tertiary and Cretaceous Formations of Sussex* in 1850 (Dixon 1850). This unethical treatment of Bowerbank sufficiently incensed Mantell such that he wrote informally to his good friend Sir Charles Lyell, then President of the Geological Society, in protest (Wennerbom 1999). Shortly after, Owen (June 1851) provided a lengthy, and somewhat obsequious, explanation for his actions in the pages of the Palaeontographical Society, but only history knows if this is because Lyell 'had a word' with Owen or because Owen felt a pang of guilt (see below).

Taxonomic subterfuge and an albatross for Owen

Famed for his encyclopaedic knowledge of osteology and his skill in interpreting even fragmentary specimens, Richard Owen was, like Mantell, slow to realize the pterosaurian nature of many early discoveries. Even when it was becoming clear that birds were not part of the British Mesozoic fossil assemblage, Owen tenaciously clung to the opinion that some specimens at least were avian and probably with affinities to extant forms (Owen 1846*a*, *b*). This view may reflect a reluctance to admit previous errors of identification, although Owen was usually adept at turning such things to his advantage. Initially, all thin-walled, hollow bones from the Wealden Group were considered avian, and most accounts make comparisons only with extant birds (Mantell 1827). As it became clear that the small, so-called bird bones of Stonesfield were pterosaurian (Buckland 1836), so too it transpired that similar but larger bones from the Wealden and Chalk formations were pterosaurian

Fig. 9. (**a**) Engraving by John Martin entitled *The Country of the Iguanodon*. This haunting scene of reptilian ferocity involving *Iguanodon*, *Megalosaurus* and *Hylaeosaurus* is observed by a rather bat-like pterosaur (lightened for clarity). This image and accompanying text in Mantell's *The Wonders of Geology* is the first document confirming the presence of pterosaurs in the English Wealden. It appeared in the same year (1838) that George Richardson included the engraving (**b**) by George Nibb in his '*Prose and Verse*'. Image in (**a**) is scanned from the 4th edition (Mantell 1840) of '*The Wonders*' and has been digitally lightened to enhance the pterosaur.

(e.g. Bowerbank as discussed earlier). Thus, in his description of a fragmentary pterosaur metacarpal IV (at that time thought to be metacarpal V), Owen (1846*b*) goes to great pains to explain why it (BMNH 39411), and another long bone fragment, were avian rather than pterosaurian (Fig. 12). Indeed, Owen makes an extremely good case and clearly convinces himself, despite the considerable

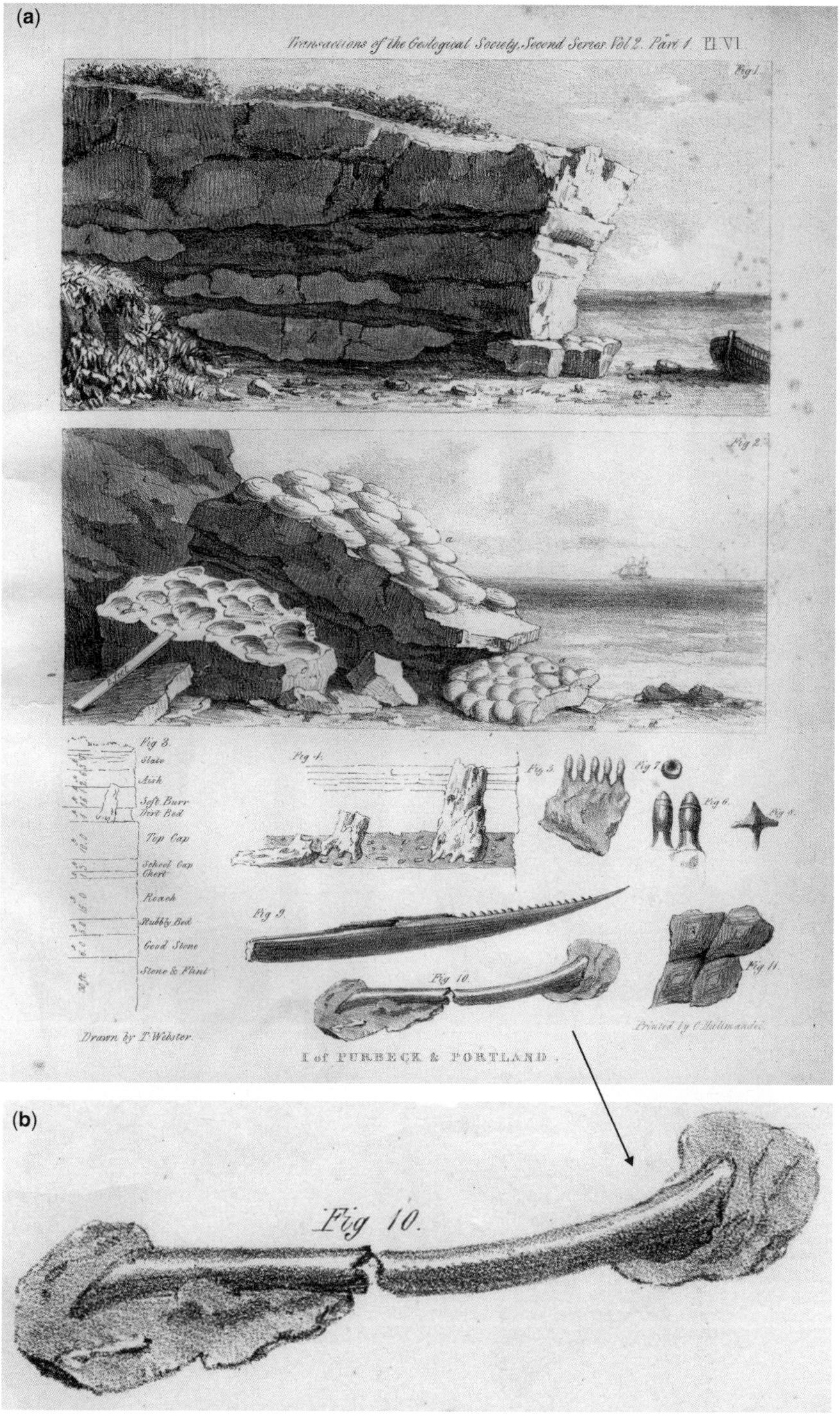

Fig. 10. (**a**) Reproduction of plate VI from Webster (1829). Webster recorded bones of birds from the Hastings beds of Sussex in 1824 and figured one of them in 1829. (**b**) The bone in Webster's figure is difficult to interpret, unfortunately, its whereabouts is not known. It may have been pterosaurian.

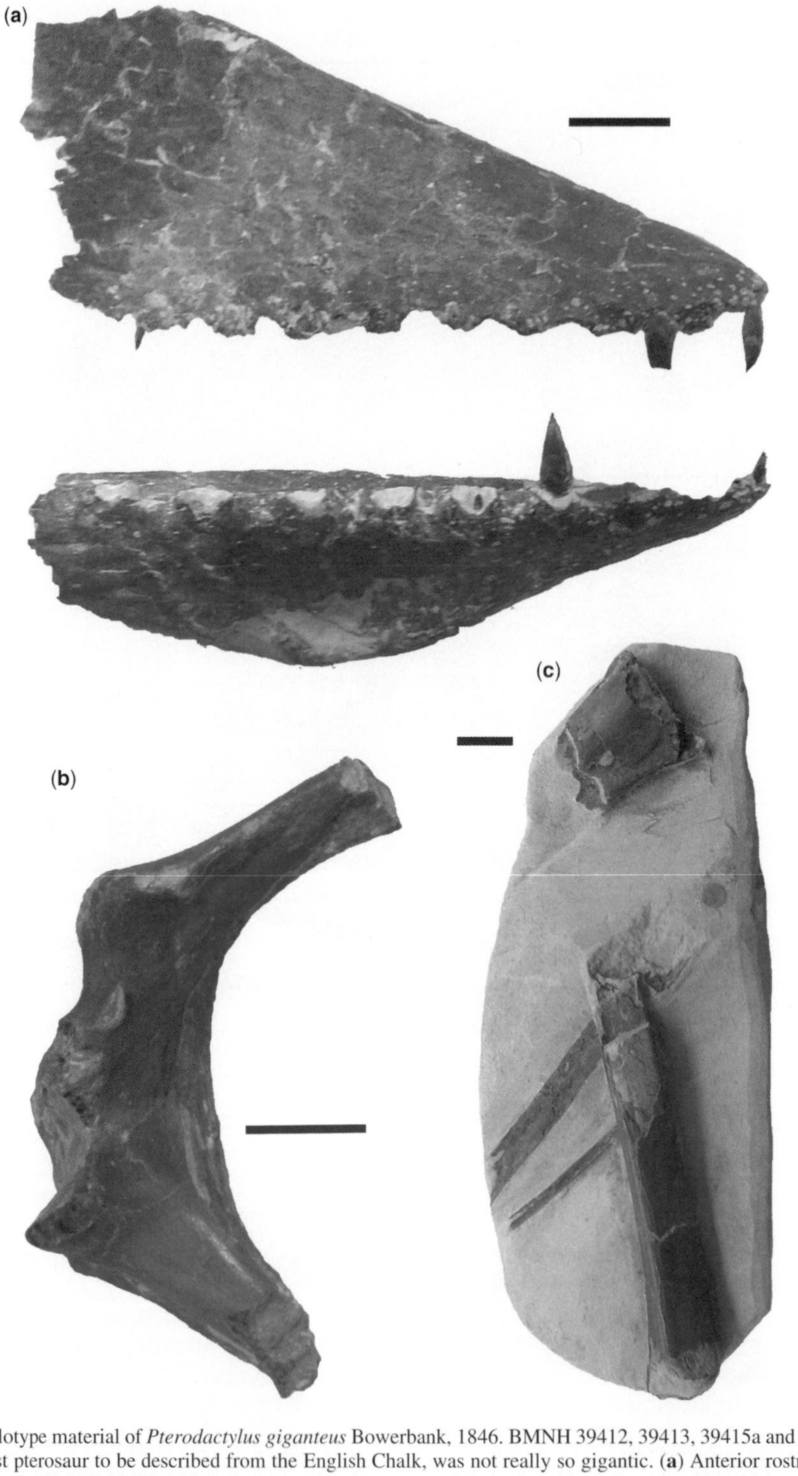

Fig. 11. Holotype material of *Pterodactylus giganteus* Bowerbank, 1846. BMNH 39412, 39413, 39415a and 39415b). This, the first pterosaur to be described from the English Chalk, was not really so gigantic. (**a**) Anterior rostrum with some teeth, BMNH 39412. This is the piece that Owen named *Pterodactylus conirostris*; (**b**) partial scapulocoracoid; (**c**) assemblage of broken log bones. Note that (a) and (b) have been digitally removed from the matrix. Scale bars, 10 mm. Currently, this pterosaur is placed in the genus *Lonchodectes* by Unwin (2001).

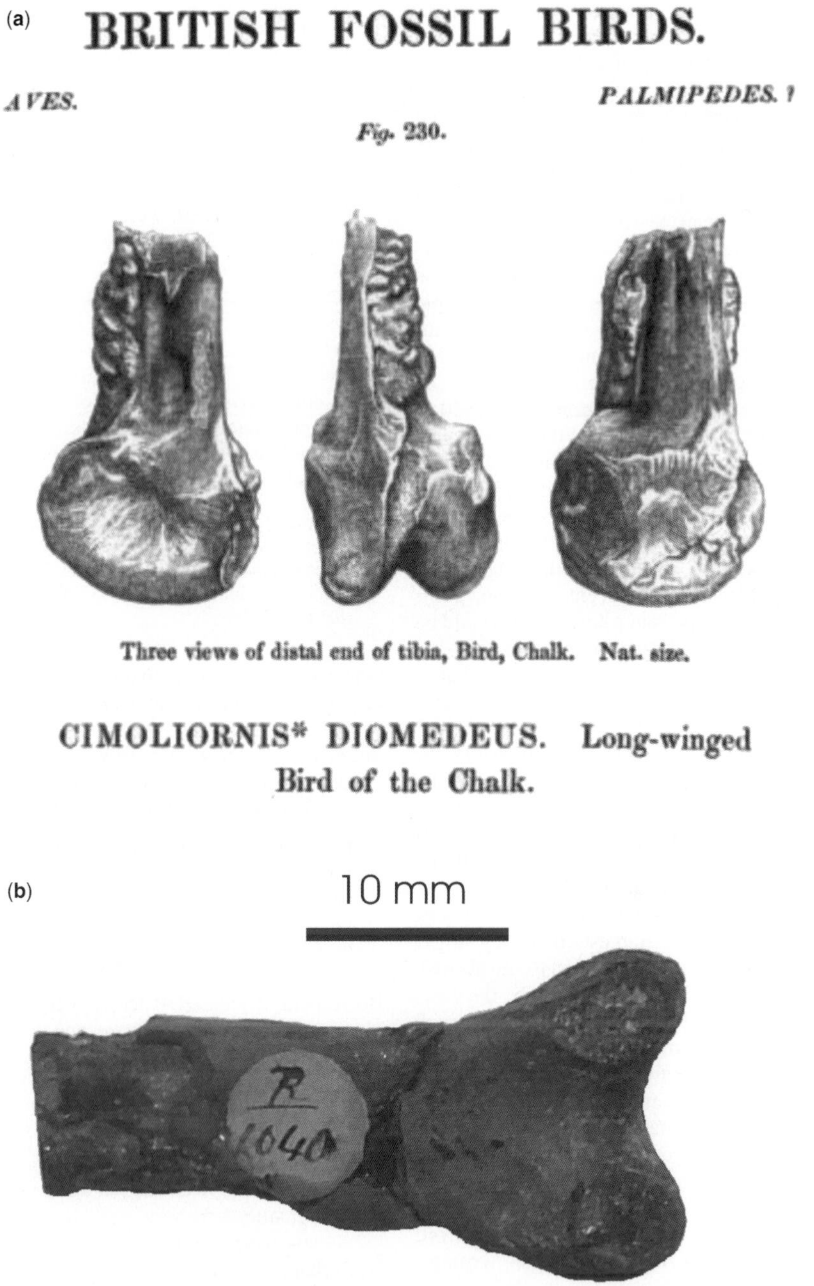
(a)
BRITISH FOSSIL BIRDS.
AVES.
PALMIPEDES.?
Fig. 230.
Three views of distal end of tibia, Bird, Chalk. Nat. size.
CIMOLIORNIS* DIOMEDEUS. Long-winged Bird of the Chalk.
(b)
10 mm
R
1640

Fig. 12. *Cimoliornis diomedius* Owen 1850. (**a**) Owen's (1846*a*) illustrations of the distal metacarpal, BMNH 1640; (**b**) caudal aspect of the original distal carpal, a view not given by Owen. Owen originally thought that this animal was a bird, perhaps close to the Recent albatross. It was James Scott Bowerbank who suggested it was pterosaurian, much to Owen's chagrin.

differences between the pterosaur bone and the Recent avian equivalents. Owen did a significantly better job describing *Cimoliornis* than Mantell did for *Palaeornis*, although Mantell's *Palaeornis* was broken with only the proximal and distal ends preserved. With the diaphysis missing Mantell did not know for certain if the two pieces belonged to the same bone, and even if they did, he had no idea how long the missing portion was. Therefore, Mantell identified the distal end of a pterosaurian humerus as the distal end of a bird's metatarsal, which in detail it did not compare at all well. It is, nevertheless, a perfectly forgivable mistake, but one that Mantell was reluctant to admit. Owen, on the other hand, identified a pterosaur metacarpal IV as an avian metacarpal: right bone, wrong animal. Owen too can be forgiven. Fragments of pterosaur long bones have often caused considerable confusion and still frustrate pterosaur workers today[8]. Eventually Owen came to the inevitable conclusion that *Cimoliornis* was a pterosaur (Owen 1859*a*, 1874). His pro-bird stance through to grudging acceptance as pterosaurian can be traced trough a series of publications from 1840 to 1852. In 1840 Owen announces the 'discovery' (most probably a purchase) by the Earl Enniskillen of three portions of bone that both Eniskillen and William Buckland had identified as belonging to a species of bird (according to Owen 1840, p. 411). Owen notes several differences that the fossil bones display from those of Recent birds, and comments that should it represent a humerus, it would be the size of an albatross. However, in suggesting that it might instead be a radius, Owen notes that it would represent a bird of gigantic proportions comparable with the '*fabulous Roc of Arabian romance*' (Owen 1840, p. 411). In his *History of British Fossil Mammals and Birds* Owen (1846*a*) figures the material for a second time and erects for it the new genus and species *Cimoliornis diomedius*, colloquially naming it the Long-winged bird of the Chalk (Owen 1846*a*, figs 230 and 231).

James Scott Bowerbank referred to the bones described by Owen, and suggests that they might belong to a pterosaur (Bowerbank 1846 see above). Bowerbank also stated that should this be the case, then the animal might have had a wingspan of 8 or 9 ft (*c.* 2.5–3 m). Bowerbank's gentle criticism of Owen attracted ire from the great man who responded with considerable venom (Owen in Dixon 1850) and a certain degree of petulance. Owen notes that no Cretaceous pterosaur that he has seen (Owen had seen Bowerbank's material at the Geological Society) had a wingspan greater than that of *Pterodactylus macronyx* from the Oxford Oolite[9] (Owen 1850, p. 401) and goes on, writing:

> the idea of gigantic proportions of the Pterodactyle of our chalk-deposits has, in fact, been founded on the assumption that the fossil bones of *Cimoliornis* figured by me in my 'British Fossil Mammals and Birds,' pp. 545, 546, figs. 230, 231, and in Tab. XXXIX. Figs 11 & 12 of the present work [Owen 1850], belong to the genus *Pterodactylus* . . . .

Then continues:

> I have yet obtained no evidence which shakes my original conclusion that the bone is part of the shaft of a humerus of a longi-pennae bird, like the Albatros (sic).

Owen's criticisms were even stronger in his footnote (Owen 1850, p. 403), where he takes Bowerbank to task for his statement that the microstructure of Owen's *Cimoliornis* bone and confirmed pterosaur bones from the Chalk is identical.

When Owen replaced the trivial epithet *giganteus* coined by Bowerbank with the new species name *conirostris* (on account of the former being an inappropriate name for a pterosaur that Owen considered was not gigantic), he insensitively rubbed salt in the wound by stating:

> The mere coining of names for things glanced at and imperfectly understood, – the fabrication of signs without due comprehension of the things signified, – becomes a hindrance instead of a furtherance of true knowledge.
>
> (Owen 1850, p. 404)

One can only conclude that this petty tirade played out in the pages of the learned journals reflects Owen's arrogance and inability to accept that he might have been wrong. Bowerbank did not take Owen's criticism lying down and was forthright in his condemnation of Owen stating:

> I certainly did not lend my specimens to my late friend Mr. Dixon for the illustration of his work with a view of having the name which I had assigned to this new and gigantic species subverted, and without in the slightest degree being consulted on the subject.
>
> (Bowerbank 1852*c*, p. 377)

Bowerbank discussed at length why Owen had no case for suppressing *giganteus* and adopting a new specific name, rather cleverly citing a ruling on p. 4 of the Committee of Nomenclature of the British Association (the forerunner of the International Commission on Zoological Nomenclature (ICZN) and essentially the rule of priority): a committee on which Owen sat and a ruling to which he was a signatory.

As discussed in the section on 'James Scott Bowerbank' earlier in this paper, Owen's snub of Bowerbank so incensed Gideon Mantell, that he wrote to his friend Charles Lyell, then President of the Geological Society, in protest. Very shortly after, Owen (1851) provided an in-depth and rather

---

[8]French palaeontologist Camille Arambourg described an elongate pterosaur cervical vertebrae as a metacarpal IV. He never could have known that a pterosaurian cervical vertebra might have approached an astonishing 80cm in length (Frey & Martill *et al.* 1996).

[9]Owen is here confusing *Pterodactylus macronyx* Buckland 1829 from the Lias with *Pterodactylus bucklandi* Meyer 1832 from the Stonesfield Slate.

sycophantic explanation for his actions, but, as is detailed earlier in this chapter, the reason for this is not recorded. Certainly in previous years Lyell had been a drinking and dining friend of Owen's, as Lyell recorded in a letter to Adam Sedgwick (James 1986). One might have thought that for someone publishing in the Palaeontographical Society Monographs, falling out with Bowerbank, who was Secretary of the Society at the time, would not have been a wise course of action. Even so, in the very same publication where Owen attempts to make amends he (Owen 1851, p. 80) could not help but take yet another swipe at Bowerbank. In a footnote beneath his somewhat grovelling explanation for his previous actions Owen points out that Bowerbank had said the bones came from the Upper Chalk, but were in fact from the Middle Chalk, an error that Bowerbank himself had corrected 3 years earlier (Bowerbank 1848, p. 2, footnote). Nevertheless, Owen did reinstate Bowerbank's *Pterodactylus giganteus* in this work and, goes on to say regarding fossil birds in the Chalk:

> Let me not be supposed, however, to be concerned in excusing my own mistake. I am only reducing the unamiable exaggeration of it. Above all things, in our attempts to gain a prospect of an unknown world by the difficult ascent of the fragmentary ruins of a former temple of life, we ought to note the successful efforts, as well as the occasional deviations from the right track, with a clear and unprejudiced glance, and record them with a strict regard to truth.
>
> (Owen 1851 p. 83)

It is difficult to estimate a wingspan for *Cimoliornis* as the remains are highly fragmentary, but clearly it was larger than anything hitherto described. But there was to be no triumphalism: any glorification of this event for a Victorian media would only have highlighted Owen's error, and credit may have gone to Bowerbank. Even after Owen had reluctantly reinstated *Pterodactylus giganteus*, he still took one more opportunity to rubbish Bowerbank's taxon. In his 1861 monograph supplement Owen refers to *Pterodactylus giganteus* Bk. as 'this comparatively small species' (Owen 1861*a*, p. 3).

By way of a taxonomic aside, Lydekker (1888) retained Owen's *Cimoliornis diomedius* as a distinct species, but refers it instead to the genus *Ornithochirus* (sic) as *O. diomedius*. Lydekker (1888, p. 13) suggests that it is probably identical to *Ornithochirus* (?) *giganteus* (Bowerbank) and presumably the question mark suggests Lydekker had some reservation about its referral to the genus. In his systematic index (Lydekker 1888, p. xiii) he also considers it a doubtful species, ranking it with the dreaded Lydekkeran double asterisk thus: ***Ornithocheirus diomedius*. In fact, the subtriangular cross-sectional shape of the bone (BMNH 39411) probably precludes referral to *Ornithocheirus*, it probably being closer to Azhdarchoidea than Ornithocheiroidea. But whatever its pterosaurian affinities, until 1859 it ranked as the largest known pterosaur.

The volant giants of Cambridgeshire

During the latter half of the nineteenth century the remains of fragmentary, but uncrushed pterosaur bones from the Cretaceous Cambridge Greensand began to find their way into museum collections and into scientific debate (numerous papers by Owen and Seeley reviewed by Unwin 2001). These fossils were obtained as a by-product of phosphate mining for fertilizer to the north and east of Cambridge (Worssam & Taylor 1969), and occurred as a remané deposit with bones and teeth of marine reptiles and dinosaurs. Among the material both Owen and Seeley recognized a number of distinct taxa characterized mainly by features of the distal rostrum and dental configuration (Unwin 2001). Although Owen was an enthusiast for erecting new taxa on scant remains, describing four Cambridge Greensand species, Seeley, by describing approximately 48 Cambridge Greensand species, made Owen appear like an 'also ran' in this respect. The Cambridge Greensand material was certainly perplexing. Despite its fragmentary nature, the bones were clearly pterosaurian, and many indicated animals of immense size. Owen's 1859 paper on *Pter. fittoni* and *Pter. sedgwickii* (Owen 1859*b*) was entitled 'On remains of new and gigantic species of pterodactyle' while his description of *Pter. simus* in his 1861 Palaeontographical Society Monograph supplement begins 'The first evidence I have to offer of this truly gigantic flying reptile' (Owen 1861*a*).

Dodgy systematics aside, these pterosaur fragments do indicate the presence of some very large animals, but getting an accurate grasp on their overall size from small fragments was never going to be easy. Owen's estimates of size for the Cambridge Greensand material were based on scaling up from a small, but near complete, example of *Pterodactylus* (=*Cycnorhamphus*) *suevicus* Quenstedt 1855 from the Nüsplingen lithographic limestone of Wurttemburg, Germany[10]. Owen felt that his *Pterodactylus* (=*Ornithocheirus*) *simus* 'must have acquired double the dimensions of *Pterodactylus sedgwickii* (Owen 1861*a*). In fact, Owen (1859*b*, p. 19) calculates *Pt. sedgwickii* wing span as 'not less than 22 ft [*c*. 6.55 m] from tip to tip'. Thus,

[10]The Nüsplingen lithographic limestone of Kimmeridgian age should not be confused with the Tithonian age Solnhofen limestone.

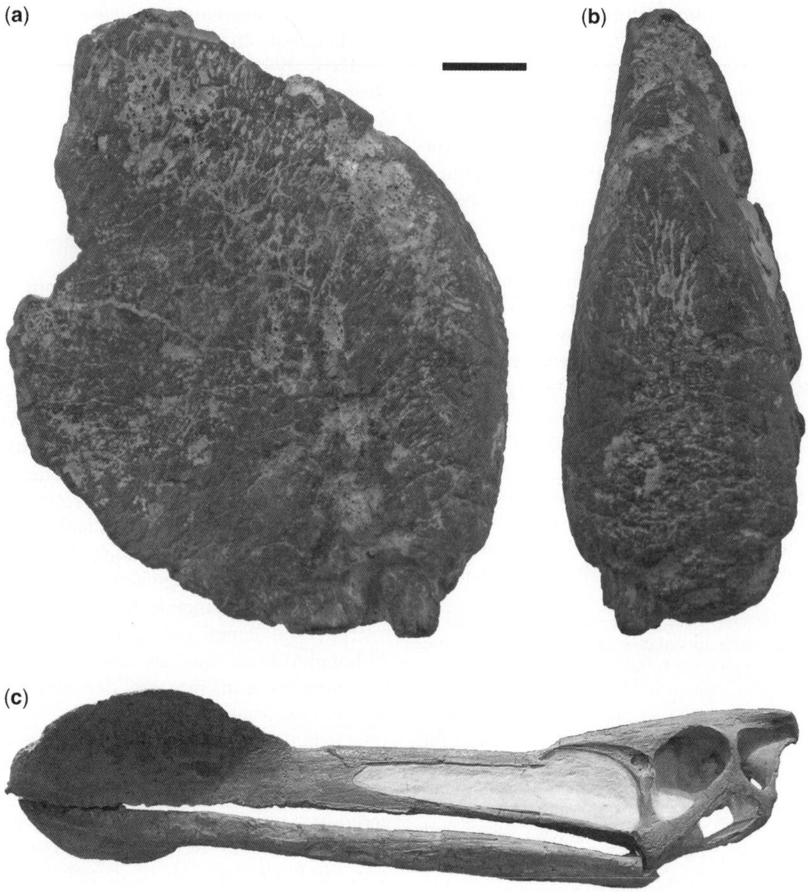

Fig. 13. *Ornithocheirus simus* (Owen 1861*a*) from the Cretaceous Cambridge Greensand of Cambridgeshire. (**a**) right lateral and (**b**) anterior aspects of BMNH 35412; (**c**) a complete skull of '*Tropeognathus*' *mesmbrinus* Wellnhofer 1987. Owen estimated this pterosaur to have been about twice the size of *Pterodactylus sedgwickii*, and therefore with a wingspan of around 13 m. Both this specimen (BMNH 35412) and the holotype (CAMSM B54.428) are just small pieces of a much larger skull. The skull in (c) is 630 mm long.

although Owen does not explicitly provide a dimension, he must have imagined *Pt.* (= *Orn.*) *simus* to have had a wingspan of approximately 44 ft (*c.* 13.4 m). If this was an accurate estimate, then today *Orn. simus* would rank among the largest of pterosaurs. In fact, the holotype fragment of *Orn. simus*, an anterior rostrum (Fig. 13), incorporates an expanded dorsal crest of which Owen was unaware, leading to an erroneous size estimate.

In 1884 Owen donated to the collections of the Natural History Museum, London a fragment of pterosaur prexamilla from the Cambridge Greensand that he never described or figured. Any attempt at anything other than a general identification would be pointless, but it is clearly from an ornithocheirid, probably close to *Coloborhynchus*. The specimen (BMNH R 481; Fig. 14) is an ugly chunk of bone with few features of note apart from two broken teeth seen in cross-section and its enormous size. The teeth have diameters of 13 mm at their base and the specimen is 60 mm wide across the palate. It, thus, is from an animal larger than any other ornithocheirid, and most probably had a wing span in excess of 9 m. Perhaps Owen chose not to describe this specimen as by now *Pteranodon* had been discovered in Kansas and the fragments from the Cambridge Greensand now appeared inadequate or, perhaps in the later years of his life, he simply had just had enough of pterosaurs.

Not a big pterosaur at all

Although the title suggests a monumental blunder, Harry Govier Seeley's (1870*b*) description of

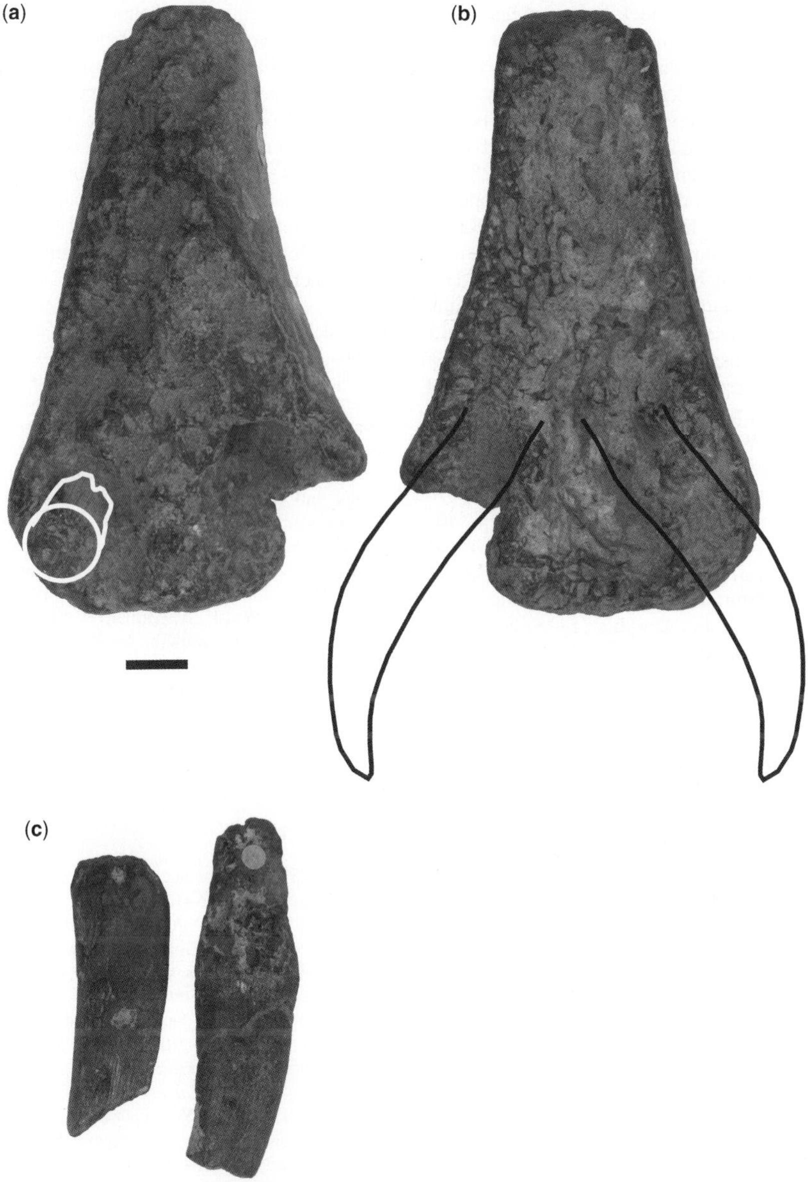

Fig. 14. An ugly chunk of bone from the Cambridge Greensand. Presented to the NHM collection (BMNH R 481) by Sir Richard Owen in 1884, this fragment of mandible from the Cambridge Greensand of the ornithocheirid *Coloborhynchus* sp. possibly represents the largest such pterosaur yet known. (**a**) Anterior view with a broken tooth in the alveolus indicated; (**b**) caudal view of same with outline of two teeth; (**c**) two isolated, but extremely large teeth (BMNH 35418 and 35418a) from the same horizon as R 481. These teeth were figured by Owen (1860, plate IV, fig. 4). Scale bar, 10 mm.

Ornithopsis hulkei, a sauropod dinosaur, as 'A gigantic animal of the pterodactyle kind' (p. 279) was an extremely insightful osteological essay that can be seen as a harbinger of Gauthier's (1986) concept of Ornithodira: the clade containing Pterosauria and Dinosauria, including Aves. Taken literally, Seeley's referral of *Ornithopsis* to 'an animal of the pterodactyle kind' would have been a grave error. *Ornithopsis* subsequently proved to be a sauropod dinosaur, an animal that could not have been more different from a pterosaur. Just for fun, had it really been a 'pterodactyle', then

Seeley's calculation of a neck length of between 4 and 5 ft (*c.* 1.22–1.52 m) for the animal would imply a wingspan of about 56 ft (*c.* 17.07 m)[11].

In his paper, Seeley describes the anatomy of two opisthocoelous cervical vertebra with extensive and large pneumatic foramina. The vertebrae, both in the Natural History Museum, London (BMNH 28632), possess 'paper-thin' bony walls internally supported by thin honeycomb-like cells. Although Seeley makes extensive comparisons between these vertebrae and those of birds and pterosaurs, he concludes that they belong to an intermediate animal between the two, and 'probably manifest some affinity with the dinosaurs' (p. 280). He certainly did not suggest or imply that *Ornithopsis* was volant, or indeed that it possessed wings. Although sauropod dinosaurs were known at this time – *Cetiosaurus* was represented mainly by limb bones and massive lumbar vertebrae (Upchurch & Martin 2002); *Cardiodon* only by teeth (Owen 1840–1845); *Oplosaurus* by a single tooth (Gervais 1852); *Pelorosaurus* by a humerus and four caudal vertebrae (Upchurch *et al.* 2004) – they were poorly understood, and Marsh's (1878) concept of Sauropoda did not yet exist.

The discovery of *Pteranodon* and the beginning of the end of English Pterosauria

Discovered in 1870, *Pteranodon* is one of the best-studied and perhaps best-known creatures of the Mesozoic after *Tyrannosaurus rex*, having gained a position in the public eye as the archetypal 'pterodactyl'. The unearthing of *Pteranodon* eclipsed previous pterosaur discoveries from the English Chalk and Cambridge Greensand but there is little need to recount its early history, which has been adequately examined by Bennett (1994, 2001) and Everhart (2005). *Pteranodon* was the first of the giant pterosaurs to be known from more than just fragments (see Witton 2010) and it became iconic as one of the central 'prehistoric characters' in film versions of Arthur Conan Doyle's (1922) *Lost World* and, latterly, Michael Crichton's *Jurassic Park: The Lost World* (*Cearadactylus* in the novel, *Pteranodon* in the film). The discovery of this incredible animal, with a wingspan now reliably known to be around 6–7 m, projected Othniel C. Marsh into the limelight and drew attention away from Britain: the Great American dinosaur rush had begun. Even though Harry G. Seeley continued to work on Cambridge Greensand pterosaurs through the rest of the nineteenth century, and his death in 1909 effectively brought to an end any substantial pterosaur research until the latter part of the twentieth century. Only Hooley (1913) made any significant contribution, with his remarkable discovery of *Istiodactylus latidens* (Hooley 1913) in the Early Cretaceous Wessex Formation of the Isle of Wight (Howse *et al.* 2001), and, with this, work on the British pterosaur assemblage abruptly ended for most of the twentieth century. It was revived in the 1980s when Beverly Halstead appointed a young researcher, David Unwin.

I an indebted to D. Frey for introducing me to *Arambourgiania*, truly a giant pterosaur, and to Dr J. Washington Evans for sharing a moment of ornithocheirid discovery several years ago. I especially thank D. Unwin for discussions on Cambridge Greensand pterosaurs, D. Hone for making historically important specimens available for photography at the Bavarian State Collection of Palaeontology and Historical Geology, M. Witton for musings on measuring wingspan and on what constitutes a giant among pterosaurs. A. Veldmeijer and E. Endenburg very kindly allowed me to reproduce photographs of *O. brevis*. Thanks also to K. Padian, D. Naish, E. Buffetaut, R. Moody, S. Walsh, A. Milner, S. Chapman, L. Steel, R. Loveridge, M. Godwin, P. Pursglove, E. Malone, G. White, Professors Challenger and Summerlee, Lord J. Roxton, the folks at Google Books and Internet Archive. R. Strachan of the School of Earth and Environmental Sciences, and the University of Portsmouth supported this research.

References

ANON. 1757. [Further accounts of fossils.] *Gentleman's Magazine*, **27**, 122–123.

BENNETT, S. C. 1995. A statistical study of *Rhamphorhynchus* from the Solnhofen Limestone of Germany – year classes of a single large species. *Journal of Paleontology*, **69**, 569–580.

BENNETT, S. C. 1994. Taxonomy and Systematics of the Late Cretaceous pterosaur *Pteranodon* (Pterosauria, Pterodactyloidea). *Occasional Papers of the Natural History Museum, Kansas*, **169**, 1–70.

BENNETT, S. C. 1996. Year classes of pterosaurs from the Solnhofen Limestone of Germany: taxonomic and systematic implications. *Journal of Vertebrate Paleontology*, **16**, 432–444.

BENNETT, S. C. 2001. The osteology and functional morphology of the Late Cretaceous pterosaur *Pteranodon*. Part II. Size and functional morphology. *Palaeontographica A*, **260**, 113–153.

BENTON, M. J. & SPENCER, P. S. 1995. *Fossil Reptiles of Great Britain*. Geological Conservation Review Series. Chapman & Hall, London.

BOWERBANK, J. S. 1846. On a new species of pterodactyle found in the Upper Chalk of Kent. *Quarterly Journal of the Geological Society, London*, **2**, 7–8.

[11]Calculation based on the proportion of neck length to wingspan in the ornithocheiroid pterosaur *Anhanguera* figured by Wellnhofer (1991*b*).

BOWERBANK, J. S. 1848. Microscopical observations on the structure of the bones of *Pterodactylus giganteus* and other fossil animals. *Quarterly Journal of the Geological Society, London*, **4**, 2–10.

BOWERBANK, J. S. 1851. On the pterodactyls of the Chalk Formation. *Proceedings of the Zoological Society, London*, **1851**, 14–20.

BOWERBANK, J. S. 1852*a*. On the probable dimensions of the great shark (*Carcharias megalodon*) of the Red Crag. *In*: *Report of the British Association for the Advancement of Science for 1851, Ipswich*. John Murray, London, 54–55.

BOWERBANK, J. S. 1852*b*. On the pterodactyls of the Chalk Formation. *In*: *Report of the British Association for the Advancement of Science for 1851, Ipswich*. John Murray, London, 55.

BOWERBANK, J. S. 1852*c*. On the pterodactyls of the Chalk Formation. *Annals of the Magazine of Natural History*, **10**, 372–378.

BOWERBANK, J. S. 1854. On the remains of a gigantic bird (*Lithornis emuinus*) from the London Clay of Sheppey. *Annals of the Magazine of Natural History*, **2**, 263–264.

BRAMWELL, C. & WHITFIELD, G. R. 1974. Biomechanics of *Pteranodon*. *Philosophical Transactions of the Royal Society of London*, (B), **267**, 503–581.

BUCKLAND, W. 1829. On the discovery of a new species of pterodactyle in the Lias at Lyme Regis. *Transactions of the Geological Society of London*, Series 2, **3**, 217–222.

BUCKLAND, W. 1836. *Geology and Mineralogy Considered with Reference to Natural Theology*. The Bridgewater Treatises on the Power, Wisdom and Goodness of God as Manifested in Creation, Treatise VI (2 vols). William Pickering, London.

BUFFETAUT, E. 2004. A giant pterosaur from the Lower Cretaceous of the eastern Paris Basin. *Bulletin de la Société Géologique de France*, **175**, 573–577.

BUFFETAUT, E., GRIGORESCU, D. & CSIKI, Z. 2002. A new giant pterosaur with a robust skull from the latest Cretaceous of Romania. *Naturwissenschaften*, **89**, 180–184.

BUFFETAUT, E., GRIGORESCU, D. & CSIKI, Z. 2003. Giant azhdarchid pterosaurs from the terminal Cretaceous of Transylvania (western Romania). *In*: BUFFETAUT, E. & MAZIN, J.-M. (eds) *Evolution and Palaeobiology of Pterosaurs*. Geological Society, London, Special Publications, **217**, 91–104.

BUFFETAUT, E. & MAZIN, J.-M. 2003. Evolution and palaeobiology of pterosaurs. *In*: BUFFETAUT, E. & MAZIN, J.-M. (eds) *Evolution and Palaeobiology of Pterosaurs*. Geological Society, London, Special Publications, **217**, 1–3.

CADBURY, D. 2000. *The Dinosaur hunters*. Fourth Estate, London.

CHATTERJEE, S., TEMPLIN, R. J. & CAMPBELL, K. E. 2007. The aerodynamics of *Argentavis*, the world's largest flying bird from the Miocene of Argentina. *Proceedings of the National Academy of Sciences*, **104**, 12,398–12,403; doi: 10.1073/pnas.0702040104.

COLLINI, C. A. 1784. Sur quelques zoolithes du cabinet d'Histoire Naturelle de S.A.S.E. Palatine et de Baviere, a Manheim. *Acta Acadamiae Theodoro-Palatinae, Manheim, Pars Physica*, **5**, 58–103.

CONAN DOYLE, A. 1922. *The Lost World*. Hodder & Stoughton, London.

CONYBEARE, W. D. & PHILLIPS, W. 1822. *Outlines of the Geology of England and Wales with an Introductory Compendium of the General Principles of that Science and Comparative Views of the Structure of Foreign Countries*. William Phillips and George Yard, London.

CUVIER, G. 1801. Extrait d'un ouvrage sur les espèces de quadrupèdes dont on a trouvé les ossemens dans l'intérieur de la terre. *Journal de Physique, de Chemie et d'Histoire Naturelle*, **52**, 253–267.

CUVIER, G. 1809. Mémoire sur le squelette fossile d'un reptile Volant des environs d'Aichstedt, que quelques naturalistes ont pris pour un oiseau, et don't nous formons un genre de Sauriens, sous le nom de Pter-Dactyle. *Annales du Muséum national d'Histoire Naturelle, Paris*, **13**, 424–437.

CUVIER, G. 1819. (*Pterodactylus longirostris*). *Isis* von Oken, **2**, 1128, 1788.

DALLA VECCHIA, F. M. & LIGABUE, G. 1993. On the presence of a giant pterosaur in the Lower Cretaceous (Aptian) of Chapada do Araripe (northeastern Brazil). *Bollettin della Società Paleontologica Italiana*, **32**, 131–136.

DEAN, D. R. 1998. *Gideon Algernon Mantell: A Bibliography with Supplementary Essays*. Delmar, New York.

DEAN, D. R. 1999. *Gideon Mantell and the Discovery of Dinosaurs*. Cambridge University Press, Cambridge.

DENNIS, J. 1856. The existence of birds during the deposition of the Stonesfield Slate proved by a comparison of the microscopic structure of certain bones from that formation with that of Recent bones. *Quarterly Journal of Micrsocopical Science*, **5**, 63–77.

DIXON, F. 1850. *The Geology and Fossils of the Tertiary and Cretaceous Formations of Sussex*. Longman, London.

EATON, G. F. 1910. Osteology of *Pteranodon*. *Memoires of the Connecticut Academy of Sciences*, **2**, 1–38.

EVERHART, M. J. 2005. *Oceans of Kansas: A Natural History of the Western Interior Sea*. Indiana University Press, Bloomington, IN.

FRASER, N. C. & UNWIN, D. M. 1990. Pterosaur remains from the Upper Triassic of Britain. *Neues Jahrbuch für Geologie und Paläontologie, Monatshefte*, **5**, 272–282.

FREY, E. & MARTILL, D. M. 1996. A reappraisal of *Arambourgiania* (Pterosauria, Pterodactyloidea): one of the world's largest flying animals. *Neues Jahrbuch für Geologie und Paläontologie, Abhandlungen*, **199**, 221–247.

GAUTHIER, J. A. 1986. Saurischian monophyly and the origin of birds. *In*: PADIAN, K. (ed.) *The Origin of Birds and the Evolution of Flight*. Memoirs of the Californian Academy of Sciences, **8**, 1–55.

GERVAIS, P. 1852. *Zoologie et Paléontologie Françaises (Animaux Vertébrés)*, 1st edn. A. Bertrand, Paris.

GOLDFUSS, A. 1831. Beiträge zur kenntnis verschiedener Reptilien der Vorwelt. *Nova Acta Academiae Leopoldinae*, **15**, 61–128.

HOWSE, S. C. B., MILNER, A. R. & MARTILL, D. M. 2001. Pterosaurs. *In*: MARTILL, D. M. & NAISH, D. (eds), *Dinosaurs of the Isle of Wight*. Palaeontological Association, London, 324–355.

James, K. W. 1986. 'Damned nonsense!': the geological career of the Third Earl of Enniskillen (1807–1886). *Geology Today*, **2**, 184–186.

Jenkins, F. A., Shubin, N. H., Gatesy, S. M. & Padian, K. 2001. A dimunitive pterosaur (Pterosauria: Eudimorphodontidae) from the Greenlandic Triassic. *Bulletin of the Musuem of Comparative Zoology, Harvard*, **156**, 151–170.

Jensen, J. A. & Padian, K. 1989. Small pterosaurs and dinosaurs from the Uncompahgre fauna (Brushy Basin Member, Morrison Formation: ?Tithonian), Late Jurassic, western Colorado. *Journal of Paleontology*, **63**, 364–373.

Kaup, J. J. 1834. Versuch einer Eintheilung der saugethiere in 6 Stämme und der Amphibien in 6 Ordungen. *Isis*, **3**, 311–315.

Lawson, D. A. 1975. Pterosaur from the latest Cretaceous of West Texas: discovery of the largest flying creature. *Science*, **187**, 947–948.

Lear, E. 1832. *Illustrations of the Family of the Pittacidae or Parrots*. 1–4. Privately published, London.

Lydekker, R. 1888. *Catalogue of the fossil Amphibia and Reptilia in the British Museum (Natural History), Part I*. Trustees of the BM(NH), London.

Mantell, G. A. 1824. Description of some fossil vegetables of the Tilgate Forest in Sussex. *Transactions of the Geological Society, London*, **1**, 421–424, plates XLV–XLVII.

Mantell, G. A. 1827. *Illustrations of the Geology of Sussex*. Lupton Relfe, London, xii.

Mantell, G. A. 1835. A tabular arrangement of the organic remains of the county of Sussex. *Transactions of the Geological Society, London*, **3**, 201–216.

Mantell, G. A. 1837. On the bones of birds discovered in the strata of Tilgate Forest, in Sussex. *Transactions of the Geological Society, London*, **5**, 175–177, plate 19.

Mantell, G. A. 1840. *The Wonders of Geology*, 4th edn, Volume 1, 1–429, plates I–IV; Volume 2, i–vii431–804, plates V–X. Relfe & Fletcher, London.

Mantell, G. A. 1844. *The Medals of Creation; or, First Lessons in Geology and in the Study of Organic Remains*. Henry G. Bohn, London.

Mantell, G. A. 1846. On the fossil remains of birds in the Wealden strata of the South-east of England. *Quarterly Journal of the Geological Society, London*, **2**, 104–106.

Mantell, G. A. 1847. Birds vs reptiles. *London Geological Journal, and Record of Discoveries in British and Foreign Palaeontology*, **1**(3), 130–131.

Mantell, G. A. 1851. *Petrifactions and their Teachings or a Hand-book to the Gallery of Organic Remains of the British Museum*. Henry G. Bohn, London.

Marsh, O. C. 1871. Note on a new and gigantic species of *Pterodactyle. American Journal of Science*, Series 3, **1**, 472.

Marsh, O. C. 1878. Principal characters of American Jurassic dinosaurs, Part 1. *American Journal of Science*, Series 3, **16**, 411–416.

Martill, D. M., Frey, E., Green, M. & Green, M. E. 1996. Giant pterosaurs from the Lower Cretaceous of the Isle of Wight, UK. *Neues Jahrbuch für Geologie und Paläontologie, Monatsefte*, **1996**, 672–683.

Martill, D. M., Gale, A. & Witton, M. 2008. Possible azhdarhoid pterosaur remains from the Coniacian (Late Cretaceous) of England. *Zitteliana*, **B28**, 209–218.

Meyer, H. von 1832. *Palaeologica zur Geschichte der Erde*. Frankfurt.

Meyer, H. von 1834. Beitrage zur Petrefactenkunde. [*Gathosaurus subulatus*, ein Saurus aus dem lithographischen Schiefer von Solnhofen.] *Museum Senckenbergianum*, **1**, 1–26.

Meyer, H. von 1859. *Zur fauna der Vorwelt. Vierte Abteilung: Die Reptilian aus dem Lithographischen Schiefer des Jura in Deutschland und Frankreich*. Heinrich Keller, Frankfurt am Maine (pterosaurs pp. 1–90 + plates I–X, XXI).

Meyer, H. von 1861. Vogel-federn und *Palpipes priscus* von Solnhofen. *Neues Jahrbuch für Mineralogie, Geologie und Palaeontologie*, **1861**, 561.

Müller, I. 1985. *Ornithocephalus oder Pterodactylus? Die rekonstruktion von Fossilien durch S. Th. Soemmerring und Georges Cuvier als Experimentierfeld anatomischer Forschung*. Gustav Fischer, Stuttgart, 89–118.

Münster, G. G. zu. 1830. *Nachtrag zu der Abhandlungen des Professor Goldfuss über den* Ornithocephalus Münsteri *(Goldf.)*. Bayreuth.

Münster, G. G. zu. 1839. Ueber einige neue Versteinerungen in der lithographischen Schiefer von Baiern. *Neues Jahrbuch für Mineralogie, Geologie und Palaeontologie*, **1839**, 676–682.

Owen, R. 1840. Description of the remains of a bird, tortoise and lacertilian saurian, from the chalk. *Proceedings of the Geological Society of London*, **3**, 298–300.

Owen, R. 1840–1845. *Odontography*. Hippolyte Bailliere, London, **1–4**, Atlas.

Owen, R. 1846*a*. *A history of British Fossil Mammals and Birds*. John Van Vorst, London.

Owen, R. 1846*b*. On the supposed fossil bones of birds from the Wealden. *Quarterly Journal of the Geological Society, London*, **2**, 96–102.

Owen, R. 1850. Reptilia. *In*: Dixon, F. (ed.) *The Geology and Fossils of the Tertiary and Cretaceous Formations of Sussex*. Longman, London, 378–404. (published posthumously by R. Owen).

Owen, R. 1851. *Fossil Reptilia of the Cretaceous Formations*. Palaeontographical Society Monograph, June 1851, Part I, 1–118, plates I–XXXVII, VIIa, IXa.

Owen, R. 1852. On a new species of pterodactyle (*Pterodactylus compressirostris*, Owen) from the Chalk; with some remarks on the nomenclature of the previously described species. *Annals of the Magazine of Natural History*, **10**, 378–391.

Owen, R. 1859*a*. *A Monograph on the Fossil Reptilia of the Cretaceous Formations. Supplement I*. Palaeontographical Society Monograph, 1–19, plates I–IV.

Owen, R. 1859*b*. On remains of new and gigantic species of pterodactyle (*Pter. Fittoni* and *Pter. Sedgwickii*) from the Upper Greensand, near Cambridge. *In*: *Report of the British Association for the Advancement of Science, for* 1858, Leeds. John Murray, London, 98–103.

Owen, R. 1860. *Palæontology*. Adam and Charles Black, Edinburgh.

OWEN, R. 1861*a*. *Fossil Reptilia of the Cretaceous formations. Supplement III*. Palaeontographical Society Monograph, 1–19, plate I–VI.

OWEN, R. 1861*b*. *Fossil Reptilia of the Liassic Formations. Supplement 3*, Plesiosaurus, Dimorphodon *and* Ichthyosaurus. Palaeontographical Society Monograph, 41–81, plates XVII–XX.

OWEN, R. 1874. *Fossil Reptilia of the Mesozoic formations, I. Pterosauria*. Palaeontographical Society Monograph, **27**, 1–14.

PADIAN, K. 1984. A large pterodactyloid pterosaur from the Two Medicine Formation (Campanian) of Montana. *Journal of Vertebrate Paleontology*, **4**, 516–524.

PARKINSON, J. 1811. *Organic Remains of a Former World, an Examination of the Mineralised Remains of the Vegetables and Animals of the Antediluvian World; Generally Termed Extraneous Fossils. Volume 3, the fossil starfish, echini, shells, insects, Amphibia, Mammalia, &c.* Sherwood, Neely and Jones, London.

QUENSTEDT, F. A. 1855. *Über* Pterodactylus suevicus *im lithographischen Schiefer Würtembergs*. Universität Tübingen, Tübingen, 1–52.

SEELEY, H. G. 1870*a*. *The Ornithosauria. An Elementary Study of the Bones of Pterodactyls*. Cambridge University Press, Cambridge.

SEELEY, H. G. 1870*b*. On *Ornithopsis*, a gigantic animal of the pterodactyle kind from the Wealden. *Annals of the magazine of Natural History*, Series 4, **5**, 279–283.

SEELEY, H. G. 1901. *Dragons of the Air. An Account of extinct Flying Reptiles*. Methuen, London.

SOEMMERRING, S. T. 1812. Uber einen *Ornithocephalus*. *Denkschriften der Akademie der Wissenschaften München, Mathematisch–Physik*, **3**, 89–158.

SOEMMERRING, S. T. 1817. Uber einer *Ornithocephalus brevirostris* der Vorwelt. *Denkschriften der Akademie der Wissenschaften München, Mathematisch–Physik*, **6**, 89–104.

STEEL, L. 2003. The John Quekett sections and the earliest pterosaur histological studies. *In*: BUFFETAUT, E. & MAZIN, J.-M. (eds) *Evolution and Palaeobiology of Pterosaurs*. Geological Society, London, Special Publications, **217**, 325–334.

TAQUET, P. & PADIAN, K. 2004. The earliest known restoration of a pterosaur and the philosophical origins of Cuvier's *Ossemens Fossiles*. *Comptes Rendus Palevol*, **3**, 157–175.

THEODORI, C. 1830. Knochen von *Pterodactylus* aus der Liasformation von Banz. *Frorieps Notizen für Natur und Heilkunde*, **632**, 101.

UNWIN, D. M. 2001. An overview of the pterosaur assemblage from the Cambridge Greensand (Cretaceous) of eastern England. *Mitteilungen aus dem Museum für Naturkunde, Berlin, Geowissenschaftlichen, Reihe* **4**, 189–221.

UNWIN, D. M. 2003. On the phylogeny and evolutionary history of pterosaurs. *In*: BUFFETAUT, E. & MAZIN, J.-M. (eds) *Evolution and Palaeobiology of Pterosaurs*. Geological Society, London, Special Publications, **217**, 139–190.

UPCHURCH, P. & MARTIN, J. G. 2002. The Rutland *Cetiosaurus*: the anatomy and relationships of a Middle Jurassic British sauropod dinosaur. *Palaeontology*, **45**, 1049–1074.

UPCHURCH, P., BARRETT, P. M. & DODSON, P. 2004. Sauropoda. *In*: WEISHAMPEL, D. B., DODSON, P. & OSMOLSKA, H. (eds) *The Dinosauria*. University of California Press, Berkeley, CA, 259–399.

VIGORS, N. A. 1825. Sketches in ornithology; or observations on the leading affinities of some of the more extensive groups of birds: on a group of Psittacidae known to the ancients. *Zoological Journal*, **2**, 47–65. (*Palaeornis* erected p. 46.)

WEBSTER, T. 1824. Geological Observations on the sea cliffs of Hastings, with some remarks on the beds immediately below the chalk. *Annals of Philosophy, New Series*, **8**, 66–67.

WEBSTER, T. 1829. Observations on the strata at Hastings, Sussex. *Transactions of the Geological Society*, Series 2, **2**, 33–36, plate VI.

WELLNHOFER, P. 1970. Die Pterodactyloidea (Pterosauria) der Oberjura-Plattenkalke Süddeutschlands. *Bayerische Akademie der Wissenschaften Mathematisch–Naturwissenschaftliche Klasse*, **141**, 1–133.

WELLNHOFER, P. 1987. New crested pterosaurs from the Lower Cretaceous of Brazil. *Mitteilungen der Bayerischen Staatssammlungen für Paläontologie und historische Geologie*, **27**, 175–196.

WELLNHOFER, P. 1991*a*. *The Illustrated Encyclopedia of Pterosaurs*. Salamander, London, 192 pp.

WELLNHOFER, P. 1991*b*. Weitere pterosaurierfunde aus der Santana-Formation (Apt) der Chapada do Araripe, Brasilien. *Palaeontographica*, **215**, 43–101.

WENNERBOM, A. J. 1999. *Charles Lyell and Gideon Mantell, 1821–1852: Their Quest for Elite Status in English Geology*. PhD thesis, University of Sydney.

WITTON, M. P. 2010. *Pteranodon* and beyond: the history of giant pterosaurs from 1870 onwards. *In*: MOODY, R. T. J., BUFFETAUT, E., NAISH, D. & MARTILL, D. M. (eds) *Dinosaurs and Other Extinct Saurians: A Historical Perspective*. Geological Society, London, Special Publications, **343**, 313–323.

WITTON, M., MARTILL, D. M. & GREEN, M. 2009. On pterodactyloid diversity in the British Wealden (Lower Cretaceous) and a reappraisal of '*Palaeornis cliftii*' Mantell, 1844. *Cretaceous Research*, **30**, 676–686.

WORSSAM, B. C. & TAYLOR, J. H. 1969. *Geology of the Country Around Cambridge*. Memoirs of the Geological Survey of Great Britain.

Pteranodon and beyond: the history of giant pterosaurs from 1870 onwards

MARK P. WITTON

Palaeobiology Research Group, School of Earth and Environmental Sciences, Burnaby Building, Burnaby Road, University of Portsmouth, Portsmouth, PO1 3QL, UK

(e-mail: mark.witton@port.ac.uk)

Abstract: The immense size of many pterosaurs is now well known to academics and laymen alike, but truly enormous forms with wingspans more than twice those of the largest modern birds were not discovered until 83 years after the first pterosaur fossils were found. These remains were discovered in an expedition to the Cretaceous chalk deposits of Kansas led by O.C. Marsh in 1870: initially revealing animals with 6.6 m wingspans, Marsh eventually found material from animals estimated to span 7.6 m. Marsh's record breaking pterosaur – the largest flying animal known for nearly 80 years – was equalled by a supposed wing bone described by C.A. Arambourg in 1954, and then surpassed with the discovery of the 10 m span azhdarchid *Quetzalcoatlus northropi* by D. Lawson in 1972. Subsequent fragmentary azhdarchid discoveries suggest even larger forms: reinterpreting Arambourg's 'wing bone' as a cervical vertebra suggests an animal with an 11–13 m wingspan, while the Romanian taxon *Hatzegopteryx thambema* is a particularly large and robust form with a 12 m wingspan. Giant pterosaur footprints are also known, with the largest footprints recording walking azhdarchids of comparable size to those suggested by body fossils.

The spectacular size of many prehistoric animals has almost certainly contributed to their popularity amongst scientists and laymen alike. The Mesozoic seems to have been particularly well stocked with large creatures, bearing enormous dinosaurs on land and gigantic marine reptiles in the seas and oceans. Another Mesozoic group, the pterosaurs, are renowned for not only being the largest Mesozoic vertebrates capable of flight but also the biggest volant animals of all time, with the largest pterodactyloids dwarfing any bird, bat or flying insect known from the past or present (e.g. Buffetaut *et al.* 2002, 2003). Such sizes have ingrained giant pterosaurs into popular culture, and their expansive wingspans have featured prominently in popular books on prehistoric life, television documentaries as well as innumerable films and novels. Their size has captured the imagination of palaeontologists too, and multiple generations of pterosaur workers have felt compelled to estimate the total size of even those animals known from only fragmentary remains (e.g. Marsh 1871; Gilmore 1928; Arambourg 1954; Lawson 1975; Buffetaut *et al.* 2002). Some authors have even openly admitted that they find the size of these pterosaurs so impressive that they are willing to estimate gross proportions of animals not known from even one complete bone, despite the large degree of uncertainty associated with such calculations (Frey & Martill 1996).

The enormous size of pterosaurs was not truly appreciated until their fossils had been known for over 80 years. Prior to 1870, the largest pterosaur fossils known were fragmentary remains from the Cretaceous Chalk of southern England that hinted at forms with wingspans of 3 m (Bowerbank 1854), a wingspan comparable with those of the largest modern birds (see Martill 2010). It was not until pterosaur remains were uncovered outside of Europe in 1870 that their gargantuan sizes were appreciated, while the truly enormous forms we know of today would have to wait another century before discovery. The pterosaur trackway record has also recently been found to record giant forms. There have also been several – sometimes rather unsubstantiated – claims of record pterosaur size, citing the existence of forms that may have defied all understanding of animal flight. The 140-year history of giant pterosaur discoveries are reviewed here, beginning with the discovery of the best known of all giant pterosaurs, *Pteranodon*.

Pteranodon and the discovery of pterosaurs in North America

The first discovery of gigantic pterosaurs is an event synonymous with the first uncovering of pterosaurs in North America, an accolade traditionally credited to O. C. Marsh and his teams working in the Smoky Hill Member of the Niobrara Formation, Kansas, in 1870. However, the story of discovering the first pterosaurs in the New World is not without

From: Moody, R. T. J., Buffetaut, E., Naish, D. & Martill, D. M. (eds) *Dinosaurs and Other Extinct Saurians: A Historical Perspective*. Geological Society, London, Special Publications, **343**, 313–323.
DOI: 10.1144/SP343.19 0305-8719/10/$15.00

complications. In actuality, Marsh's bitter rival, E. D. Cope, reported and named supposed American pterosaur material 5 years before Marsh's teams discovered their own. Marsh never mentioned these reports in any of his publications on pterosaurs, suggesting he was either unaware of their existence or simply ignoring them. Unlike Marsh's gigantic pterosaur material from Kansas, Cope's alleged pterosaur remains were of considerably smaller forms sourced from Triassic strata of Pennsylvania, making them the first claims of Triassic pterosaurs anywhere in the world. Cope initially called this material *Pterodactylus longispinis* (Cope 1866), but were placed in his new genus *Rhabdopelix* in his 1870 paper 'Synopsis of the extinct Batrachia, Reptilia and Aves of North America' (Cope 1870; note that the first portion of this paper appeared in 1869: *Rhabdopelix* was erected in the second section, published in 1870 – see Colbert 1966 for more details). The *Rhabdopelix* holotype was reported as being lost five decades later by F. von Huene, but this was supplemented by additional reports of possible pterosaur remains from the same deposit (Huene 1921). Ultimately, however, doubts over the pterosaurian affinities of Cope's finds became apparent. Colbert (1966) noted some similarities between the gliding reptile *Icarosaurus* and the *Rhabdopelix* holotype figured in Cope's 1866 publication, concluding that at least some of the bones identified by Cope as pterosaurian were probably from an *Icarosaurus*-like animal (now recognized as a kuehneosaurid lepidosauromorph – see Gauthier *et al.* 1988), and that *Rhabdopelix longispinis* be considered a *nomen dubium* on account of the fragmentary nature of the holotype and its unknown whereabouts. Wellnhofer (1978) retained *Rhabdopelix* within Pterosauria and referred Huene's (1921) pterosaur discoveries to the same genus, but could only identify them as 'Pterosauria indet.'. Wellnhofer (1991) later questioned the pterosaurian identity of this material and highlighted its possible kuehneosaurid affinities. Dalla Vecchia (2003) was even less confident about the identity of *Rhabdopelix*, stating that all material referred to this taxon could belong to any reptile with slender, hollow bones (e.g. small theropods, protosaurs, kuehneosaurids) and is not necessarily pterosaurian. Thus, while Cope pre-empted Marsh with the first claims of North American pterosaur fossils, his discoveries were apparently insufficient to credit him with the first discovery of pterosaurs on American soil.

Of course, even if Cope had found the first American pterosaurs, he would not have not found the first real pterosaurian giants, whereas Marsh certainly did. Marsh's discoveries were made in the Coniacian–Campanian Smoky Hill Chalk of Kansas, a deposit famous for its rich assemblage of marine reptiles, sharks, bony fishes and marine birds (Everhart 2005). Marsh's expeditions to the Niobrara Chalk found their first pterosaur remains in 1870 and, on their first expedition, uncovered pterosaur remains of unprecedented size. Amongst several pterosaur bones representing two individuals, Marsh's team recovered a wing metacarpal that suggested 'an expanse of wings not less than 20 feet [6.6 m]!' (Marsh 1871, p. 472). This estimate was more than twice that of the largest pterosaurs known at that time in Europe and provided the first indication that pterosaurs grew to wingspans in considerable excess of any modern flying animals. Marsh named these isolated remains '*Pterodactylus Oweni*' in honour of the famed British naturalist Sir Richard Owen (Marsh 1871), and would name another eight pterosaur species from the Niobrara Chalk over the next 11 years. Marsh described the supposed teeth of his first pterosaur species as being 'smooth and compressed', perhaps assuming that teeth associated with the pterosaur remains (Everhart 2005) belonged to the same animal. Given that virtually all pterosaurs known up until this time were toothed, Marsh's assumption that these associated teeth belonged to the pterosaur remains was reasonable. However, and possibly unbeknownst to Marsh, toothless pterosaurs had just been identified in Britain with a reappraisal of the Cambridge Greensand pterosaur *Ornithostoma*, a fragmentary specimen described – as a metacarpal – by Owen (1851) but reinterpreted by Seeley (1871) as the jaw of an edentulous pterosaur. Had Marsh known such pterosaurs existed, he may not have been so confident about allocating the loose teeth he discovered to his first pterosaur finds.

A return to Kansas allowed Marsh to procure additional material of his first pterosaur species (renamed '*Pterodactylus occidentalis*' following the discovery that '*Pterodactylus Oweni*' had already been used by Seeley 1864), including a virtually complete wing that verified his 6.6 m wingspan estimate (Marsh 1872). He also discovered additional specimens that hinted at a species spanning almost 22 ft (7.3 m), and placed these remains in a separate species, *Pterodactylus ingens* (Marsh 1872). Once again, Marsh assumed that this species bore teeth and described them as being relatively slender compared to *Pterodactylus occidentalis*. In fact, it was not until more complete skull remains were found in 1876 that Marsh discovered that the jaws of these pterosaurs were actually edentulous (Marsh 1876*a*) (see Fig. 1a for Marsh's first (1884) reconstruction of the *Pteranodon* skull). Marsh was clearly surprised at this discovery, emphasizing the words 'absence of teeth' in his two 1876 pterosaur papers (Marsh 1976*a*, *b*). Both papers emphasized the difference between the edentulous Niobrara forms and 'all forms known in the

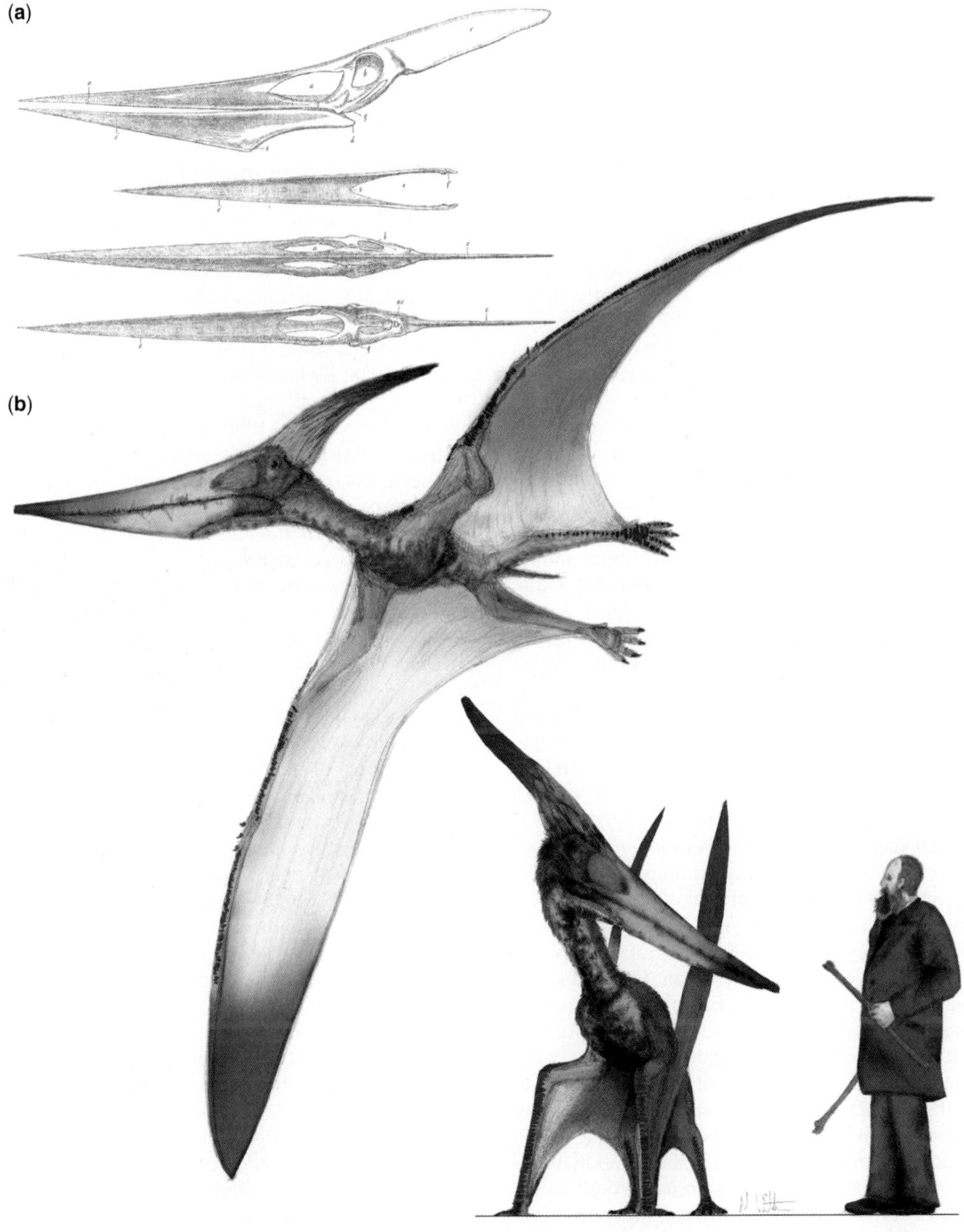

Fig. 1. The giant pterosaur *Pteranodon*. (**a**) Marsh's 1884 reconstruction of the *Pteranodon* skull, his first published figure of any *Pteranodon* material (from Marsh 1884). (**b**) Restoration of a 7.25 m span *Pteranodon longiceps* in flight and standing compared to a human of 1.75 m height (proportions of *Pteranodon* based on FMNH PR 464; see Bennett 2001 for more details).

old world', suggesting that Marsh was still unaware of *Ornithostoma*. Marsh used the edentulousness of these forms, along with a distinctive posterodorally directed cranial crest, to establish a new genus, *Pteranodon*, and erected a third species, *Pteranodon longiceps*, as its type (Marsh 1876*a*). In the same publication Marsh placed all of his other Niobrara pterosaur species in the same genus and also commented on the enormous size of some *Pteranodon* skulls, with some fragments indicating skull lengths of over 4 ft (1.3 m). The same year saw Marsh report *Pteranodon* with wingspans of 7.6 m (Fig. 2c) and reallocate a previously named species of *Pteranodon*, *P. gracilis*, to a new genus of Niobrara pterosaur, *Nyctosaurus* (Marsh 1876*b*; note that Marsh (1881) renamed this genus *Nyctodactylus* following presumption that his first name was preoccupied; this was shown to be erroneous by Williston 1903). His description of this 'eight to ten feet' (2.4–3 m) span taxon as 'medium size' (Marsh 1876*b*, p. 480) demonstrates that the definition of a 'giant pterosaur' had shifted significantly in the 6 years since Marsh first reported *Pteranodon*.

Following Marsh's (1876*a*) claim of 7.6 m span *Pteranodon*, no pterosaur remains were found that could challenge it for the title of largest flying animal for almost a century, despite Eaton (1910) downsizing *Pteranodon* to a wingspan of 6.8 m. This reduced estimate was, in part, attributable to Eaton (1910) factoring flexion between wing bones into his span estimates, giving a more realistic wingspan of the living animal than simply adding the lengths of the wing bones and shoulder width. However, he provided no methodological details as to how he factored this flexion into his wingspan estimates, making his accuracy against other *Pteranodon* size estimates difficult to fathom. Larger pterosaurs were reported in 1966 when an almost complete skull of a new *Pteranodon* species, *Pteranodon sternbergi*, was described and suggested to belong to an individual spanning 30 ft (9.1 m) across the wings (Fig. 2e) (Harksen 1966).

This species, along with *Pteranodon longiceps*, are the only *Pteranodon* taxa still considered valid (Bennett 1994), but a reappraisal of the *Pteranodon* wingspan in a comprehensive review of all *Pteranodon* material by Bennett (2001) suggests that its size estimates have fared better than its taxonomy. Bennett (2001) agreed with Eaton (1910) that estimates of pterosaur wingspans should allow for flex in the wing joints and suggested that the wing bone lengths be added without the shoulder girth, the absence of which from the span-total accounting for the flexion between wing bones. Bennett (2001) did not consider the wingspan of the individual represented by the *Pteranodon sternbergi* skull as the largest *Pteranodon* known, instead suggesting that the biggest *Pteranodon* individual known is represented by an isolated radius and ulna that give an estimated wingspan of 7.25 m (Fig. 1b). This specimen is not from the Niobrara Formation, however, but the overlying Pierre Formation: the largest Niobrara individual, and also the largest *Pteranodon* recorded by relatively complete remains, suggests a wingspan of 6.25 m. These dimensions have been eclipsed in recent decades by the discovery of larger pterosaurs, but with almost 140 years of research history, over 1100 specimens known and comprehensive descriptions of its entire osteology (Eaton 1910; Bennett 2001), the status of *Pteranodon* as the most completely known giant pterosaur has yet to be challenged.

Azhdarchidae: long-necked giants

No pterosaur remains were discovered that indicated animals larger than *Pteranodon* for the first seven decades of the twentieth century. The average wingspans of Cretaceous pterosaurs, however, rose so that spans of 2–5 m became appreciated as typical for pterodactyloids (e.g. Hooley 1913; Gilmore 1928; Swinton 1948; Young 1964; Miller 1971). A potential record of a giant pterosaur was mentioned in a 1936 *Time* article (entitled 'Diggers' published 16 November) in which T. A. Stoyanow was reported to have discovered an enormous pterosaur in Jurassic deposits of Arizona. With a reported 10 m wingspan (Fig. 2d), this find would have been significant in not only being larger than *Pteranodon* but also in being three being times larger than any Jurassic pterosaur known, even today (see Carpenter *et al.* 2003). The find, however, was never documented beyond the *Time* article and was never followed up by other pterosaur workers. This lull in discoveries of giant pterosaurs was broken when C. A. Arambourg recovered the first evidence of non-American pterosaurs that rivalled *Pteranodon* in size around 1940. This 500 mm-long bone from Campanian phosphate mines in Jordan was interpreted as a wing metacarpal (Fig. 3a) and was suggested to represent an animal spanning 7 m, a size equal to the wingspan of *Pteranodon* (Arambourg 1954). The specimen was named *Titanopteryx philidelphiae* 5 years later (Arambourg 1959), but its affinities and significance would not become clear for several more decades.

It was not until the 1970s that relatively frequent discoveries of giant pterosaurs began again and the concept of giant pterosaur size was heightened further. A 544-mm long humerus (Fig. 3b) and other elements of a huge wing were recovered by D. Lawson in the Maastrichtian Javelina Formation of Texas in 1972, revealing that pterosaurs with wingspans far greater than 7 m once existed. The humerus of this giant is twice the size of even the largest *Pteranodon* humerus and suggested that this pterosaur, named *Quetzalcoatlus northropi* in 1975, had a wingspan of between 11 and 21 m, depending on which pterosaurs were used to extrapolate its size (Lawson 1975). A medial figure of 15.5 m was provisionally accepted until work on several smaller, more complete, *Quetzalcoatlus* skeletons (designated *Quetzalcoatlus* sp.) found at the same time as their giant brethren, but 40 km distant, indicated that an 11–12 m wingspan

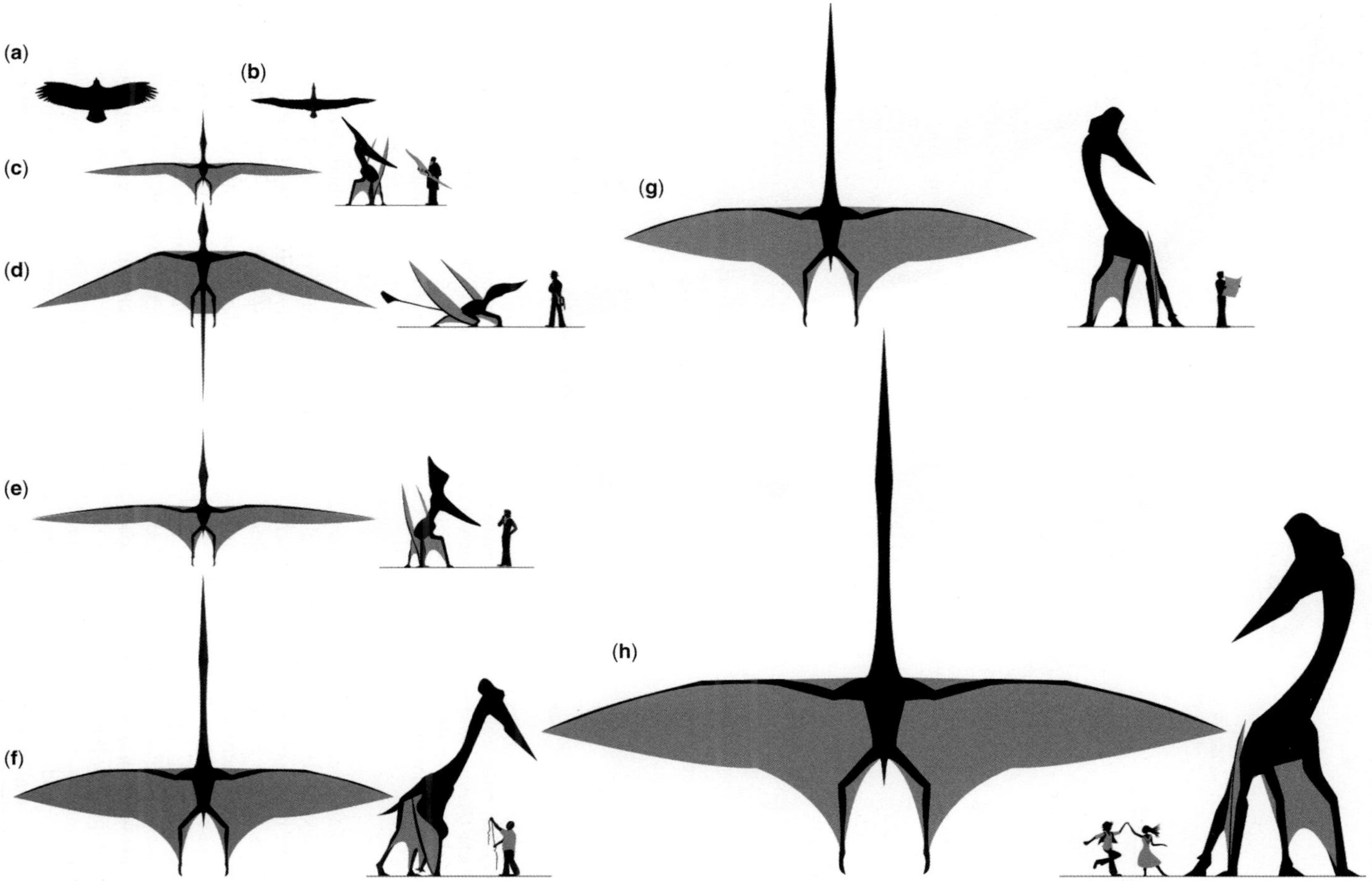

Fig. 2. Record claims of pterosaur wingspans and equivalent standing heights compared to (**a**) a 3 m span Andean condor (*Vultur gryphus*) and (**b**) a 3 m span wandering albatross (*Diomedea exulans*). (**c**) Marsh's (1876*a*) 7.6 m span *Pteranodon longiceps*. (**d**) Stoyanow's (16 November 1936, *Time Magazine*) apocryphal 10 m span Jurassic pterosaur. (**e**) Harksen's (1966) 9.1 m span *Pteranodon sternbergi*. (**f**) Lawson's (1975) 11 m span *Quetzalcoatlus northropi*. (**g**) The Buffetaut *et al.* (2002) 12 m span *Hatzegopteryx thambema*. (**h**) The erroneously reported BA Festival of Science 20 m span pterosaur. Humans used for scale are 1.75 m tall.

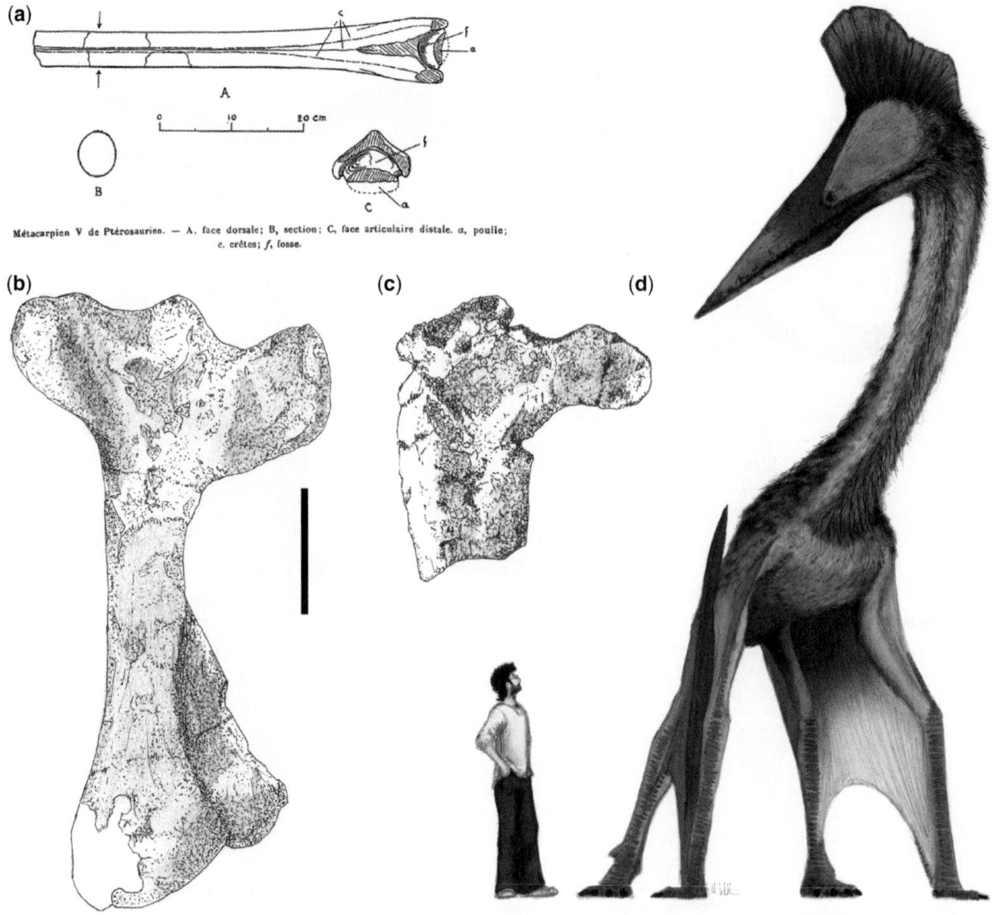

Fig. 3. Giant azhdarchids. (**a**) The earliest figured azhdarchid material: Arambourg's 1954 figure and figure caption of the *Arambourgiania* 'wing metacarpal', later revealed to be a cervical vertebra (modified from Arambourg 1954). (**b**) The 544 mm-long *Quetzalcoatlus northropi* left humerus (TMM 41450-3; drawn from Wellnhofer 1991). (**c**) Proximal left humerus fragment of *Hatzegopteryx thambema* (FGGUB R 1083; drawn from Buffetaut *et al.* 2002). Scale bar of (b) and (c) represents 100 mm. (**d**) Life restoration of 12 m span *Hatzegopteryx* next to a 1.75 m tall human.

estimate for *Quetzalcoatlus northropi* was more accurate (Langston 1981). This revision also appears to have incorporated arguments from aeronautical engineers who proposed that the skeleton of a 15–20 m span pterosaur would suffer overwhelming stresses during flight, a point with which Bakker (1986) argued strongly against. Stating that too little was known of the *Q. northropi* wing joints to curb wingspan estimates on account of engineering pitfalls, Bakker suggested that the original 15 m wingspan estimate should be accepted until there was good evidence to the contrary. However, given that a complete wing of the smaller *Quetzalcoatlus* species indicates that their wing fingers were proportionally short (Langston 1981), an 11 m wingspan seems more in keeping with *Quetzalcoatlus* anatomy than 15 or 20 m span estimates. Later discoveries of complete skeletons from smaller but closely related forms such as *Zhejiangopterus* (Cai & Wei 1994) add further confidence to the lower wingspan estimate of *Quetzalcoatlus northropi*. These estimates suggest that *Quetzalcoatlus northropi* had a wingspan almost 40% larger than that of *Pteranodon* (Fig. 2f), and it remains one of the largest known flying animals.

The long neck of *Quetzalcoatlus* generated almost as much interest upon its discovery as its large size and short wings. With several elongate, sub-cylindrical vertebrae – the longest of which is 8 times its width – the neck of *Quetzalcoatlus* provided an insight to the real identity of the

Titanopteryx holotype: Lawson (1975) re-identified Arambourg's pterosaur metacarpal as a cervical vertebra from a *Quetzalcoatlus*-like animal, and one with similar proportions to *Quetzalcoatlus northropi*. The following decade revealed another form similar to *Quetzalcoatlus* and *Titanopteryx*; *Azhdarcho* (Nessov 1984), and a new pterosaur group, Azhdarchinae, was erected to house them. Contemporaneously, Padian (1984) acknowledged the similarities between *Quetzalcoatlus* and *Titanopteryx*, and erected Titanopterygiidae as a group containing these taxa. Despite exclusively containing the world's largest pterosaurs, Padian (1984) stated of his Titanopterygiidae that '[g]reat size is not a diagnostic character' (p. 522) and used only features of the cervical vertebrae to qualify his group. By contrast, Nessov (1984) suggested that gigantic size was apomorphic for Azhdarchinae, a puzzling statement considering that *Azhdarcho* was not particularly large, with typical wingspans of 4–5 m and only rare individuals reaching 6 m (Bakhurina & Unwin 1995). Realizing that Azhdarchinae had precedence over Titanopterygiidae, Padian (1986) elevated the former to 'familial' rank – Azhdarchidae, and, again, defined the group exclusively by their elongate cervical vertebrae. More recent analyses have identified other azhdarchid characters (e.g. Unwin 2003), but their vertebrae remain highly diagnostic and are still used in determining the relationships of azhdarchids to other pterosaurs (e.g. Howse 1986; Bennett 1994; Unwin 2003; Kellner 2003; Andres & Ji 2008).

With the discovery of *Quetzalcoatlus* redefining the term 'giant pterosaur' from the 1970s onwards, the remains of a large Cretaceous pterosaur from Montana received little hyperbole despite indicating an animal of enormous size (wingspan 7.5–9 m; Padian 1984). A fragmentary femur from the Campanian Judith River Formation of Alberta (now the Oldman Formation of the Judith River Group: see Eberth 2005) was suggested to indicate an animal with a wingspan of 13 m (Currie & Russell 1982), providing the first evidence of an azhdarchid significantly larger than *Quetzalcoatlus*. This material has since been re-examined and is probably an ulna (Bennett pers. comm. 2009), suggesting the wingspan cited for this specimen by Currie & Russell (1982) is too high. A reappraisal of *Titanopteryx* provided alternative evidence for 13 m span pterosaurs, however, despite the misplacing of the *Titanopteryx* holotype by the late 1980s. Nessov & Jarkov (1989) saw fit to rename this pterosaur *Arambourgiania* after it became apparent that *Titanopteryx* was preoccupied by a blackfly, and a re-description of the specimen as a cervical vertebra by Frey & Martill (1996) was performed using plaster casts deposited in European and American museums. The holotype was later rediscovered in Jordan and additional descriptions of features not observable on the plaster cast were made by Martill *et al.* (1998). Comparing the incomplete *Arambourgiania* vertebra with those of *Quetzalcoatlus* sp. suggested that the former spanned 11–13 m: thus, Arambourg's *c.* 1940 discovery makes it the earliest find of a pterosaur larger than *Pteranodon*, albeit one that took 60 years to appreciate.

While work on *Arambourgiania* was underway, European deposits began to yield their first remains of giant pterosaurs. Martill *et al.* (1996) reported on a wing-finger fragment from a giant pterosaur found in Barremian–Aptian shales of the Isle of Wight, southern England, and suggested it may have spanned 9 m. The taxonomic position of this specimen could not established, but it remains noteworthy as the geologically oldest record of a giant pterosaur. Buffetaut *et al.* (1997) reported an azhdarchid cervical vertebra from Maastrichtian deposits of the French Pyrenees that indicated an animal of a similar size, while Company *et al.* (2001) reported a larger azhdarchid from the Maastrichtian of Valencia, Spain, with a wingspan of over 12 m. Recently, fragmentary remains of the largest pterosaur yet reported were recovered from the Maastrichtian Haţeg Basin of Romania (Buffetaut *et al.* 2002, 2003). The remains, named *Hatzegopteryx thambema*, include the only skull material known from a giant azhdarchid and are noteworthy for their unusually robust construction. The fragmentary skull bones indicate a jaw width of 500 mm (Buffetaut *et al.* 2003): if a 'typical' neoazhdarchian jaw length/width ratio (averaged to 0.2 across seven taxa: see Witton 2008, table 2) is assumed for *Hatzegopteryx*, its jaws may have been around 2.5 m long. Such a figure grants *Hatzegopteryx* with one of the longest skulls of any non-marine vertebrate, an accolade made all the more remarkable when it is considered that most non-marine animals with atypically large skulls – such as ceratopsian dinosaurs – only achieve comparable lengths through 'accessory' structures such as supraoccipital frills and spikes. If *Hatzegopteryx* has a skull like those of other azhdarchids, the estimated 2.5 m length would represent the jaws alone, granting it a larger gape than even the biggest theropod dinosaurs (see Dal Sasso *et al.* 2005). The *Hatzegopteryx* humerus (Fig. 3c) is also more robust than that of *Quetzalcoatlus*, suggesting it had a minimum wingspan of 12 m (Fig. 2g) and, when standing, a shoulder height of 3 m (Fig. 3d).

Grounded giants: giant pterosaur footprints

The 1952 discovery of pterosaur footprints in Upper Jurassic deposits of Arizona by W. L. Stokes (Stokes 1957) was integral to understanding pterodactyloid terrestrial locomotion. Controversy reigned over the identification and interpretation of these tracks for several years, and, although a rough consensus has since been reached, some arguments remain to be settled (see Lockley *et al.* 1995; Bennett 1997; Unwin 1997, 2005; Mazin *et al.* 2003; Padian 2003). Stokes' pterosaur tracks were made by pterosaurs of moderate size, with 76 mm-long pes prints and 83 mm-long manus prints, and most pterosaur prints found subsequently are of comparable size or smaller (e.g. Mazin *et al.* 1995; Lockley & Wright 2003; Padian 2003; Rodriguez-de la Rosa 2003). Two possible pterosaur track sites contain prints considerably larger than those in Stokes' (1957) trackway, however, and suggest that larger pterosaurs – perhaps even giants – also have an ichnological record. *Purbeckopus pentadactylus* was first described by J. B. Delair (1963) from Lower Cretaceous deposits of the Purbeck Group, southern England, and later interpreted as a pterosaur trace by Wright *et al.* (1997). With 150 mm-long manus prints and 200 mm-long pes prints (Fig. 4b and c), *Purbeckopus* records a large pterosaur with an estimated 5–6 m wingspan: while this size may not constitute a 'giant' pterosaur as known from the pterosaur body fossil record, *Purbeckopus* is a relatively enormous pterosaur track with prints roughly twice those of other pterosaur footprints. A more specific identification of the *Purbeckopus*-trackmaker is not clear, but possible 'beakprod' marks made by the *Purbeckopus* trackmaker suggest it bore at least partially edentulous jaws. Note, however, that the identification of *Purbeckopus* as a pterosaur track has recently been questioned: Billon-Bruyat & Mazin (2003) argued that crucial details of the *Purbeckopus* tracks are indeterminable, and that there is no clear association between alleged pes and manus prints, suggesting further work is needed to confirm its status as a pterosaur trace.

More confidently identified and considerably larger pterosaur tracks were described in 2002. The prints, including several isolated footprints and trackways from Santonian–Campanian age deposits of South Korea, were placed in the new ichnotaxon *Haenamichnus*, with some particularly large specimens placed in the new ichnospecies *Haenamichnus uhangriensis* (Hwang *et al.* 2002). Unlike most pterosaur trackways, the distinctive form of *Haenamichnus* has allowed for a more precise identification of its maker to be established, with several aspects of their morphology showing similarities with what is known of azhdarchid feet. Although only known from few specimens, azhdarchids seem to bear slender but robust pedes, metatarsals of almost equal length, digits approximately half the metatarsal length and reduced pedal claws (Hwang *et al.* 2002). Because many of these details are demonstrated by the *Haenamichnus* prints, it is likely that they record the movements of azhdarchids, and their size and age corroborate this hypothesis. Thus far, only large *Haenamichnus* prints are known: virtually all pes prints are over 150 mm long and most are over 200 mm. A trackway comprised of 14 footprint pairs (average pes print length of 228 mm) constitute the longest continuous pterosaur trackway known at 7.3 m long. Scaling these prints with complete azhdarchid skeletons suggest a pterosaur with an 8 m wingspan and standing shoulder height of 2 m. However, the largest *Haenamichnus* pes prints are up to 350 mm in length with only marginally shorter manus prints (Fig. 4d and e): scaling these prints suggests animals standing 3 m tall at their shoulders and wingspans comparable with those predicted for the largest azhdarchid body fossils.

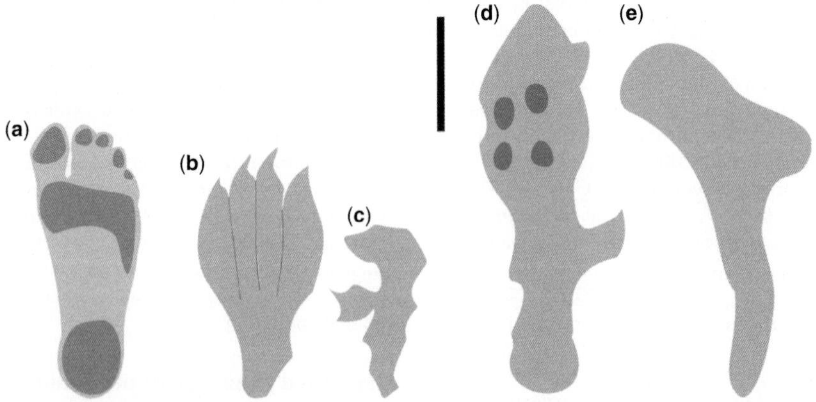

Fig. 4. Giant pterosaur footprints compared to a human (280 mm-long) footprint (**a**). (**b**) and (**c**) *Purbeckopus pentadactylus* right pes and left manus print (drawn from Wright *et al.* 1997). (**d**) and (**e**) *Haenamichnus uhangriensis* right pes and manus prints (drawn from Hwang *et al.* 2002). Scale bar represents 100 mm.

Even larger?

Since the discovery of the 10 m span *Quetzalcoatlus*, evidence of pterosaurs of equal or larger proportions have been reported in relatively quick succession (e.g. Padian 1984; Frey & Martill 1996; Martill *et al.* 1996; Buffetaut *et al.* 1997, 2002; Company *et al.* 2001; Hwang *et al.* 2002). Even these giants, however, were dwarfed by the claim of a 20 m span pterosaur made in 2005 (Fig. 2h). Tales of enormous pterosaur footprints in Mexico and a huge wing bone from Israel were revealed in a press conference at the 2005 British Association Festival of Science prior to any formal publication of either find, and an excited media quickly widely reported this announcement in newspapers, magazines and numerous websites around the world (for examples of coverage in the British press, see 9 September 2005 editions of *The Guardian* (p. 9) and *The Daily Mail* (p. 25). However, subsequent reappraisals of the alleged discoveries suggest that the footprints belong to a large theropod dinosaur and the 'wing bone' is, in fact, a particularly large piece of fossil wood (Frey pers. comm. 2007). Clearly, the claims of 20 m flying reptiles were made somewhat prematurely. It is intriguing to speculate, however, whether or not such a pterosaur *could* exist. Several lines of biomechanical evidence suggest that known pterosaur skeletal morphology may not permit them to obtain such sizes: any pterosaur with a wingspan above 12 or 13 m is likely to have considerable difficulty in becoming airborne, and would render its wing long bones and joints highly vulnerable to buckling and torsional forces once in flight (Cunningham & Habib pers. comm. 2008). Hence, although the fossil record has repeatedly confounded vertebrate palaeontologists and biomechanists who have attempted to speculate on the maximum size of extinct animals, a 20 m span pterosaur would be a surprise to any pterosaur researcher and would need to be a wholly different beast to any flying reptile currently known.

Tip of the hat to D. Martill, R. Moody and D. Naish for stimulating this research and providing the forum in which to display it; D. Martill for suggesting improvements on an early version of the manuscript; D. Frey and C. Bennett for helpful information and reviews; and J. Cunningham and M. Habib for tolerating my constant questioning about pterosaur size limits.

References

ANDRES, B. & JI, Q. 2008. A new pterosaur from the Liaoning Province of China, the phylogeny of the Pterodactyloidea, and the convergence in their cervical vertebrae. *Palaeontology*, **51**, 453–469.

ARAMBOURG, C. 1954. Sur la présence d'un ptérosaurien gigantesue dans les phosphates de Jordanie. *Canadian Royal Academy of Science, Paris*, **283**, 133–134.

ARAMBOURG, C. 1959. *Titanopteryx phildelphiae* nov. gen., nov. sp., pterosaurien géant. *Notes et Mémoirses du Moyen Orient*, **7**, 229–234.

BAKHURINA, N. A. & UNWIN, D. M. 1995. A survey of pterosaurs from the Jurassic and Cretaceous of the former Soviet Union and Mongolia. *Historical Biology*, **10**, 197–245.

BAKKER, R. T. 1986. *The Dinosaur Heresies*. Citadel Press, New York.

BENNETT, S. C. 1994. Taxonomy and systematics of the Late Cretaceous pterosaur *Pteranodon* (Pterosauria, Pterodactyloidea). *Occasional Papers of the Natural History Museum, University of Kansas*, **169**, 1–70.

BENNETT, S. C. 1997. Terrestrial locomotion of pterosaurs: a reconstruction based on *Pteraichnus* trackways. *Journal of Vertebrate Paleontology*, **17**, 104–113.

BENNETT, S. C. 2001. The osteology and functional morphology of the Late Cretaceous pterosaur *Pteranodon*. *Palaeontographica Abteilung A*, **260**, 1–153.

BILLON-BRUYAT, J. P. & MAZIN, J.-M. 2003. The systematic problems of tetrapod ichnotaxa: the case study of *Pteraichnus* Stokes, 1957 (Pterosauria, Pterodactyloidea). *In*: BUFFETAUT, E. & MAZIN, J.-M. (eds) *Evolution and Palaeobiology of Pterosaurs*. Geological Society, London, Special Publications, **217**, 315–324.

BOWERBANK, J. S. 1854. On a new species of pterodactyl found in the Upper Chalk of Kent (*Pterodactylus giganteus*). *Quarterly Journal of Geological Society*, London, **2**, 7–9.

BUFFETAUT, E., GRIGORESCU, D. & CSIKI, Z. 2002. A new giant pterosaur with a robust skull from the latest Cretaceous of Romania. *Naturwissenschaften*, **89**, 180–184.

BUFFETAUT, E., GRIGORESCU, D. & CSIKI, Z. 2003. Giant azhdarchid pterosaurs from the terminal Cretaceous of Transylvania (western Romania). *In*: BUFFETAUT, E. & MAZIN, J.-M. (eds) *Evolution and Palaeobiology of Pterosaurs*. Geological Society, London, Special Publications, **217**, 91–104.

BUFFETAUT, E., LAURENT, Y., LE LŒUFF, J. & BILOTTE, M. 1997. A terminal Cretaceous giant pterosaur from the French Pyrenees. *Geological Magazine*, **134**, 553–556.

CAI, Z. & WEI, F. 1994. *Zhejiangopterus linhaiensis* (Pterosauria) from the Upper Cretaceous of Linhai, Zhejiang, China. *Vertebrata PalAsiatica*, **32**, 181–194.

CARPENTER, K., UNWIN, D., CLOWARD, K., MILES, C. & MILES, C. 2003. A new scapognathine from the Upper Jurassic Morrison Formation of Wyoming, USA. *In*: BUFFETAUT, E. & MAZIN, J.-M. (eds) *Evolution and Palaeobiology of Pterosaurs*. Geological Society, London, Special Publications, **217**, 45–54.

COLBERT, E. H. 1966. A gliding reptile from the Triassic of New Jersey. *American Musuem Novitates*, **2246**, 1–23.

COMPANY, J., UNWIN, D. M., PEREDA SUBERBIOLA, X. & RUIZ-OMEÑACA, J. I. 2001. A giant azhdarchid pterosaur from the latest Cretaceous of Valencia, Spain – the largest flying creature ever? *Journal of Vertebrate Paleontology*, **21**, 41A–42A.

Cope, E. D. 1866. Communication in regard to the Mesozoic sandstone of Pennsylvania. *Proceedings of the Academy of Natural Sciences of Philadelphia*, **1866**, 290–291.

Cope, E. D. 1870. Synopsis of the extinct Batrachia, Reptilia and Aves of North America. *Transactions of the American Philosophy Society*, **14**, 105–252.

Currie, P. J. & Russell, D. A. 1982. A giant pterosaur (Reptilia: Archosauria) from the Judith River (Oldman) Formation of Alberta. *Canadian Journal of Earth Sciences*, **19**, 894–897.

Dal Sasso, C., Maganuco, S., Buffetaut, E. & Mendez, M. A. 2005. New information on the skull of the enigmatic theropod *Spinosaurus*, with remarks on its size and affinities. *Journal of Vertebrate Paleontology*, **25**, 888–896.

Dalla Vecchia, F. M. 2003. A review of the Triassic pterosaur fossil record. *Rivista del Museo Civico di Scienze Naturali 'E. Caffi'* Bergamo, **22**, 13–29.

Delair, J. B. 1963. Notes on Purbeck fossil footprints, with descriptions of two hitherto unknown forms from Dorset. *Proceedings of the Dorset Natural History and Archaeological Society*, **84**, 92–100.

Eaton, G. F. 1910. *Osteology of* Pteranodon. Memoirs of the Connecticut Academy of Arts and Sciences, **2**, 1–38.

Eberth, D. A. 2005. The geology. *In*: Currie, P. J. & Koppelhus, E. B. (eds) *Dinosaur Provincial Park: A Spectacular Ancient Ecosystem Revealed*. Indiana University Press, Bloomington, IN, 54–82.

Everhart, M. J. 2005. *Oceans of Kansas: A Natural History of the Western Interior Sea*. Indiana University Press, Bloomington, IN.

Frey, E. & Martill, D. M. 1996. A reappraisal of *Arambourgiania* (Pterosauria, pterodactyloidea): One of the world's largest flying animals. *Neues Jahrbuch für Geologie and Paläeontologie, Abhandlungen*, **199**, 221–247.

Gauthier, J., Estes, R. & de Queiroz, K. 1988. A phylogenetic analysis of Lepidosauromorpha. *In*: Estes, R. & Pregill, G. (eds) *Phylogenetic Relationships of the Lizard Families: Essays Commerating Charles L. Camp*. Stanford University Press, Stanford, CA, 15–98.

Gilmore, C. W. 1928. A new pterosaurian reptile from the marine Cretaceous of Oregon. *Proceedings of the US National Museum*, **73**, 1–5.

Harksen, J. C. 1966. *Pteranodon sternbergi*, a new fossil pterodactyl from the Niobrara Cretaceous of Kansas, *Proceedings of the South Dakota Academy of Sciences*, **45**, 74–77.

Hooley, R. W. 1913. On the skeleton of *Ornithodesmus latidens*; an Ornithosaur from the Wealden Shales of Atherfield (Isle of Wight). *Quarterly Journal of the Geological Society, London*, **96**, 372–422.

Howse, S. C. B. 1986. On the cervical vertebrae of the Pterodactyloidea (Reptilia: Archosauria). *Zoological Journal of the Linnean Society, London*, **88**, 307–328.

Huene, F. von 1921. Reptilian and stegocephalian remains from the Triassic of Pennsylvania in the Cope collection. *Bulletin of the American Museum of Natural History*, **44**, 561–574.

Hwang, K. G., Huh, M., Lockley, M. G., Unwin, D. M. & Wright, J. L. 2002. New pterosaur tracks (Pteraichnidae) from the Late Cretaceous Uhangri Formation, S. W. Korea. *Geological Magazine*, **139**, 421–435.

Kellner, A. W. A. 2003. Pterosaur phylogeny and comments on the evolutionary history of the group. *In*: Buffetaut, E. & Mazin, J.-M. (eds) *Evolution and Palaeobiology of Pterosaurs*. Geological Society, London, Special Publications, **217**, 105–137.

Langston, Jr. W. 1981. Pterosaurs. *Scientific American*, **244**, 92–102.

Lawson, D. A. 1975. Pterosaur from the Latest Cretaceous of West Texas: discovery of the largest flying creature. *Science*, **185**, 947–948.

Lockley, M. G. & Wright, J. L. 2003. Pterosaur swim tracks and other ichnological evidence of behaviour and ecology. *In*: Buffetaut, E. & Mazin, J.-M. (eds) *Evolution and Palaeobiology of Pterosaurs*. Geological Society, London, Special Publication, **217**, 297–313.

Lockley, M. G., Logue, T. J., Moratalla, J. J., Hunt, A. P. P., Schultz, J. & Robinson, J.-M. 1995. The fossil trackway *Pteraichnus* is pterosaurian, not crocodilian: implications for the global distribution of pterosaur reacks. *Ichnos*, **4**, 7–20.

Marsh, O. C. 1871. Note on a new and gigantic species of Pterodactyle. *American Journal of Science*, **1**, 472.

Marsh, O. C. 1872. Discovery of additional remains of Pterosauria with description of two new species. *American Journal of Science*, **3**, 1–9.

Marsh, O. C. 1876*a*. Notice of a new sub-order of Pterosauria. *American Journal of Science*, **11**, 507–509.

Marsh, O. C. 1876*b*. Principal characters of American pterodactyls. *American Journal of Science*, **12**, 479–480.

Marsh, O. C. 1881. Note on American pterodactyls. *American Journal of Science*, **21**, 342–343.

Marsh, O. C. 1884. Principal characters of American Cretaceous pterodactyls. Part I. The skull of *Pteranodon*. *American Journal of Science*, **27**, 422–426.

Martill, D. M. 2010. The early history of pterosaur discovery in Great Britain. *In*: Moody, R. T. J., Buffetaut, E., Naish, D. & Martill, D. M. (eds) *Dinosaurs and Other Extinct Saurians: A Historical Perspective*. Geological Society, London, Special Publications, **343**, 287–311.

Martill, D. M., Frey, E., Green, M. & Green, M. E. 1996. Giant pterosaurs from the Lower Cretaceous of the Isle of Wight, UK. *Neues Jahrbuch fur Geologie und Paläontologie, Monatshefte*, **1996**, 672–683.

Martill, D. M., Frey, E., Sadaqah, R. M. & Khoury, H. N. 1998. Discovery of the holotype of the giant pterosaur *Titanopteryx philadephia* Arambourg, 1959 and the status of *Arambourgiania* and *Quetzalcoatlus*. *Neues Jahrbuch für Geologie and Paläontologie, Abhandlungen*, **207**, 57–76.

Mazin, J.-M., Hantzpergue, P., Lafaurie, G. & Vignaud, P. 1995. Des pistes de pterosaurs dans le Tithonien de Crayssac (Quercy, France). *Comptes rendus de l'Académie des Sciences de Paris*, **321**, 417–424.

Mazin, J.-M, Billon-Bruyat, J, Hantzepergue, P. & Lafaurie, G. 2003. Ichnological evidence for quadrapedal locomotion in pterodactyloid pterosaurs: trackways from the late Jurassic of Crayssac.

In: BUFFETAUT, E. & MAZIN, J.-M. (eds) *Evolution and Palaeobiology of Pterosaurs*. Geological Society, London, Special Publications, **217**, 283–296.

MILLER, H. W. 1971. A skull of *Pteranodon (Longicepia) longiceps* Marsh associated with wing and body bones. *Transactions of the Kansas Academy of Science*, **74**, 20–33.

NESSOV, L. A. 1984. Pterosaurs and birds of the Late Cretaceous of Central Asia. *Paläontologische Zeitschrift*, **1**, 47–57.

NESSOV, L. A. & JARKOV, A. A. 1989. New Cretaceous Paleogene birds of the USSR and some remarks on the origin and evolution of the class Aves. *Proceedings of the Zoological Institute, Leningrad, USSR Academy of Science*, **197**, 78–97 (in Russian).

OWEN, R. 1851. *Monograph on the fossil Reptilia of the Cretaceous Formations. Part I. Chelonia, Lacertilia, etc.* Palaeontographical Society Monograph, **1**, 80–104.

PADIAN, K. 1984. A large pterodactyloid pterosaur from the Two Medicine Formation (Campanian) of Montana. *Journal of Vertebrate Paleontology*, **4**, 516–524.

PADIAN, K. 1986. A taxonomic note on two pterodactyloid families. *Journal of Vertebrate Paleontology*, **6**, 289.

PADIAN, K. 2003. Pterosaur stance and gait and the interpretation of trackways. *Ichnos*, **10**, 115–126.

RODRIGUREZ-DE LA ROSA, R. A. 2003. Pterosaur tracks from the latest Campanian Cerro del Pueblo Formation of southeastern Coahuila, Mexico. *In*: BUFFETAUT, E. & MAZIN, J.-M. (eds) *Evolution and Palaeobiology of Pterosaurs*. Geological Society, London, Special Publications, **217**, 275–282.

SEELEY, H. G. 1864. On the osteology and classification of Pterodactyles, Part II, with descriptions of the new species, *P. Hopkinsi* and *P. Oweni*. *Proceedings of the Cambridge Philosophy Society*, **1**, 238.

SEELEY, H. G. 1871. Additional evidence of the structure of the head in Ornithosaurs from the Cambridge Upper Greensand; being a supplement to 'The Ornithosauria'. *Annals and Magazine of Natural History*, **37**, 20–36.

STOKES, W. L. 1957. Pterodactyl tracks from the Morrison Formation. *Journal of Paleontology*, **31**, 952–954.

SWINTON, W. E. 1948. A Cretaceous pterosaur from the Belgian Congo. Bull. Soc. Belge Geol. Paléont. Hydr. Liège **77**, 234–238.

UNWIN, D. M. 1997. Pterosaur tracks and the terrestrial ability of pterosaurs. *Lethaia*, **29**, 373–386.

UNWIN, D. M. 2003. On the phylogeny and evolutionary history of pterosaurs. *In*: BUFFETAUT, E. & MAZIN, J.-M. (eds) *Evolution and Palaeobiology of Pterosaurs*. Geological Society, London, Special Publications, **217**, 139–190.

UNWIN, D. M. 2005. *The Pterosaurs from Deep Time*. Pi Press, New York.

WELLNHOFER, P. 1978. *Handbuch der Paläoherpetologie. Teil 19: Pterosauria*. Gustav Fischer Verlag, Stuttgart.

WELLNHOFER, P. 1991. *The Illustrated Encyclopaedia of Pterosaurs*. Salamander, London.

WILLISTON, S. W. 1903. *On the Osteology of* Nyctosarus (Nyctodactylus). Field Columbian Museum Publications, Geological Series, **2**, 125–163.

WITTON, M. P. 2008. A new azhdarchoid pterosaur from the Crato Formation (Lower Cretaceous, Aptian?) of Brazil. *Palaeontology*. **51**, 1289–1300.

WRIGHT, J. L., UNWIN, D. M., LOCKLEY, M. G. & RAINFORTH, E. C. 1997. Pterosaur tracks from the Purbeck Limestone Formation of Dorset, England. *Proceedings of the Geologists' Association*, **108**, 39–48.

YOUNG, C. C. 1964. On a new pterosaurian from Sinkiang, China. *Vertebrate Palasiatica*, **8**, 221–225.

Art and palaeontology in German-occupied France: *Les Diplodocus* by Mathurin Méheut (1943)

JEAN LE LOEUFF

Musée des Dinosaures, 11260 Espéraza, France (e-mail: jean.leloeuff@dinosauria.org)

Abstract: Geologist Yves Milon, the Dean of the Faculty of Sciences of Rennes, hired the painter Mathurin Méheut in 1941 to produce a large mural decoration for the new Geological Institute. This resulted in a little known 130 m^2 artwork that includes a Mesozoic triptych, the genesis of which is described here. The work was executed during the World War II, when Milon's illegal activities in several English intelligence services-led Resistance movements possibly prevented him from supervising the artist's work and which led to some anatomical inaccuracies. This decoration has survived several threats and constitutes a unique example of a large decorative palaeontological artwork in France. It has a special place in the history of dinosaur reconstructions as the choice of a decorative painting style is far from the usual forms of natural history illustration.

In the long history of dinosaur reconstructions, France does not have realizations comparable to the Crystal Palace sculptures of Waterhouse Hawkins or the great dinosaur murals painted by Charles R. Knight and Rudolph F. Zallinger in various North American museums. The lack of interest of most French palaeontologists for dinosaurs in the nineteenth century and the first half of the twentieth century can explain this quasi-absence of original dinosaur reconstructions in France during this period, as the dinosaur-fossil material from France discovered then was extremely scanty and did not warrant spectacular exhibitions (Buffetaut *et al.* 1991). One major exception is the remarkable dinosaur painting kept at the Museum of the Geological Institute in Rennes, a work that is unique in France because of its size (9 m^2), the status of the artist (painter and decorator Mathurin Méheut), and it having been created in German-occupied France during World War II.

A geologist and a painter

Les Diplodocus is a masterpiece of large artwork commissioned by the head of the Geological Institute in Rennes, Yves Milon (1896–1987), and includes 25 palaeontological and geological paintings created for the decoration of the new Geological Institute that had opened in 1937. The son of a pharmacist, Yves Milon had undertaken medical studies in Rennes at the beginning of World War I. In 1916 he was enrolled in the army and fought at the battle of Verdun. He was injured in May 1918 during a poison gas attack and was hospitalized until March 1919. He then abandoned his medical vocation and turned studies in geology in Rennes, where he became the assistant of geologist Fernand Kerforne (Rannou 2006). Milon was appointed Professor of Geology at the University of Rennes in 1930 and soon conceived the idea of a new building for the Geological Institute, a project that was successfully realized in a few years and opened in 1938 (Milon 1939). In Milon's mind, the building should have been decorated by large murals representing geological landscapes from Brittany, as well as faunas and floras of the past. However, he did not obtain funds for this decoration before the end of 1941.

As soon as German troops defeated the French Army in June 1940, Milon and his 21 year-old son Jean (the latter had survived the bombing of the French Navy by the British Navy in the harbour of Mers-el-Kebir in Algeria in July 1940) decided to fight against the German occupation. Jean Milon went to Gibraltar and then London where he was recruited by British Intelligence, MI6, and was eventually sent back to western France as a member of the so-called 'Johnny's Group' to spy on the activities of the German troops on the coast of Britanny (Rannou 2006). It is at this time that Yves Milon also joined this French Resistance group and agreed to make geological studies for the German Army, including hydrogeological research for anti-aircraft installations. Very precise information on the location of these installations was sent directly to the British Intelligence agencies. After Jean Milon died while crossing the Channel back to England in March 1941, Yves Milon entered even more into illegal activities and became a local leader of the Resistance, while retaining his university positions (he was the Dean of the Faculty of Science and the Director of the Geological Institute). It was at this time that he hired the painter Mathurin Méheut and started the project for the decoration of the Geological

From: Moody, R. T. J., Buffetaut, E., Naish, D. & Martill, D. M. (eds) *Dinosaurs and Other Extinct Saurians: A Historical Perspective*. Geological Society, London, Special Publications, **343**, 325–333.
DOI: 10.1144/SP343.20 0305-8719/10/$15.00

Institute. One might think that this was a new way to show his intense activity as an inoffensive scientist to the German services, one more smokescreen to conceal his hidden activities. However, Milon himself never suggested that, and it seems more likely that he was only following his 10 year-old project for the decoration of his new institute. As a result of his 4 years of 'field' activities (he used his geological field trips authorized by the Germans to contact the members of his organization in Brittany), Milon was eventually appointed Mayor of Rennes when the Allied troops took the town in August 1944, and was subsequently elected twice as the mayor of the town (Fig. 1). He left the office in 1953, going back to his geological studies.

Mathurin Méheut (1882–1958) is still well known for his paintings of rural Brittany in the first half of the last century (Fig. 2). He had begun his career with natural history illustrations at a laboratory of marine zoology in Roscoff in westernmost France. During World War I he was a soldier in the trenches until early 1916, when he was appointed to the topographical service of the army. Later he settled in Paris and devoted himself to the decorative arts. He illustrated many books between the two world wars and, as other artists of his generation, he undertook almost all possible commissions to support himself financially. He worked as a sketcher, a painter, an engraver, a painter–decorator and also as a book illustrator, a stained-glass windows and tapestry designer, and a ceramist (Delouche *et al.* 2004). He was also well known for the large murals he painted for the ocean-going liners of this period.

Fig. 1. Yves Milon in 1944. To the right is General Charles de Gaulle.

Fig. 2. Mathurin Méheut in the 1940s.

The majority of Méheut's larger artworks have been destroyed, as most of his great murals were painted for ocean-going liners of the Compagnie Générale Transatlantique and the Compagnie des Messageries Maritimes, and either sank with the ships in some instances (the *Georges-Philippar* was lost at sea in the Indian Ocean in 1932) or disappeared when the ships were broken up. Today, art historians have become interested in Méheut's work. A museum bearing his name and exhibiting his work was opened in 1972 in his home town of Lamballe, in western Britanny. Since the beginning of the twenty-first century, several retrospective exhibitions devoted to his work, the publication of books, as well as the success of recent auctions clearly demonstrate that he is recognized as an important artist of the first half of the twentieth century in France (Delouche *et al.* 2004, 2008), and especially as a remarkable draughtsman. His painting style is less characteristic, although it shows influences of post-impressionism. Méheut remained completely outside the main artistic tendencies of his time (cubism, surrealism, etc.) and was at odds with his contemporary fellow painters, such as Picasso, Braque or Matisse (see later).

Painting *Les Diplodocus*

Back in 1941, Milon apparently also had an excellent relationships with the German-appointed French authorities, as he took the opportunity of special credits from the Education Ministry to hire Mathurin Méheut that year and to realize the long-awaited decoration of the institute. Milon was not a vertebrate palaeontologist (he was a geologist) and his department was more involved in Palaeozoic projects; but he decided to devote a triptych to the Mesozoic, which would depict the most impressive creatures of this time, that is dinosaurs, pterosaurs and ichthyosaurs. Milon did not explain his choice of a North American dinosaur for a mural painting in a French institute; however, *Diplodocus* was extremely well known as Andrew Carnegie had offered casts of *D. carnegii* to major museums in the world, including the Paris Natural History Museum where it was installed in 1908 (Rea 2001). Admittedly, French dinosaurs were still extremely poorly known in the 1940s when Milon decided on the subjects of the paintings. Besides the Mesozoic paintings, the order included 22 other paintings of geological and palaeontological scenes for a total area of 134 m^2.

Méheut and Milon met in January 1942, and decided that the artist would make decorative paintings ‘d'une facture large, soit l'opposé d'un art de

Fig. 3. *Apatosaurus* by Ch. Knight (1898), cover page of *La Nature*, February 1942.

chevalet, tout de précision et de nuance' (with a large facture as opposed to very detailed easel paintings) using the special technique of camaieu, that is a painting with few colours and many tones (Le Bihan & Plusquellec 1989). The selected colours were brown, yellow and grey, which would fit well with the furniture housing the geological collections. This decision allowed the production of an artwork quite different from the usual canonical format of the 'genre of scenes from deep time' issued from the classical natural history illustrations (see Rudwick 1992), as a large facture implied a less figurative work.

Méheut took with him different documents such as a copy of Othenio Abel's (1925) *Geschichte und Methode der Rekonstruktion vorzeitlicher Wirbeltiere*, which includes (among others) drawings by Charles R. Knight, the master of the genre in the late nineteenth century and first half of the twentieth century. He also spent some time at Vincennes zoological park where he sketched models for the Quaternary paintings (bears, wolves, etc.), as well as at the National Natural History Museum in Paris where he could see the skeleton of *Diplodocus* and discuss it with palaeontologists (namely with palaeomammalogist Camille Arambourg). Unfortunately, it seems that the drawings given by Milon to Méheut (other than Abel's book) have not been preserved, so that we can only speculate on the artist's sources. One probable source is a

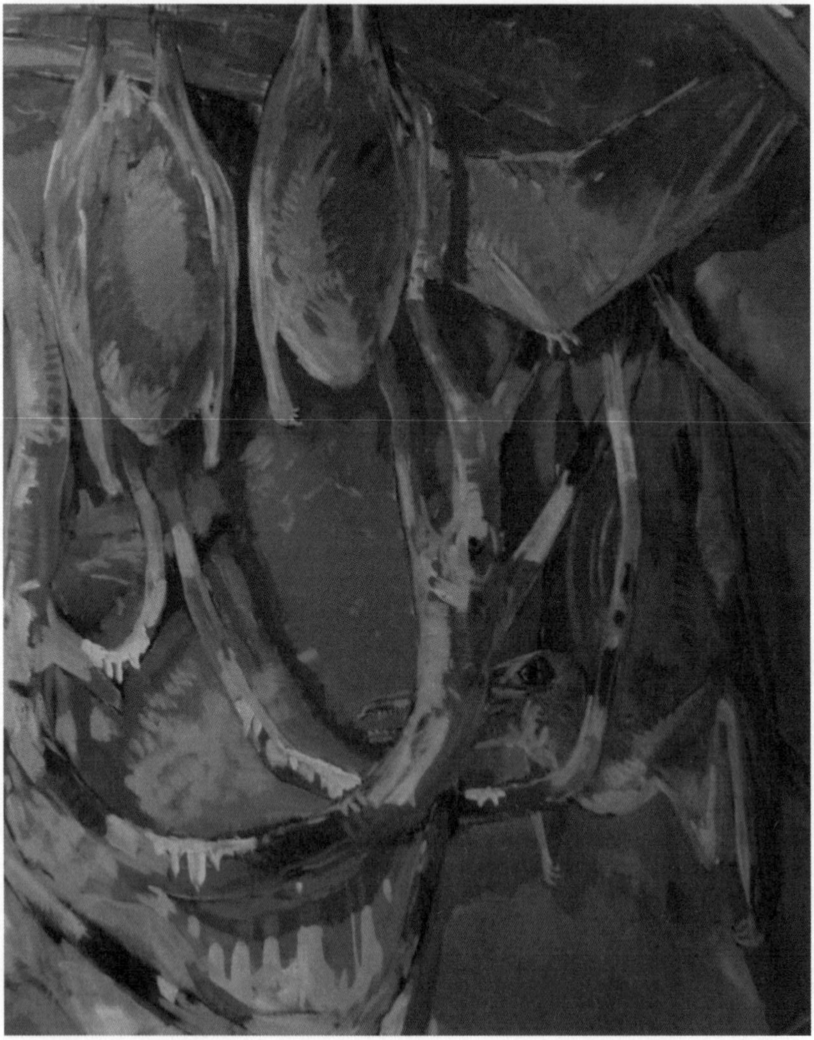

Fig. 4. *Les Ptérodactyles* (1943) by Méheut, detail.

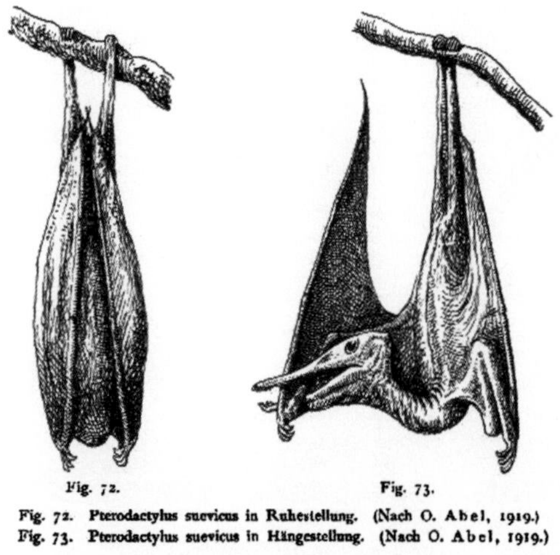
Fig. 72.
Fig. 73.
Fig. 72. Pterodactylus suevicus in Ruhestellung. (Nach O. Abel, 1919.)
Fig. 73. Pterodactylus suevicus in Hängestellung. (Nach O. Abel, 1919.)

Fig. 5. Abel's pterodactyls (1919).

general article on dinosaurs by Perruche published in February 1942 in the French scientific magazine *La Nature*, where it is recalled that sauropods lived in swamps. The article is illustrated by Knight's paintings (Fig. 3), including one commissioned in 1897 by the American Museum of Natural History (Czerkas & Glut 1982) depicting two individuals of the related sauropod genus, *Apatosaurus* (then popularly known as *Brontosaurus*). One clear influence from Abel's book that can be recognized are the pterosaurs hanging in a bat-like pose (Figs 4 and 5).

The major painting (190.5 × 486.5 cm) shows seven *Diplodocus* in a swamp close to the sea (Fig. 6). It was executed in less than 10 days (Le Bihan & Plusquellec 1989) in early August 1943. Letters from Méheut, in his usual colourful style, to his student Yvonne Jean-Haffen reveal that he often visited the Paris Natural History Museum during this period to draw the skeleton of *Diplodocus* 'pour l'avoir bien en main (façon de causer) avant de commencer cette grande tartine' ['to have it at hand (so to speak) before beginning this large slice of bread'] (Le Bihan & Plusquellec 1989). A sketch of his artwork in a letter to Jean-Haffen (Fig. 7) indicates well his decorative concerns with the necks and tails of the dinosaurs (structuring the composition in biomechanically impossible positions). Two of the dinosaurs are standing on a small island in the foreground, one curiously seen from behind. There is no other animal in the composition. It seems that they are feeding in a swamp close to the seashore with huge waves in the background. This painting is described by art historians as 'a surprising mixture of scientific realism, fantastic and decorative concern' (Delouche *et al.* 2004, page 177). Fantastic and decorative aspects are indisputable, whereas scientific accuracy is more problematic. The painting shows three circular depressions in the foreground, which are in all likelihood sauropod footprints: this kind of dinosaur footprints had just been described, in1939, by Roland T. Bird in *Natural History*. The drawing by Georges F. Mason, illustrating Bird's paper (Fig. 8), shows a '*Brontosaurus*' leaving the water and impressing footprints on the ground – a work based on a painting made by artist James E. Allen for *The Sinclair Dinosaur Book* (1934), a popular booklet apparently written by American palaeontologist Barnum Brown

Fig. 6. *Les Diplodocus* (1943) by Méheut.

Fig. 7. *Les Diplodocus*, letter to Y. Jean-Haffen (1943).

Fig. 8. *Sauropod* by George F. Mason (in Bird 1939).

(Glut 1980). It is likely that Milon had sent Bird's paper (or an unknown French version of it) to Méheut, as there are some clear similarities between all three of these pieces of art. Mason's (as well as Allen's) sauropod has characteristic flutings on its neck, legs and tail, which are also recognizable on Méheut's *Diplodocus*.

Milon was probably very busy with his official and unofficial activities, and it seems that he did not carefully examine Méheut's work because many inaccuracies can be observed, from pterosaurs with bat-like wings (Fig. 9) to ichthyosaurs with fish-like fins (Fig. 10). As for the *Diplodocus* painting, the limbs of the sauropods are anatomical monstrosities, but fortunately most of them have their legs concealed by high vegetation. It is not unlikely that Méheut made his own synthesis from Abel's *Diplodocus* reconstructions, where Hay's lizard-like dinosaurs are presented next to Charles Knight's classical '*Brontosaurus*'. It is remarkable that in the letters Milon and Méheut exchanged during the war (at least those that are kept at the Geological Museum in Rennes) there is no mention of the anatomical accuracy of the paintings. Although Méheut wrote 'j'ai à coeur de ne pas faire de blagues' ['I don't want to make blunders'], he made a number of mistakes and Milon did not correct them. A single preserved telegram from Méheut asks whether he could add horsetails and ferns around the *Diplodocus*, to which Milon surprisingly answered: no horsetails, but reeds. Either Milon was completely ignorant of the anatomy of Mesozoic reptiles or he considered that the paintings had a decorative rather than an educational function. The *Geological Fieldtrip* (Fig. 11), another painting for the decoration of the Geological Institute, clearly shows that the work was not figurative, however. Long after the war, when writing his reminiscences of Méheut's work, Milon mentions very precisely the technical, artistic and administrative aspects of the story, but fails completely to evoke the accuracy of the reconstructions (in Morzadec-Kerfourne 2000). He considered Méheut to be an accomplished naturalist painter and probably considered that the painter was better able than himself to draw accurate prehistoric animals. Milon was, thus, definitely more a patron ordering an artwork than a scientific supervisor in this endeavour, which puts the Milon–Méheut pair quite apart from the famous pairs Osborn–Knight or Augusta–Burian. American palaeontologist Henry F. Osborn (1857–1935) and artist Charles R. Knight (1874–1953) worked together for many years and Knight's entire career was that of a scientific illustrator. Czechoslovakian scientist Josef Augusta (1903–1968) later collaborated with the painter Zdenek Burian (1905–1981), Knight's successor as the world-leading palaeoartist. Méheut's palaeontological contribution, on the other hand, was only a short episode in a long and prolific artistic career.

The paintings were installed in Rennes after the war and the Geological Institute was officially opened in 1947 by the Ministry of National Education (although it was functional 10 years before this, the war had prevented its official opening). Milon, at that time, suggested to Méheut an exhibition in Paris, an idea that the painter rejected, fearing a possible rejection of his work by art critics: 'Les Picasso, Matisse, Braque, etc ... ont faussé, pour un bout de temps, tout esprit critique. L'on dirait que l'on s'efforce de détruire ce que nous appelions autrefois le goût Français. Je suis persuadé qu'en ce moment nous irions à un four plus que noir et ce serait dommage pour tous deux', the painter wrote ['We would head for a disaster, as good taste was destroyed by Picasso, Matisse, Braque, etc.']. They also tried to publish a book on the decoration

Fig. 9. *Les Ptérodactyles* (1943), detail.

Fig. 10. *Les Ichthyosaures* (1943) by Méheut.

Fig. 11. *Geological fieldtrip* by Méheut (1946).

of the institute but they never found a publisher. It was more than 40 years later, in 1989, that the first comprehensive monograph on the topic was published in the rather restricted regional natural history journal *Penn ar Bed* by René Le Bihan, the curator of the Art Museum in Brest, and Yves Plusquellec, a geologist from the University of Brest, both former students of Yves Milon. Méheut's authoritative composition for the Geological Institute fell short of suffering the same fate as his murals for the ocean going liners when a new university was built in Rennes in the early 1960s. University bureaucrats were apparently unaware of the major importance of Méheut's paintings, which were removed without care. Thanks to the action of the successive heads of the Geology department, the paintings were eventually restored, classified as historical monuments by the Ministry of Culture and then reinstalled in a new geological museum in 1995 (see Morzadec-Kerfourne 2000).

Conclusions

Méheut's *Diplodocus* have many anatomical flaws, as have his ichthyosaurs and pterodactyls, and do not really reflect the scientific knowledge of the 1940s, with the exception of the up-to-date footprints. The orthodoxy of that period, however, still considered sauropods as aquatic animals feeding on soft food in swamps; and Méheut's flaws are strictly anatomical. However, their delicate camaïeu gives an interesting decorative aspect to the paintings; it is the opinion of the author that his paintings are an exceptional example of the use of a palaeontological theme for decorative, more than educational, purposes; and they are definitely better suited for decoration than Zallinger's artwork at the Yale Peabody Museum (which, incidentally, was painted exactly at the same time). Despite its flaws, which might be related to the troubled times during which it was painted, a doubtful documentation and an absence of scientific supervision, Méheut's artwork (which also includes Palaeozoic and Cenozoic scenes) is a remarkable example of palaeontological art in mid-twentieth century France. It is also a departure from the norms of the genre, as the main goal was to produce a decorative artwork more than a scientifically accurate reconstruction (the reverse is better known in museums worldwide, where sometimes artistically doubtful paintings are no longer accurate after a few decades). In this respect, it was a success that has remained almost ignored for 60 years and has not, so far, inspired recent artists. It seems that leading French geologists and palaeontologists of the time had neither the fighting spirit nor the artistic skills of Milon, and these paintings at the Geological Institute in Rennes remained an oasis in the French palaeoartistical desert.

I thank J. Plaine (Musée de Géologie, University of Rennes) and D. Néraudeau (University of Rennes) for allowing me to work on Méheut's correspondence with Milon and to reproduce Méheut's artwork. Thanks to V. Girard for sending me pictures of Méheut's paintings. This work was inspired by the very complete study by R. Le Bihan and Y. Plusquellec on Mathurin Méheut, and the decoration in the Geological Institute in Rennes. I also thank D. Glut and E. Buffetaut who provided useful reviews.

References

ABEL, O. 1925. *Geschichte und Methode der Rekonstruktion vorzeitlicher Wirbeltiere*. Gustav Fisher, Jena, 1–327.

BUFFETAUT, E., CUNY, G. & LE LOEUFF, J. 1991. The discovery of French dinosaurs. *Modern Geology*, **18**, 161–182.

CZERKAS, S. M. & GLUT, D. F. 1982. *Dinosaurs, Mammoths and Cavemen: The Art of Charles R. Knight*. Dutton, New York, 1–120.

DELOUCHE, D., DE STOOP, A. & LE TIEC, P. 2004. *Mathurin Méheut*. Edition du Chasse-Marée, Douarnenez, 1–376.

DELOUCHE, D., DE STOOP, A. & ROZÉ, C. 2008. *Mathurin Méheut. De Bretagne et d'ailleurs*. Editions Palantines, Quimper, 1–144.

GLUT, D. F. 1980. *The Dinosaur Scrapbook*. Citadel Press, New York, 1–320.

LE BIHAN, R. & PLUSQUELLEC, Y. 1989. Animaux disparus et paysages géologiques. La décoration de l'Institut de Géologie de Rennes. *Penn Ar Bed*, **133**, 1–56.

MILON, Y. 1939. Le nouvel Institut de Géologie de la Faculté des Sciences de Rennes. *Comptes rendus des séances de la Société Géologique et Minéralogique de Bretagne*, **1937**, 42–53.

MORZADEC-KERFOURNE, M. T. 2000. La décoration de l'Institut de Géologie, l'œuvre commune d'un géologue et d'un artiste-peintre. *In*: BRUN, J. P., OLLIVIER, M. A. & FALAISE, A. (eds) *150 Ans de Géologie à Rennes*. Mémoires de Géosciences Rennes, hors-série, **3**, 93–105.

PERRUCHE, L. 1942. Les dinosaures. *La Nature*, **3078**, 33–38.

RANNOU, Y. 2006. *Yves Milon. De la Résistance à la mairie de Rennes*. Editions Apogées, Rennes, 1–93.

REA, T. 2001. *Bone Wars. The Excavation and Celebrity of Andrew Carnegie's Dinosaur*. University of Pittsburg Press, Pittsburg, PA, 1–276.

RUDWICK, M. J. S. 1992. *Scenes From Deep Time. Early Pictorial Representations of the Prehistoric World*. University of Chicago Press, Chicageo, IL, 1–280.

2000 A.D. and the new 'Flesh': first to report the dinosaur renaissance in 'moving' pictures

J. J. LISTON

Hunterian Museum, University of Glasgow, University Avenue, Glasgow G12 8QQ, UK (e-mail: j.liston@museum.gla.ac.uk)

Abstract: Prior to recent developments in computer-generated images, reconstructions of dinosaurs and other prehistoric animals were limited to static images or objects. Although a dynamic tension could be introduced to a composition or construction, it fundamentally lacked the ability to convey the motion of a now-extinct animal to its viewer. Before digital art forms the one exception to this was graphic or sequential art, generally in the form of 'comic' strips. This article explores how one particular comic strip came to be the mass communicator of a new dynamism in dinosaur reconstructions within 2 years of the data for the so-called 'dinosaur renaissance' being presented in the scientific press.

The wide and effective dissemination of new scientific ideas to a public audience is arguably the most important challenge to a scientist. It can often take generations for the concepts to take root in a significant portion of the population. As the archetypal extinct animal, dinosaurs are particularly problematic in this regard: ever since their discovery, young children in particular have found dinosaurs to be utterly fascinating, and this has seemed to trivialize their study to the equivalent level of 'fairy tales' in the popular mind. To an extent, this state of affairs can only recently be argued to have been somewhat alleviated with the advent of moving computer-generated images ('CGI') in *Jurassic Park* and *Walking With Dinosaurs*. For as much as these CGI dinosaurs have been derided by some sections of the palaeontological community (as discussed in Liston 2000*a*), they have at least managed to achieve a broadening of the audience willing to engage with dinosaur-related media.

The key palaeontological idea of communicating to the general public what an extinct animal would have been like can be particularly difficult to convey: the fossil evidence that we have does not move or even stand in a semblance of the fashion that palaeontologist's envisage the animal to have had in life. The crux of the success of the CGI-based digital media franchises lies in their ability to communicate recreations of these animals that appear lifelike, with an evident sophistication that runs counter to the perhaps anticipated cliché of a 'cold-blooded lumbering slow-witted reptile'. This image of the dinosaur persisted in the public imagination for almost 20 years from the time that the 'dinosaur renaissance' sparked by the work of Ostrom and Bakker (Bakker 1975) first challenged these ideas within the scientific establishment. However, as this work will demonstrate, the first attempt to communicate the ideas inherent in this fundamental reappraisal of these animals was made in a populist graphic medium within 2 years of this change of thinking being proposed in the scientific literature.

First reconstructions: impact and appetite

Dinosaurs have not always been seen by the public as merely of interest to children. The impact of dinosaurs in literary (and therefore popular) culture came soon after their formal announcement to the world (Owen 1842). In 1851 the Great Exhibition ran in London's Hyde Park for almost 6 months from 1 May to 15 October. One of the important exhibits displayed there was Waterhouse Hawkins's collection of life-size reconstructions of Owen's 'founder members' of this extinct group of animals (but models of many other sorts of creatures were depicted too – not just Dinosauria). Six million people visited the Great Exhibition, and it seems that – as this represented a third of the population of Britain at the time – it is highly likely that Charles Dickens was amongst them: 2 years later, in the fourth sentence of *Bleak House* (1853), he used the image of a lumbering *Megalosaurus* to convey the idea that the streets of London had the muddy appearance of a world only recently revealed by the departure of the waters of The Flood:

> London. Michaelmas Term lately over, and the Lord Chancellor sitting in Lincoln's Inn Hall. Implacable November weather. As much mud in the streets, as if the waters had but newly retired from the face of the earth, and it would not be wonderful to meet a Megalosaurus, forty feet long or so, waddling like an elephantine lizard up Holborn-hill.

From: Moody, R. T. J., Buffetaut, E., Naish, D. & Martill, D. M. (eds) *Dinosaurs and Other Extinct Saurians: A Historical Perspective*. Geological Society, London, Special Publications, **343**, 335–360.
DOI: 10.1144/SP343.21 0305-8719/10/$15.00

Dickens's use of *Megalosaurus* not only reflects the impact that the coverage (regardless of whether or not he personally saw the sculptures) of the dinosaurs had had on him – as a writer – but his use of the name indicates his judgement that the animal would *already* be both recognizable, and impressive, to his readers.

Twenty years later, the power of Waterhouse Hawkins's realization of these animals had not diminished, and so a series of six lithographic sheets were produced for distribution to schools and technical colleges. The successful fossil vertebrate collector Alfred Leeds (1847–1917) appears to have found his first dinosaur around this time (Noè & Liston 2010), and he certainly had a set of these lithographic prints (GLAHM 132304–132309) in his home. Two years after his death, they passed (along with over 600 specimens) to the Hunterian Museum when his family finally left their home at Eyebury. However, it is perhaps a reflection of how much had changed in the way that these extinct animals were envisaged, that these lithographic sheets were merely ignominiously disposed off as packing, padding some of the 22 crates of bones sent to the University of Glasgow in 1919 (Fig. 1). A photograph exists of Leeds's smaller attic 'bone room' with a version of the Dollo–DePauw's (*c.* 1882) reconstruction of *Iguanodon bernissartensis*, which suggests that Waterhouse Hawkins had been superceded in Alfred Leeds's eyes.

Portraiture of rare and extinct animals

As an indication of how Waterhouse Hawkins's reconstructions fit within wildlife depiction, it is worth looking at the work of an artist, George Stubbs, working earlier, in the late eighteenth century, at a time of great interest in new discoveries

(a)

Fig. 1. (**a**) *Megalosaurus* (GLAHM 132305) and (**b**) *Iguanodon* (GLAHM 132306) prints by Waterhouse Hawkins from Alfred Leeds' collection. When the crates were eventually unpacked by the Hunterian Museum's Keith Ingham in 1963, the sheets were salvaged, and have recently been expertly conserved. Background details in photographs of Alfred Leeds' 'bone rooms' show that he had a Dollo–DePauw's reconstruction propped on his workbench, probably rendering Waterhouse Hawkins' prints a trifle superfluous. © Hunterian Museum & Art Gallery, University of Glasgow.

(b)

Fig. 1. *Continued.*

of 'exotic' animals with the expansion of empires. Stubbs was highly regarded, and as such was employed by William and John Hunter to record some of these animals (Rolfe & Grigson 2006). Although such animals were sometimes encountered alive by the artist (*The Nilgai* 1769; *The Moose* 1770) (Fig. 2a, b), they were occasionally reconstructed in imagined poses from their remains (e.g. skins and skeletons from Cook's expedition: Egerton 2007). The level of contact of the artist with his subject was sometimes apparent in some of the more speculative compositions (e.g. note the lion in Stubbs's etching *Horse Frightened by a Lion* 1788) (Fig. 2c). As knowledge of such rare animals increased over time, such depictions became more informed. With extinct animals there was no opportunity for the knowledge of an artist to expand based on direct experience or even anecdotal reports, and reconstructions generally remained conservative, staying within the purview of statuesque portraiture. Wildlife subjects had a tradition in portraiture in static poses, sometimes metaphorical or symbolic (Rolfe & Grigson 2006), lacking motion or dynamism. Waterhouse Hawkins's lithographic sheets expressed this tradition.

An early example of widespread dissemination of post-Waterhouse Hawkins reconstructions is the series of Vernon Edwards's two-dimensional models generated by the British Museum (Natural History) [hereafter referred to as the BM(NH)], one of the earliest examples of dinosaur merchandise in the world. Sold by Hilda Bather [daughter of Francis Arthur Bather, the BM(NH) Keeper of Geology 1924–1928] as a souvenir of their visit to the museum, they were drawn and painted by Edwards onto wood, then placed in wooden stands (Snell & Tucker 2003). This set of eight dinosaurs (and the synapsid *Dimetrodon*, which was destined to be regarded by the toy industry as an 'honorary' dinosaur for the next 80 years) made reconstructions available for visitors to take from their visit to the Museum in South Kensington, and continue to interact with at home. The only known complete set survives in the collections of the Hunterian Museum (University of Glasgow: GLAHM 132405–132413) (Fig. 3). Of particular historical interest in

Fig. 2. (**a**) *The Nilgai* 1769 (GLAHA 43821), (**b**) *The Moose* 1770 (GLAHA 43823) and (**c**) *Horse Frightened by a Lion* 1788 (GLAHA 51579), printed in black, all by George Stubbs (1724–1806). © Hunterian Museum & Art Gallery, University of Glasgow.

Fig. 3. Vernon Edwards's 1920s models of extinct reptiles (GLAHM 132405–132413), as on display in 'EarthLife' in the Hunterian Museum, June 2005. © Hunterian Museum & Art Gallery, University of Glasgow.

the Vernon Edwards set is a *Hypsilophodon* placed in a tree, and a large sauropod almost entirely submerged in water, both very dated settings for these animals by today's standards. These objects were generated in response to public demand, as even in the 1920s the enthusiasm of child visitors was a significant governing force for steering the market towards the commercial outputs of dinosaur-related science.

The significance of graphic art in post-war Britain

Such individual images as these colour 'portraits' are important in terms of how they communicate the activity, movement and dynamism of the animals in question, and therefore reflect our understanding and ability to visualize ancient life. Although this dynamism can be inherent in a single picture, sequential art with a progression of images is what depicts, to varying degrees, the pace of that dynamism and the vigour or response of the subject. Sequential art forms, with their frame-by-frame change (whether as cinema, television or graphic art), can deliver and communicate this aspect of an extinct animal's existence, adding a life to our perception of it. Progression of images through time enables far greater understanding of interaction and development, rather than dealing with a static isolated slice of time. In short, although a picture may be worth a thousand words, a sequence of pictures is worth far more.

In cinema, the major figure in dinosaur-related work is Ray Harryhausen, with his stop motion animation technique. However, Harryhausen has displayed little interest in accuracy over the years, noting that 'visually ... I feel it is far more important to create a dramatic illusion than to be bogged down with detailed accuracy' (Jones 1993, p. 79), and even responding to criticism of his reconstructions by 5-year olds that he was not 'making pictures for palaeontologists' (Harryhausen & Dalton 2005, p. 75), doubting that 'professors' went to the cinema anyway. As such, the access of palaeontologists to cinema or television for the creation of reasonably convincing dinosaur reconstructions (whether by CGI or other means) is a comparatively recent development. Today, in the wake of the cinema's *Jurassic Park* (1993) and television series such as *Walking With Dinosaurs* (1999) and *Primeval* (2007), with their varying levels of palaeontological input and output, it is easy to forget that graphic art was the only pre-existing medium of sequential art that depicted extinct animals for many decades. Even then, the quality of that graphic art was not just dependent on the ability of the artist, but on the quality of the reference images and how up-to-date the associated information was.

But there are other constraints – the story itself. In the post-*Walking With Dinosaurs* world we have had Ricardo Delgado's *Age of Reptiles* (Delgado 1997), published by Dark Horse Comics, which, while lacking both dialogue and text, managed to convey the narrative surrounding its dinosaur characters very well indeed. However, over 30 years earlier, the idea of a strip-based story without humans was almost unthinkable. This attitude is reflected in Hollywood's insistence on placing cavemen in the same time frame as dinosaurs [for example, in Harryhausen's *One Million Years B.C.* (1966): Jones 1993]. There was at least a perceived need for humans to be present in sequential stories told concerning dinosaurs – although such things could not happen in the real world. As such, one had to enter the realms of science fiction for a means of juxtaposing human characters with prehistoric animals for an audience to connect to. Although such a mechanism is fantastical, science fiction acts as a valuable narrative device for humans to be placed into a context with living dinosaurs. As such, it is in science fiction strips that the few early examples of dinosaur-based stories can be found, wherein a reflection can be divined of what the public (in the form of its predominantly young audience) was presented with as the closest approximation to dynamic reconstructions of these extinct animals.

The use of dinosaurs in US comics has been dealt with elsewhere, and an excellent introduction to this area is provided by Glut & Brett-Surman (1997). But the appearance of dinosaurs in a medium that fused both text and artwork in a form of sequential or graphic art would only happen in Britain after World War II. The linkage between dinosaurs and comics is perhaps a natural one: it could be argued that both have been demeaned in the eyes of the general public through their strong association with children. They therefore become marginalized as 'childish things', to be put away and not regarded seriously once an adult. But this devalues and underestimates the true power and influence of this medium: image-rich, mass produced for a younger generation to be shared, retained and re-experienced, they had an accessibility and influence that far outweighed books, cinema or television in post-war Britain. Where had so-called 'comics' come from in the UK to achieve this kind of communicative power? In order to look at this, it is necessary not only to look briefly at the history of comics in Britain, but also how they related to educational children's magazines of the 1960s.

Ranger, *Look and Learn* and the rise of the post-war British comic strip

In May 1890 Alfred Harmsworth launched a halfpenny comic paper that included cartoons and strips taken from US humour papers, called *Comic Cuts*. This was an alternative to the UK tradition up to that date of the 'story paper', where one or two illustrations were scattered across a page of text. The majority of these were cancelled owing to paper shortages in the UK during the 1940s. Post-war, in the absence of the same pre-war level of 'home-grown' titles, there was a market for US horror and crime comics (e.g. *Eerie* in 1947: McAlpine 1997*b*, p. 331) that started to be imported via Canada (Barker 1992). Although the numbers of both titles and issues were small, a few agitators (Barker 1992) began to argue that they were having a deleterious effect on the young. The evidence for this was poor, but it sparked a press campaign that led to the enactment of the Children and Young Persons Act of 1955 (Barker 1992), paralleling the US experience with the establishment of the Comics Code Authority the same year (McAlpine 1997*a*, p. 165). It also provided an opportunity for new publishers, such as the Reverend Marcus Morris, to present themselves as a wholesome alternative, providing traditional (perhaps old-fashioned) role models as heroes – authority figures without flaws or weaknesses. Against the background of the press outcry against the imports from North America, and with a sudden increase in paper availability (Holland pers. comm. 12 August 2008), Morris launched *Eagle* comic through Hulton Press on 14 April 1950. Thanks primarily to artist Frank Hampson, the publication had an unusually high standard of artwork, aiming for a far more lifelike feel than had so far been produced in British comics (Holland 1997*a*). It built up a huge following, particularly with its creation of the immensely popular character Dan Dare, an officer in the 'Interplanet Space Fleet'.

The success of *Eagle* established that there was a market for high-quality graphic narratives in Britain. By the 1960s, educational magazines like *Look and Learn* were starting to tap into that influence in order to 'sweeten the educational pill' and break up the text-heavy 'story paper' format of the rest of the magazine. The *Look and Learn* magazine was launched in January 1962 by Fleetway Publications, designed to be an educational magazine bought by parents or grandparents for children to read. Covering science, history and the arts, it was an instant success, selling over a million copies a week in its early issues. Within a couple of years this figure had fallen to the still impressive quantity of 350 000 (Holland pers. comm. 17 April 2008). By 18 September 1965 Fleetway (now called International Publishing Corporation, or IPC, Ltd) had started a slightly different title, *Ranger*, 'the only national magazine for boys', with a similar mix of educational content (similar to *Look and Learn*'s 'story paper' format of one–three pages of text accompanied by one or two illustrations scattered across each page), but a heavier emphasis on narrative graphic strips. This, perhaps, reflected a move towards the children themselves lobbying for the purchase of the publication, rather than being presented with it by family members.

Mike Butterworth was the person responsible for writing virtually all of the strips in *Ranger*, the most enduring of which was the full-colour painted 'Rise and Fall of the Trigan Empire' with artist Don Lawrence (Holland 1997*a*). Another full-colour strip written by Butterworth for this new magazine would feature a rare outing for reconstructions of dinosaurs and other prehistoric animals, and serves as a marker for the market's expectations at the time. Inspired by the success of 'Dan Dare' in *Eagle*, 'Space Cadet' was the adventures of Jason January of the Royal Space Force Academy (based, naturally, in Portsmouth). Whereas Dan Dare had been a serving officer (chief pilot of the Interplanet Space Fleet) intended as an aspirational role model (Dare was originally designed as a military service chaplain or padre), Jason January was an attempt to splice the same ideas of space adventure with traditional school-based stories so popular with young audiences, a hero that they could more directly identify with rather than simply aspire to eventually be. Illustrated in full colour by Geoff Campion, 'Space Cadet' ran all through the run of *Ranger*, and when that magazine was amalgamated with *Look and Learn* in June 1966, it ran for a further year and a half. (To simply cancel a publication lost money for the company, so Fleetway/IPC had a policy of amalgamation rather than cancellation for ailing publications, which would artificially boost sales. In order to merge two titles, roughly 40% of the content had to be incorporated into the more successful 'host' publication. (Mills pers. comm. 4 August 2008) – thus 'Space Cadet' and the 'Trigan Empire' found a new adoptive home in *Look and Learn*.)

The rationale behind the presence of dinosaurs in the opening 'Space Cadet' story is thin, to say the least, but it does reflect the 1960s sensibilities of the strip. In 2805 the HMS *Victory* is stolen from Portsmouth and held to ransom in the lagoonal waters of an island in the China Sea called Wu Chung. Devastation by atomic bomb testing in 1965 has resulted (in a rather unclear fashion) in the resurrection of prehistoric animals on the island. The scenario is highly reminiscent of 'Godzilla' (no doubt reflecting the perceived level of sophistication of the public's knowledge of these animals) and, unfortunately, so is the quality of depiction of some of the 'prehistoric animals' in the strip (Fig. 4). Although one or two of the images vaguely resemble some of Burian's works from the 1950s (collected in Špinar 1972), they do not come anywhere close to Zallinger (Werner Watson 1960) and are fundamentally frozen and static animals, often closer to the work of Waterhouse Hawkins than the contemporary palaeontological reconstructions of the 1960s. As a rare example of the depiction of extinct animals portrayed in narrative art, the strip is a disappointment – particularly in a publication with an overtly educational agenda and responsibility.

It would be more than 10 years before another significant opportunity to present dinosaurs in a graphic science fiction narrative arose.

'Flesh': from the ashes of *Action*

On 6 July 1976 *Daily Mail* journalist David Lewin wrote an article which noted that the previous month's cinema release *Logan's Run* was only the vanguard of a horde of 15 science fiction films (including *Star Wars*, *Close Encounters of the Third Kind*, *Damnation Alley*, *Demon Seed*) due to arrive in UK film theatres in the coming year (Lewin 1976). With some prescience, he commented on the move by Hollywood away from disaster movies to putting significant funding (some £ 50 million – quite a lot at the time) into these more positive escapist scenarios. Kelvin Gosnell of IPC (International Publishing Corporation) Ltd's Competitions Department had read the article, and sent a memo to John Sanders (Managing

(a)

Fig. 4. Portsmouth Space Cadets: Composite of artwork from *Ranger* Magazine (**a**) issues 5 (16 October 1965), 8 (6 November 1965), and (**b**) issues 4 (9 October 1965) and 9 (13 November 1965), art by Geoff Campion, written by Mike Butterworth. 'Space Cadet' © IPC Media Ltd.

(b)

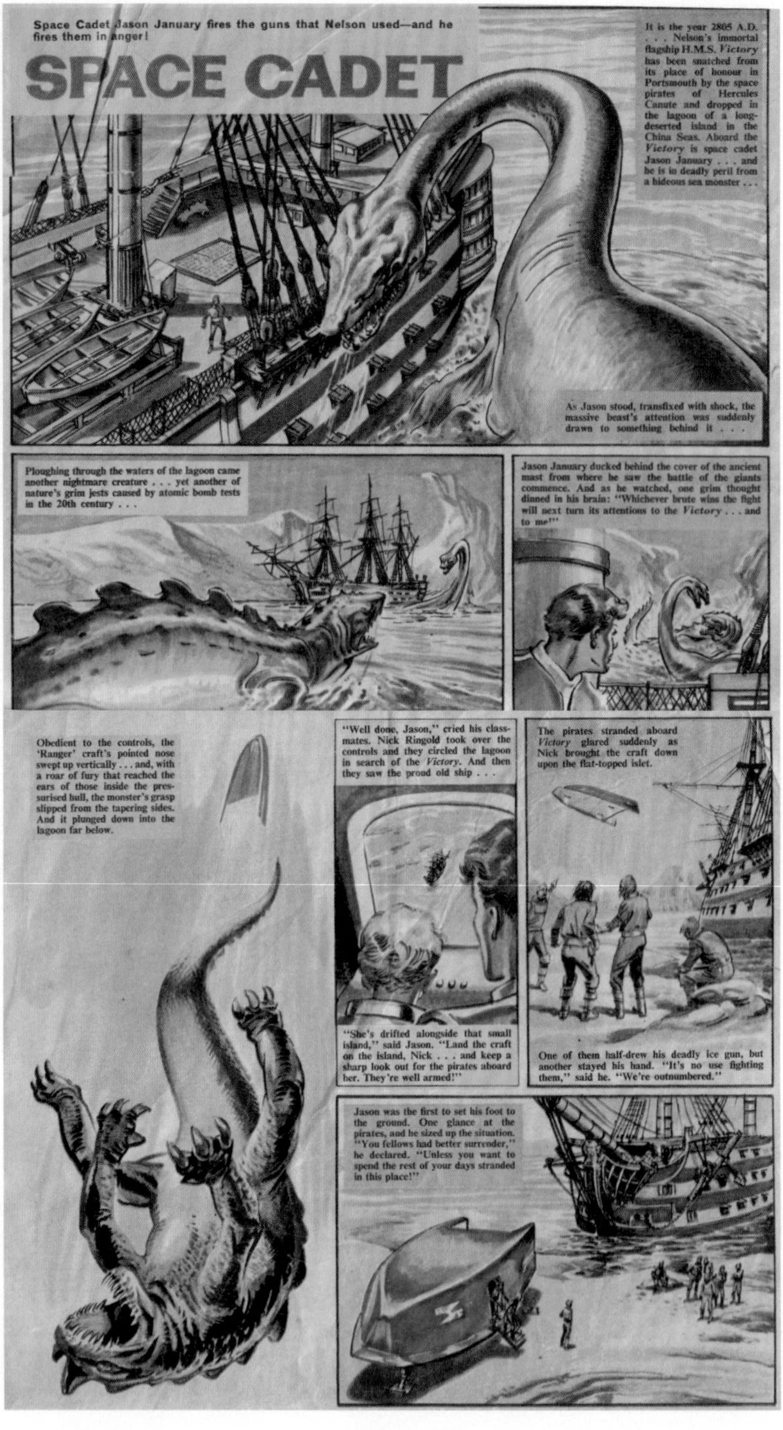

Fig. 4. *Continued.*

Editor of IPC's Comics Division) suggesting that a science fiction comic would be able to take advantage of the 'new market' that the release of these films would encourage (Holland 1997*b*). In order to take advantage of this, Sanders asked Pat Mills, a veteran of Dundee-based publishers DC Thompson as well as IPC Ltd, to put together a new science fiction comic for IPC. Mills had successfully done this twice before for IPC: the war comic *Battle Picture Weekly* (launched March 1975) and *Action* (launched February 1976), an anthology comic of different genres that appropriated successful contemporary film and television shows and repackaged the themes. Both titles had been part of the British 'new wave' in comics, with cynical, non-stereotypical working class heroes, and often including flawed authority figures. *Action* thus provoked a backlash from the tabloid press (reminiscent of the hysteria over Wertham's *Seduction of the Innocent* in 1954) for what Barker has referred to as its 'melodramas of social and political cynicism' (Barker 1989 p. 60), and IPC came under mounting pressure to scrap this extremely commercially successful title. Eventually, IPC suspended it 7 months after its launch, rewrote subsequent issues to avoid anything that could be construed as criticism of authority and, ultimately, merged the title into extinction in *Battle*.

Mills was aware that the same tabloid press that had emasculated *Action* would have problems applying similar criticism to a title where all the stories were presented with the trappings of science fiction, as they would thus not be so obviously challenging and critical of the everyday world. Looking to the future, the new comic would be called *2000 A.D.*, and to continue this futuristic feel the individual issues were referred to as 'Programmes' or 'Progs' (an abbreviation to make it sound like a computer program experience) that were 'In Orbit Every Saturday' for the price of '8p Earth Money' (Fig. 5). With Mills as founder and supervising editor, it was an opportunity for him to continue writing with the same sort of realism that had made *Action* so successful, albeit in an abstracted science fiction context.

The new comic would feature the same genre stories as *Action* (sport, war, crime, espionage, adventure) and, through the process of publishing house amalgamations, IPC now owned the rights to characters from the *Eagle*, so 'Dan Dare' could be 'reincarnated' to give *2000 A.D.* the pedigree of a classic British science fiction comic. But one story or genre would not translate quite so obviously into a science fiction setting: *Action*'s most popular story was 'Hook Jaw', inspired by the film *Jaws*, but told from the perspective of a great white shark. Rewritten by Mills from Ken Armstrong's original story (Mills pers. comm. 20 August 2008) and illustrated by Ramon Sola, Hook Jaw's victims were invariably human embodiments of some form of immorality, whether greed, violence or treachery, with the shark's attacks effectively expressing a judgement by the natural world on human activities. If Mills was to repeat the same successful mix of story genres that *Action* had possessed, he would have to come up with a science fiction equivalent of this successful 'wildlife' story. He had been working on an idea with a polar bear as the central character, but once the press campaign against *Action* gathered steam he became concerned that this story was not strong enough to be part of the launch of the new title (Mills pers. comm. 19 May 2008). He began to carry out background research on dinosaurs, and commenced writing the strip – called 'Flesh' – in late 1976 (Mills pers. comm. 19 May 2008).

The timing was propitious: in 1964 John Ostrom had been excavating in the early Cretaceous Cloverly Formation of Billings near Bridger, Montana, when he had come across the remains of *Deinonychus* (as recalled in Ostrom 1978) – an apparently agile small theropod dinosaur, with a skeletal structure that linked it neatly into the ancestry of birds (reviewed in Liston 2000*b*). Ostrom had published his description of the animal in 1969 (Ostrom 1969*a*, *b*), but one of Ostrom's students, Robert Bakker (who had been in Ostrom's 1964 field party as an undergraduate: Bakker 1975), published his landmark paper 'Dinosaur renaissance' in *Scientific American* in April 1975. It raised a series of controversial questions regarding thermoregulation, the connections with *Archaeopteryx*, interpretation of the implications of 'Arctic dinosaurs', the role of integument/pelage in the pterosaur *Sordes* and the fact that theropod dinosaurs had, for their time, the largest brains of any land animal. These questions challenged the scientific establishment's view that, to a large extent, mirrored that of the public's 'cold-blooded lumbering slow-witted reptile'.

The impact of the *Scientific American* piece on the creation of 'Flesh' was felt in two ways. First, Kelvin Gosnell, now editor-designate for Mills' planned science fiction comic, was alerted to the article through IPC's news-cuttings service. Interested in science, he had brought it to the attention of Mills (Mills pers. comm. 2 April 2008). Secondly, the Bakker article fed directly into a popular dinosaur book that came out in the same year and which would also heavily influence the design of the strip: *The Evolution and Ecology of the Dinosaurs*, written by Beverly Halstead (1975) and illustrated by Giovanni Caselli. Mills was captivated by Caselli's artwork, and effusive about its dynamism. From the agile leaping *Deinonychus* to the butting pachycephalosaurs, the book had a

Fig. 5. Pat Mills and his 'Space Age Dinosaurs' in the comic he founded, *2000 A.D.* 'Flesh' presented one of the more novel 'theories' for the passing of the dinosaurs: harvested to extinction by people from the future – after slaughtering, the meat is sent from the Late Cretaceous to the twenty-third century for consumption. Artwork by Boix, from Programme 1 (pp. 1 and 10) and Programme 2 (p. 8). 'Flesh' © 2008 Rebellion A/S. All rights reserved.

lot of fairly revolutionary depictions between its covers. Following on from the hair-like insulation referred to by Bakker, Caselli had painted all pterosaurs (including *Pterodactylus* and *Rhamphorhynchus*) with a similar fur-like covering on their bodies. And it was not just Caselli's artwork that inspired Mills – photographs of specimens like the 2.5 m arms of the Mongolian dinosaur

Deinocheirus (named by the late Halska Osmólska with Ewa Roniewicz in 1970) would also impact on the story. Mills sent the images as references to his artists, and they set to work.

The two primary artists selected for the strip were Juan Boix Sola Segales and Ramon Sola (from 'Hook Jaw') – both Spaniards worked for Josep Toutain's Selecciones Illustradas agency. The Spanish artists preferred to visually reference films and actors for their characters and looks: the lead human, Earl Reagan, was somewhere between John Wayne and Kirk Douglas; Claw Carver was based on Lee Marvin; and Reagan's sidekick, Joe Brontowski, referenced Robert Redford (Mills pers. comm. 19 May 2008). For its look, 'Flesh' drew heavily on the 1973 film *Westworld* (based on the Michael Crichton novel) for designs of uniforms and technology (Mills pers. comm. 19 May 2008).

Mills's dinosaur story presented the scenario of a future Earth that humanity had ravaged of its food supplies. The large meat-distribution companies (represented by the 'Trans-Time Corporation') have resorted to time travel to solve the shortage of meat, going back to the Late Cretaceous to harvest the untapped resource of the large herbivorous dinosaur herds, slaughtering and processing them in their thousands for the appetites of humans in the future (Fig. 5). This set-up meant that, rather unusually, the humans became the villains of the piece, with the dinosaurs as the principal characters of a five–six page per week story, as opposed to having subsidiary or accessory roles in a one–two pages per week story (as in *Ranger*). Key to the successful utilization of these pages was IPC's art editor Doug Church (Mills pers. comm. 14 August 2008). Church's unconventional layouts for the first eight issues, followed by Boix and Sola, were unorthodox, imbuing 'Flesh' and the other fledgling stories with a memorable dynamism, grabbing the attention of the reader with the opening scenes each week.

Although fulfilling the traditional requirements of an action science fiction strip, Mills's 'Flesh' had an underlying environmental message about humanity's squandering of the planet's resources in both the past and the future. The story opens with horse-borne cowboys on a cattle drive, rounding up stray beasts on the plains to take back to their base for slaughter – except the 'cattle' being led by trail boss Earl Reagan are styracosaurs. During an overnight break, some tyrannosaurs attack the herd – the human harvesting of the herbivores has led to food shortages for the predators, who are emboldened by their hunger. The styracosaurs stampede towards a cliff (echoing the herd of *Iguanodon* charging over a ravine illustrated by Caselli in Halstead 1975, p. 85), but are intercepted by the intervention of Reagan and his deputy Brontowski. The second issue sees another excursion, this time to round up a herd of alamosaurs ('pin heads') and, in the wake of a pterosaur assault, Brontowski is mauled by another tyrannosaur, which this time attacks the humans rather than the herbivores. In order to save Joe, Earl jams an electric goad (a large cattle prod) into the animal's right eye, blinding and stunning it (Fig. 6). This creates the central protagonist ('Old One Eye') and establishes the conflict in the story. From this point onwards, Reagan and the other human characters are mere antagonists: as they flee through a variety of locations back to the Trans-Time base, they serve only to provide obstacles to Old One Eye in her quest for revenge. Inexorably, she drives the plot forward towards her eventual triumph at the conclusion.

The second half of the story consists of a 7 day siege of the Trans-Time base, with the meat-processing station surrounded by starving theropods (Figs 7 & 8): again, a consequence of the removal of herbivore herds to the station for slaughter by humans. These theropods have travelled hundreds of miles, following the herds, to surround the base before breaking in and delivering their Gaia-like judgement on humanity's actions (Fig. 9). Here Mills and Sola went beyond the text in Halstead's book, making an intuitive leap to connect Bakker's Arctic dinosaurs with Caselli's hairy pterosaurs: amongst the streams of spinosaurs and *Deinocheirus* approaching the base 'From the north came the furry tyrannosaurs...'. This was 20 years before the first reports of any theropods with hair-like plumage emerged from Liaoning Province in China (Ackerman 1998), never mind large (around 2 m long) theropods, for example, *Beipiaosaurus* (Xu *et al.* 1999), with the same characteristics. Others have drawn attention to the ability of popular culture to make similar 'predictions' for future palaeontological finds; for example, the production design of the enlarged dromaeosaur in the film *Jurassic Park*, before the reconstruction of the newly excavated *Utahraptor* the same year (Bakker 1993; Lessem & Davis 1993). Similarly, on Friday 11 September at the 1998 Symposium of Vertebrate Palaeontology and Comparative Anatomy (SVPCA) meeting in Bournemouth, Frey & Martill presented a Crato Formation pterosaur as 'The pterosaur predicted by the toy industry' (SVPCA 1998; Frey *et al.* 2003; pers. obs.).

Significantly, for the introduction of Old One Eye in the third issue Mills used Ramon Sola, his former artistic collaborator for Hook Jaw in *Action*. 'Hook Jaw' is clearly the 'spiritual ancestor' of Old One Eye, both animal nemeses representing the natural world and sharing the rare animal kingdom ability of being able to swallow their human prey whole. Although Mills and Boix are

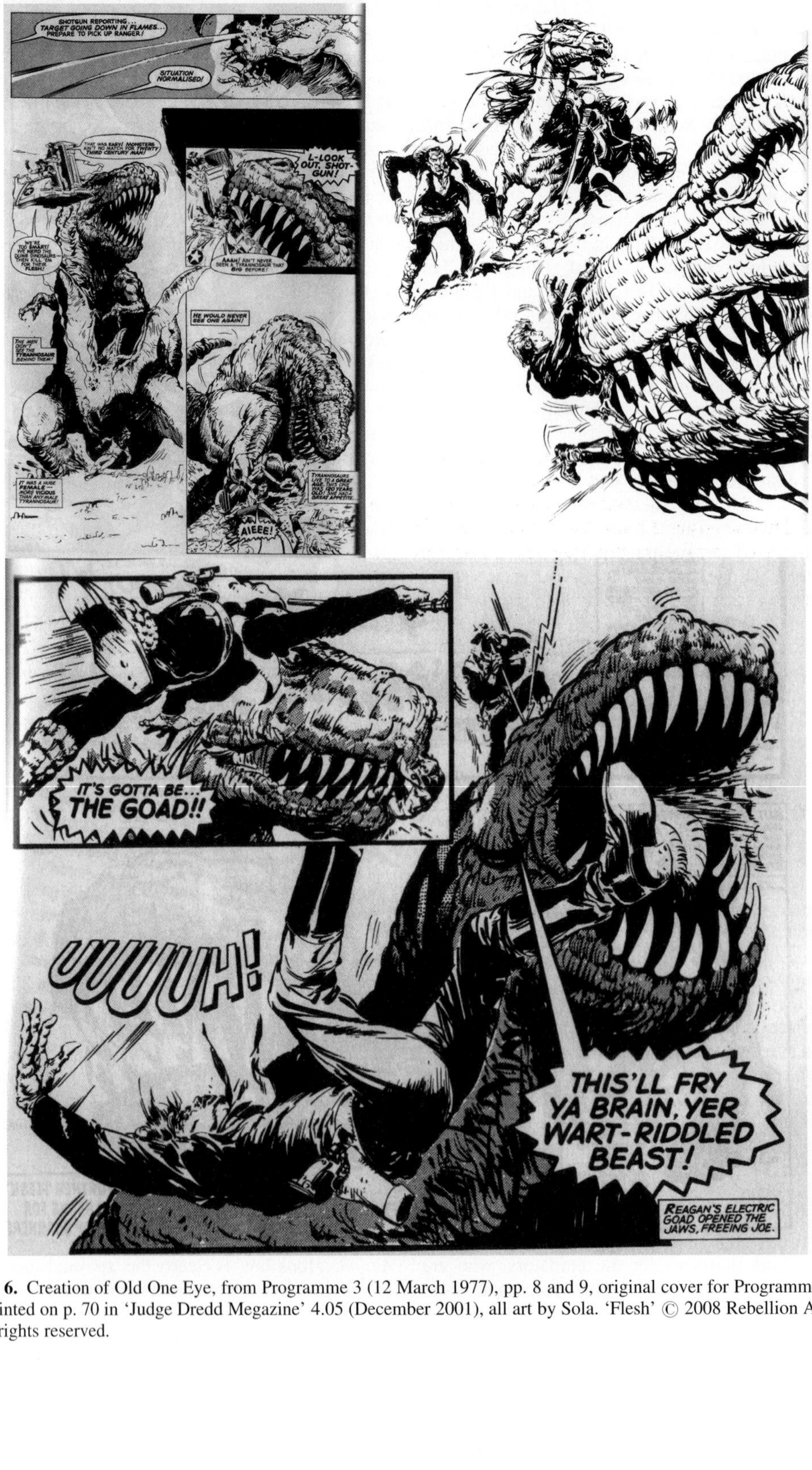

Fig. 6. Creation of Old One Eye, from Programme 3 (12 March 1977), pp. 8 and 9, original cover for Programme 3 reprinted on p. 70 in 'Judge Dredd Megazine' 4.05 (December 2001), all art by Sola. 'Flesh' © 2008 Rebellion A/S. All rights reserved.

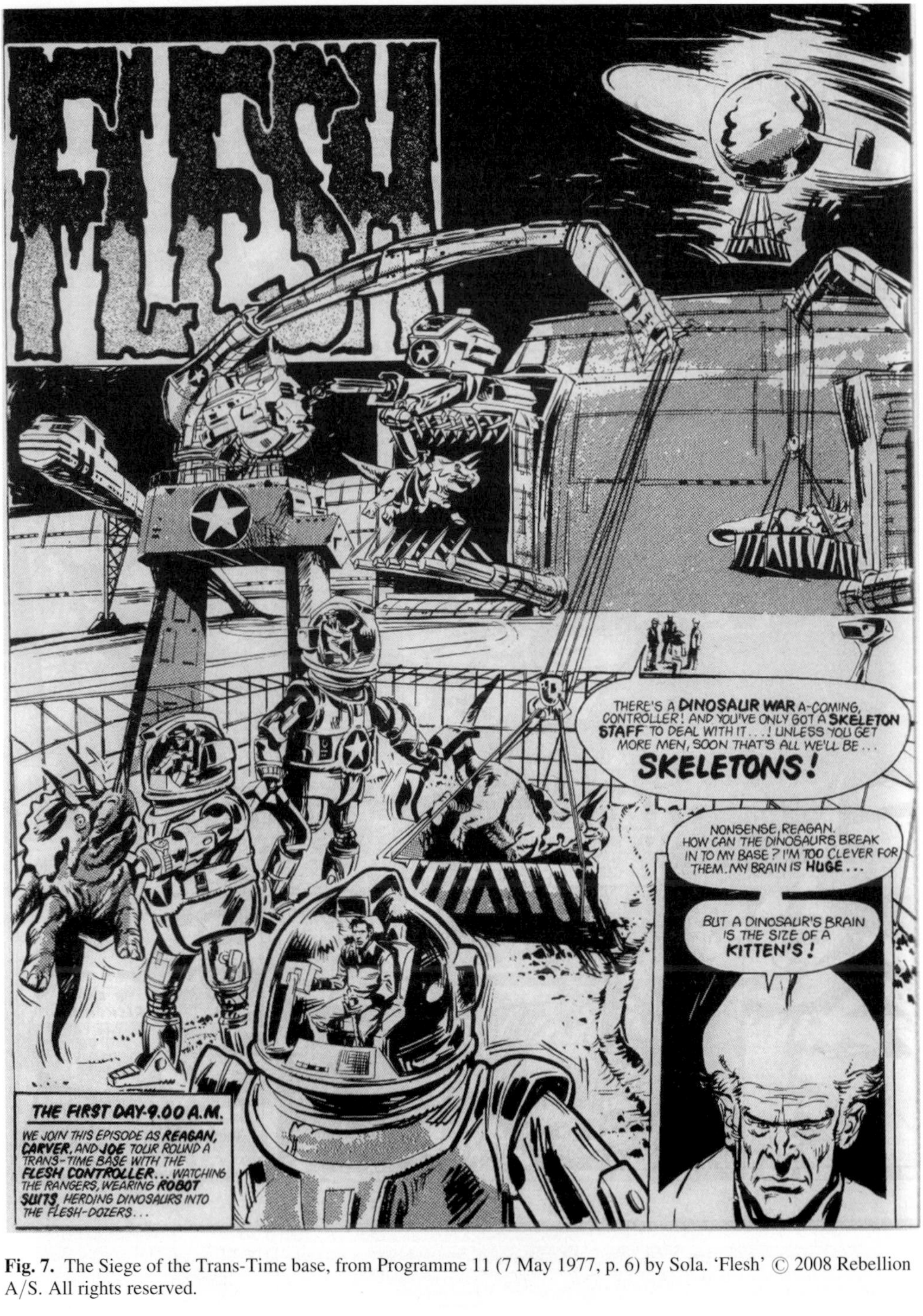

Fig. 7. The Siege of the Trans-Time base, from Programme 11 (7 May 1977, p. 6) by Sola. 'Flesh' © 2008 Rebellion A/S. All rights reserved.

Fig. 8. A diversity of Cretaceous predators lays siege to the base, from Programme 11 (7 May 1977, pp. 8 and 9) by Sola. 'Flesh' © 2008 Rebellion A/S. All rights reserved.

Fig. 9. With a suitably violent electrical storm, the final assault begins in Programme 14 (28 May 1977, p. 11), art by Boix.

credited as creators of 'Flesh', Mills clearly apportions the credit for the visual creation of Old One Eye to Sola. The design of Old One Eye is stylized, with her hide looking particularly scaly, as though to express her great age (Fig. 10). But in many ways it is the portrayal of the secondary dinosaurs that is of greater interest: their representation was radically different to any previously available to a popular audience.

First, scattered amongst the more commonly seen dinosaurs (styracosaurs, *Triceratops*, tyrannosaurs, hadrosaurs) and associates (*Pteranodon*), Mills introduces comparatively unknown or recently discovered dinosaur genera into his 'cast', occasionally introducing slang-terms employed by the cowboys to make them more accessible to readers unfamiliar with their names: spinosaurs, alamosaurs ('pin heads'), *Deinocheirus* ('terrible hands'), *Deinonychus* ('terrible claws'), *Ouranosaurus*. The large crocodilian *Phobosuchus* (= *Deinosuchus*) also appeared as a recurring character.

Secondly, to emphatically get rid of the idea of the dinosaur as the 'cold-blooded swamp-dweller', Mills brought dinosaurs out of the swamps and into the forests and plains (significantly leaving *Phobosuchus* behind in this regard).

Thirdly, having removed the dinosaurs from this traditional context, they behave in a far more dynamic way: the herbivores stampede, tyrannosaurs lock muzzles and Ostrom's *Deinonychus* (referred to as 'terrible claws', the translation of the generic name, throughout the strip) are presented in a particularly agile fashion, on one occasion able to leap onto a passing jeep (Fig. 11). One *Deinonychus* duels almost balletically (albeit unsuccessfully) with Claw Carver (Fig. 12), the human character who is utterly unrepentant about humanity's abuse of the environment, and solely values money. Although the animal loses the fight, the frames of Sola's artwork show it moving in an unusually lithe way.

For all that Mills upgrades the presentation of these animals in this strip, it is also interesting what he does not do, in terms of common mistakes. Traditional popular representations would indiscriminately mix taxa from all three Mesozoic periods (see, e.g., Harryhausen & Dalton 2005): by and large, the dinosaurs used are correctly constrained to the Late Cretaceous, although a couple of taxa from the very end of the Early Cretaceous (*Ouranosaurus* and the 'terrible claws') are also featured. Although the central character is a tyrannosaur, Mills labours to play down her intelligence and move away from anthropomorphism, constantly referring to her 'kitten-sized brain' and reinforcing the idea that intelligence does not mean innate superiority when she consumes the large-brained controller of the Trans-Time base.

This idea is reinforced in the epilogue to the story in *2000 A.D.* Prog. 19. After her exertions in the final conflict at the base, Old One Eye goes off to die of old age. Her fossilized remains are excavated in 1983 by a particularly unpleasant and egotistical academic, given the almost Dickensian name of Professor Gizzard. In a homage to the famous Waterhouse Hawkins event, he decides to bask in the glory of the find with his fellow professors by holding a meal within her rib cage (Fig. 13a) the night before her reconstructed skeleton is due to go on public display at the Natural History Museum (London). Arguing over the superiority of humans with his colleagues, Professor Gizzard climbs up to the skull to demonstrate that such an animal could never kill a human. In his enthusiasm, he accidentally knocks away the support that is holding the jaw open (Fig. 13b). It closes, rendering him a victim of his own conceit and arrogance: 'Even in death ... Old One Eye was triumphant!' (Prog. 19, p. 11).

The impact of 'Flesh'

2000 A.D. was launched on 26 February 1977, less than 2 years after Bakker's piece in *Scientific American* (April 1975). As a new science fiction comic, its commercial timing (3 months before a film called *Star Wars* was released) probably could not have been better. The sales of 215 000 copies a week of this new comic, passed enthusiastically around the playgrounds of 1977 Britain to reach a far wider audience, ensured that after 89 pages of 'Flesh' in *2000 A.D.*'s first 19 issues, a generation had been weaned on a distilled version of Bakker's 'dinosaur renaissance' less than 2 years after it was first published in the scientific literature. Not only was it ahead of its time with its 'green' subtext, within which humans are judged harshly for mismanagement of Earth's resources (in two time frames, the future and the Late Cretaceous), but it was also the first popular graphic art form to represent these animals in a modern and dynamic fashion, almost 20 years before Steven Spielberg would bring similar images to a worldwide audience with the film *Jurassic Park* (1993).

'Flesh' was one of the most popular strips of *2000 A.D.*, and so it has returned in a variety of reincarnations, as well as being reprinted several times (most recently in the 'Judge Dredd Megazine' 4.04–4.07 in 2002, under the promotional slogan of 'Stalking With Dinosaurs'). In 1978 Mills incorporated the 'son' of Old One Eye within the futuristic dystopian Judge Dredd epic 'The Cursed Earth' (Fig. 14). The mechanism for resurrecting a Late Cretaceous tyrannosaur is (so to speak) ahead of its time: DNA has been extracted from dinosaur

Fig. 10. ‘Carver City’: the tyrannosaurs break into the dome. Artwork from Programme 4 (19 March 1977, p. 10) and Programme 1526 (28 February 2007, ‘Flesh: Hand of Glory’, p. 21), all art by Sola. ‘Flesh’ © 2008 Rebellion A/S. All rights reserved.

Fig. 11. 'The Driving *Deinonychus*': a pair accidentally commandeer a jeep in the final siege at the Trans-Time base. Artwork from Programme 15 (4 June 1977, pp. 7 and 8), art by Sola. 'Flesh' © 2008 Rebellion A/S. All rights reserved.

Fig. 12. 'The Dancing *Deinonychus*': in 'Flesh', these animals are by far the most agile, introduced in the break-in to the domed Carver City, and duelling with Claw Carver. Artwork from Programme 6 (2 April 1977, pp. 7 and 8) and reprinted in *Judge Dredd* magazine 4.05 (December 2001, p. 62) art by Sola. 'Flesh' © 2008 Rebellion A/S. All rights reserved.

(**a**)

Fig. 13. (**a**) Dinner with the prophetically-named Professor Gizzard. (**b**) Note the panel at the bottom of the final page advertising the replacement strip the following week: Shako, the polar bear story that Mills held back from using in *2000 A.D.*'s starting line-up, in favour of 'Flesh'. Artwork from Programme 19, pp. 10 and 11, art by Sola. 'Flesh' © 2008 Rebellion A/S. All rights reserved.

(b)

Fig. 13. *Continued.*

bones and used to 'grow' a new dinosaur (Fig. 15). The scientists eventually decide to use the increasing number of dinosaurs created by this process as the basis of a recreational theme park. This is clearly highly reminiscent of Michael Crichton's 1990 *Jurassic Park*, although Mills himself has resisted the idea that this inspired Crichton, and the *Jurassic Park* template surely owes more to Robert Wells's 1969 novel *The Parasaurians*.

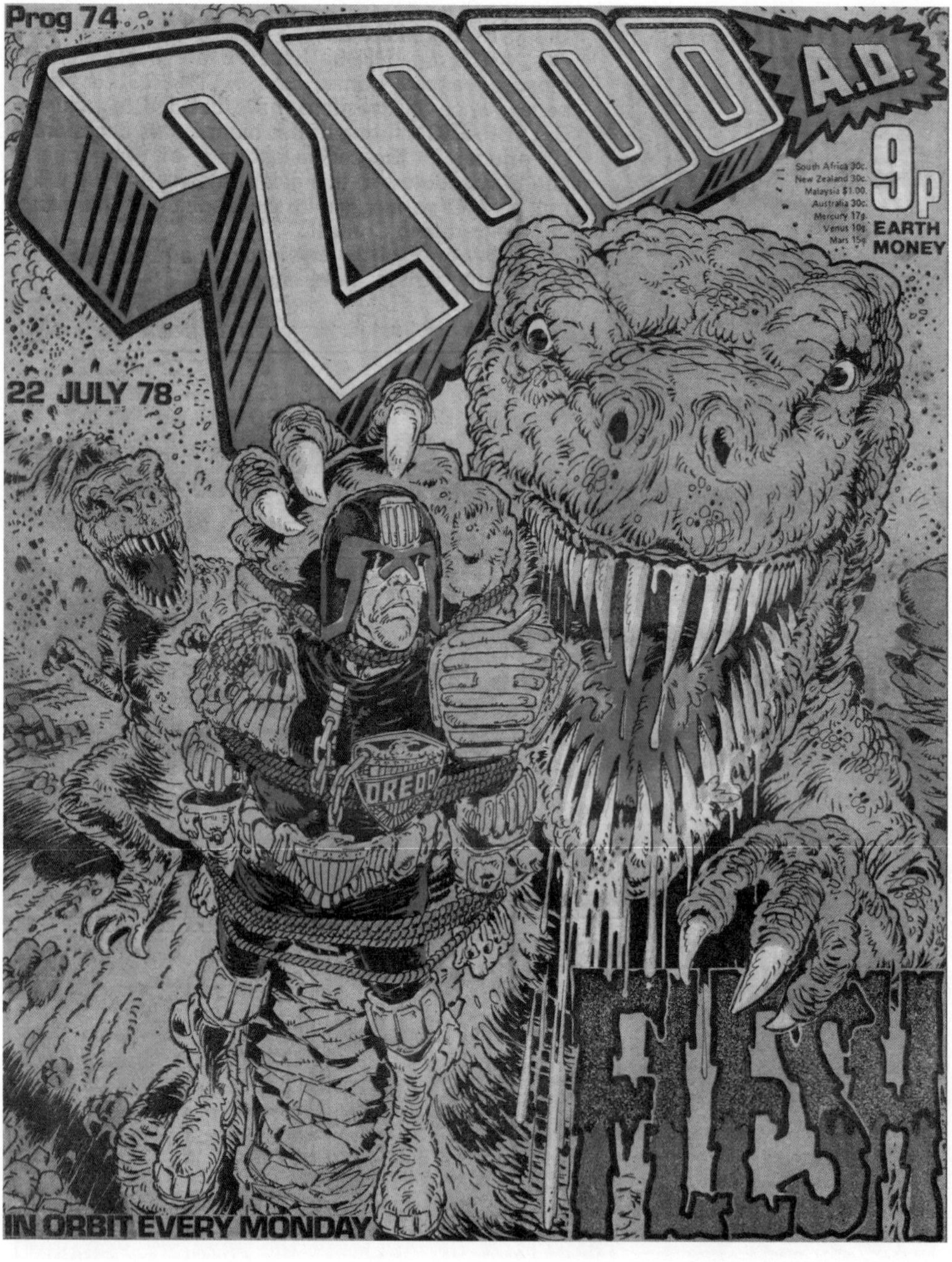

Fig. 14. Judge Dredd meets 'Flesh': cover of Programme 74 (22 July 1978), artwork by Mick McMahon: 'They were to be strong characters, not a herd but a gang!' (McMahon pers. comm. 19 October 2008). World wide web address: http://mickmcmahon.onlinefolio.biz/index.asp. 'Flesh' © 2008 Rebellion A/S. All rights reserved.

In 1992 (*2000 A.D.* again pre-empting a cinema release, this time of Spielberg's *Jurassic Park*) Mills returned to writing 'Flesh', producing 'The Legend of Shamana' with Carl Critchlow as primary artist (Fig. 16). In this story Mills takes the idea of human greed and self-destruction through intelligence even further: amongst the 'cast' of dinosaurs there is a thinly disguised version of Dale Russell's

Fig. 15. Beyond 'Flesh': as part of Mills' classic pioneering Judge Dredd Saga 'The Cursed Earth', scientists extract DNA from dinosaur remains and (using alligator eggs) grow a new generation of dinosaurs that form a theme park for tourists. Following the collapse of society, the dinosaurs run free. Programme 73 (15 July 1978, pp. 19 and 21), artwork by Mick McMahon. 'Flesh' © 2008 Rebellion A/S. All rights reserved.

Fig. 16. 'Flesh' Revived: 'The Legend of Shamana' as featured on the cover of Programme 808 (7 November 1992), art by Carl Critchlow. 'Flesh' © 2008 Rebellion A/S. All rights reserved.

'dinosauroid' concept (Russell & Séguin 1982; Russell 1987), a speculative projection of the possible results of the troodontid trend of descent towards an enlarged brain, opposable digits and bipedal posture, following the idea suggested by Carl Sagan (1977, pp. 135–136). Towards the climax of Book One of this story (Prog. 808), this slightly more intelligent breed of dinosaur emerges from the background and, in a pastiche of Kubrick's 'Dawn of Man' sequence from the film *2001: A Space Odyssey* (Jones 1993, p. 87), shoots one of the humans from the future before throwing the gun, spinning, into the air. The 'Gaia' judgement is again applied – the other dinosaurs annihilate these more intelligent animals, recognizing them (and, by implication, intelligence) as an abnormality to be wiped out before it threatens their genetic stock.

Discussion

The comic strip has long been looked down upon as the 'poor relation' of communicative media, the purveyor of mindless and often gratuitous storylines. But as an image-rich, mass produced medium or format directed at a younger generation that can be distributed, retained and re-experienced, it has an accessibility and influence that far outweighed books, cinema or television in post-war Britain. Although dinosaurs had been, to an extent, marginalized as 'kidstuff' in the view of the general public, it is also perhaps the reason why popular breakthroughs in the understanding of dinosaurs could be communicated most quickly and effectively through channels or media formats that were specifically aimed at children, instead of more expensive media involving longer production times, such as television and cinema. Thus, the dinosaurs presented in 'Flesh', radically different to any popular depiction previously available to a general audience, made a long-lasting and influential impact on how a generation in Britain viewed these animals. In this regard, it was ahead of its time even when compared to *National Geographic Magazine*, which today strives to report new developments in dinosaur science as soon as it can. It was not until August 1978 that *National Geographic* ran an article by John Ostrom on the new way of looking at dinosaurs in the light of the recent discoveries (Ostrom 1978).

2000 A.D. appealed to a number of sections of the population when it first appeared. The deluge of science fiction films from the United States of America had provided a fertile ground for an audience appreciative of popular science fiction to grow on, and *2000 A.D.* was both an accessible outlet and a natural receptacle for this enthusiasm. The comic also had appeal for a 'post-punk anti-authority generation', as well as an art-school-centred appreciation of the artwork. It might be argued that the circulation of *2000 A.D.* to its predominantly teenage audience would be insignificant in terms of its impact, but this would be missing the point: the under 20s that read 'Flesh' in 1977 grew to be the next generation, with a far better informed view of the current understanding of dinosaurs than their peers who had not done so. These readers would also be more likely to be receptive to scientific discoveries relating to dinosaurs than if they had only ever thought of them in the clichéd terms of slow and lumbering reptiles. They, as an audience, would also be prepared in advance for, and more receptive to, the style of dinosaurs that Steven Spielberg would present to them in the cinema in *Jurassic Park* in 1993.

Conclusions

Serendipitously, a time of upheaval in dinosaur science coincided with a period of significant change in comics in Britain, bridged by a UK 'coffee table' book. The result was an extremely powerful series of dinosaur depictions in a sequential art narrative that effectively and widely disseminated across a generation, a significant percentage of whom would never again see dinosaurs as lumbering cold-blooded creatures messing around in swamps.

Thanks go to S. Holland, P. Mills, A. Barnes, L. Noè for encouragement, A. Brown, R. Sola, J. Boix, E. Harkness (for selling his collection of the first 85 Progs to me for £3.60 in 1981), M. Smith, I. Rolfe, D. Bishop and M. McMahon for helpful comments, A. A. Wilson of Conservation Consortium (Scotland) Ltd for expert conservation of the Waterhouse Hawkins prints. Thanks also go to P. Mills, L. Noè, M. Barker and S. Holland, who provided comments on an earlier version of this manuscript, and to D. Norman for useful information on historical reconstructions of *Iguanodon*. Finally, special thanks to the reviewers and The Dinosaur Society, the Carnegie Trust for the Universities of Scotland (for a Carnegie Illustration Grant), the Blodwyn Lloyd Bins Bequest Fund of the Glasgow Natural History Society and the Curry Fund of the Geologists' Association for financial support towards the production of colour figures in this work.

References

Ackerman, J. 1998. Dinosaurs take wing. *National Geographic Magazine*, **194**, 74–99. (July).

Bakker, R. T. 1975. Dinosaur renaissance. *Scientific American*, **232**, 58–78. (April).

Bakker, R. T. 1993. Bakker's field guide to Jurassic Park dinosaurs. *Earth Magazine*, September, 33–43.

Barker, M. 1989. *Comics: Ideology, Power and the Critics*. Manchester University Press, Manchester.

Barker, M. 1992. *A Haunt of Fears: The Strange History of the British Horror Comics Campaign*. University Press of Mississippi, Jackson, MI.

Crichton, M. 1991. *Jurassic Park*. Ballantine Books, New York.

DELGADO, R. 1997. *The Age of Reptiles*. Dark Horse Comics.

DICKENS, C. 1853. *Bleak House*. Bradbury & Evans, Bouverie Street, London.

EGERTON, J. 2007. *George Stubbs, Painter: Catalogue Raisonne*. Yale University Press, New Haven, CT.

FREY, E., MARTILL, D. M. & BUCHY, M.-C. 2003. A new crested ornithocheirid from the Lower Cretaceous of northeastern Brazil and the unusual death of an unusual pterosaur. *In*: BUFFETAUT, E. & MAZIN, J.-M. (eds) *Evolution and Palaeobiology of Pterosaurs.*, Geological Society, London, Special Publications, **217**, 55–63.

GLUT, D. F. & BRETT-SURMAN, M. K. 1997. Chapter 43. Dinosaurs and the media. *In*: FARLOW, J. O. & BRETT-SURMAN, M. K. (eds) *The Complete Dinosaur*. Indiana University Press, Bloomington, IN, 675–706.

HALSTEAD, B. 1975. *The Evolution and Ecology of the Dinosaurs* (illustrated by G. CASELLI). Eurobook Ltd. London.

HARRYHAUSEN, R. & DALTON, T. 2005. *The Art of Ray Harryhausen*. Aurum Press, London.

HOLLAND, S. 1997*a*. An introduction to British comics. *In*: MCALPINE, D. (ed.) *The Comic Book Price Guide 1997/1998*, Volume 8. Titan Books, London, 722–725.

HOLLAND, S. 1997*b*. *2000 A. D.* – Introduction: millennium fever. *In*: MCALPINE, D. (ed.) *The Comic Book Price Guide 1997/1998*, Volume 8. Titan Books, London, 781.

JONES, S. 1993. *The Illustrated Dinosaur Movie Guide*, Volume **2**. Titan Books, London.

LESSEM, D. & DAVIS, S. 1993. *The Real Jurassic Park*. Channel 4 Television, London, 1–24.

LEWIN, D. 1976. Why the future is going to be more than a little early this year ... *Daily Mail*, 6 July, 20.

LISTON, J. J. 2000*a*. Tiptoeing amongst the egos. *Quarterly Journal of the Dinosaur Society*, **3**, 3.

LISTON, J. J. 2000*b*. *Archaeopteryx* and the evolution of feathered flight: the hidden story. *Quarterly Journal of the Dinosaur Society*, **4**, 6–14.

MCALPINE, D. 1997*a*. The historical ages of comic books. *In*: MCALPINE, D. (ed.) *The Comic Book Price Guide 1997/1998*, Volume 8. Titan Books, London, 164–166.

MCALPINE, D. 1997*b*. UK comic book guide: DC/Marvel/Independent comics. *In*: MCALPINE, D. (ed.) *The Comic Book Price Guide 1997/1998*, Volume 8. Titan Books, London, 183–714.

NOÈ, L. F. & LISTON, J. J. 2010. 'Old bones, dry subject': the dinosours and pterosaur collected by Alfred Nicholson Leeds of Peterborough, England. *In*: MOODY, R. T. J., BUFFETAUT, E., NAISH, D. & MARTILL, D. M. (eds) *Dinosours and Other Extinct Saurians: A Historical Perspective*. Geological Society, London, Special Publications, **343**, 49–77.

OSMÓLSKA, H. & RONIEWICZ, E. 1970. Deinocheiridae, a new family of theropod dinosaurs. *Palaeontologica Polonica*, **21**, 5–19.

OSTROM, J. H. 1969*a*. A new theropod dinosaur from the Lower Cretaceous of Montana. *Postilla* **128**, 1–17.

OSTROM, J. H. 1969*b*. Osteology of *Deinonychus antirrhopus*, an unusual theropod from the Lower Cretaceous of Montana. *Bulletin of the Peabody Museum of Natural History*, **30**, 1–165.

OSTROM, J. H. 1978. A new look at dinosaurs. *National Geographic Magazine*, **154**, 152–185. (August).

OWEN, R. 1842. Report on British fossil reptiles. Part II. *In*: *Report of the Eleventh meeting of the British Association for the Advancement of Science*, Plymouth, England, July 1841. John Murray, London, 60–204.

ROLFE, W. D. I. & GRIGSON, C. 2006. Stubbs's 'Drill and albino hamadryas baboon' in conjectural historical context. *Archives of Natural History*, **33**, 18–41.

RUSSELL, D. A. 1987. Models and Paintings of North American dinosaurs. *In*: CZERKAS, S. J. & OLSON, E. C. (eds) *Dinosaurs Past and Present*, Volume 1. A Symposium held at the Natural History Museum of Los Angeles County on 15 February 1986. University of Washington Press, Seattle, WA, 114–131.

RUSSELL, D. A. & SÉGUIN, R. 1982. Reconstruction of the small Cretaceous theropod *Stenonychosaurus inequalis* and a hypothetical dinosauroid. *Syllogeus*, **37**, 1–43.

SAGAN, C. 1977. *The Dragons of Eden: Speculations on the Evolution of Human Intelligence*. Random House: New York.

SNELL, S. & TUCKER, P. 2003. *Life through a Lens: Photographs from the Natural History Museum 1880–1950*. Natural History Museum, Cromwell Road, London, 66.

ŠPINAR, Z. 1972. *Life Before Man* (illustrated by BURIAN, Z.). Thames and Hudson, London.

SVPCA 1998. The Annual Symposium of Vertebrate Palaeontology and Comparative Anatomy, Bournemouth 1998, Talks and posters. World wide web address:http://www.svpca.org/general/pages/talksAndPosters.php?y=1998.

WELLS, R. 1969. *The Parasaurians*. Berkley Medallion Books, New York.

WERNER WATSON, J. 1960. *Dinosaurs and Other Prehistoric Reptiles* (illustrated by ZALLINGER, R. F.). Hamlyn, London.

WERTHAM, F. 1954. *Seduction of the Innocent*. Rinehart & Company Inc., New York.

XU, X., TANG, Z.-L. & WANG, X.-L. 1999. A therizinosauroid dinosaur with integumentary structures from China. *Nature*, **399**, 350–354.

Sauropod dinosaur research: a historical review

MICHAEL P. TAYLOR

Palaeobiology Research Group, School of Earth and Environmental Sciences, University of Portsmouth, Burnaby Road, Portsmouth PO1 3QL, UK and Department of Earth Sciences, University College London, Gower Street, London WC1E 6BT, UK (e-mail: dino@miketaylor.org.uk)

Abstract: In the 169 years since Owen named a tooth as *Cardiodon*, the study of sauropod dinosaurs has gone through several distinct periods. In the early years, a sequence of descriptions of isolated skeletal elements gave rise to a gradually emerging understanding of the animals that would later be known as sauropods. The second phase began in 1871 with Phillips's description of *Cetiosaurus oxoniensis*, the first reasonably complete sauropod, and continued with the Marsh-Cope Bone Wars and the description of the nearly complete sauropods *Camarasaurus* and '*Brontosaurus*' (= *Apatosaurus*). As these and other genera became better known, a third phase began, exploring not just the remains but the lives of these giants, with arguments about posture and habitat to the fore, and with the public becoming increasingly aware of sauropods owing to skeletal mounts. A 'dark age' followed during and after World War II, with sauropods considered uninteresting evolutionary dead ends and largely ignored. This was brought to an end by the 'dinosaur renaissance' that began in the late 1960s, since when work has recommenced with new vigour, and the public has been introduced to a more vigorous and terrestrial image of sauropods through film and television. Both diversity and disparity of sauropods continue to increase through new descriptive work, and the group is now seen as more fascinating and worthy of study than ever before.

Sauropod dinosaurs are the terrestrial superlative: they were not just the largest animals ever to have walked on land, but an order of magnitude heavier than their nearest rivals – the hadrosaurid dinosaurs, and the proboscidean and indricotherian mammals. Although the first genera now recognized as sauropods were named in 1841, the nature of the animals was not understood for some time, and many aspects of their palaeobiology remained controversial for considerably longer; some, including habitual neck posture, remain unresolved to this day. Throughout the 169 years of research into sauropods, an increasingly clear picture has gradually emerged. This paper traces the process of discovery through five distinct eras: an initial period of studies restricted to isolated elements; the period in which near-complete specimens first became available; the age of interpretation and controversy; the 'dark ages'; and the modern renaissance.

Institutional abbreviations: AMNH, American Museum of Natural History, New York, NY, USA; BMNH, Natural History Museum, London, UK; CM, Carnegie Museum of Natural History, Pittsburgh, PA, USA; HMN, Humboldt Museum für Naturkunde, Berlin, Germany; OUMNH, Oxford University Museum of Natural History, Oxford, UK; USNM, National Museum of Natural History, Washington, DC, USA; YPM, Yale Peabody Museum, New Haven, CT, USA.

Stage 1: early studies, isolated elements (1841–1870)

It was only 17 years after the naming of the first dinosaur recognized by science, *Megalosaurus* Buckland 1824, and a year before the coinage of the name Dinosauria Owen 1842, that the first sauropods were named: *Cardiodon* Owen 1841*a* and *Cetiosaurus* Owen 1841*b*. The former was named on the basis of a single tooth crown from the Middle Jurassic Forest Marble Formation of Bradford-on-Avon, Wiltshire. It was later figured by Owen (1875*a*, plate IX, figs 2–5), but has since been lost (Fig. 1a). A second tooth crown, BMNH R1527, was referred to this genus by Lydekker (1890, p. 236), and was later figured by Barrett (2006, fig. 2a,b). These two teeth are the only elements to have been assigned to *Cardiodon*, and this genus – the first sauropod – is now all but forgotten. Various workers have suggested that *Cardiodon* might be a senior synonym of *Cetiosaurus*, but this putative synonymy was refuted by Upchurch & Martin (2003, pp. 214–215).

It is with the genus *Cetiosaurus*, named later that same year, that the story of sauropods really begins. Owen (1841*b*) used a wide variety of specimens from six different localities as the basis for the new genus *Cetiosaurus*, for which no specific name was initially given. Despite the large amount

From: Moody, R. T. J., Buffetaut, E., Naish, D. & Martill, D. M. (eds) *Dinosaurs and Other Extinct Saurians: a Historical Perspective*. Geological Society, London, Special Publications, **343**, 361–386.
DOI: 10.1144/SP343.22 0305-8719/10/$15.00

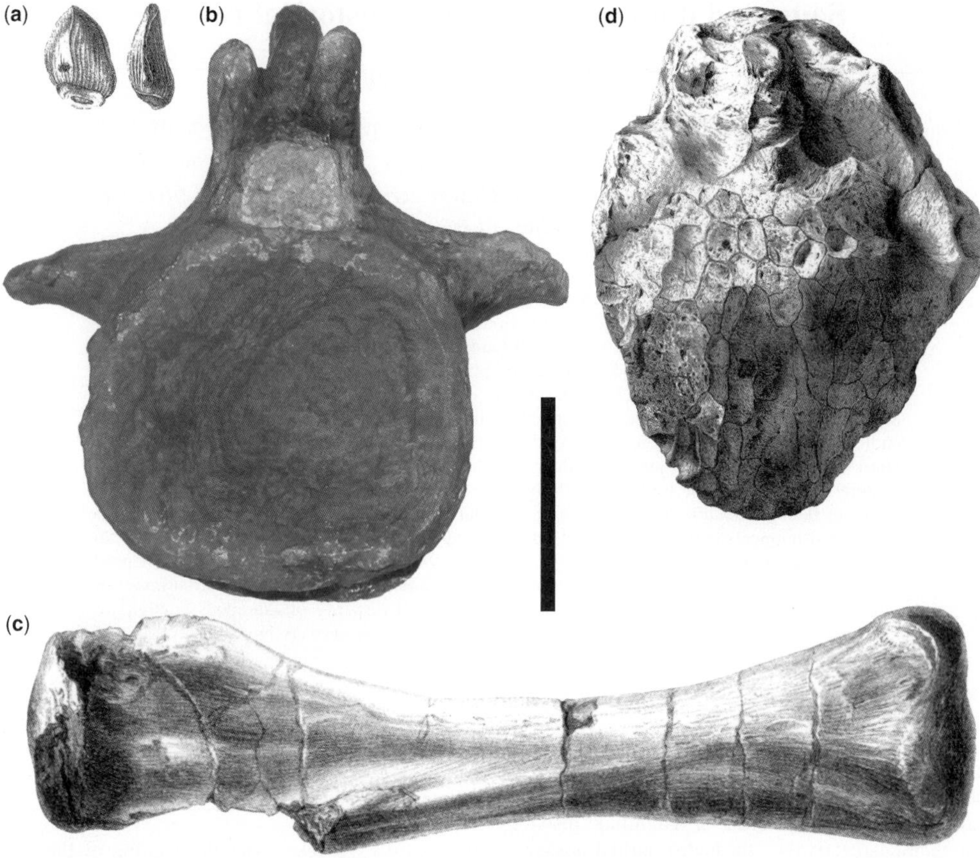

Fig. 1. Historically significant isolated sauropod elements. (**a**) The holotype tooth of *Cardiodon* in labial and distal views, modified from Owen (1875*a*, plate IX, figs 2 and 3); (**b**) anterior caudal vertebra of *Cetiosaurus brevis* in anterior view, part of the holotype, photograph by the author; (**c**) holotype right humerus of *Pelorosaurus* in anterior view, modified from Mantell (1850, plate XXI, fig. 1b); and (**d**) lectotype dorsal vertebra of *Ornithopsis* (see Blows 1995, p. 188) in anterior view, exposing pneumatic cavities owing to erosion of the anterior articular surface, modified from Owen (1875*a*, plate IX, fig. 1). The scale bar is 5 cm for (a), 10 cm for (b) and (d), and 30 cm for (c).

of material most of it was rather poor, consisting largely of partial caudal vertebrae and appendicular fragments. Owen noted that in their size, and in the size and proportions of their neural spines and chevron articulations, the vertebrae resembled those of whales; but that the concavity of their articular surfaces and high position of the transverse processes suggested a reptilian affinity. Accordingly, he named the new genus *Cetiosaurus* or 'whale lizard' (Fig. 1b).

It is often said that Owen (1841*b*) described *Cetiosaurus* as a gigantic crocodilian, but in fact this assignment came later. In his initial description, Owen (1841*b*, p. 462) explicitly separated his new animal from crocodiles, concluding that 'the surpassing bulk and strength of the *Cetiosaurus* were probably assigned to it with carnivorous habits, that it might keep in check the Crocodilians and Plesiosauri'. What is certain is that when, a year later, Owen (1842, p. 103) created the name Dinosauria, he omitted *Cetiosaurus* from it; limiting its initial content to 'the gigantic Crocodile-lizards of the dry land', *Megalosaurus*, *Iguanodon* Mantell 1825 and *Hylaeosaurus* Mantell 1833. *Cetiosaurus*, then thought aquatic, was explicitly excluded.

In subsequent years, a total of 13 species of *Cetiosaurus* were named by Owen and others on the basis of British material, although nearly all of these are now considered nomina nuda or nomina dubia (Upchurch & Martin 2003, pp. 209–215). It was not until 1871 that truly informative *Cetiosaurus* remains would be described. Before this, though, several more historically important sauropods would be named on the basis of isolated elements.

The first of these, and the first sauropod to be named on the basis of appendicular material, was

Pelorosaurus Mantell 1850 (Fig. 1c), based on a humerus from the Early Cretaceous Wealden Supergroup that at the time seemed 'stupendous' (p. 379) at a length of 4.5 ft – although this is little more than 60% the length of the humeri of the subsequently described brachiosaurids *Brachiosaurus altithorax* Riggs 1903*a* and *Brachiosaurus brancai* Janensch 1914, animals which if they were isometrically similar to *Pelorosaurus* would have weighed four times as much as it did. The significance of *Pelorosaurus* is that it was the first-named sauropod that was recognized by its describer as being terrestrial – ironically, owing to its possession of a medullary cavity, a feature that seems to be unique among sauropods. Although Owen (1859*a*, p. 40) tried to portray Mantell as having mistaken the 'anterior for the posterior of the bone', it is clear from Mantell's description, and particularly his correct identification of the deltoid process (deltopectoral crest), that he oriented the humerus correctly and that the error was only in the caption of Mantell's plate XXI. Mantell subsequently described a second species, *Pelorosaurus becklesii* Mantell 1852, which in fact is not closely related to the type species (Upchurch 1995, p. 380). The type specimen of '*Pelorosaurus*' *becklesii*, BMNH R1868, is important because as well as a humerus, radius and ulna, it includes a skin impression – the first known from any sauropod, and still one of only very few sauropod skin impressions. Because Mantell referred to *Pelorosaurus* the same caudal vertebrae that Owen (1842) used as the type specimen for *Cetiosaurus brevis* Owen 1842, the taxonomy of *Cetiosaurus* and *Pelorosaurus* is complex and intertwined. This situation is being addressed by a petition to the International Commission on Zoological Nomenclature (ICZN) (Upchurch *et al.* 2009). *Pelorosaurus*, including the misassigned species '*Pelorosaurus*' *becklesii*, is being restudied to better determine its affinities but the type material appears to represent a basal titanosauriform, possibly a brachiosaurid (Upchurch & Martin 2003, p. 210).

As with dinosaurs in general, England was very much the home of sauropods during the early days of their study. The first sauropod named from outside England was *Aepisaurus* Gervais 1852, based on a subsequently lost humerus of which the proximal part has since been found; it is now considered a nomen dubium. The first sauropod from outside Europe was *Astrodon* Johnston 1859 from the USA, which, like *Cardiodon*, was named on the basis of a single tooth crown and not initially given a specific name. Six years later, the tooth was referred to the new species *Astrodon johnstoni* Leidy 1865, although this is often misspelled as A. *johnsoni* (e.g. Carpenter & Tidwell 2005). (*Pleurocoelus* Marsh 1888, based on mostly juvenile vertebral centra, has sometimes been considered separate from *Astrodon*, but is now generally considered a junior synonym of that genus despite the inadequate *Astrodon* type material – see the overview in Carpenter & Tidwell 2005.)

Another significant find was *Ornithopsis* Seeley 1870, named on the basis of two partial presacral vertebrae from different localities that are now known to belong to sauropods (probably two different sauropod taxa) but thought by Seeley (p. 279) to be 'of the Pterodactyle kind' (Fig. 1d; see Martill 2010). Seeley's mistake was based on his recognition of pneumatic features in the bones – internal air spaces giving rise to a honeycombed internal structure, and lateral foramina through which air entered these spaces from the sides of the bones. At the time of Seeley's writing, almost all animals known to have pneumatized bones in their postcranial skeletons were birds and pterosaurs, the only exception being the theropod *Becklespinax altispinax* Paul 1988*b*, then thought to belong to *Megalosaurus* (Naish 2010). As both birds and pterosaurs are flying vertebrates, Seeley's assumption that an animal with postcranial skeletal pneumaticity (PSP) was closely related to, or even intermediate between, the flying vertebrate groups was perfectly sensible. We now know that PSP also occurs in sauropods, non-avian theropods and in some basal sauropodomorphs (Wedel 2006), and possibly also in some crocodile-line archosaurs (Gower 2001; Nesbitt & Norell 2006, p. 3). Sauropod pneumaticity has been subsequently studied by Longman (1933) and Janensch (1947), but thereafter remained largely overlooked until the more recent work of Britt (1993) and Wedel (2003*a*, *b*, 2005). A picture has now emerged of a complex range of vertebral pneumatic features, encompassing everything from gentle lateral depressions in basal sauropods such as *Barapasaurus* Jain *et al.* 1975, via large internal spaces in basal neosauropods such as *Camarasaurus* Cope 1877*a*, to the dense, irregularly honeycombed, internal structure of derived titanosaurs such as *Saltasaurus* Bonaparte & Powell 1980.

Stage 2: the emerging picture (1871–1896)

Understanding of sauropods took a giant leap forward with the description of *Cetiosaurus oxoniensis* Phillips 1871 (Fig. 2), a Middle Jurassic sauropod from England, described and illustrated in detail by Phillips in 50 pages of his book on the geology of Oxford and the Thames Valley. Phillips described remains from several localities, all near Oxford, and there is no compelling reason not to accept his assessment that they all belong to the same species. Most important are the associated remains of several individuals from Kirtlington Station, north of Oxford, of which the largest is

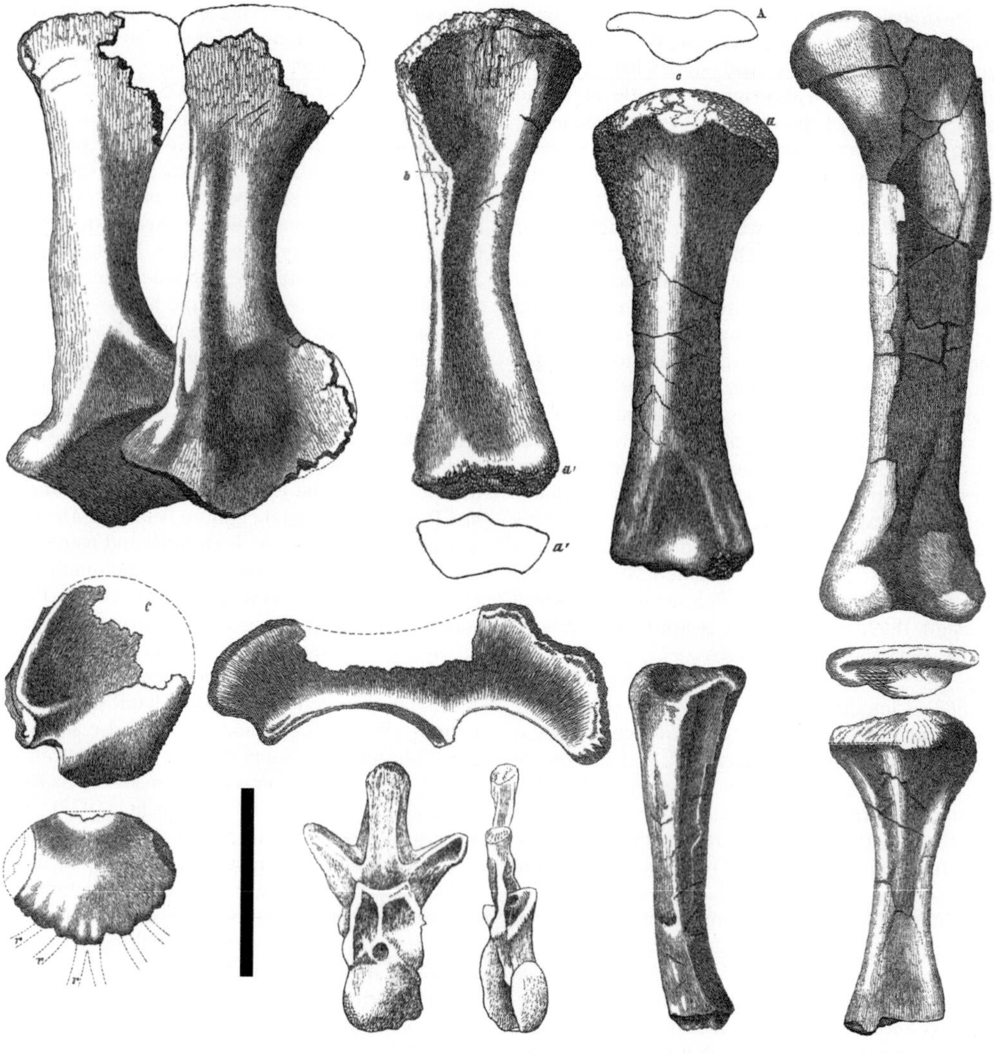

Fig. 2. Elements of *Cetiosaurus oxoniensis*. Top row, left to right: right scapula in lateral view and left scapula in medial view; right humerus in anterior and distal views, and left humerus in proximal and posterior views; left femur in anterior view. Bottom row, left to right: left coracoid in medial view and ?left sternal plate in ?dorsal view; right ilium in lateral view and ?fourth dorsal vertebra in anterior and right lateral views; ?right ulna in ?posterolateral view; right tibia in proximal and posterolateral views. Dorsal vertebra modified from Phillips (1871, fig. 86), other elements modified from Owen (1875*b*, figs 1–9), which were reproduced from Phillips (1871). The scale bar is 50 cm.

also the best represented and was accordingly nominated by Upchurch & Martin (2003, p. 216) as the lectotype. Material described and figured by Phillips included: a tooth; dorsal, sacral and caudal vertebrae; dorsal ribs; sternal plate, coracoids and scapulae; humeri and ulnae; ilium, pubis and ischium; femora, tibiae and fibula; metatarsals and pedal phalanges. The only parts of the skeleton not represented were the skull, cervical vertebrae, radius and manus – although recent work by Galton & Knoll (2006) has tentatively agreed with Woodward's (1910) and Huene's (1926) assignment of the isolated saurischian braincase OUMNH J13596 to *Cetiosaurus oxoniensis*. Given the lack of prior information about sauropods, Phillips's identification of the various bones was impressively accurate. He made only two errors: he interpreted the sole recovered sternal plate as a median element rather then as one of a pair; and he interpreted the ischiadic and pubic articular surfaces of the pubis and ischium, respectively, as articulating with the ilium. Phillips did not attempt a skeletal reconstruction – unfortunately, as it would have been of great historical importance.

Armed with all of this material, Phillips was able to envisage the sauropod body plan for the first time (although he could not have known about the long neck and small head), recognizing it as capable of terrestrial locomotion and possessing erect posture:

> all the articulations [of the limb bones] are definite, and made so as to correspond to determinate movements in particular directions, and these are such as to be suited for walking. In particular, the femur, by its head projecting freely from the acetabulum, seems to claim a movement of free stepping more parallel to the line of the body, and more approaching to the vertical than the sprawling gait of the crocodile.
>
> (pp. 293–294)

However, Phillips hedged his bets with regard to lifestyle, concluding that 'we have, therefore, a marsh-loving or river-side animal' (p. 294). Phillips was also first to suggest the dinosaurian affinities of *Cetiosaurus*, albeit tentatively:

> The [femur] is nearly straight, in this respect differing much from the crocodilian, and approaching towards the deinosaurian type
>
> (p. 280)

> 'a lizard of such vast proportions would seem to claim easy admission to the deinosaurians, and to take its place naturally with megalosaurus or iguanodon ... but its fore-limbs are more crocodilian, its pelvic girdle more lacertilian, while its vertebral system is of a peculiar type'.
>
> (p. 291)

Phillips's work on *Cetiosaurus* marked a significant step forward, giving the first meaningful window on the morphology and ecology of a sauropod dinosaur. However, his work was to be largely superseded just six years later by a sequence of important announcements in 1877: the first recognized Gondwanan sauropod, *Titanosaurus* Lydekker 1877; the onset of the Bone Wars, with the descriptions of the sauropods *Camarasaurus*, *Apatosaurus* Marsh 1877*b*, *Atlantosaurus* Marsh 1877*b*, *Amphicoelias* Cope 1877*b* and *Dystrophaeus* Cope 1877*c*; and the first skeletal reconstruction of a sauropod.

Titanosaurus was named by Lydekker (1877) on the basis of a partial femur and two incomplete caudal vertebrae, and was diagnosed by only a single character – procoelous caudal vertebrae (i.e. having centra that are concave anteriorly and pronouncedly convex posteriorly). Although the original *Titanosaurus* material was from India, similar procoelous caudal vertebrae from other countries were subsequently referred to the genus, eventually resulting in a total of 14 species! It has since been shown by Wilson & Upchurch (2003, p. 152) that the type species of *Titanosaurus*, *T. indicus* Lydekker 1877 is invalid as it can no longer be diagnosed: the single diagnostic character identified by Lydekker, procoelous caudal vertebrae, is now recognized as synapomorphic of the much larger clade Titanosauria, which at the last count encompasses more than 50 valid genera. Lydekker's initial naming of *Titanosaurus* on the basis of this morphology remains historically significant, however, as not only the first recognition of the important group now known as Titanosauria but also as the first sauropod recognized from the Gondwanan supercontinent (Table 1).

The year 1877 also marked the beginning of the Bone Wars – a period of intense, aggressive competition between Othniel Charles Marsh and his great rival Edward Drinker Cope to find and name dinosaurs from the newly discovered Morrison

Table 1. *First sauropods named from each continent*

Continent	First named genus Earliest still valid	Author and date	Clade
Europe	*Cardiodon**	Owen (1841*a*)	?Cetiosauridae
	Cetiosaurus	Owen (1841*b*)	Cetiosauridae
North America	*Astrodon*	Johnston (1859)	Titanosauriformes
Asia	*Titanosaurus*†	Lydekker (1877)	Titanosauria
	Tienshanosaurus‡	Young (1937)	Eusauropoda
South America	*Argyrosaurus*	Lydekker (1893)	Titanosauria
Africa	*Algoasaurus*§	Broom (1904)	Sauropoda
	Tornieria	Sternfeld (1911)	Diplodocinae
Australasia	*Rhoetosaurus*	Longman (1926)	Sauropoda
Antarctica	(None named)		

*The type specimen of *Cardiodon* is lost and the referred specimen is not diagnosable.
†*Titanosaurus* was diagnosed by a character that now characterizes the large clade Titanosauria (see the text).
‡The Chinese genus *Helopus* Wiman 1929 predates *Tienshanosaurus*, but because the name *Helopus* was preoccupied by a bird, the genus was renamed *Euhelopus* Romer 1956.
§*Algosaurus* is not diagnosable.

Formation of the western United States (Colbert 1997). Besides such well-known non-sauropod dinosaurs as *Allosaurus* Marsh 1877*b* and *Stegosaurus* Marsh 1877*c*, this year saw the establishment of two classic sauropods in *Apatosaurus* and *Camarasaurus*, as well as the less well known sauropod genera, *Amphicoelias*, *Atlantosaurus* (probably synonymous with *Apatosaurus ajax* Marsh 1877*b*; Berman & McIntosh 1978, p. 11) and *Dystrophaeus* (probably a nomen dubium). Unfortunately, in their haste to beat each other to press, both Marsh and Cope published rushed and inadequate descriptions, often without illustrations, most of which would not be considered taxonomically valid if published today. Synonymies also abounded: for example, Marsh's genus *Atlantosaurus* was first published under the name *Titanosaurus montanus* Marsh 1877*a*, until Marsh became aware of Lydekker's slightly earlier use of this generic name, and so renamed it *Atlantosaurus*; and this is now thought to be probably synonymous with *Apatosaurus*, as is the slightly later *Brontosaurus* Marsh 1879. While the Marsh–Cope rivalry undoubtedly benefited palaeontology by catalysing work that would not otherwise have been done so quickly, the net results of this race were negative, yielding a set of specimens with very poor locality documentation and a trail of shoddy scientific work that had to be redone subsequently (Barbour 1890): so while, for example, Marsh is credited with the names *Apatosaurus* and *Brontosaurus*, most of his publications on these animals are now of purely historical interest, while the subsequent monographs on this genus by Riggs (1903*b*) and Gilmore (1936) are still widely used.

The year after the initial Morrison 'Dinosaur Rush', *Camarasaurus* became the first sauropod to be adequately figured (Cope 1878), but prior to this it had already been made the subject of the first attempt to reconstruct the skeleton of a sauropod: that of Dr John Ryder, executed in 1877 under the direction of Cope (Fig. 3a). Astonishingly, the reconstruction was life sized, 'over fifty feet in length' (Osborn & Mook 1921, p. 252), and was based on material from several individuals. Although it was exhibited at a meeting of the American Philosophical Society on 21 December 1877, and subsequently exhibited at the AMNH, it was not published until 37 years later (Mook 1914), and is now best known from the excellent reproduction in the monograph of Osborn & Mook (1921, plate LXXXII). In the light of subsequent work, Ryder's reconstruction can be seen to be replete with mistakes: the head is a complete fiction, the neck is too short, the vertebrae in the region of the pectoral girdle are coalesced like the sacrum, there are far too many dorsal vertebrae, the tail is clearly modelled on those of aquatic animals, being dorsoventrally tall for much of its length but not in the proximal region, and the manus does not at all resemble the correct arrangement in sauropods, with the distinctive vertical arcade of near-parallel metacarpals. Nevertheless, Ryder's work remains admirable in some respects: the animal depicted is immediately recognizable as a sauropod, having the distinctive long neck and erect posture, and the dorsal vertebrae are recognizable as those of *Camarasaurus*.

It was not until a year after Ryder's reconstruction that the group Sauropoda got its name – at the fourth attempt. Owen (1859*b*, pp. 164–165) had previously proposed the name Opisthocoelia for the group consisting of *Cetiosaurus* and *Streptospondylus* Meyer 1832, and as the first suprageneric taxon containing a genus now recognized as a sauropod, this name has some claim to priority. A second candidate name for this group, Ceteosauria [sic], was raised by Seeley (1874, p. 690) in a paper describing the partial dorsal neural arch of a stegosaur, which he misinterpreted as part of the braincase of a sauropod, but this name has been mostly overlooked. Marsh (1877*b*, p. 514) ignored both of these prior names and, instead, referred his genera *Atlantosaurus* and *Apatosaurus* to the new family Atlantosauridae, diagnosed by pneumatic vertebra and the absence of the third trochanter on the femur. Finally, the very next year, Marsh (1878*b*, p. 412) subsumed this family within yet another new taxon, Sauropoda:

> A well marked group of gigantic Dinosaurs ... has been characterized by the writer as a distinct family, Atlantosauridae, but they differ so widely from typical Dinosauria, that they belong rather in a suborder, which may be called Sauropoda, from the general character of the feet.

The name is a strange one, as the feet of sauropods do not resemble those of lizards, but it was quickly adopted. Marsh's diagnosis consisted of 10 characters and, while most of these are now known to be plesiomorphies characterizing a larger clade, two or three remain diagnostic. Marsh's name did not immediately win unanimous acceptance: Osborn (1898, p. 227) used the name Cetiosauria, listing 12 included genera that encompass diplodocoids, camarasaurs and titanosaurs; Riggs (1903*b*, pp. 166–169) discussed the names Opisthocoelia, Cetiosauria and Sauropoda in detail, concluding that 'the three terms are essentially co-ordinate and co-extensive. "Opisthocoelia" has priority, and is entitled to preference'; and Matthew (1915) also preferred the name Opisthocoelia. However, Hatcher (1903*b*, pp. 47–48) considered the name Cetiosauria 'of subordinal rank only' (i.e. less inclusive than Sauropoda), and also rejected Owen's Opisthocoelia on the grounds that 'it was

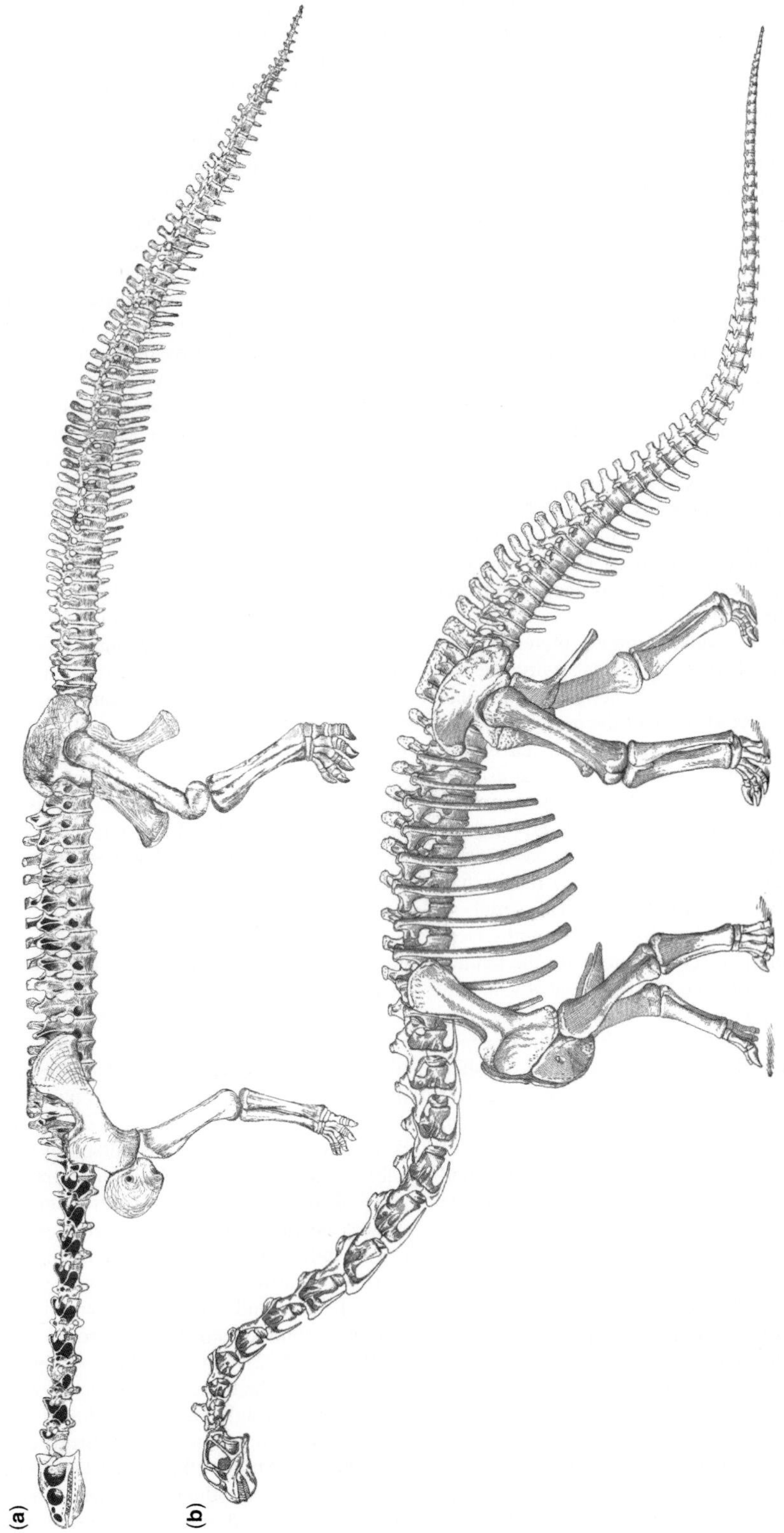

Fig. 3. Early reconstructions of *Camarasaurus*. Top: Ryder's 1877 reconstruction, the first ever made of any sauropod, modified from Osborn & Mook (1921, plate LXXXII). Bottom: Osborn & Mook's own reconstruction, modified from Osborn & Mook (1921, plate LXXXIV).

initially proposed as a suborder of the Crocodilia' and that Owen 'did not adequately define his proposed suborder and did not recognize its real relationships as being with the Dinosauria rather than the Crocodilia'. Instead, Hatcher (p. 48) concluded that 'Sauropoda, proposed and defined by Marsh ... should be accepted as the first adequately defined name for this group of dinosaurs', and this usage has since been followed almost unanimously.

Diplodocus Marsh 1878*a* was described in the same year as the name Sauropoda was first used, and *Brontosaurus* a year later. Both would become the subjects of important developments: *Brontosaurus* as the first sauropod to be satisfactorily reconstructed and *Diplodocus* as the first sauropod for which a complete skull was described (Marsh 1884). Both would also become among the most iconic of sauropods owing to the discovery of complete or near-complete skeletons and the erection of famous mounts in museums around the world. Marsh (1883) reconstructed *Brontosaurus* far more accurately than Ryder had been able to do with *Camarasaurus* 6 years earlier, correctly depicting the anterior dorsals as not coalesced, reducing the trunk to 10 dorsal vertebrae, greatly increasing the height of the sacral neural spines, showing the tail as decreasing evenly in height along its length and wrapping the coracoids around the anterior part of the trunk (Fig. 4a). Marsh also gave a reasonably accurate estimate of the mass of *Brontosaurus* as 'more than twenty tons' (Marsh 1883, p. 82). Some important mistakes were made, though: most importantly, the wrong skull was used, based on that of a camarasaur (YPM 1911) rather than that of a diplodocid; only 11 cervical vertebrae were included, rather than 15; the forelimbs were posed in a strongly flexed posture, with the humeri at 25° and 55° from the vertical; and the manus was reconstructed as plantigrade, like the pes, rather than with a vertical arcade of metacarpals. Marsh's errors in the forelimb and manus resulted in the shoulder girdle, and hence the cervicodorsal transition, being much too low, and therefore in the neck leaving the shoulders anteroventrally so that even pronounced extension of the neck resulted only in the head being at the same height as the scapula. Eight years later, Marsh (1891) provided a revised reconstruction of *Brontosaurus* (Fig. 4b), but while this correctly increased the number of cervicals, it also incorrectly increased the dorsal count from 10 to 14, and failed to correct the skull even though the new reconstruction's skull was based on a different specimen, YPM 1986 (now USNM 5730), now thought to belong to *Brachiosaurus* Riggs 1903*a* (Carpenter & Tidwell 1998). Osborn (1899, p. 213) criticized Marsh's reconstructions for making the mid-dorsal vertebrae the highest point of the axial column rather than the sacrum, thereby relegating the tail to being 'an appendage of the body instead of an important locomotor organ of the body', and provided his own reconstruction of the posterior dorsals, sacrum and tail of *Diplodocus* (Osborn 1899, fig. 1), the only parts of that animal then available to him. (The articulation of the sauropod manus would not be properly understood until 21 years later, when Osborn (1904, p. 181) began a paper with the refreshingly honest statement, 'my previous figures and descriptions of the manus are all incorrect', and figured a correctly articulated manus.)

Having already named the first Gondwanan sauropod, the globe-trotting Englishman Richard Lydekker (1893) also named the first sauropods from South America, which has subsequently become a very important region for sauropods: two new species of his genus *Titanosaurus*, *T. australis* and *T. nanus*, and two new genera, *Argyrosaurus* and *Microcoelus*. Of these taxa, only *Argyrosaurus* remains valid, with *T. australis* having been referred to the new titanosaurian genus *Neuquensaurus* Powell 1992, and *Microcoelus* and *T. nanus* being nomina dubia (Powell 2003, p. 44; Wilson & Upchurch 2003, p. 140). Huene (1929*a*, fig. 10) would go on to provide the first reconstruction of a titanosaur; and, in the same year, Huene (1929*b*, p. 497) was also to provide what was probably the first life restoration of a titanosaur. This figure is remarkable not so much for the rather poorly proportioned main individual as for the sketch of two more individuals fighting in the background, one of them rearing on its hind legs.

Stage 3: interpretation and controversy (1897–1944)

By the end of the nineteenth century sauropod osteology was sufficiently well understood that it had become possible to make palaeobiological inferences. Three controversies have dominated discussions of sauropod palaeobiology ever since: habitat, athleticism and neck posture. Although early illustrations of sauropods used a variety of neck postures, the subject was not explicitly discussed until relatively recently, beginning with the work of Martin (1987). By contrast, arguments about habitat and athleticism date right back to Phillips's comments in his 1871 book.

Ballou (1897) included, as one of his six figures, the first published life restoration of a sauropod, executed by Knight under the direction of Cope (Fig. 5a). This illustration, subsequently republished by Osborn & Mook (1921, fig. 127), depicted four *Amphicoelias* individuals in a lake, two of them entirely submerged and two with only their heads

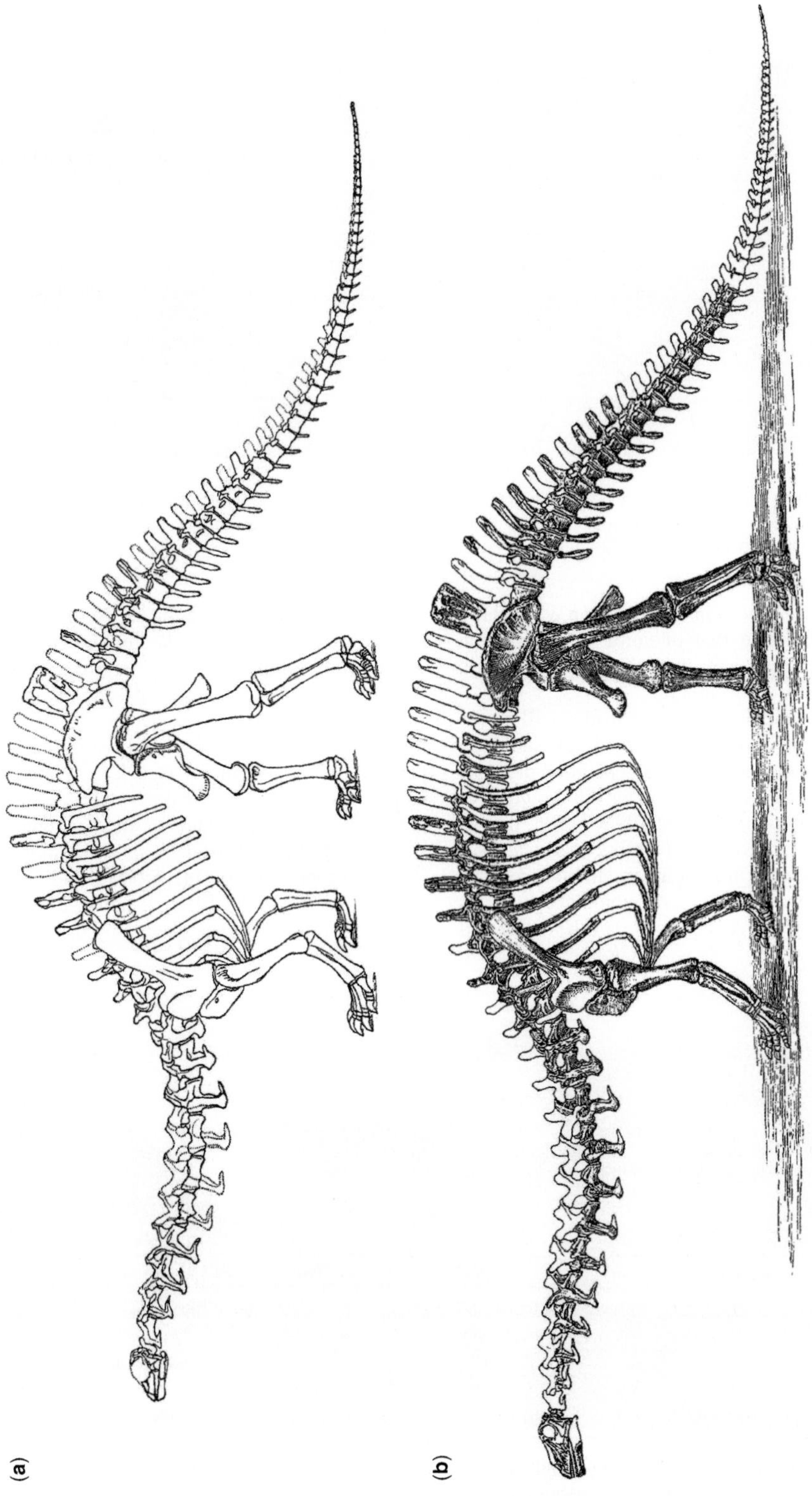

Fig. 4. Marsh's reconstructions of '*Brontosaurus*' (now *Apatosaurus*). Top: first reconstruction, modified from Marsh (1883, plate I). Bottom: second reconstruction, modified from Marsh (1891, plate XVI).

Fig. 5. Snorkelling sauropods. Left: the first-ever life restoration of a sauropod, Knight's drawing of *Amphicoelias*, published by Ballou (1897), modified from Osborn & Mook (1921, fig. 127). Right: a similar scene with '*Helopus*' (now *Euhelopus*), modified from Wiman (1929, fig. 5).

above the water. The skins were shown with a bold mottled pattern like that of some lizards, which would not be seen again in a sauropod restoration for the best part of a century.

Later the same year came what may still be the most immediately recognizable of all sauropod depictions: Charles Knight's 1897 painting of *Brontosaurus* (Fig. 6a), executed under the direction of Osborn and reproduced by Matthew (1905, fig. 4). The centrepiece of Knight's painting was an amphibious *Brontosaurus* in right anterolateral aspect, its legs, tail and most of its torso submerged, with its back projecting above the surface of the water and its neck nearly vertical. In the background, a *Diplodocus* grazed on the lake shore, shown in lateral view. Both animals were a uniform dull grey. Knight was unwittingly setting the template for how sauropods would be depicted for the next three quarters of a century, not least in the Jurassic part of Zallinger's mural (see later). In Knight's world, sauropods were clumsy, lumbering behemoths, barely able to support their weight out of water: even the terrestrial *Diplodocus*, lighter than its swamp-bound cousin, looks ponderous and inert. A dramatically different opinion, at least as regards *Diplodocus*, was offered by Osborn (1899,

Fig. 6. Two classic sauropod paintings by Knight. Left: swamp-bound '*Brontosaurus*' (now *Apatosaurus*), painted in 1897, with static terrestrial *Diplodocus* in background. Right: athletic *Diplodocus*, painted in 1907.

pp. 213–214), who considered sauropods much more athletic and not restricted to an aquatic lifestyle – although still at least partially aquatic by habit:

> The animal was capable not only of powerful but of very rapid movements. In contrast with *Brontosaurus* it was essentially long and light-limbed and agile. Its tail was a means of defence upon land and a means of rapid escape by water from its numerous carnivorous foes.

Osborn also asserted that *Diplodocus* was capable of rearing to feed:

> the tail ... functioned as a lever to balance the weight of the dorsals, anterior limbs, neck, and head, and to raise the entire forward portion of the body upwards. This power was certainly exerted while the animal was in the water, and possibly also while upon land. Thus the quadrupedal Dinosaurs occasionally assumed the position characteristic of the bipedal Dinosaurs – namely, a tripodal position, the body supported upon the hind feet and the tail.
>
> (p. 213)

Ironically, it was the same artist, Knight, who was to depict this more nimble *Diplodocus*, in his painting of 1907 (Fig. 6b), created as a cover image for *Scientific American* to celebrate the American Museum of Natural History's donation of one of its *Diplodocus* skeletons to the Senckenberg Museum in Frankfurt, Germany. In this painting, the animal is depicted with its torso raised about 60° from the horizontal, its forefeet raised to knee height and its neck high in the air – well above the foliage that it seems to be trying to eat, in fact. Even this athletic *Diplodocus*, however, is accompanied by the traditional aquatic counterpart, whose head and neck are visible peering into the frame from the body of water on the right of the picture.

One of the most important sauropod workers of the early twentieth century was Elmer S. Riggs of the Field Columbian Museum (now the Field Museum of Natural History, Chicago). Riggs (1903*a*) named and briefly described *Brachiosaurus*, which had been found by the expedition that he led to Grand Junction, Colorado in 1900. It was at that time the largest known dinosaur. In the same year as the description of *Brachiosaurus*, Riggs published an important monograph on *Apatosaurus* that argued that Marsh's genus *Brontosaurus* was synonymous with his own earlier *Apatosaurus*, and that the difference in the number of sacral vertebrae between the two genera was an ontogenetic character, the latter having been described from a juvenile specimen in which not all the sacral vertebrae had fused by the time of death (Riggs 1903*b*). Although Riggs's argument has since proven conclusive for most palaeontologists, so that the older name *Apatosaurus* takes priority over its junior synonym, the more euphonious and resonant name *Brontosaurus* continued to be used in scientific publication for some time after Riggs's work, and remains popular with the public even today (e.g. Chapman & Cleese 1989). The next year, Riggs (1904) published a full monographic description of *Brachiosaurus*, erecting the family Brachiosauridae to contain this genus and *Haplocanthosaurus* Hatcher 1903*a*. This work was also important for its forceful argument in favour of a terrestrial lifestyle for sauropods:

> There is no evidence among [sauropods] of that shortening or angulation of limb, or the broadening of foot, which is common to amphibious animals. Nor is there anything in the structure of the opisthocoelians [i.e. sauropods] which is not found in some terrestrial forms. The straight hind leg occurs in quadrupeds only among those forms which inhabit the uplands ... The short, stout metapodials and blunted phalanges ... would be as ill adapted for propulsion in water or upon marsh lands as are those of the elephant ... In short, if the foot structure of these animals indicates anything, it indicates specialization for terrestrial locomotion.
>
> (pp. 244–245)

Riggs also argued that, while *Apatosaurus* and *Diplodocus* were capable of rearing on their hind limbs, *Brachiosaurus* would have found this much more difficult – a finding consonant with current thinking.

February 1905 saw the unveiling of the mounted skeleton of *Brontosaurus* at the American Museum of Natural History, its posture based on the results of dissections of alligators and other reptiles to elucidate the functioning of the joints (Matthew 1905). This mount, the first of a sauropod, consisted primarily of the remains of a single individual, AMNH 460, with some elements from AMNH 222, AMNH 339 and AMNH 592, and the remainder cast or modelled in plaster. Most important among these constructed elements was the *Camarasaurus*-like skull, modelled after the reconstructions of Marsh (1883, 1891) discussed above. Osborn's thoughts on *Brontosaurus* have not aged well: he estimated the mass of the mounted specimen as 'not less than ninety tons' (p. 64) and its age as 'some eight millions of years' (p. 66), and followed Owen and Cope in considering sauropods as 'spending their lives entirely in shallow water, partly immersed, wading about on the bottom or, perhaps, occasionally swimming, but unable to emerge entirely upon dry land' (p. 67), 'Hence we can best regard the *Brontosaurus* as a great, slow-moving animal-automaton' (p. 69). Based on the mounted skeleton, Knight modelled a 1:16 scale life restoration of *Brontosaurus*, illustrated by Matthew (1905, fig. 3), and, at Osborn's request, Gregory (1905) used this model to calculate the mass of *Brontosaurus* more rigorously, using the volume of water displaced by the model. Gregory's estimate of 38 tons was the first scientifically calculated mass estimate for a sauropod. While much better than Osborn's, the estimate is still rather high: this is partly because it was based on the assumption that *Brontosaurus* was 10% more dense than water – an assumption now known to be incorrect because of the increased understanding of the pneumatic cavities in the skeleton and soft tissue. Gregory's volume estimate was 31.13 m^3, which, using a density of 0.8 kg L^{-1} (Wedel 2005, p. 220), would yield a mass of 24 900 kg, corresponding well to more recent estimates such as 26 000 kg (Anderson *et al.* 1985) and 23 000 kg (Paul 1988*a*) for comparable specimens.

The AMNH *Brontosaurus* mount was followed only 3 months later by the second mounted sauropod, that of *Diplodocus carnegii* Hatcher 1901. The type and cotype specimen of this species (CM 84 and CM 94, respectively) had been discovered at Sheep Creek, Albany County, Wyoming, and collected by J.L. Wortman and O.A. Peterson in expeditions funded by Andrew Carnegie. Hatcher's (1901) description was based on both of these specimens, and included a skeletal reconstruction (Hatcher 1901, plate XIII) based primarily on these two individuals, but with the missing forelimbs provided by an AMNH specimen that subsequently proved to be from *Camarasaurus*. A cast of the combined skeleton was prepared under the direction of first Hatcher and then, after his death, Holland. At the request of King Edward VII, this was sent to the British Museum (Natural History) (BMNH) in London in January 1905, assembled there in April and unveiled on 12 May (Holland 1905, pp. 443–446). Further casts of the same material were subsequently sent to museums in Berlin, Paris, Vienna, Madrid, St Petersburg, Bologna, La Plata, Mexico City and Munich, and the original material mounted at the Carnegie Museum in 1907 (McIntosh 1981, p. 20); making this, perhaps, the single most viewed skeleton of any animal in the world.

The availability of the skeleton of *Diplodocus carnegii* provoked much speculation about its lifestyle. Hay (1908) proposed that it sprawled like a crocodile: 'The mammal-like pose attributed to the Sauropoda is one that is not required by their anatomy and one that is improbable' (p. 677); 'The weight of *Diplodocus* and *Brontosaurus* furnishes a strong argument against their having had a mammal-like carriage' (pp. 679–680); '*Diplodocus* ... could creep about on land, with perhaps laborious effort' (p. 681). Tornier (1909) also rejected Hatcher's mammal-like erect-legged posture for *Diplodocus*, despite its pedigree going all the way back to Phillips, in favour of an interpretation in which *Diplodocus* sprawled like a lizard. Tornier (1909, plate II) provided a bizarre skeletal reconstruction of *Diplodocus* (Fig. 7) in which the scapulae were vertical and articulated with the last cervical rather than the first few dorsals, the glenoid faced directly to the posterior with no ventral component, the radius and ulna formed an acute angle with the humerus, the tibia and fibula formed an acute angle with the femur, and the neck was so flexible that the fifth most proximal cervical was vertical, C6–C10 were inclined

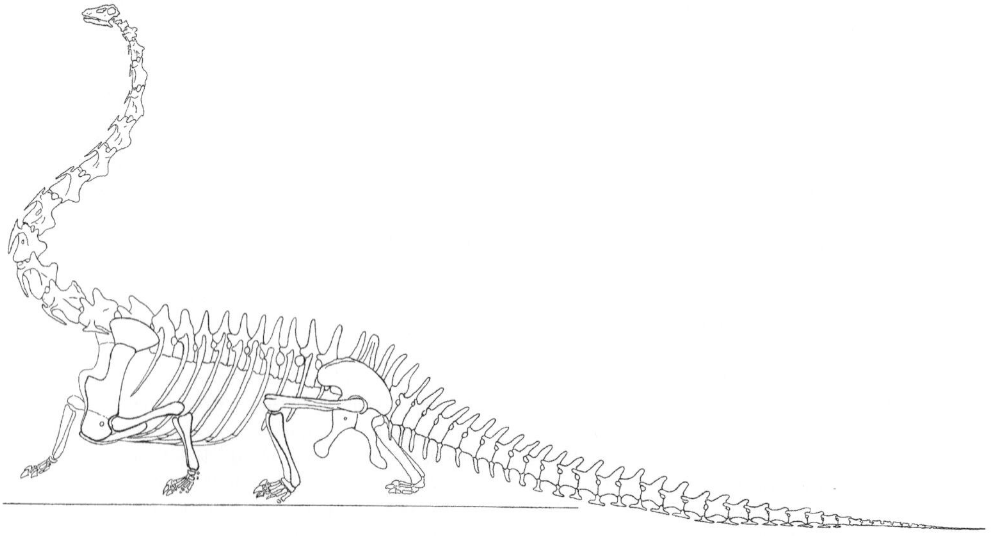

Fig. 7. Tornier's sprawling, disarticulated reconstruction of *Diplodocus*, modified from Tornier (1909, plate II).

backwards, and the skull was held directly dorsal to the shoulder. Hay (1910) reaffirmed and amplified his position, concluding his paper with a drawing by Mary Mason, executed under his instruction, that depicted four *Diplodocus* individuals. In the foreground, two individuals sprawl on dry land, one of them trailing its right leg painfully behind it. Further back, a nearly submerged individual swims towards them; further back still, a fourth lies absolutely flat on a distant shore, its neck, torso and tail all lying on the ground.

The unconventional posture suggested independently by Hay and Tornier was rebutted by Holland (1910), whose paper combined solid anatomical analysis with devastating sarcasm and rhetoric to convincingly demonstrate that the sprawling posture was impossible for *Diplodocus*, and other sauropods, to adopt:

> It was a bold step for [Tornier] immediately to transfer the creature from the order Dinosauria, and evidently with the skeleton of a *Varanus* and a *Chameleon* before him, to proceed with the help of a pencil, the powerful tool of the closet-naturalist, to reconstruct the skeleton upon the study of which two generations of American paleontologists have expended considerable time and labor, and squeeze the animal into the form which his brilliantly illuminated imagination suggested.
>
> (p. 262)

Holland demonstrated that Tornier's posture requires the greater trochanter of the femur to articulate with the ischiadic peduncle of the ilium, 'thus locking the femur into a position utterly precluding all motion whatsoever' and that it disarticulates the knee, leaving the distal articular surface of the femur unused, and the tibia and fibula articulating with the posterior edges of the condyles. He commented on Tornier's skeletal reconstruction that 'As a contribution to the literature of caricature the success achieved is remarkable' (p. 264). Holland (1910, fig. 9) showed that, were the Tornierian posture actually achieved, the chest and belly of *Diplodocus* would be much lower than its feet, so that it would have required deep grooves in the ground to walk along. Although Hay (1911) attempted to counter Holland's arguments, the debate was effectively over. Whatever doubt may have remained was dispelled by the description of a complete and articulated juvenile *Camarasaurus* by Gilmore (1925), which clearly showed that the posture advocated by Holland was correct, and by the fossilized sauropod trackways later described by Bird (1939, 1941, 1944).

The years 1909–1912 saw what was, perhaps, the most ambitious palaeontological undertaking in history: the German expeditions to collect fossils from the Tendaguru region of German East Africa (now Tanzania), under the leadership of Werner Janensch and, subsequently, Hans Reck (Maier 2003). The scale of the undertaking was immense: the Germans recruited 170 native labourers for the 1909 season, rising to 400 and then 500 in subsequent years. In total, 235 tonnes of fossils were shipped back to Germany, having been carried from Tendaguru to the port of Lindi in 5400 4-day-long marches. Much of this material remains unprepared nearly a century later, but the prepared specimens include some of the most spectacular sauropod material in the world, including the *Brachiosaurus brancai* specimen HMN SII (officially MB.R.2181), which is the largest known reasonably complete skeleton of any terrestrial animal. Other new sauropods recognized from the Tendaguru fossils include *Dicraeosaurus* Janensch 1914, *Tornieria* Sternfeld 1911, *Janenschia* Wild 1991, *Tendaguria* Bonaparte *et al.* 2000 and *Australodocus* Remes 2007 – all but the first of which were previously subsumed under the name *Gigantosaurus* Fraas 1908, which was abandoned when found to be a synonym of the nomen dubium *Gigantosaurus* Seeley 1869. The Tendaguru sauropods have a complex nomenclatural history that is only now being resolved (e.g. Remes 2006; Taylor 2009). These sauropods represent several groups: Brachiosauridae (*B. brancai*), Dicraeosauridae (*Dicraeosaurus*), Diplodocinae (*Tornieria* and *Australodocus*) and probably Titanosauria (*Janenschia* and *Tendaguria*, although the former may instead represent a camarasaurid or an apatosaurine, and the latter is enigmatic, known only from a few presacral vertebrae that do not closely resemble those of any other known sauropod). Together with the theropods, ornithopods and stegosaurs of Tendaguru, these taxa constitute one of the richest known dinosaur faunas – all the more amazing in light of the difficult working conditions in which the fossils were excavated and the scarcity of materials, such as plaster for jacketing. Janensch devoted much of his career to an exhaustive series of detailed monographs on the sauropods of Tendaguru (Janensch 1922, 1929*a*, 1935–1936, 1947, 1950*a*, 1961), so that his work on these sauropods spanned more than half a century. Between 1919 and 1930, the British Museum (Natural History) mounted a series of under-resourced expeditions to Tendaguru, but the results were disappointing, with only one good specimen recovered and even that not properly described. A very brief preliminary report was provided by the expedition leader, Migeod (1931), but a full description and analysis of this specimen is only now under way (Taylor 2005), with preliminary results suggesting that Migeod's specimen may represent yet another new taxon.

Matthew (1915) wrote the first book about dinosaurs for non-specialists, which included (fig. 24) the first attempt to reconstruct the skeleton of *Brachiosaurus*, based on both the American *B. altithorax* and the German *B. brancai* material. Given that it was executed only 1 year after Janensch's (1914) initial, brief report of the German brachiosaur material, this reconstruction is impressively accurate: it is instantly recognizable as *Brachiosaurus*, and has all the proportions essentially correct. Unfortunately, sauropods otherwise receive short shrift in Matthew's book, the relevant chapter of which consists primarily of a reprint of his own (1905) account of the mounting of the AMNH *Brontosaurus*, and includes a reproduction of Knight's 1897 *Brontosaurus* painting. The book undoubtedly helped to establish swamp-bound sauropods as conventional wisdom, despite the earlier opposite conclusions of Phillips (1871), Osborn (1899), Riggs (1904) and others. This perception, once established, would prove difficult to shake off.

The 1920s opened with the publication of the sauropod monograph that stands alone: the detailed redescription of *Camarasaurus* by Osborn & Mook (1921). In 141 pages, 127 stunningly detailed figures and 25 large plates, and working from excellent and abundant material, Osborn & Mook did in detail the work that Cope had rushed through so inadequately 40 years earlier (Fig. 3b). So exhaustive was their work that, nearly 90 years on, it remains the most comprehensive guide not only to *Camarasaurus* but to sauropod anatomy in general. The monograph also redescribed *Amphicoelias*, resolved some synonymies and other nomenclatural issues, and reproduced important earlier figures, including the pioneering 1877 *Camarasaurus* reconstruction of Ryder. While palaeobiological hypotheses have come and gone, and as papers that were once highly regarded are now seen as hopelessly wrong, Osborn & Mook's careful and comprehensive descriptive work remains as relevant as ever. Four years later, Gilmore (1925) described the marvellously preserved juvenile *Camarasaurus* CM 11338 in great detail, and was able to correct the vertebral formula and other minor errors of Osborn & Mook. Gilmore presented a skeletal reconstruction in his plate XVII, which was the first reconstruction of a sauropod based on the remains of a single individual. Also significant in the 1920s was the description of *Helopus* Wiman (1929), the first of many Chinese sauropods. Like Gilmore, Wiman was fortunate enough to work from material so complete that it would have been the envy of earlier workers such as Owen and Seeley: the skull, axial and appendicular elements are all figured in multiple views. Like *Amphicoelias* before it, *Helopus* was conceived as a snorkeler (Fig. 5b). (The name *Helopus* was preoccupied, and so this genus is now known as *Euhelopus* Romer 1956.)

Around 1930, during an economic slump in Germany precipitated in part by the Wall Street Crash, plans were made to mount the skeleton of the *Brachiosaurus brancai* type specimen HMN SII at the Humboldt Museum in Berlin (Maier 2003, pp. 260–268). Original plans to mount cast and replica bones were superseded by the yet more ambitious goal of using original bones (from SII and referred specimens) for all but the skull, the fragile presacral vertebrae and a few other minor bones. The Herculean effort took 7 years to complete, and the mounted skeleton was unveiled, to a backdrop of swastika banners, in August 1937 – the year after the Berlin Olympics and just 2 years before the start of World War II. The war would interrupt further work on the Tendaguru material so that it would be a further 13 years before a paper describing the skeletal mount could be published (Janensch 1950*b*).

Bird (1939, 1941, 1944) was the first to describe sauropod tracks from several sites, including Glen Rose and Davenport Ranch, both in Texas. Bird (1944, p. 65) noted that, at the Davenport Ranch site, all 23 individual trackways were headed in the same direction, and concluded 'this suggests that they passed in a single herd, an important conclusion, borne out by the consistency of the preserved tracks'. Equally significantly, despite assuming that the tracks were made on a stream bed, Bird (1944, p. 65) noted that:

> if the the smallest animals in the herd were wading, as the depth of their tracks indicates, then, by comparison, the larger creatures were progressing well out of water. The question 'Could *Brontosaurus* walk on land?' can be answered in all probability in the affirmative.

This evidence of a terrestrial lifestyle continued to be widely overlooked, however, as in Zdeněk Burian's widely reproduced 1941 painting of three snorkelling *Brachiosaurus* individuals – a painting that seems directly descended from Knight's 1897 *Amphicoelias* drawing. In the foreground and the background two of the animals are standing on the bottom of a lake, with only their heads and the anterior part of their necks protruding above water; between them, the third has lowered its neck to eat vegetation growing on the lake bed, and is entirely submerged. This kind of lifestyle was later proved impossible by Kermack (1951), who pointed out that snorkelling cannot be achieved by means of a long neck as water pressure would make it impossible to ventilate lungs below a certain depth.

Stage 4: the dark ages (1945–1967)

Understandably, little effort was put into palaeontology during World War II (1939–1945); more surprisingly, the study of dinosaurs, including sauropods, did not resume after the war, because dinosaurs were perceived as an evolutionary dead end, and mammal palaeontology was perceived as more interesting and important (Bakker 1975, p. 58). Despite the huge popular appeal of Rudolf F. Zallinger's gigantic *Age of Reptiles* mural at the Yale Peabody Museum, completed in 1947 and reproduced in *Life Magazine*'s 1952 series *The World We Live In*, it can only have helped reinforce the popular perception of dinosaurs in general, and sauropods in particular, as sluggish and unathletic. The Jurassic part of the mural, which contains its sauropods, owes a massive debt to Knight's 1897 *Brontosaurus* painting, both compositionally and in terms of the palaeobiology that it represents. Like Knight's image, Zallinger's has as its principal subject an amphibious *Brontosaurus*, in right anterolateral aspect, submerged to the shoulders in a lake and with its neck raised to a near-vertical posture. Also, like Knight's painting, the mural depicts a *Diplodocus* in the background, on land, in lateral view and with a horizontal neck. As with Knight, both sauropods are an undistinguished grey colour. Half a century of palaeobiological work had resulted in absolutely no visible progress in how sauropods were perceived. That Zallinger had a tendency to repeat himself as well as to recycle others' compositions was demonstrated by his 1966 painting of *Brachiosaurus*, published in Watson (1966, pp. 20–21). Once more, the principal subject was depicted in right anterolateral view, up to its shoulders in water, with a steeply inclined neck, in dull grey, and with a second sauropod (this time, another *Brachiosaurus* individual) shown in the background, standing on the shore of the lake. In both the Zallinger paintings, a small, red rhamphorynchoid pterosaur flies with the tip of its left wing in front of the principal subject's neck. Outdated ideas were further propagated by a stream of children's books, such as *The How and Why Wonder Book of Dinosaurs* (Geis 1960) with its grotesquely fat sauropods in poses recycled from the work of Knight.

Apart from work mentioned earlier (e.g. Janensch's monographs on the Tendaguru sauropods and Bird's work on tracks), little significant research was published on sauropods during this period. One exception was the recognition of the first rebbachisaurid, *Rebbachisaurus* Lavocat 1954, from Morocco, although this specimen has never been properly described; another was the description of *Mamenchisaurus* Young 1954, from China, although the extreme neck elongation in this genus would not be recognized until the subsequent description of the referred species *Mamenchisaurus hochuanensis* Young & Zhao 1972.

Of more general interest was the work of Colbert (1962) on dinosaur masses, the first systematic attempt to estimate and compare the masses of different dinosaurs. Colbert used a variation on the method of Gregory (1905), measuring the volumes of scale models by the amount of sand displaced, and multiplying up by the scale to determine the volume of the modelled animal and then by an estimated density of 0.9 kg l^{-1} to determine its mass. Colbert (1962, p. 10) obtained values of 27.87 and 32.42 tonnes for *Brontosaurus* (using two different models, of which he favoured the heavier), 10.56 tonnes for *Diplodocus*, and 78.26 tonnes for *Brachiosaurus* – the latter figure being widely quoted in popular books. Since Colbert's efforts, several further surveys have been made of the masses of various dinosaurs, among which those of Alexander (1985, 1989) and Anderson *et al.* (1985) are of particular interest – the former based on the volumes of models, and the latter based on regression equations that relate limb-bone measurements to mass in extant animals and which extrapolates them to yield the masses of sauropods whose limb bones are known. Mass estimation has progressed significantly in recent years, especially with the growing understanding of how important pneumaticity was for weight reduction. Table 2 presents a summary of the history of mass estimates for *Brachiosaurus brancai*, a much studied taxon owing to its large size and the existence of an excellent near-complete skeleton. Several trends are evident: first, the improvement in methods, from simple *gestalt* estimates via volume measurements of physical models to computer models; second, a tendency to assume lower densities in recent years; and third, generally decreasing estimates of volume owing to the use of more scientifically rigorous models than the grossly obese models available to the earlier studies. The net result of the last two of these is that modern estimates tend to be much lower than older ones, especially if the aberrant result of Gunga *et al.* (1995) is ignored because of its use of circular rather than elliptical conic sections in its model. This trend towards lower mass estimates also applies to other sauropods, although it is more difficult to quantify in the case of, for example, *Apatosaurus* owing to different authors' use of different specimens.

Stage 5: the modern renaissance (1968–present)

Having fallen into dormancy, dinosaur palaeontology reawakened dramatically as the 1960s closed. The beginnings of the 'dinosaur renaissance' (Bakker 1975) are usually attributed to the description of the bird-like theropod *Deinonychus* Ostrom 1969*a* and its full osteology (Ostrom 1969*b*), which pointed out many aspects of its anatomy indicative of an active lifestyle. However, the first shoots of revival had appeared a year earlier, in

Table 2. *Changing mass estimates for* Brachiosaurus brancai

Author and date	Method	Volume (l)	Density (kg/l)	Mass (kg)
Janensch (1938)	Not specified	–	–	'40 t'
Colbert (1962)	Displacement of sand	86 953	0.9	78 258
Russell *et al.* (1980)	Limb-bone allometry	–	–	13 618*
Anderson *et al.* (1985)	Limb-bone allometry	–	–	29 000
Paul (1988*a*)	Displacement of water	36 585	0.861†	31 500
Alexander (1989)‡	Weighing in air and water	46 600	1.0	46 600
Gunga *et al.* (1995)	Computer model	74 420	1.0	74 420
Christiansen (1997)	Weighing in air and water	41 556	0.9	37 400
Henderson (2004)	Computer model	32 398	0.796	25 789
Henderson (2006)	Computer model	–	–	25 922
Gunga *et al.* (2008)	Computer model	47 600	0.8	38 000
Taylor (2009)	Graphic double integration	29 171	0.8	23 337

*Russell *et al.* give the mass as '14.9 t', which has usually been interpreted as representing metric tonnes, for example, 14 900 kg. However, they cite 'the generally accepted figure of 85 tons' (p. 170), which can only be a reference to Colbert (1962). Colbert stated a mass of 85.63 US tons as well as the metric version, so we must assume that Russell et al. were using US tons throughout.
†Paul used a density of 0.9 kg L^{-1} for most of the model and 0.6 kg L^{-1} for the neck, which was measured separately and found to constitute 13% of the total volume, yielding an aggregate density of $(0.9 \times 87\%) + (0.6 \times 13\%) = 0.861$ kg L^{-1}.
‡Alexander did not state which *Brachiosaurus* species his estimate was for, only that it was based on the BMNH model. This model is simply stamped '*Brachiosaurus*'.

Bakker's article 'The Superiority of Dinosaurs', in the magazine of the Yale Peabody Museum (Bakker 1968). Bakker (1968, pp. 14–20) discussed sauropods specifically and at length, advocating a vigorous, endothermic, terrestrial lifestyle on the basis of limb articulations, torso shape, neck length and palaeoenvironmental evidence, and included a revolutionary life restoration (Bakker 1968, fig. 4) showing two individuals of *Barosaurus* Marsh 1890, heads held high and alert, striding briskly across dry land. It is difficult, 40 years on, to appreciate how radical this image seemed at the time: the visual impact of *Jurassic Park*, *Walking With Dinosaurs* and the new generation of palaeoartists has brought such images so firmly into the mainstream that Bakker's drawing no longer surprises. But against the then ubiquitous backdrop of swamp-bound, sluggish sauropods exemplified by the art of Knight, Zallinger and Burian, it was a remarkable departure. As indicated by the title of a subsequent paper (Bakker 1980) and a popular book (Bakker 1986), Bakker was preaching 'dinosaur heresies', and old views were not quick to change – for example, Weaver (1983) argued that *Brachiosaurus* would be physically unable to gather food quickly enough to support the metabolic demands of endothermy, although this study was flawed by its assumption that the head of *Brachiosaurus* was only the size of that of a giraffe; and Dodson (1990) continued to advocate ectothermy for sauropods, with correspondingly long lifespans of multiple centuries.

The first shots had been fired in the battle to bring sauropods out of the swamps, and Coombs (1975) provided many compelling arguments for sauropod terrestriality. In a careful study that found that some anatomical evidence was equivocal, Coombs found that the tall and relatively narrow sauropod torso both resembles that of terrestrial rather than amphibious extant species, and is mechanically optimized for load-bearing. Using this and several other lines of evidence (e.g. lack of secondary palate, weight reduction through pneumaticity, straight-limbed posture, compact feet and the terrestrial sediments in which sauropod remains occur), he concluded that sauropods were primarily terrestrial, although they probably spent some time in water – as do elephants.

McIntosh & Berman (1975) reconsidered the problem of the skull of *Apatosaurus*, which had long been thought, following the reconstructions of Marsh (1883, 1891), to resemble the robust skull of *Camarasaurus*. On reviewing the historical evidence concerning the large *Diplodocus*-like skull CM 11162, they concurred with the earlier suggestion of Holland (1915) that it belonged to *Apatosaurus*. This conclusion has now been widely accepted, although in Holland's time it had been rejected due to the disagreement of Osborn. It is widely believed that the use of the name *Apatosaurus* for the animal previously known as *Brontosaurus* is related to the recognition of the correct skull, but in fact no such connection exists.

Jensen (1985) formally described and named three new giant sauropods, although he had been referring to them informally in print since the late 1970s: *Supersaurus* Jensen 1985, *Dystylosaurus* Jensen 1985 and *Ultrasaurus* Jensen 1985. These attracted much media attention because of the enormous sizes attributed to them: in particular,

Ultrasaurus, considered a brachiosaurid on the basis of a referred scapulocoracoid, was estimated to weigh as much as 180 tonnes (McGowan 1991, p. 118) – a ludicrously inflated estimate that was based on Colbert's (1962) 78 tonne estimate for *Brachiosaurus*, scaled for an animal 32% larger in linear dimension. Unfortunately, spectacular though they are, Jensen's finds have not proven to be all that he claimed. First, it became apparent that *Ultrasaurus* Jensen 1985 was a junior homonym of *Ultrasaurus* Kim 1983, and so it was given the rather inelegant replacement name *Ultrasauros* Olshevsky 1991. Next, Curtice *et al.* (1996) showed that the dorsal vertebra that was the holotype of *Ultrasauros* belonged to the same individual as the *Supersaurus* holotype, so that *Ultrasauros* was synonymized with *Supersaurus*. This meant that the brachiosaurid scapulocoracoid that had been considered to belong to *Ultrasauros* could not belong to the same animal as the diplodocid *Ultrasauros* = *Supersaurus*. Curtice *et al.* (1996) also showed that this scapulocoracoid was not larger than the largest Tendaguru brachiosaur specimens. Finally, Curtice & Stadtman (2001) showed that the *Dystylosaurus* holotype and only specimen, a dorsal vertebra, also belonged to the same individual as the *Supersaurus* holotype, so that this name became another junior synonym. In short, all of Jensen's three giant sauropods proved to be a single sauropod, with only the referred scapulocoracoid belonging to a different taxon. Nevertheless, *Supersaurus* remains a gigantic animal; its neck is longer than any other for which there is osteological evidence, probably about 15 m in length.

With the debate about sauropod terrestriality having been effectively settled by the mid-1980s, neck posture and flexibility became the next point of contention. From the early days of sauropod palaeontology, it had been assumed that the long necks of sauropods were flexible: for example, 'The slender skull ... was supported by a very long and flexible neck which permitted of an almost unlimited variety of movements throughout a considerable arc' (Hatcher 1901, p. 57). Skeletal reconstructions had shown necks held in a variety of postures. Horizontal and near-horizontal postures had been illustrated by, among others, Ryder for his 1877 *Camarasaurus*, Marsh (1883, 1891) for *Brontosaurus* (= *Apatosaurus*), Hatcher (1901, plate XIII) for *Diplodocus* and Gilmore (1936, plate XXXIV) for *Apatosaurus*. Upward-inclined and near-vertical necks had been depicted by Osborn & Mook (1921, plate LXXXIV) for *Camarasaurus*, Wiman (1929, fig. 3) for *Helopus* (= *Euhelopus*), Janensch (1950*b*, plate VIII) for *Brachiosaurus brancai* and Bakker (1968, fig. 4) for *Barosaurus*. However, as it was generally assumed that sauropod necks were very flexible, it is not clear how much importance these authors attached to the illustrated postures: they probably considered each illustrated posture to be just one of many that were habitually adopted. In contradiction to this, Martin (1987), having investigated the range of motion between adjacent cervical vertebrae during the mounting of the Rutland specimen of *Cetiosaurus* at the Leicester City Museum, concluded that the neck would have been much less flexible than previously assumed – only just able to lower the head to the ground and only able to lift the head about 1 m above shoulder height. Martin also found horizontal flexibility to be limited to only a 4.5 m arc. These findings were later corroborated by the work of Stevens & Parrish (1999) on DinoMorph. a computer program for modelling such articulations digitally. Stevens & Parrish (1999, p. 799) found that both *Apatosaurus louisae* CM 3018 and *Diplodocus carnegii* CM 84 were limited in their ability to raise their heads, but that their osteology did not prevent them from lowering their heads well below ground level – an adaptation that they interpreted as facilitating browsing on aquatic plants from the shore. This interpretation has been opposed by, among others, Paul (1998), who disputed the morphological evidence; Upchurch (2000), who pointed out that the *Apatosaurus* reconstruction was based on badly damaged vertebrae; Christian & Heinrich (1998) and Christian & Dzemski (2007), who argued from the pattern of stresses in the intervertebral joints that *Brachiosaurus brancai* held its neck erect; and Taylor *et al.* (2009), who argued from the behaviour of extant tetrapods that sauropods held their necks raised rather than in neutral pose. The issue is not yet settled.

The release of the film *Jurassic Park* in 1993 marked a turning point in public perception of dinosaurs, and particularly sauropods. Until then, the dinosaur renaissance of Bakker, Ostrom and others, while challenging the traditional views of palaeontologists, had had little impact on non-specialists. The terrestrial and athletic *Brachiosaurus* that is the first dinosaur clearly seen in the film brought this revolution to a far wider audience. Similarly, the depiction of sauropods in the BBC's 1999 documentary series *Walking with Dinosaurs* helped to publicize new ideas, including both the relatively inflexible and horizontal necks advocated by Stevens & Parrish, and rearing in order to feed and to mate. Subsequent films, including the *Jurassic Park* sequels, and TV programmes, including *When Dinosaurs Roamed America*, have continued to present a view of sauropods that is largely in keeping with current thought.

The evolutionary relationships of sauropods were very poorly understood up until the mid-1990s, and their classification had not progressed beyond the establishment of a handful of families – Diplodocidae, Brachiosauridae, Titanosauridae, Cetiosauridae – whose content was unstable, and whose interrelationships were obscure and, indeed, largely unexplored. For example, the evolutionary diagram of Bonaparte (1986) consisted only of a Prosauropoda block leading to a central block representing Cetiosauridae, and with branches leading from it to further undifferentiated and unrelated blocks for Brachiosauridae, Camarasauridae, Diplodocidae and Dicraeosauridae. Against this backdrop, Russell & Zheng (1993) performed the first phylogenetic analysis on sauropods as part of their paper describing the new species *Mamenchisaurus sinocanadorum* (Russell & Zheng 1993). Their analysis consisted of only 21 characters applied to nine taxa, and produced a tree that, in light of more recent work, appears wrong in placing the basal eusauropods *Mamenchisaurus*, *Omeisaurus* Young 1939 and *Shunosaurus* Dong *et al.* 1983 as closely related to the diplodocoids *Dicraeosaurus* and *Apatosaurus*. However, their analysis was quickly followed by others using more characters and taxa, notably those of Upchurch (1995), using 174 characters and 27 taxa; Upchurch (1998), using 205 characters and 26 taxa; Wilson & Sereno (1998), using 109 characters and 10 taxa; Wilson (2002), using 234 characters and 29 taxa; and Upchurch *et al.* (2004), using 309 characters and 47 taxa. The results of Wilson's and Upchurch's independent series of analyses are largely in agreement, with only the position of *Euhelopus* and the nemegtosaurids differing greatly between them. A subsequent collaboration between the authors of these studies (Wilson & Upchurch 2009) has established a consensus phylogeny, in which a sequence of basal sauropods leads to the great clade Neosauropoda, which comprises Diplodocoidea (Diplodocidae, Dicraeosauridae and Rebbachisauridae) and Macronaria (Camarasauridae, Brachiosauridae and Titanosauria). Although some work remains to be done, this basic structure now seems quite well established.

The advent of rigorous phylogenetic methods has dramatically affected the field of sauropod palaeontology by placing classification on a sound theoretical basis and making it possible to trace the evolution of particular features. Before the pioneering studies of the early and mid-1990s, much sauropod work was undertaken by non-specialists, and ideas about the group's classification were arbitrary and often contradictory. Since then, the establishment of a consensus on sauropod phylogeny has made it possible for the first time to carry out meaningful work on palaeobiogeography, diversity and palaeoecology, and these opportunities have attracted a crop of specialist workers who continue to expand the boundaries of sauropod science.

Until relatively recently, discussions on of the feeding strategy of sauropods have been speculative and dominated by then-prevailing ideas about sauropod habitats – hence, the claim of Hatcher (1901, p. 60) and many others that sauropods subsisted on 'tender, succulent aquatic or semi-aquatic plants'. This began to change in 1994, with the publication of two papers in the same volume (Barrett & Upchurch 1994; Calvo 1994) on feeding mechanisms. These papers established the modern approach by forsaking analogies with extant megaherbivores, instead relying on the direct evidence of functional anatomy, tooth wear and stomach contents when available. These and subsequent studies have yielded a consensus view that sauropods used minimal oral processing, although various groups seem to have differed in details of feeding strategy.

Chiappe *et al.* (1998) reported the first known sauropod embryos, those of titanosaurs, from the Auca Mahuevo site of Patagonia. The site covers more than 1 km^2 and has furnished many hundreds of specimens – for example, 200 whole eggs in a single 25 m^2 area (Chiappe *et al.* 2000). The preservation of the embryos is also excellent, including skin as well as bone, and articulated near-complete skulls (Chiappe *et al.* 2001), the first known from any titanosaur.

Curry (1999) applied the techniques of bone histology to sauropod remains for the first time, yielding insights into the growth history of *Apatosaurus*. By sampling bones from juvenile, sub-adult and adult specimens, she determined that growth was rapid and not seasonal, and that near-adult size was attained in about 10 years. Sander (2000) analysed the microstructure of a wide selection of bones from four different Tendaguru sauropods, and was able to demonstrate that the bones of different taxa can be differentiated on histological features alone. He also found two distinct types of histology in the bones of '*Barosaurus*' *africanus* Fraas 1908 (probably *Tornieria* sensu Remes 2006), which he tentatively interpreted as representing sexual dimorphism.

The recognition and description of new sauropod taxa has continued and accelerated in recent years, with significant new genera including *Rapetosaurus* Curry Rogers & Forster 2001, from Madagascar, a titanosaur much more complete than any known up until that time. The association of its skull with an unquestionably titanosaurian postcranial skeleton finally established the nature of titanosaur skulls, and resolved the phylogenetic position of nemegtosaurids as titanosaurs closely related to *Rapetosaurus*.

Today and tomorrow

As with other dinosaurs (Taylor 2006), the rate at which new sauropods are being recognized, described and named is far greater now than at any previous time. Of the 137 valid sauropod genera known at the end of 2006, more than half had been named in the previous 13 years, and all six of the most fruitful years have fallen since 1999. Figure 8 shows the rate of accumulation of valid sauropod genera, broken down by clade and in total. The general trend is towards exponential growth – not a trend that can be maintained indefinitely, but one that shows no signs of slowing yet. While brachiosaurid and diplodocid genera began to accumulate early in the history of sauropod palaeontology, it is only relatively recently that recognized titanosaur diversity has begun to climb, primarily due to the growth of work in South America. Titanosauria now represents one third of valid sauropod genera, whereas of the 20 valid sauropod genera that had been named by 1921 only a single titanosaur genus had been named that is still considered valid today, *Argyrosaurus*. (*Titanosaurus* and *Microcoelus* had also been named, but are no longer considered valid.)

Not only is sauropod diversity rising steeply, so is sauropod disparity – that is, the degree of morphological variation between different sauropods. The sauropod body plan has traditionally been described as conservative, but this prejudice is breaking down in light of the many bizarre forms

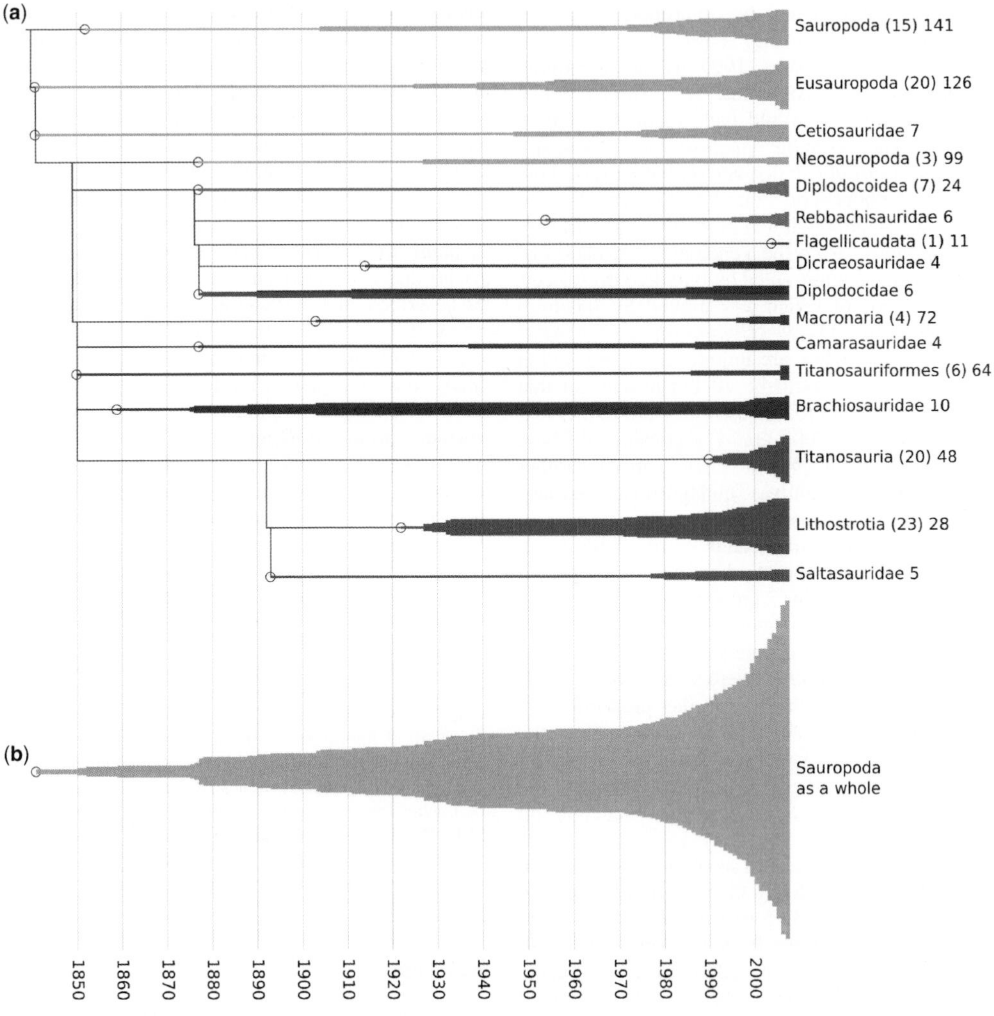

Fig. 8. Growing recognition of sauropod diversity through history. Only genera now considered valid are included. (**a**) Broken down by clade. The vertical thickness of the lines is proportional to the number of genera; the earliest valid genus in each clade is marked by a circle. Terminal clades have simple counts; for non-terminal clades, parentheses enclose the number of basal genera, that is, not members of depicted subclades, and are followed by total counts that include those of all subclades. (**b**) Total recognized diversity.

that have been described in recent years. These include the following.

- *Amargasaurus* Salgado & Bonaparte 1991 is an Argentinian dicraeosaurid with enormously elongated forked neural spines on the cervical and dorsal vertebrae. These spines may have appeared in life as individual spikes or may have supported long, tall, parallel sails.
- *Nigersaurus* Sereno *et al.* 1999 is an African rebbachisaurid whose well-preserved skull has a distinctive dentary with a completely straight, transversely oriented tooth row, extending further laterally than the posterior part of the skull does. The skull is also extraordinarily lightly built, even by sauropod standards (Sereno *et al.* 2007, fig. 1E).
- *Agustinia* Bonaparte 1999 is an armoured sauropod from Argentina, with spiked dorsal osteoderms that would have made the animal somewhat resemble *Stegosaurus*. Bonaparte found *Agustinia* so distinctive that he raised the new monogeneric family Agustiniidae to contain it, although it is probably a titanosaur.
- *Tendaguria*, from the Tendaguru Formation of Tanzania, is represented by only two dorsal vertebrae, one of which was figured by Janensch (1929*b*, fig. 11) as '*Gigantosaurus*' *robustus* Fraas 1908. They are unique in having neural spines so low as to be all but absent, so that they are much broader than they are tall. Bonaparte *et al.* (2000, p. 47) considered these vertebrae sufficiently distinct to merit another monogeneric family, Tendaguriidae, perhaps related to Camarasauridae.
- *Brachytrachelopan* Rauhut *et al.* 2005 is an Argentinian dicraeosaurid unique among known sauropods in having a proportionally short neck, so that in profile it more closely resembles an ornithopod than a classic sauropod.
- Conversely, *Erketu* Ksepka & Norell 2006 seems likely to have had the proportionally longest neck of any known sauropod, as the anterior cervical vertebrae from which it is principally known are more elongate even than the mid-cervicals of *Sauroposeidon* Wedel *et al.* 2000.
- *Europasaurus* Mateus, Laven and Knötschke in Sander *et al.* 2006 is a German titanosauriform somewhat resembling *Brachiosaurus*, except in its diminutive size: it is the smallest of all known sauropods, with adults measuring up to 6.2 m and weighing, perhaps, 500 kg – about the mass of a cow.
- At the other end of the size scale, *Futalognkosaurus* Calvo *et al.* 2007 joins its fellow Argentinian titanosaurs *Argentinosaurus* Bonaparte & Coria 1993 and *Puertasaurus* Novas *et al.* 2005 as one of the largest known sauropods. All three of these animals would have massed in the region of 50–100 tonnes.
- *Xenoposeidon* Taylor & Naish 2007, a British neosauropod, is known from a single partial dorsal vertebra, but has several features unique among all sauropods (e.g. neural arch is taller than centrum, covers dorsal surface of centrum, slopes forward by 35° and has featureless areas of unlaminated flat bone on its lateral surfaces). *Xenoposeidon* may represent a major new group of sauropods, of which further specimens are greatly to be desired.

The study of sauropods has come a long way since Owen named the tooth of *Cardiodon* 169 years ago, and the future looks very bright: with new sauropods being named at an ever-increasing rate, new techniques being applied to their study and old specimens being re-evaluated in the light of new knowledge, our understanding of sauropod morphology, ecology and phylogeny seems set to grow in richness and scope for the foreseeable future. At the same time, a great deal of work remains to be done. New specimens are being found and excavated more quickly than they can be described, and many sauropods named in recent years still await the monograph to follow up an often inadequate preliminary description. Also, many historical genera are long overdue for revision: for example, no modern analysis exists of the various species of *Diplodocus* or *Camarasaurus*. Much is being done, and much must be done in the future. Although they have been dead for 65 Ma, history continues to roll relentlessly on for sauropods.

This article would never have been written without the opportunity offered by the editors of this volume, R.T.J. Moody, E. Buffetaut, D. Naish and D.M. Martill, all of whom I thank for their enlightened interest in the history of our discipline. My work would have been shapeless without F. J. Taylor's invaluable advice on fitting all of the information into a coherent structure. In an undertaking of this kind, old literature is indispensable, and I thank M.J. Wedel, D. Naish, R. Irmis, S. Werning and D. Fowler for their aid in obtaining many crucial papers. M.J. Wedel also provided helpful comments on an earlier draft. Reviews of the submitted manuscript by P. Upchurch and D. Schwarz-Wings were detailed and constructive.

References

ALEXANDER, R. M. 1985. Mechanics of posture and gait of some large dinosaurs. *Zoological Journal of the Linnean Society*, **83**, 1–25.

ALEXANDER, R. M. 1989. *Dynamics of Dinosaurs and Other Extinct Giants.* Columbia University Press, New York.

ANDERSON, J. F., HALL-MARTIN, A. & RUSSELL, D. A. 1985. Long-bone circumference and weight in mammals, birds and dinosaurs. *Journal of Zoology*, **207**, 53–61.

BAKKER, R. T. 1968. The superiority of dinosaurs. *Discovery: Magazine of the Peabody Museum of Natural History*, **3**, 11–22.

BAKKER, R. T. 1975. Dinosaur renaissance. *Scientific American*, **232**, 58–78.

BAKKER, R. T. 1980. Dinosaur heresy, dinosaur renaissance: why we need endothermic archosaurs for a comprehensive theory of bioenergetic evolution. *In*: THOMAS, R. D. K. & OLSEN, E. C. (eds) *A Cold Look at the Warm-blooded Dinosaurs*. American Association for the Advancement of Science, Selected Symposia, **28**, 351–462.

BAKKER, R. T. 1986. *The Dinosaur Heresies*. Morrow, New York.

BALLOU, W. H. 1897. Strange creatures of the past: gigantic saurians of the reptilian age. *The Century*, **55**(1), 15–23.

BARBOUR, E. H. 1890. Scientific news 5: notes on the paleontological laboratory of the United States Geological Survey under Professor Marsh. *The American Naturalist*, **24**, 388–400.

BARRETT, P. M. 2006. A sauropod dinosaur tooth from the Middle Jurassic of Skye, Scotland.*Transactions of the Royal Society of Edinburgh: Earth Sciences* **97**, 25–29.

BARRETT, P. M. & UPCHURCH, P. 1994. Feeding mechanisms of *Diplodocus*. *Gaia*, **10**, 195–203.

BERMAN, D. S. & MCINTOSH, J. S. 1978. Skull and relationships of the Upper Jurassic sauropod *Apatosaurus* (Reptilia, Saurischia). *Bulletin of the Carnegie Museum*, **8**, 1–35.

BIRD, R. T. 1939. Thunder in his footsteps. *Natural History*, **43**, 254–261.

BIRD, R. T. 1941. A dinosaur walks into the museum. *Natural History*, **47**, 74–81.

BIRD, R. T. 1944. Did *Brontosaurus* ever walk on land? *Natural History*, **53**, 60–67.

BLOWS, W. T. 1995. The Early Cretaceous brachiosaurid dinosaurs *Ornithopsis* and *Eucamerotus* from the Isle of Wight, England. *Palaeontology*, **38**, 187–197.

BONAPARTE, J. F. 1986. The early radiation and phylogenetic relationships of the Jurassic sauropod dinosaurs, based on vertebral anatomy. *In*: PADIAN, K. (ed) *The Beginning of the Age of Dinosaurs*. Cambridge University Press, Cambridge, 247–258.

BONAPARTE, J. F. 1999. An armoured sauropod from the Aptian of northern Patagonia, Argentina. *In*: TOMIDA, Y., RICH, T. H. & VICKERS-RICH, P. (eds) *Proceedings of the Second Gondwanan Dinosaur Symposium*. National Science Museum, Tokyo, 1–12.

BONAPARTE, J. F. & CORIA, R. A. 1993. Un nuevo y gigantesco sauropodo titanosaurio de la Formacion Río Limay (Albiano-Cenomaniano) de la Provincia de Neuquén, Argentina. *Ameghiniana*, **30**, 271–282.

BONAPARTE, J. F. & POWELL, J. E. 1980. A continental assemblage of tetrapods from the Upper Cretaceous beds of El Brete, northwestern Argentina (Sauropoda–Coelurosauria–Carnosauria–Aves). *Mémoires de la Société Géologique de France, Nouvelle Série*, **139**, 19–28.

BONAPARTE, J. F., HEINRICH, W.-D. & WILD, R. 2000. Review of *Janenschia* Wild, with the description of a new sauropod from the Tendaguru beds of Tanzania and a discussion on the systematic value of procoelous caudal vertebrae in the Sauropoda. *Palaeontographica A*, **256**, 25–76.

BRITT, B. B. 1993. *Pneumatic postcranial bones in dinosaurs and other archosaurs*. PhD dissertation, University of Calgary.

BROOM, R. 1904. On the occurrence of an opisthocoelian dinosaur (*Algoasaurus bauri*) in the Cretaceous beds of South Africa. *Geological Magazine, new series, decade 5*, **1**, 445–447.

BUCKLAND, W. 1824. Notice on the *Megalosaurus* or great fossil lizard of Stonesfield. *Transactions of the Geological Society*, London, **21**, 390–397 (plates 40–44).

CALVO, J. O. 1994. Jaw mechanics in sauropod dinosaurs. *Gaia*, **10**, 184–193.

CALVO, J. O., PORFIRI, J. D., GONZÁLEZ-RIGA, B. J. & KELLNER, A. W. A. 2007. A new Cretaceous terrestrial ecosystem from Gondwana with the description of a new sauropod dinosaur. *Anais da Academia Brasileira de Ciências*, **79**, 529–541.

CARPENTER, K. & TIDWELL, V. 1998. Preliminary description of a *Brachiosaurus* skull from Felch Quarry 1, Garden Park, Colorado. *Modern Geology*, **23**, 69–84.

CARPENTER, K. & TIDWELL, V. 2005. Reassessment of the Early Cretaceous Sauropod *Astrodon johnsoni* Leidy 1865 (Titanosauriformes). *In*: TIDWELL, V. & CARPENTER, K. (eds) *Thunder Lizards: the Sauropodomorph Dinosaurs*. Indiana University Press, Bloomington, IN, 78–114.

CHAPMAN, G. & CLEESE, J. 1989. Anne Elk's Theory on Brontosauruses. *In*: CHAPMAN, G., CLEESE, J., GILLIAM, T., IDLE, E., JONES, T. & PALIN, M. (eds) *Just the Words, Volume 2*. Methuen, London, 118–120.

CHIAPPE, L. M., CORIA, R. A., DINGUS, L., JACKSON, F., CHINSAMY, A. & FOX, M. 1998. Sauropod dinosaur embryos from the Late Cretaceous of Patagonia. *Nature*, **396**, 258–261.

CHIAPPE, L. M., DINGUS, L. ET AL. 2000. Sauropod eggs and embryos from the Late Cretaceous of Patagonia. *In*: BRAVO, A. M. & REYES, T. (eds) *First International Symposium on Dinosaur Eggs and Babies – Extended Abstracts*. Isona I Conca Dellà Catalonia, Spain, 23–29.

CHIAPPE, L. M., SALGADO, L. & CORIA, R. A. 2001. Embryonic skulls of titanosaur sauropod dinosaurs. *Science*, **293**, 2444–2446.

CHRISTIAN, A. & DZEMSKI, G. 2007. Reconstruction of the cervical skeleton posture of *Brachiosaurus brancai* Janensch, 1914 by an analysis of the intervertebral stress along the neck and a comparison with the results of different approaches. *Fossil Record*, **10**, 38–49.

CHRISTIAN, A. & HEINRICH, W.-D. 1998. The neck posture of *Brachiosaurus brancai*. *Mitteilungen aus dem Museum für Naturkunde, Berlin, Geowissenschaften*, **1**, 73–80.

CHRISTIANSEN, P. 1997. Locomotion in sauropod dinosaurs. *Gaia*, **14**, 45–75.

COLBERT, E. H. 1962. The weights of dinosaurs. *American Museum Novitates*, **2076**, 1–16.

COLBERT, E. H. 1997. North American dinosaur hunters. *In*: FARLOW, J. O. & BRETT-SURMAN, M. K. (eds) *The Complete Dinosaur*. Indiana University Press, Bloomington, IN, 24–33.

COOMBS, W. P. 1975. Sauropod habits and habitats. *Palaeogeography, Palaeoclimatology, Palaeoecology*, **17**, 1–33.

COPE, E. D. 1877*a*. On a gigantic saurian from the Dakota Epoch of Colorado. *Paleontology Bulletin*, **25**, 5–10.

COPE, E. D. 1877*b*. On *Amphicoelias*, a genus of saurians from the Dakota Epoch of Colorado. *Paleontology Bulletin*, **27**, 1–5.

COPE, E. D. 1877*c*. On a dinosaurian from the Trias of Utah. *Proceedings of the American Philosophical Society*, **16**, 579–584.

COPE, E. D. 1878. On the vertebrata of the Dakota Epoch of Colorado. *Proceedings of the American Philosophical Society*, **17**, 233–247.

CURRY, K. A. 1999. Ontogenetic histology of *Apatosaurus* (Dinosauria: Sauropoda): new insights on growth rates and logevity. *Journal of Vertebrate Paleontology*, **19**, 654–665.

CURRY ROGERS, K. & FORSTER, C. A. 2001. Last of the dinosaur titans: a new sauropod from Madagascar. *Nature*, **412**, 530–534.

CURTICE, B. D. & STADTMAN, K. L. 2001. The demise of *Dystylosaurus edwini* and a revision of *Supersaurus vivianae*. *Western Association of Vertebrate Paleontologists and Mesa Southwest Paleontological Symposium, Mesa Southwest Museum Bulletin*, **8**, 33–40.

CURTICE, B. D., STADTMAN, K. L. & CURTICE, L. J. 1996. A reassessment of *Ultrasauros macintoshi* (Jensen, 1985). *Museum of Northern Arizona Bulletin*, **60**, 87–95.

DODSON, P. 1990. Sauropod paleoecology. *In*: WEISHAMPEL, D. B., DODSON, P. & OSMÓLSKA, H. (eds) *The Dinosauria*. University of California Press, Berkeley, CA, 402–407.

DONG, Z., ZHOU, S. & ZHANG, Y. 1983. The dinosaurian remains from Sichuan Basin, China. *Palaeontologica Sinica* (Series C), **23**, 1–145.

FRAAS, E. 1908. Ostafrikanische Dinosaurier. *Palaeontographica*, **55**, 105–144.

GALTON, P. M. & KNOLL, F. 2006. A saurischian dinosaur braincase from the Middle Jurassic (Bathonian) near Oxford, England: from the theropod *Megalosaurus* or the sauropod *Cetiosaurus*? *Geological Magazine*, **143**, 905–921.

GEIS, D. 1960. *The How and Why Wonder Book of Dinosaurs*. Price Stern Sloan, Los Angeles, CA.

GERVAIS, P. 1852. *Zoologie et paléontologie française (animaux vertébrés)*. A. Bertrand, Paris.

GILMORE, C. W. 1925. A nearly complete articulated skeleton of *Camarasaurus*, a saurischian dinosaur from the Dinosaur National Monument, Utah. *Memoirs of the Carnegie Museum*, **10**, 347–384 (plates 13–17).

GILMORE, C. W. 1936. Osteology of *Apatosaurus*, with special reference to specimens in the Carnegie Museum. *Memoirs of the Carnegie Museum*, **11**, 175–298 (plates XXI–XXXIV).

GOWER, D. J. 2001. Possible postcranial pneumaticity in the last common ancestor of birds and crocodilians: evidence from *Erythrosuchus* and other Mesozoic archosaurs. *Naturwissenschaften*, **88**, 119–122.

GREGORY, W. K. 1905. The weight of *Brontosaurus*. *Science*, **22**, 572–572.

GUNGA, H.-C., KIRSCH, K. A. ET AL. 1995. New data on the dimensions of *Brachiosaurus brancai* and their physiological implications. *Naturwissenschaften*, **82**, 190–192.

GUNGA, H.-C., SUTHAU, T. ET AL. 2008. A new body mass estimation of *Brachiosaurus brancai* Janensch, 1914 mounted and exhibited at the Museum of Natural History (Berlin, Germany). *Fossil Record*, **11**, 28–33.

HATCHER, J. B. 1901. *Diplodocus* (Marsh): its osteology, taxonomy and probable habits, with a restoration of the skeleton. *Memoirs of the Carnegie Museum*, **1**, 1–63.

HATCHER, J. B. 1903*a*. A new name for the dinosaur *Haplocanthus* Hatcher. *Proceedings of the Biological Society of Washington*, **16**, 100.

HATCHER, J. B. 1903*b*. Osteology of *Haplocanthosaurus* with description of a new species, and remarks on the probable habits of the Sauropoda and the age and origin of the Atlantosaurus beds. *Memoirs of the Carnegie Museum*, **2**, 1–72 (plates I–V).

HAY, O. P. 1908. On the habits and the pose of the sauropodous dinosaurs, especially of *Diplodocus*. *The American Naturalist*, **42**, 672–681.

HAY, O. P. 1910. On the manner of locomotion of the dinosaurs especially *Diplodocus*, with remarks on the origin of the birds. *Proceedings of the Washington Academy of Science*, **12**, 1–25.

HAY, O. P. 1911. Further observations on the pose of the sauropodous dinosaurs. *The American Naturalist*, **45**, 396–412.

HENDERSON, D. M. 2004. Tipsy punters: sauropod dinosaur pneumaticity, bouyancy and aquatic habits. *Proceedings of the Royal Society of London, Series B (Biology Letters)*, **271**, S180–S183.

HENDERSON, D. M. 2006. Burly Gaits: centers of mass, stability, and the trackways of sauropod dinosaurs. *Journal of Vertebrate Paleontology*, **26**, 908–921.

HOLLAND, W. J. 1905. The presentation of a reproduction of *Diplodocus carnegiei* to the trustees of the British Museum. *Annals of the Carnegie Museum*, **3**, 443–452 (plates 17–18).

HOLLAND, W. J. 1910. A review of some recent criticisms of the restorations of sauropod dinosaurs existing in the museums of the United States, with special reference to that of *Diplodocus carnegiei* in the Carnegie museum. *The American Naturalist*, **44**, 259–283.

HOLLAND, W. J. 1915. Heads and tails: a few notes relating to the structure of the sauropod dinosaurs. *Annals of the Carnegie Museum*, **9**, 273–278.

HUENE, F. V. 1926. The carnivorous Saurischia in the Jura and Cretaceous formations principally in Europe. *Revista del Museo de La Plata*, **29**, 35–114.

HUENE, F. V. 1929*a*. Los Saurisquios y Ornitisquios del Cretaceo Argentina. *Annales Museo de La Plata, Serie 2a*, **3**.

HUENE, F. V. 1929*b*. Die Besonderheit der Titanosaurier. *Centralblatt für Mineralogie, Geologie und Paläontologie*, **1929B**, 493–499.

JAIN, S. L., KUTTY, T. S. & ROY-CHOWDHURY, T. K. 1975. The sauropod dinosaur from the Lower Jurassic Kota Formation of India. *Proceedings of the Royal Society of London A*, **188**, 221–228.

JANENSCH, W. 1914. Übersicht über der Wirbeltierfauna der Tendaguru-Schichten nebst einer kurzen Charakterisierung der neu aufgefuhrten Arten von Sauropoden. *Archiv für Biontologie*, **3**, 81–110.

JANENSCH, W. 1922. Das Handskelett von *Gigantosaurus robustus* u. *Brachiosaurus Brancai* aus den Tendaguru-Schichten Deutsch-Ostafrikas. *Centralblatt für Mineralogie, Geologie und Paläontologie*, **15**, 464–480.

JANENSCH, W. 1929*a*. Die Wirbelsaule der Gattung *Dicraeosaurus*. *Palaeontographica*, **2**, 35–133.

JANENSCH, W. 1929*b*. Material und Formengehalt der Sauropoden in der Ausbeute der Tendaguru-Expedition. *Palaeontographica*, **2**, 1–34.

JANENSCH, W. 1935–1936. Die Schadel der Sauropoden *Brachiosaurus*, *Barosaurus* und *Dicraeosaurus* aus den Tendaguru-Schichten Deutsch-Ostafrikas. *Palaeontographica*, **2**, 147–298.

JANENSCH, W. 1938. Gestalt und Größe von *Brachiosaurus* und anderen riesigwüchsigen Sauropoden. *Der Biologe*, **7**, 130–134.

JANENSCH, W. 1947. Pneumatizitat bei Wirbeln von Sauropoden und anderen Saurischien. *Palaeontographica*, **3**, 1–25.

JANENSCH, W. 1950*a*. Die Wirbelsaule von *Brachiosaurus brancai*. *Palaeontographica*, **3**, 27–93.

JANENSCH, W. 1950*b*. Die Skelettrekonstruktion von *Brachiosaurus brancai*. *Palaeontographica*, **3**, 97–103 (plates VI–VIII).

JANENSCH, W. 1961. Die Gliedmaszen und Gliedmaszengürtel der Sauropoden der Tendaguru-Schichten. *Palaeontographica*, **3**, 177–235 (plates XV–XXIII).

JENSEN, J. A. 1985. Three new sauropod dinosaurs from the Upper Jurassic of Colorado. *Great Basin Naturalist*, **45**, 697–709.

JOHNSTON, C. 1859. Note on odontography. *American Journal of Dental Science*, **9**, 337–343.

KERMACK, K. A. 1951. A note on the habits of sauropods. *Annals and Magazine of Natural History, Series 12*, **4**, 830–832.

KIM, H. M. 1983. Cretaceous dinosaurs from Korea. *Journal of the Geology Society of Korea*, **19**, 115–126.

KSEPKA, D. T. & NORELL, M. A. 2006. *Erketu ellisoni*, a long-necked sauropod from Bor Guve (Dornogov Aimag, Mongolia). *American Museum Novitates*, **3508**, 1–16.

LAVOCAT, R. 1954. Sur les Dinosauriens du continental intercalaire des Kem-Kem de la Daoura. *Comptes Rendus 19th International Geological Congress 1952*, **1**, 65–68.

LEIDY, J. 1865. Cretaceous reptiles of the United States. *Smithsonian Contribution to Knowledge*, **192**, 1–135.

LONGMAN, H. A. 1926. A giant dinosaur from Durham Downs, Queensland. *Memoirs of the Queensland Museum*, **8**, 183–194.

LONGMAN, H. A. 1933. A new dinosaur from the Queensland Cretaceous. *Memoirs of the Queensland Museum*, **10**, 131–144.

LYDEKKER, R. 1877. Notices of new and other Vertebrata from Indian Tertiary and Secondary rocks. *Records of the Geological Survey of India*, **10**, 30–43.

LYDEKKER, R. 1890. *Catalogue of the fossil Reptilia and Amphibia in the British Museum, part IV, containing the orders Anomodontia, Ecaudata, Caudata and Labyrinthodontia.* British Museum of Natural History, London.

LYDEKKER, R. 1893. The dinosaurs of Patagonia. *Anales del Museo de La Plata*, **2**, 1–14.

MAIER, G. 2003. *African Dinosaurs Unearthed: The Tendaguru Expeditions.* Indiana University Press, Bloomington, IN.

MANTELL, G. A. 1825. Notice on the *Iguanodon*, a newly discovered fossil reptile, from the sandstone of Tilgate Forest, in Sussex. *Philosophical Transactions of the Royal Society*, **115**, 179–186.

MANTELL, G. A. 1833. *The Geology of the South-east of England.* Longman, London.

MANTELL, G. A. 1850. On the *Pelorosaurus*: an undescribed gigantic terrestrial reptile, whose remains are associated with those of the *Iguanodon* and other saurians in the strata of Tilgate Forest, in Sussex. *Philosophical Transactions of the Royal Society of London*, **140**, 379–390.

MANTELL, G. A. 1852. On the structure of the *Iguanodon* and on the fauna and flora of the Wealden Formation. *Notice: Proceedings of the Royal Institute of Great Britain*, **1**, 141–146.

MARSH, O. C. 1877*a*. Notice of a new and gigantic dinosaur. *American Journal of Science and Arts*, **14**, 87–88.

MARSH, O. C. 1877*b*. Notice of new dinosaurian reptiles from the Jurassic Formation. *American Journal of Science and Arts*, **14**, 514–516.

MARSH, O. C. 1877*c*. A new order of extinct Reptilia (Stegosauria) from the Jurassic of the Rocky Mountains. *American Journal of Science and Arts*, **14**, 513–514.

MARSH, O. C. 1878*a*. Principal characters of American Jurassic dinosaurs. Part I. *American Journal of Science, Series 3*, **16**, 411–416.

MARSH, O. C. 1878*b*. Notice of new dinosaurian reptiles. *American Journal of Science, Series 3*, **15**, 241–244.

MARSH, O. C. 1879. Notice of new Jurassic reptiles. *American Journal of Science, Series 3*, **18**, 501–505.

MARSH, O. C. 1883. Principal characters of American Jurassic dinosaurs. Pt. VI. Restoration of *Brontosaurus*. *American Journal of Science, Series 3*, **26**, 81–85 (plate 1).

MARSH, O. C. 1884. Principal characters of American Jurassic dinosaurs. Pt. VII. On the Diplodocidae, a new family of the Sauropoda. *American Journal of Science, Series 3*, **27**, 161–167 (plates 3–4).

MARSH, O. C. 1888. Notice of a new genus of Sauropoda and other new dinosaurs from the Potomac Formation. *American Journal of Science, Series 3*, **35**, 89–94.

MARSH, O. C. 1890. Description of new dinosaurian reptiles. *American Journal of Science, Series 3*, **39**, 81–86 (plate I).

MARSH, O. C. 1891. Restoration of *Brontosaurus*. *American Journal of Science, Series 3*, **41**, 341–342.

MARTILL, D. M. 2010. The early history of pterosaur discovery in Great Britain. *In*: MOODY, R. T. J., BUFFETAUT, E., NAISH, D. & MARTILL, D. M. (eds) *Dinosaurs and Other Extinct Saurians: A Historical Perspective*. Geological Society, London, Special Publications, **343**, 287–311.

MARTIN, J. 1987. Mobility and feeding of *Cetiosaurus* (Saurischia: Sauropoda) – why the long neck?

Occasional Papers of the Tyrrell Museum of Palaeontology (Fourth Symposium on Mezozoic Terrestrial Ecosystems), **3**, 154–159.

Matthew, W. D. 1905. The mounted skeleton of *Brontosaurus*. *The American Museum Journal*, **5**, 62–70.

Matthew, W. D. 1915. *Dinosaurs, with Special Reference to the American Museum Collections*. American Museum of Natural History, New York.

McGowan, C. 1991. *Dinosaurs, Spitfires and Sea Dragons*. Harvard University Press, Cambridge, MA.

McIntosh, J. S. 1981. Annotated catalogue of the dinosaurs (Reptilia, Archosauria) in the collections of Carnegie Museum of Natural History. *Bulletin of the Carnegie Museum*, **18**, 1–67.

McIntosh, J. S. & Berman, D. S. 1975. Description of the palate and lower jaw of the sauropod dinosaur *Diplodocus* (Reptilia: Saurischia) with remarks on the nature of the skull of *Apatosaurus*. *Journal of Paleontology*, **49**, 187–199.

Meyer, H. V. 1832. *Palaeologica zur Geschichte der Erde und ihrer Geschöpfe*. Schmerber, Frankfurt am Main.

Migeod, F. W. H. 1931. British Museum East Africa Expedition: Account of the work done in 1930. *Natural History Magazine*, **3**, 87–103.

Mook, C. C. 1914. Notes on *Camarasaurus* Cope. *Annals of the New York Academy of Sciences*, **24**, 19–22.

Naish, D. 2010. Pneumaticity, the early years: Wealden Supergroup dinosaurs and the hypothesis of saurischian pneumaticity. *In*: Moody, R. T. J., Buffetaut, E., Naish, D. & Martill, D. M. (eds) *Dinosaurs and Other Extinct Saurians: A Historical Perspective*. Geological Society, London, Special Publications, **343**, 229–236.

Nesbitt, S. J. & Norell, M. A. 2006. Extreme convergence in the body plans of an early suchian (Archosauria) and ornithomimid dinosaurs (Theropoda). *Proceedings of the Royal Society of London B*, **273**, 1045–1048.

Novas, F. E., Salgado, L., Calvo, J. & Agnolin, F. 2005. Giant titanosaur (Dinosauria, Sauropoda) from the Late Cretaceous of Patagonia. *Revista del Museo Argentino dei Ciencias Naturales, Nuevo Serie*, **7**, 37–41.

Olshevsky, G. 1991. A revision of the parainfraclass Archosauria Cope, 1869, excluding the advanced Crocodylia. *Mesozoic Meanderings*, **2**, 1–196.

Osborn, H. F. 1898. Additional characters of the great herbivorous dinosaur *Camarasaurus*. *Bulletin of the American Museum of Natural History*, **10**, 219–233.

Osborn, H. F. 1899. A skeleton of *Diplodocus*. *Memoirs of the American Museum of Natural History*, **1**, 189–214 (plates 24–28).

Osborn, H. F. 1904. Manus, sacrum and caudals of Sauropoda. *Bulletin of the American Museum of Natural History*, **20**, 181–190.

Osborn, H. F. & Mook, C. C. 1921. *Camarasaurus*, *Amphicoelias* and other sauropods of Cope. *Memoirs of the American Museum of Natural History, new series*, **3**, 247–387 (plates LX–LXXXV).

Ostrom, J. H. 1969*a*. A new theropod dinosaur from the Lower Cretaceous of Montana. *Postilla*, **128**, 1–17.

Ostrom, J. H. 1969*b*. Osteology of *Deinonychus antirrhopus*, an unusual theropod from the Lower Cretaceous of Montana. *Bulletin of the Peabody Museum of Natural History*, **30**, 1–165.

Owen, R. 1841*a*. *Odontography, Part II*. Hippolyte Bailliere, London.

Owen, R. 1841*b*. A description of a portion of the skeleton of the *Cetiosaurus*, a gigantic extinct Saurian Reptile occurring in the Oolitic formations of different portions of England. *Proceedings of the Geological Society*, London, **3**, 457–462.

Owen, R. 1842. Report on British fossil reptiles, Part II. *Reports of the British Association for the Advancement of Science*, **11**, 60–204.

Owen, R. 1859*a*. Monograph on the fossil Reptilia of the Wealden and Purbeck Formations. Supplement no. II. Crocodilia (*Streptospondylus*, &c.). *Palaeontographical Society Monograph*, **11**, 20–44.

Owen, R. 1859*b*. On the orders of fossil and recent Reptilia, and their distribution in time. *Report on the British Association for the Advancement of Science, 29th Meeting*, **1859**, 153–166.

Owen, R. 1875*a*. Monograph of the Mesozoic Reptilia, part 2: Monograph on the genus *Bothriospondylus*. *Palaeontolographical Society Monograph*, **29**, 15–26.

Owen, R. 1875*b*. Monograph of the Mesozoic Reptilia, part 2: Monograph on the genus *Cetiosaurus*. *Palaeontolographical Society Monograph*, **29**, 27–43.

Paul, G. S. 1988*a*. The brachiosaur giants of the Morrison and Tendaguru with a description of a new subgenus, *Giraffatitan*, and a comparison of the world's largest dinosaurs. *Hunteria*, **2**, 1–14.

Paul, G. S. 1988*b*. *Predatory Dinosaurs of the World*. Simon & Schuster, New York.

Paul, G. S. 1998. Terramegathermy and Cope's Rule in the land of titans. *Modern Geology*, **23**, 179–217.

Phillips, J. 1871. *Geology of Oxford and the Valley of the Thames*. Clarendon Press, Oxford.

Powell, J. E. 1992. Osteología de *Saltasaurus loricatus* (Sauropoda–Titanosauridae) del Cretácico Superior del Noroeste Argentino. *In*: Sanz, J. L. & Buscalioni, A. D. (eds) *Los Dinosaurios y su Entorno Biotico. Actas del Segundo Curso de Paleontologia en Cuenca*. Instituto Juan de Valdés, Ayuntamiento de Cuenca, 165–230.

Powell, J. E. 2003. Revision of South American Titanosaurid dinosaurs: palaeobiological, palaeobiogeographical and phylogenetic aspects. *Records of the Queen Victoria Museum*, **111**, 1–94.

Rauhut, O. W., Remes, K., Fechner, R., Cladera, G. & Puerta, P. 2005. Discovery of a short-necked sauropod dinosaur from the Late Jurassic period of Patagonia. *Nature*, **435**, 670–672.

Remes, K. 2006. Revision of the Tendaguru sauropod dinosaur *Tornieria africana* (Fraas) and its relevance for sauropod paleobiogeography. *Journal of Vertebrate Paleontology*, **26**, 651–669.

Remes, K. 2007. A second Gondwanan diplodocid dinosaur from the Upper Jurassic Tendaguru beds of Tanzania, East Africa. *Palaeontology*, **50**, 653–667.

Riggs, E. S. 1903*a*. *Brachiosaurus altithorax*, the largest known dinosaur. *American Journal of Science*, **15**, 299–306.

Riggs, E. S. 1903*b*. Structure and relationships of opisthocoelian dinosaurs. Part I, *Apatosaurus* Marsh. *Field Columbian Museum*, Geological Series, **2**, 165–196.

RIGGS, E. S. 1904. Structure and relationships of opisthocoelian dinosaurs. Part II, the Brachiosauridae. *Field Columbian Museum, Geological Series*, **2**, 229–247.

ROMER, A. S. 1956. *Osteology of the Reptiles*. University of Chicago Press, Chicago, IL.

RUSSELL, D. A. & ZHENG, Z. 1993. A large mamenchisaurid from the Junggar Basin, Xinjiang, People's Republic of China. *Canadian Journal of Earth Sciences*, **30**, 2082–2095.

RUSSELL, D. A., BELAND, P. & MCINTOSH, J. S. 1980. Paleoecology of the dinosaurs of Tendaguru (Tanzania). *Memoires de la Société Geologique de France*, **139**, 169–175.

SALGADO, L. & BONAPARTE, J. F. 1991. Un nuevo sauropodo Dicraeosauridae, *Amargasaurus cazaui* gen. et sp. nov., de la Formacion La Amarga, Neocomiano de la Provincia del Neuquen, Argentina. *Ameghiniana*, **28**, 333–346.

SANDER, P. M. 2000. Longbone histology of the Tendaguru sauropods: implications for growth and biology. *Paleobiology*, **26**, 466–488.

SANDER, P. M., MATEUS, O., LAVEN, T. & KNÖTSCHKE, N. 2006. Bone histology indicates insular dwarfism in a new Late Jurassic sauropod dinosaur. *Nature*, **441**, 739–741.

SEELEY, H. G. 1869. *Index to the fossil remains of Aves, Ornithosauria, and Reptilia, from the Secondary System of Strata, arranged in the Woodwardian Museum of the University of Cambridge*. Deighton, Bell, and Co., Cambridge.

SEELEY, H. G. 1870. On *Ornithopsis*, a gigantic animal of the Pterodactyle kind from the Wealden. *Annals of the Magazine of Natural History*, Series 4, **5**, 279–283.

SEELEY, H. G. 1874. On the base of a large lacertian cranium from the Potton Sands, presumably dinosaurian. *Quarterly Journal of the Geological Society, London*, **30**, 690–692.

SERENO, P. C., BECK, A. L. *ET AL*. 1999. Cretaceous sauropods from the Sahara and the uneven rate of skeletal evolution among dinosaurs. *Science*, **282**, 1342–1347.

SERENO, P. C., WILSON, J. A., WITMER, L. M., WHITLOCK, J. A., MAGA, A., IDE, O. & ROWE, T. A. 2007. Structural extremes in a Cretaceous dinosaur. *PLoS ONE*, **2**, e1230.

STERNFELD, R. 1911. Zur Nomenklatur der Gattung *Gigantosaurus* Fraas. *Sitzungsberichte der Gesellschaft Naturforschender Freunde zu Berlin*, **1911**, 398.

STEVENS, K. A. & PARRISH, J. M. 1999. Neck posture and feeding habits of two Jurassic sauropod dinosaurs. *Science*, **284**, 798–800.

TAYLOR, M. P. 2005. Sweet seventy-five and never been kissed: the Natural History Museum's Tendaguru brachiosaur. *In*: BARRETT, P. M. (ed.) *Abstracts Volume for 53rd Symposium of Vertebrae Palaeontology and Comparative Anatomy*. Natural History Museum, London.

TAYLOR, M. P. 2006. Dinosaur diversity analysed by clade, age, place and year of description. *In*: BARRETT, P. M. (ed.) *Ninth International Symposium on Mesozoic Terrestrial Ecosystems and Biota, Manchester, UK*. Cambridge Publications, Cambridge, 134–138.

TAYLOR, M. P. 2009. A re-evaluation of *Brachiosaurus altithorax* Riggs 1903 (Dinosauria, Sauropoda) and its generic separation from *Giraffatitan brancai* (Janensch 1914). *Journal of Vertebrate Paleontology*, **29**, 787–806.

TAYLOR, M. P. & NAISH, D. 2007. An unusual new neosauropod dinosaur from the Lower Cretaceous Hastings Beds Group of East Sussex, England. *Palaeontology*, **50**, 1547–1564.

TAYLOR, M. P., WEDEL, M. J. & NAISH, D. 2009. Head and neck posture in sauropod dinosaurs inferred from extant animals. *Acta Palaeontologica Polonica*, **54**, 213–220.

TORNIER, G. 1909. Wie war der *Diplodocus carnegii* wirklich gebaut? *Sitzungsbericht der Gesellschaft naturforschender Freunde zu Berlin*, **4**, 193–209.

UPCHURCH, P. 1995. The evolutionary history of sauropod dinosaurs. *Philosophical Transactions of the Royal Society of London B*, **349**, 365–390.

UPCHURCH, P. 1998. Phylogenetic relationships of sauropod dinosaurs. *Zoological Journal of the Linnean Society*, **124**, 43–103.

UPCHURCH, P. 2000. Neck posture of sauropod dinosaurs. *Science*, **287**, 547b.

UPCHURCH, P. & MARTIN, J. 2003. The anatomy and taxonomy of *Cetiosaurus* (Saurischia, Sauropoda) from the Middle Jurassic of England. *Journal of Vertebrate Paleontology*, **23**, 208–231.

UPCHURCH, P., MARTIN, J. & TAYLOR, M. P. 2009. Case 3472: *Cetiosaurus* Owen, 1841 (Dinosauria, Sauropoda): proposed conservation of usage by designation of *Cetiosaurus oxoniensis* Phillips, 1871 as the type species. *Bulletin of Zoological Nomenclature*, **66**, 51–55.

UPCHURCH, P., BARRETT, P. M. & DODSON, P. 2004. Sauropoda. *In*: WEISHAMPEL, D. B., DODSON, P. & OSMÓLSKA, H. (eds) *The Dinosauria*. 2nd edn. University of California Press, Berkeley, CA, 259–322.

WATSON, J. W. 1966. *Dinosaurs and Other Prehistoric Reptiles*. Hamlyn, London.

WEAVER, J. C. 1983. The improbable endotherm: the energetics of the sauropod dinosaur *Brachiosaurus*. *Paleobiology*, **9**, 173–182.

WEDEL, M. J. 2003*a*. Vertebral pneumaticity, air sacs, and the physiology of sauropod dinosaurs. *Paleobiology*, **29**, 243–255.

WEDEL, M. J. 2003*b*. The evolution of vertebral pneumaticity in sauropod dinosaurs. *Journal of Vertebrate Paleontology*, **23**, 344–357.

WEDEL, M. J. 2005. Postcranial skeletal pneumaticity in sauropods and its implications for mass estimates. *In*: WILSON, J. A. & CURRY-ROGERS, K. (eds) *The Sauropods: Evolution and Paleobiology*. University of California Press, Berkeley, CA, 201–228.

WEDEL, M. J. 2006. Origin of postcranial skeletal pneumaticity in dinosaurs. *Integrative Zoology*, **2**, 80–85.

WEDEL, M. J., CIFELLI, R. L. & SANDERS, R. K. 2000. *Sauroposeidon proteles*, a new sauropod from the Early Cretaceous of Oklahoma. *Journal of Vertebrate Paleontology*, **20**, 109–114.

WILD, R. 1991. *Janenschia* n. g. *robusta* (E. Fraas 1908) pro *Tornieria robusta* (E. Fraas 1908) (Reptilia, Saurischia, Sauropodomorpha). *Stuttgarter Beiträge zur*

Naturkunde, Serie B *(Geologie und Paläontologie),* **173**, 1–4.

Wilson, J. A. 2002. Sauropod dinosaur phylogeny: critique and cladistic analysis. *Zoological Journal of the Linnean Society*, **136**, 217–276.

Wilson, J. A. & Sereno, P. C. 1998. *Early Evolution and Higher-level Phylogeny of Sauropod Dinosaurs.* Society of Vertebrate Paleontology, Memoir **5**, 1–68; supplement to *Journal of Vertebrate Palaeontology*, **18**.

Wilson, J. A. & Upchurch, P. 2003. A revision of *Titanosaurus* Lydekker (Dinosauria – Sauropoda), the first dinosaur genus with a 'Gondwanan' distribution. *Journal of Systematic Palaeontology*, **1**, 125–160.

Wilson, J. A. & Upchurch, P. 2009. Redescription and reassessment of the phylogenetic affinities of *Euhelopus zdanskyi* (Dinosauria: Sauropoda) from the Early Cretaceous of China. *Journal of Systematic Palaeontology*, **7**, 199–239.

Wiman, C. 1929. Die Kreide-Dinosaurier aus Shantung. *Palaeontologia Sinica* (Series C), **6**, 1–67 (plates 1–9).

Woodward, A. S. 1910. On a skull of *Megalosaurus* from the Great Oolite of Minchinhampton (Gloucestershire). *Quarterly Journal of the Geological Society, London*, **66**, 111–115.

Young, C.-C. 1937. A new dinosaurian from Sinkiang. *Palaeontologia Sinica* (Series C), **2**, 1–25,

Young, C.-C. 1939. On a new Sauropoda, with notes on other fragmentary reptiles from Szechuan. *Bulletin of the Geological Society of China*, **19**, 279–315.

Young, C.-C. 1954. On a new sauropod from Yiping, Szechuan, China. *Acta Scientia Sinica*, **3**, 491–504.

Young, C.-C. & Zhao, X. 1972. [*Mamenchisaurus*. In Chinese: description of the type material of *Mamenchisaurus hochuanensis*]. *Institute of Vertebrate Paleontology and Paleoanthropology Monograph Series I*, **8**, 1–30.

Index

Note: Page numbers in *italic* denote figures. Page numbers in **bold** denote tables.